This book is dedicated to our parents
Elizabeth and John and Dorothy and Charles

CONTENTS

PREFACE   **xiii**

O N E	WHOLE NUMBERS	**1**

1.1 Place Value   1
1.2 Addition and Subtraction   8
1.3 Multiplication and Division   17
1.4 Exponents   28
1.5 Order of Operations and Grouping Symbols   33
1.6 Prime Numbers, Divisibility Tests, and Prime Factorizations   42
1.7 LCMs and GCFs Using Primes and Exponents   50
1.8 Fundamental Algebraic Properties of Operations   58
    Summary   66
    Chapter 1 Review Problems   66
    Chapter 1 Practice Test   69

T W O	INTEGERS	**71**

2.1 The Number Line   71
2.2 Addition of Integers   78
2.3 Subtraction of Integers   88
2.4 Multiplication and Division of Integers   97
2.5 Mixed Operations and Grouping Symbols   109
    Summary   115
    Chapter 2 Review Problems   116
    Chapter 2 Practice Test   118

T H R E E   **FRACTIONS**   **121**

3.1 Expansion and Reduction of Fractions   121
3.2 Signed Fractions, Mixed Numbers, and Inequalities   133
3.3 Addition of Signed Fractions   143
3.4 Subtraction of Signed Fractions   154
3.5 Multiplication and Division of Signed Fractions
        and Signed Mixed Numbers   163
3.6 Mixed Operations and Grouping Symbols   176
3.7 Complex Fractions   184
        Summary   192
        Chapter 3 Review Problems   193
        Chapter 3 Practice Test   198

F O U R   **DECIMALS**   **201**

4.1 Decimal Notation and Place Values   201
4.2 Addition and Subtraction of Signed Decimals   209
4.3 Multiplication of Signed Decimals   218
4.4 Division of Signed Decimals   225
4.5 Square Roots as Decimals   239
4.6 Reducing Square Roots   248
4.7 Percent   258
        Summary   267
        Chapter 4 Review Problems   268
        Chapter 4 Practice Test   270

F I V E   **EXPONENTS**   **273**

5.1 Zero and Negative Exponents   273
5.2 Multiplication and Division with Signed Exponents   282
5.3 Powers of Powers   290
5.4 Decimals and Signed Powers of 10   298
5.5 Scientific Notation   306
5.6 The Metric System   315
        Summary   323
        Chapter 5 Review Problems   324
        Chapter 5 Practice Test   327

S I X   ALGEBRAIC EXPRESSIONS AND FORMULAS   329

6.1 Variables, Polynomials, and Like Terms   329
6.2 Multiplication by Monomials and Subtraction of Polynomials   342
6.3 Multiplication of Polynomials   350
6.4 Division by Monomials   356
6.5 Literal Formulas   363
Summary   376
Chapter 6 Review Problems   377
Chapter 6 Practice Test   380

S E V E N   SOLVING EQUATIONS   383

7.1 Introduction to Equations and Algebraic Expressions   383
7.2 Solving Linear Equations   392
7.3 More on Solving Equations   405
7.4 Introduction to Word Problems   418
7.5 Solving Ratio, Proportion, and Percent Problems   429
7.6 Solving Literal Equations   444
7.7 Solving Inequalities   453
Summary   460
Chapter 7 Review Problems   462
Chapter 7 Practice Test   464

E I G H T   A BRIEF INTRODUCTION TO ANALYTIC GEOMETRY   467

8.1 Rectangular Coordinate System   467
8.2 Distance Formula and Graphing Linear Equations   478
8.3 Slopes of Lines and Geometry of Similar Triangles   489
Summary   499
Chapter 8 Review Problems   500
Chapter 8 Practice Test   502
Final Exam Practice Test   503

A P P E N D I X	**TABLES**	**509**
	Prime Factors, Squares, and Square Roots	509
	Table of Common Fractions and Decimal Equivalents	513
	Table of Common Measurements	514
	Table of Geometric Formulas	516
	GLOSSARY OF SPECIAL SYMBOLS AND ABBREVIATIONS	**519**
	GLOSSARY OF SIGNIFICANT TERMS	**521**
	ANSWERS TO ODD-NUMBERED EXERCISES	**533**
	INDEX	**561**

PREFACE

Prealgebra for College Students prepares students for a first course in algebra and is designed for a one-quarter or one-semester course. It provides thorough coverage of the skills and concepts that are necessary to build a strong foundation for elementary algebra.

We introduce signed numbers before fractions and decimals, thus allowing manipulations with signs to be integrated with fractions, decimals, and grouping symbols. Throughout the text students are given problems that place additional emphasis on the use of the grouping symbols and the order of operations, thereby helping them develop sequencing skills for solving problems with several simplified steps.

The contexts of the word problems have been carefully selected to be of interest to a wide variety of students. Most of the problems are based on real-life situations that describe facts pertaining to mathematical quantities. The topics have been selected from the fields of accounting and banking, computers, consumer interests, education, the environment, health and nutrition, sports, technology, transportation, and even politics. Topics also encompass the traditional sciences of astronomy, chemistry, and physics.

Many of the word problems require critical reading and critical thinking. Students will find problems that require them to translate verbal descriptions of mathematical quantities into mathematical expressions. We also challenge students to work backwards: translating mathematical expressions into words, phrases, and sentences. We emphasize problem solving throughout the book.

In Chapter 7 on solving equations we present a six-step method for solving word problems:

1. Identify and describe the unknown and assign it a variable name.

2. Use the variable to write one or more expressions that describe other quantities in the problem.

3. Write a statement in English that summarizes the equivalence between two quantities and write an equation using the expressions from step 2.

4. Solve the equation.

5. Check the solution and determine if the answer is reasonable.

6. Write a short sentence explaining the answer.

PEDAGOGICAL FEATURES

Practice for Success

Each section begins with a statement of the objectives for that section. Within each section are numerous examples of the kinds of problems found in the exercises at the end of the section. We recommend that students first try the *Practice for Success* problems that precede each exercise set before they begin the exercises. The purpose of the Practice for Success problems is to test students' knowledge and skill level before they try the exercises. If a student has difficulty correctly completing these preliminary problems, we recommend he or she reread the material for that section and study the examples more closely. The answers to the Practice for Success problems appear at the end of each section.

 ### Looking Back

Looking Back problems remind students of techniques and major ideas that were presented earlier and thus provide a form of review. We encourage instructors to make a point of assigning most of the Looking Back problems along with the other standard problems from the section. Because many of the Looking Back problems ask conceptual types of questions, dealing with definitions and the meanings of terms and requiring critical writing and thinking skills, they are intended to help solidify understanding.

Chapter Review Problems

Chapter Review Problems appear at the end of each chapter and contain only material that appears within the given chapter. Answers to the oddnumbered exercises are provided at the back of the book.

Chapter Practice Tests

A *Chapter Practice Test* appears at the end of each chapter and consists of approximately 25 problems. A *Practice Final Exam* is included at the end of Chapter 8. Answers to all of the test questions appear at the end of the book.

Tables

Four sets of reference tables appear at the end of the book:

> *Table of Prime Factors and Squares and Square Roots* is a computational aid.
>
> *Table of Common Fractions and Decimal Equivalents* shows the decimal equivalents of fractions that are multiples of sixty-fourths.
>
> *Table of Common Measurements* provides common measurements, such as the number of yards in a mile.
>
> *Table of Geometric Formulas* provides figures and formulas for the more common two- and three-dimensional figures that concern perimeter, area, and volume.

Glossaries

In addition to the reference tables, two special glossaries are at the end of the book:

Glossary of Special Symbols and Abbreviations contains special notations and abbreviations that may be unfamiliar.

Glossary of Significant Terms provides a short form of a mathematics dictionary, containing the major concepts and terms presented in the book.

For convenience, the Special Symbols and Abbreviations and the Table of Common Measurements are reproduced inside the front and back covers of the book.

Special Markings, Numbering, and Calculator Use

Major concepts and definitions are boxed for easy reference; the end of each example is marked with a square bullet symbol; and a standard numbering system is used to identify numbered sections, figures, and tables within a chapter. The first number indicates the chapter and the second, the sequence within the chapter—for example, 3.2 indicates Chapter 3 and Section, Figure, or Table 2 within Chapter 3.

This text does not explicitly mark problems as either requiring or recommending the use of a calculator. We expect that part of a student's math education should provide practice in deciding when calculator use is appropriate. We encourage students to use a calculator for several of the sections in Chapter 4, which deal with decimals, and for financial formulas introduced in Section 6.5.

SUPPLEMENTS

The *Instructor's Manual* discusses the purpose and objectives of each chapter and contains a suggested course schedule. It contains four forms of a test for each of the chapters (1 through 8), four forms of the final exam, and answers to all even-numbered exercises.

The *Student Study Guide* contains sets of review problems that provide long-term reinforcement. Solutions to all of the problems are included in this supplement.

EXPTest, a computerized test bank for IBM-PCs and compatibles, contains over *875* test questions. The package also allows the instructor to view and edit the tests by adding or deleting questions. Both the existing and new test questions can be modified. Any number of student tests can be printed and created in multiple forms for larger class sections or individual use. The included graphics importation feature lets the instructor display and print graphs, diagrams, and maps with the tests. EXPTest is accompanied by easy-to-follow documentation and a quick-start guide. A demonstration disk is available for review.

EXAM BUILDER, a computerized test bank for the Macintosh, is a simple testing program that allows instructors to create, view, and edit tests. Questions can be stored by objective so that tests can be created using multiple choice, true/false, fill-in-the-blank, essay, and matching formats. Questions can also be scrambled to avoid duplicate testing. A demonstration disk is available for review.

Problem-generating software, consisting of programs that can be used to generate or check problems, is available to instructors through the authors. Further information can be obtained by contacting the authors: John Kennedy and Terry Green, Department of Mathematics, Santa Monica College, 1900 Pico Blvd, Santa Monica, CA 90405.

A *Developmental Mathematics Review Videotape Series*, created by Hope Florence, College of Charleston, and covering the review of arithmetic (one tape), topics in elementary algebra (three tapes), and topics in intermediate algebra (one tape), is available to adopters of this text. The videotape series includes specialized worksheets that give students the chance to work additional exercises.

ACKNOWLEDGMENTS

We would like to acknowledge the following people who were instrumental in helping transform this book from a dream to a reality. JoAnn Green and Alison Feldman provided encouragement and reassurance and were understanding whenever deadlines came along. Carrie and Jennie Green and Paige, Stacie, and Kevin Feldman kept us motivated whenever they asked, "Aren't you finished with the book yet?" Roger Murray, a former student and now friend, was invaluable in spending countless hours proofreading, problem checking, and helping with the editing. Darrell Peterson, Mathematics Department Chairperson at Santa Monica College, encouraged us to continue writing and provided the example of someone who had already written his own. We would also like to thank all the other colleagues in our department for their encouragement over the past two years.

At PWS-KENT Publishing we would like to thank Tim Anderson, Associate Editor, who took the time and interest to get this project off the ground. Tim provided continuous encouragement and guidance and always had upbeat, helpful advice. More than anyone else, he is responsible for making us authors. Robine Andrau, as Senior Production Editor, was instrumental in seeing this project make it onto the printed page. Robine made our writing and overall organization more readable and comprehensible. During our numerous discussions by telephone, she always had helpful suggestions. Now that the project is complete, we are thankful Robine kept us on task. Diana Kelley was involved in the early phases of the project and Kelle Karshick helped us with all the supplements to the text. We would also like to acknowledge all the others on the staff at PWS-KENT who did the day-to-day work in the production of the book.

We would also like to thank the following professional reviewers whose comments and suggestions were valuable in making improvements in the text:

Nancy B. Adams   Carol Atnip
Kent State University   University of Louisville

Bonita G. Breze
Winona State University

Julia Brown
Atlantic Community College

Patricia Deamer
Skyline College

Donna M. Doyle
Grossmont College

Lenore Frank
SUNY—Stony Brook

Steve E. Green
Tyler Junior College

Janet L. Hansen
Murray State University

Cora-Lynn Harrison
Grossmont College

Margaret D. Hovde
Grossmount College

Horatio H. Jen
Westmoreland County
Community College

Maryann E. Justinger
Erie Community College

Thomas Killian
Long Beach City College

Lois G. Leonard
Erie Community College

Gary Long
Mt. San Antonio College

Kent M. Neuerburg
Consumnes River College

Sybil Robert
San Diego Mesa College

Mary Teegarden
San Diego Mesa College

Sandra J. Vrem
College of the Redwoods

Prentice E. Whitlock
Jersey City State College

Kevin Yokoyama
College of the Redwoods

WHOLE NUMBERS

In this introductory chapter we review topics related to **whole numbers**, which represent a starting point for learning about the kinds of numbers used in algebra. Whole numbers can be used to represent many different quantities such as money, distance, time, temperature, and so on.

The first few topics in this chapter include place value, rounding whole numbers, writing numbers in expanded forms, and the four fundamental operations. Then we introduce the concept of prime numbers and discuss how these numbers form the fundamental building blocks of the whole number system. Next, we introduce applications of prime numbers and bases and exponents to find least common multiples and greatest common factors. In preparation for algebra, we then investigate the order of operations and the use of grouping symbols and how they relate to expressions consisting of several mixed operations. The chapter concludes by discussing some of the fundamental algebraic properties of numbers.

1.1 PLACE VALUE

OBJECTIVES

☐ To identify the place value of a digit
☐ To write whole numbers in expanded form
☐ To convert whole numbers in standard form to words
☐ To convert whole numbers in words to standard form
☐ To round whole numbers

The set of whole numbers starts at 0 and continues forever and is represented by writing {0, 1, 2, ...}. The ellipsis dots, ..., indicate that a particular sequence of numbers continues indefinitely. Numbers in the **decimal number system**, otherwise known as the "base 10" number system, are written using the digits 0, 1, 2, 3, 4, 5, 6, 7, 8, and 9. The value of a digit within a number is determined by the position of that digit; for example, the numbers 12 and 21 have the same digits, but they do not represent the same numerical value.

In the decimal number system, each digit has a **place value**. The rightmost digit of any whole number is in the ones place, and the digit to the left of the ones place is in the tens place. Because the decimal number system is base 10, each place to the left has a value 10 times that of the previous place. Therefore, the place after the tens place is the hundreds (10 times 10) place. Figure 1.1 shows the names and values of the first 12 places in the decimal number system. The place values are in groups of three called *periods*. It is important to be familiar with these 12 places because we encounter numbers such as a hundred billion in daily life—for example, when the U.S. national budget is discussed.

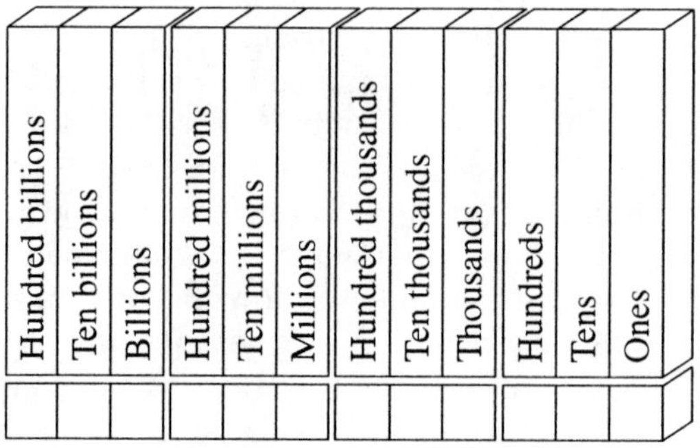

FIGURE 1.1   Place value names for whole numbers

EXAMPLE 1   Identify the place value of the 7 in 497,325.

SOLUTION   Place 497,325 into the boxes below the place value columns (see Figure 1.2). The 7 is in the thousands place.

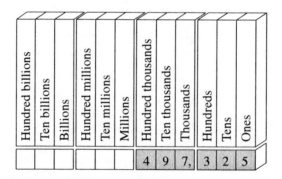

FIGURE 1.2   Place values of the digits in 497,325   ■

EXAMPLE 2   Identify the place value of the digit 4 in 43,267,580.

SOLUTION   Make a place value chart and insert 43,267,580 into the boxes. The 4 is in the ten millions place.   ■

Whole Numbers in Expanded Forms

Whole numbers can be written as sums of products of multiples of ten. For example, 735 indicates that we have $7 \cdot 100 + 3 \cdot 10 + 5 \cdot 1$. (We often use the **raised dot**, ·, to indicate multiplication.) The number 735 could also be written as $700 + 30 + 5$. These two ways of writing the number 735 are called **expanded forms**.

| EXAMPLE 3 | Write 4,236 in two expanded forms. |

SOLUTION
$$4,236 = 4 \cdot 1,000 + 2 \cdot 100 + 3 \cdot 10 + 6 \cdot 1$$
$$4,236 = 4,000 + 200 + 30 + 6$$ ■

| EXAMPLE 4 | Write 20,875,935 in two expanded forms. |

SOLUTION   20,875,935

$$= 2 \cdot 10,000,000 + 8 \cdot 100,000 + 7 \cdot 10,000 + 5 \cdot 1,000 + 9 \cdot 100 + 3 \cdot 10$$
$$+ 5 \cdot 1$$

$$= 20,000,000 + 800,000 + 70,000 + 5,000 + 900 + 30 + 5$$

It is not necessary to write 0 millions in either of the expanded forms.   ■

Whole Numbers in Word Form

When a whole number is written using digits, the number is said to be in **standard form.** Using place value and the second expanded form of a number, whole numbers written in standard form can be written in words. This skill is essential for writing checks, because the amount is written out in words as well as in decimal form. One-digit numbers have the names *zero* through *nine.* Two-digit numbers come in two groups. The numbers 10 through 20 are written as follows:

10 ten	16 sixteen
11 eleven	17 seventeen
12 twelve	18 eighteen
13 thirteen	19 nineteen
14 fourteen	20 twenty
15 fifteen	

The written forms of 21 through 99 have two parts separated by a hyphen. Here are some samples:

21 twenty-one	65 sixty-five
32 thirty-two	76 seventy-six
43 forty-three	87 eighty-seven
54 fifty-four	98 ninety-eight

For numbers with three or more digits, the names are written according to the place values listed in Figure 1.1. The number 422 is written "four hundred twenty-two." The number 1,728 is written "one thousand, seven hundred twenty-eight." Commas separate periods, and the word *and* should not be used when reading whole numbers; it is reserved for reading numbers with a decimal point. (Decimal numbers will be covered in Chapter 4.)

| **EXAMPLE 5** | Write 42,318 in words. |

SOLUTION   42,318 is forty-two thousand, three hundred eighteen.   ■

| **EXAMPLE 6** | Write 8,395,127 in words. |

SOLUTION   8,395,127 is eight million, three hundred ninety-five thousand, one hundred twenty-seven.   ■

Whole Numbers in Standard Form

| **EXAMPLE 7** | Write four thousand, eighty-seven in standard form. |

SOLUTION   Four thousand, eighty-seven is 4,087. Because this number has no hundreds, a 0 is used in the hundreds place as a **place holder**. Without the 0 holding the hundreds place, the number would be incorrectly written as 487 and the 4 would then represent four hundreds, not four thousands.   ■

| **EXAMPLE 8** | Write two billion, nine hundred in standard form. |

SOLUTION   Two billion, nine hundred is 2,000,000,900. Again, many places needed zeros as place holders.   ■

Rounding Whole Numbers

We often **round** whole numbers by finding approximate values that are easier to use. If a car cost $7,995, we would probably say we paid $8,000 for it, rounding to the nearest thousand dollars. If a television set cost $350, we might say we paid $400, rounding to the nearest hundred dollars. Or if a bill at a restaurant were $22, we would probably say we spent $20, rounding to the nearest ten dollars. In each case, the approximate value is easier to say and use.

Why was $7,995 rounded to $8,000 to the nearest thousand dollars? Because 7,995 is between 7,000 and 8,000 or $7 \cdot 1,000$ and $8 \cdot 1,000$, one of the two numbers is the approximation to the nearest thousand. Because 7,995 is nearer to 8,000 than to 7,000, $7,995 rounds to $8,000 to the nearest thousand dollars.

Why was $350 rounded to $400 to the nearest hundred dollars? Because $350 is between 300 and 400 or 3 · 100 and 4 · 100, one of the two numbers is the approximation to the nearest hundred. Because 350 is halfway between 300 and 400, it is nearer to neither number. In such cases, we agree to round to the larger number, so $350 was rounded to $400 to the nearest hundred dollars.

Why was $22 rounded to $20 to the nearest ten dollars? Because $22 is between 20 or 30 or 2 · 10 or 3 · 10, one of the two numbers is the approximation to the nearest ten. Because 22 is closer to 20 than to 30, $22 is rounded to $20 to the nearest ten dollars.

We can use the **approximately equal symbol**, ≈, to express the relationship between the original whole number and the rounded number. We write $22 ≈ $20 to mean that $22 is *approximately equal* to $20 to the nearest ten dollars. Instead of determining which number is closer each time we round, we can use the following set of rules to round whole numbers:

ROUNDING WHOLE NUMBERS

1. **Identify the digit immediately to the right of the place value to which we are rounding.**

2. **If the digit is 0, 1, 2, 3, or 4 (digits less than 5), round down. Keep the digit in the place value to which we are rounding the same and replace the digit in each subsequent place to the right with 0.**

3. **If the digit is 5, 6, 7, 8, or 9 (digits 5 or greater), round up. Add 1 to the digit in the place value to which we are rounding and replace the digit in each subsequent place to the right with 0.**

4. **When rounding up, if the digit in the place to which we are rounding is a 9, replace it with a 0 and add 1 to the digit to the left. Continue to the left until all consecutive 9s have been replaced with 0s. When the last 9 is replaced by a 0, the digit to left of the last 9 is one greater than it was before.**

EXAMPLE 9	Round 1,942,587 to the nearest hundred thousand.

SOLUTION   1,942,587 ≈ 1,900,000 to the nearest hundred thousand.
The digit immediately to the right of the digit in the hundred thousands place is a 4, indicating that we round down. Keep the 9 in the hundred thousands place and replace the digits to the right with zeros. The 1 remains in the millions place.   ■

EXAMPLE 10	Round 972,555,552 to the nearest million.

SOLUTION   972,555,552 ≈ 973,000,000 to the nearest million.
The digit immediately to the right of the digit in the millions place is a 5, indicating that we round up. The 2 in the millions place is increased by 1, making it a 3. The digits to the right of the millions place are replaced with zeros. The 9 remains in the hundred millions place, and the 7 remains in the ten millions place.   ■

| EXAMPLE 11 | Round 999,999 to the nearest thousand. |

SOLUTION   999,999 ≈ 1,000,000 to the nearest thousand.
The digit immediately to the right of the digit in the thousands place is a 9, indicating that we round up. We replace the 9 with a 0 and add 1 to the digit to the left. We continue adding to the left. When the last 9 is replaced by a 0, the digit to left of the last 9 is one greater than it was before. As the millions place had no digit, a zero can be assumed to be in the millions place. Adding 1 to 0 gives us 1 in the millions place.   ■

P R A C T I C E   F O R   S U C C E S S

Answers for each set of Practice-for-Success problems are located after the exercises.

Practice 1.   Give the place value of the 6 in 786,451,290.
Practice 2.   Write 53,297 in both expanded forms.
Practice 3.   Write 129,306,078 using words.
Practice 4.   Write six million, twelve thousand, seventy-two in standard form.
Practice 5.   Round 23,865 to the nearest thousand.

EXERCISES 1.1

In exercises 1–15, write the name for the place value of the indicated digit.

1. Give the place value of 5 in 67,500,327.
2. Give the place value of 8 in 80,945,621.
3. Give the place value of 3 in 712,563,788.
4. Give the place value of 2 in 532,679,446.
5. Give the place value of 9 in 45,371,934.
6. Give the place value of 7 in 938,442,257.
7. Give the place value of 0 in 912,909,115.
8. Give the place value of 1 in 1,000,000,000.
9. Give the place value of 4 in 4,053,221,567.
10. Give the place value of 6 in 67,547,133,927,211.
11. Give the place value of 8 in 7,934,085.
12. Give the place value of 7 in 79,233,455,621.
13. Give the place value of 2 in 214,358,843,754,563.
14. Give the place value of 3 in 23,541,971.
15. Give the place value of 0 in 7,098,342.

In exercises 16–25, write each number in two expanded forms.

16. 55,671	**17.** 340,875	**18.** 4,871
19. 5,602,809	**20.** 23,479	**21.** 1
22. 106,803	**23.** 54,663	**24.** 4,019,009
25. 45,072,190		

In exercises 26–40, write each number in words.

26. 5,632	**27.** 45,001	**28.** 506,000
29. 1,294,543	**30.** 23,439,002,213	**31.** 599,000
32. 30,000	**33.** 5,621,345,772	**34.** 603,240,999
35. 44	**36.** 72,134,246,821	**37.** 2,002,009
38. 225,520	**39.** 542,636,119,004	**40.** 444,469

In exercises 41–55, write the given number in standard form.

41. Two thousand, five hundred seventy-nine

42. Five hundred thirty-four thousand, four hundred forty-four

43. Two thousand, one

44. Two million, five hundred three thousand, seventeen

45. Twenty-four billion, twenty million, four thousand, thirteen

46. Eight thousand, eight

47. Five hundred nine thousand, ninety-nine

48. Ten thousand, twenty-eight

49. Nine hundred thousand, eighty-four

50. Thirty-two million, six hundred eighty thousand

51. Two hundred forty-four billion

52. Fifty million, fifteen thousand

53. Nine hundred ten

54. Ten thousand, seventy-four

55. Three thousand, three hundred three

In exercises 56–65, round to the indicated place.

56. 85 to the nearest ten

57. 2,486 to the nearest thousand

58. 8,975,361 to the nearest ten thousand

59. 9,876,553 to the nearest hundred

60. 8,999,999 to the nearest hundred thousand

61. 3,999,995 to the nearest ten

62. 962 to the nearest thousand

63. 965,388 to the nearest million

64. 42,611,999 to the nearest ten thousand

65. 123,456,789 to the nearest ten million

PRACTICE-FOR-SUCCESS ANSWERS

---

1. millions
2. $53{,}297 = 5 \cdot 10{,}000 + 3 \cdot 1{,}000 + 2 \cdot 100 + 9 \cdot 10 + 7 \cdot 1$
   $= 50{,}000 + 3{,}000 + 200 + 90 + 7$
3. One hundred twenty-nine million, three hundred six thousand, seventy-eight
4. 6,012,072
5. 24,000

1.2 ADDITION AND SUBTRACTION

OBJECTIVES

- To add whole numbers
- To subtract whole numbers
- To use addition and subtraction to solve word problems
- To distinguish between "find the difference" and "subtract...from..."

The four fundamental operations used in arithmetic and algebra are addition, subtraction, multiplication, and division. In this section, we will learn about addition and subtraction using whole numbers.

Addition of Whole Numbers

Addition is the method of finding the total of two or more numbers. A **number line** can be used to help us understand addition. The number line for whole numbers starts at zero and continues forever to the right (see Figure 1.3).

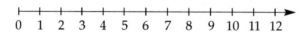

FIGURE 1.3   **Number line for whole numbers**

For the problem $3 + 4$, we place an arrow representing the first number (3) starting at zero and with a length of 3. Next, we place an arrow representing the second number (4) starting at the tip of the first arrow and extending to the right with a length of 4. The lengths of these two arrows together form the **sum** of the numbers (7) (see Figure 1.4). The sum is the result of an addition.

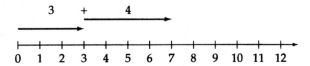

FIGURE 1.4   Number line showing addition

Of course, using a number line to add large numbers would be slow and awkward. To add large numbers, we arrange the numbers vertically, lining up the digits that have the same place value in the same column. Then, we start from the ones column and add the digits in each column going to the left.

| **EXAMPLE 1** | Add 4,812 + 3,147. |

SOLUTION
$$\begin{array}{r} 4{,}812 \\ +\ 3{,}147 \\ \hline 7{,}959 \end{array}$$ ■

In Example 1, the sum of the digits in any column is less than 10. When the sum of the digits is greater than 9, "carrying" is needed.

| **EXAMPLE 2** | Add 58 + 36. |

SOLUTION
$$\begin{array}{r} 58 \\ +\ 36 \end{array}$$ →   (5 tens) + (8 ones)
       →   (3 tens) + (6 ones)
            ─────────────────────
            (8 tens) + (14 ones)

At this point, we appear to have a problem because we cannot have a two-digit number (14) in a one-digit column. Instead, we can make use of the fact that 14 is 1 ten and 4 ones:

$$\begin{array}{r} 58 \\ +\ 36 \end{array}$$ →   (5 tens) + (8 ones)
       →   (3 tens) + (6 ones)
            ─────────────────────
            (8 tens) + (14 ones)
            (8 tens) + (1 ten) + (4 ones)
            (9 tens) + (4 ones)
94   ←   90 + 4

An easier way to write the preceding problem is to "carry" the 1 ten, which is indicated by placing a 1 above the 5 in the tens column:

$$\begin{array}{r} \overset{1}{} \\ 58 \\ +\ 36 \\ \hline 94 \end{array}$$ ■

Carrying can occur in any column and is necessary whenever the sum in a column exceeds 9. Also, the number being carried can be any digit from 1 to 9.

Addition is used to solve some application or word problems in mathematics. The first step in solving these problems is to read each problem carefully to determine exactly what is being asked. Because sometimes in real-life problems we have more information than we need, the second step is to figure out which numbers are needed to arrive at the correct solution.

EXAMPLE 3   202,500 dog owners have registered 109,236 cocker spaniels, 85,400 poodles, and 57,612 German shepherds with the American Kennel Club. How many dogs of these three varieties are registered?

SOLUTION
$$
\begin{array}{r}
{\scriptstyle 1\,2\,1} \\
109{,}236 \\
85{,}400 \\
+\quad 57{,}612 \\
\hline
252{,}248 \text{ dogs}
\end{array}
$$ ■

In Example 3 the number of dog owners is not asked for and therefore is not required to solve the problem. In a word problem, units such as "dogs" or "miles" are always included in the answer.

EXAMPLE 4   In the 1988 election, George Bush received 47,645,225 votes and Michael Dukakis received 40,797,905 votes. How many voters cast votes for these two candidates?

SOLUTION
$$
\begin{array}{r}
{\scriptstyle 1\ 111\ \ 1} \\
47{,}645{,}225 \\
+\ 40{,}797{,}905 \\
\hline
88{,}443{,}130 \text{ votes}
\end{array}
$$ ■

EXAMPLE 5   Leticia has $175 in her checking account. She gets checks for $75, $30, and $25, cashes the check for $25, and deposits the other two checks. What is her new checking account balance?

SOLUTION
$$
\begin{array}{r}
{\scriptstyle 1\,1} \\
\$175 \\
75 \\
+\quad 30 \\
\hline
\$280
\end{array}
$$

The check for $25 was not added because Leticia cashed that check.   ■

Subtraction of Whole Numbers

The second of the four fundamental operations is subtraction, which is the method of finding the difference between two numbers. The number line can also be used to illustrate subtraction (see Figure 1.5). For example, to determine the difference between 10 and 4, an arrow is drawn from 0 to 10 and then, starting at 10, another arrow with a length of 4 is drawn to the left.

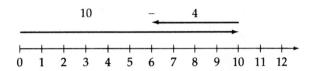

FIGURE 1.5   Number line showing subtraction of 10 and 4

The difference between the numbers is the point where the tip of the second arrow lies (6).

Because addition and subtraction are closely related, we can write two related math problems. For instance, if we borrow 10 books from a library and return 4, we have 6 remaining: $10 - 4 = 6$. Similarly, if 6 remain and we have returned 4, we know we had borrowed 10: $6 + 4 = 10$. Every subtraction problem can be restated as an addition problem, and vice versa. For this reason, addition and subtraction are called **inverse operations.**

To subtract large numbers, we arrange the numbers vertically, lining up the digits that have the same place value in the same column. As with addition, we start subtracting in the ones column and work from right to left.

EXAMPLE 6   Subtract $25,786 - 13,321$.

SOLUTION

25,786	**Check**	12,465		←difference
− 13,321		+ 13,321		←second number
12,465		25,786	√	←first number	■

We checked the answer to this example by using the inverse operation which, for a subtraction problem, is addition. If we add the difference to the second number, the sum should be the first number. Checking our work, when possible, greatly improves our chances for success and is well worth the extra time.

In Example 6 every digit in the second number is smaller than its corresponding digit in the first number. In the following examples, the lower digit is larger than the upper digit, and so "borrowing" is needed. Borrowing in subtraction is very similar to carrying in addition.

EXAMPLE 7   Subtract $82 - 67$.

SOLUTION

    82   →(8 tens) + (2 ones)
  − 67   →(6 tens) + (7 ones)

We cannot take 7 ones from 2 ones, so we "borrow" 1 ten and convert it into 10 ones. Rewriting the problem, we have:

    82   →(7 tens) + (12 ones)
  − 67   →(6 tens) + (7 ones)
    15   ←(1 ten)   + (5 ones)   ■

| **EXAMPLE 8** | Subtract $426 - 384$. |

SOLUTION

$$
\begin{array}{r}
426 \\
- \ 384 \\
\end{array}
\quad
\begin{array}{l}
\rightarrow (4\ \text{hundreds}) + (2\ \text{tens}) + (6\ \text{ones}) \\
\rightarrow (3\ \text{hundreds}) + (8\ \text{tens}) + (4\ \text{ones}) \\
\hline
\hphantom{\rightarrow (3\ \text{hundreds}) + (8\ \text{tens}) + } (2\ \text{ones})
\end{array}
$$

At this point, we cannot take 8 tens from 2 tens, so we borrow 1 hundred and convert it into 10 tens. Rewriting the problem, we have:

$$
\begin{array}{r}
426 \\
- \ 384 \\
\hline
42 \\
\end{array}
\quad
\begin{array}{l}
\rightarrow (3\ \text{hundreds}) + (12\ \text{tens}) + (6\ \text{ones}) \\
\rightarrow (3\ \text{hundreds}) + (\ 8\ \text{tens}) + (4\ \text{ones}) \\
\hline
\leftarrow (0\ \text{hundreds}) + (\ 4\ \text{tens}) + (2\ \text{ones})
\end{array}
$$
■

A more convenient way to write the preceding problem is to borrow the 1 hundred from the hundreds place by crossing out the 4 and writing a 3 above it. Next, we write a 1 next to the 2 in the tens column, making it a 12. Now it is possible to subtract in each column. When we subtract, we are now subtracting 4 from 6 in the ones column, 8 from 12 (instead of 2) in the tens column and 3 from 3 (instead of 4) in the hundreds column. Borrowing can be used as needed in any column.

$$
\begin{array}{r}
\overset{3}{\cancel{4}}{}^{1}2\,6 \\
- \ 3\,8\,4 \\
\hline
4\,2
\end{array}
$$

| **EXAMPLE 9** | Subtract $46{,}321 - 22{,}984$. |

SOLUTION

$$
\begin{array}{r}
{}^{5\,12\,11}_{} \\
4\,\cancel{6}{,}\cancel{3}\,\overset{}{2}{}^{1}\,1 \\
- \ 2\,2{,}9\,8\,4 \\
\hline
2\,3{,}3\,3\,7
\end{array}
$$

Check

$$
\begin{array}{r}
{}^{1\ 11} \\
23{,}337 \\
+ \ 22{,}984 \\
\hline
46{,}321 \quad \surd
\end{array}
$$
■

| **EXAMPLE 10** | Find the difference between 1,000,000,000 and 1,000,000. |

SOLUTION

"Find the difference" means that we are subtracting, so the calculation to be performed is $1{,}000{,}000{,}000 - 1{,}000{,}000$.

$$
\begin{array}{r}
{}^{9\ \ 9} \\
1{,}\cancel{0}{}^{1}\cancel{0}{}^{1}0{,}000{,}000 \\
- \ \ \ \ \ \ \ \ \ 1{,}000{,}000 \\
\hline
9\ 9\,9{,}000{,}000
\end{array}
$$
■

| **EXAMPLE 11** | Subtract 266 from 4,620. |

SOLUTION   When a problem says to subtract one number "from" another, it indicates that the number to subtract is the one that comes after the word *subtract* and is written second in our expression. Thus, the problem "Subtract 266 from 4,620" is written as 4,620 − 266.

$$\begin{array}{r} \overset{5\ 11}{4,\overset{1}{6}\overset{1}{2}0} \\ -\ \ \ 266 \\ \hline 4,354 \end{array}$$ ■

| **EXAMPLE 12** | A piece of lemon meringue pie has 305 calories, whereas a wedge of watermelon has 110 calories. How many more calories does the piece of lemon meringue pie have? |

SOLUTION
$$\begin{array}{r}\overset{2}{\cancel{3}}\overset{1}{}05\\-\ 110\\\hline 195 \text{ calories}\end{array}$$
Check
$$\begin{array}{r}\overset{1}{}195\\+\ 110\\\hline 305 \text{ calories} \ \sqrt{}\end{array}$$ ■

| **EXAMPLE 13** | Ms. Lucky won $10,000 in a radio station contest. She decided to use part of her winnings to pay for a Hawaiian vacation for her family and calculated that the vacation would cost $3,422. How much money would she have left over for a down payment on a Corvette? |

SOLUTION
$$\begin{array}{r}\$\ \overset{9\ \ 9\ \ 9}{\cancel{1}0\ 0\ 0\ 0}\\-\ \ \ 3,422\\\hline \$\ 6,578\end{array}$$
Check
$$\begin{array}{r}\$\ 6,578\\+\ \ 3,422\\\hline \$10,000\ \sqrt{}\end{array}$$ ■

| **EXAMPLE 14** | Nathaniel wants to buy a new car. The price of the car is $10,426, but he also wants air conditioning for an additional $485 and a compact disc system installed for an additional $272. If he has saved $2,225 for a down payment, what will be the balance he will owe the car dealership? |

SOLUTION
$$\begin{array}{r}\overset{1\ 1\ 1}{\$10,426}\\485\\+\ \ \ \ 272\\\hline \$11,183\end{array}$$
$$\begin{array}{r}\overset{10\ \ \ 7}{\$11,183}\\-\ \ \ 2,225\\\hline \$\ 8,958\end{array}$$ ■

First, we add the price of the car and the additional features to get the total cost. We then subtract the down payment to get the amount that Nathaniel will owe. ■

P R A C T I C E   F O R   S U C C E S S

Practice 1.   Add $333 + 241 + 26$.

Practice 2.   According to archaeologists, toothpicks have been used since 3500 BC (3500 BC indicates 3,500 years before the birth of Christ). Calculate the number of years humankind used the toothpick prior to 2001.

Practice 3.   Subtract $99,876 - 23,605$.

Practice 4.   Find the difference between 4,000 and 2,964.

Practice 5.   Subtract 1,000,000,000 from 1,000,000,000,000.

Practice 6.   Dr. Ruth Einstein (no relation to Albert) has built a time machine. Assuming she's currently visiting the year 2525 and that she sets the machine to go forward 1,229 years and then decides to drop back 663 years from there, in which year does she finally end up?

EXERCISES 1.2

In exercises 1–10, perform the indicated additions.

1. $76,395 + 399,488$

2. $196,996 + 1,990,025$

3. $385,807 + 687,995$

4. $39,327,797 + 15,563,769$

5. $774,656 + 2,989,796$

6. $379,583,669 + 557,398,775$

7. $2,779 + 35,669 + 576,886$

8. $54,778 + 632,997 + 1,556,887$

9. $457,873,966 + 56,887 + 544,995 + 663,779$

10. $102,130 + 371,251 + 4,294,269 + 2,026,952$

In exercises 11–24, perform the indicated subtractions.

11. $8,107,632 - 748,684$

12. $230,347 - 85,988$

13. $1,107,005 - 215,789$

14. $11,192 - 8,997$

15. $109,000 - 78,886$

16. $1,236,451 - 899,767$

17. $3,150,002 - 266,998$

18. $145,647 - 56,758$

19. $23,000,000 - 11,887,954$

20. $8,107,632 - 6,548,799$

21. $25,434,000 - 13,678,537$

22. $14,000,000 - 17,756$

23. $435,667,231 - 239,889,543$

24. $12,563,441 - 9,877,563$

Solve the word problems in exercises 25–40.

25. At one time the American Kennel Club had registered 94,803 cocker spaniels and 33,068 Yorkshire terriers. How many total registrations were there for these two breeds of dogs?

26. The deadweight tonnage of the Liberian oil tanker *Seawise Giant* is 564,739. The deadweight tonnage of the Japanese tanker *Jinko Maru* is 413,553. What is the total number of deadweight tons of these two tankers combined?

27. In one year the motor fuel consumption of cars in California was 12,628,000,000 gallons, and that for New York was 5,457,000,000 gallons. What was the total number of gallons of fuel consumed in both states for the given year?

28. In 1997 there were 70,385,073 passengers who passed through O'Hare Airport in Chicago. In the same year there were 60,142,588 passengers who passed through Los Angeles International Airport. How many more passengers passed through Chicago versus Los Angeles?

29. In 1997 there were 270,311,758 people in the United States while in the same year there were 125,931,533 people in Japan. There were 146,861,022 people living in Russia in that year. How many people total were living in the United States, Japan and Russia in 1997?

30. The following table lists the number of students enrolled in college with various majors.

Major	Number of Students
Art	2,149,000
Business	8,391,000
Engineering	5,899,000
Philosophy	2,702,000
Physical Education	2,324,000

What is the total number of enrolled students for all of the above-listed majors except philosophy?

31. An extremely rare circular-cut, purplish-red diamond sold for $926,315 per carat at Christies in New York City on April 27, 1987. Prior to this sale, the most expensive diamond sold for $127,000 per carat at Christies in Geneva. What is the total price per carat of both diamonds combined?

32. In the presidential elections in the United States for three of the recent election years, the number of people who actually voted was 91,594,693 in 1988 and 104,405,155 in 1992 and 96,456,345 in 1996. What was the total number of votes cast for these three elections?

33. Fred Newman made 20,371 basketball free throws out of a total of 22,049 shot attempts taken during a 24-hour period at Cal Tech in Pasadena, California. How many free throws did he miss?

34. In war, casualties are defined to include dead and wounded personnel but not those captured or listed as missing in action who subsequently returned to service. The following table lists the approximate number of casualties for various wars. How many more casualties have there been in wars including and after World War I compared to the number of casualties in the wars before World War I?

War	Number of Casualties
War of 1812	286,730
Mexican War	78,718
Civil War	2,213,363
Spanish–American War	306,760
World War I	4,743,826
World War II	16,353,659
Korean War	5,764,143
Vietnam War	8,744,000

35. The following table lists long-run Broadway plays in terms of days running. What is the total number of days of all these plays combined?

Play	Number of Days Running
Chorus Line	4,117
Oh, Calcutta	3,909
Grease	3,388
Fiddler on the Roof	3,242
Hello, Dolly	2,844
My Fair Lady	2,717
South Pacific	1,925

36. The following table lists the paid subscription figures for various magazines in the United States. What is the total number of paid subscriptions for all of these magazines combined?

Magazine	Subscriptions
Reader's Digest	17,866,798
TV Guide	17,115,233
Good Housekeeping	5,184,559
Ebony	1,705,455
Gentleman's Quarterly	642,156
Consumer's Digest	1,021,229
National Lampoon	451,096

37. The following table lists a few of the all-time box office movie hits. What is the total revenue of all of these movies?

Movie	Year	Box Office Receipts
Titanic	1997	$581,889,889
Star Wars	1997	$460,987,469
E.T.	1982	$399,804,539
Jurassic Park	1993	$356,839,725

38. The following table lists some of the top advertisers in the United States and the number of dollars of sales for 1983. Compared to Coca-Cola and Pepsi combined, how many more dollars are spent on the other kinds of advertisements?

Company	Number of Dollars
Procter & Gamble	$9,544,000
Sears, Roebuck & Co.	$32,637,000
General Motors Corp.	$66,160,000
K Mart Corp.	$17,785,700
PepsiCo Inc.	$6,714,000
Coca-Cola Co.	$4,071,400

39. The largest state in the United States is Alaska, which covers 591,004 square miles. The smallest state is Rhode Island, which is only 1,212 square miles. Iowa is a medium-sized state with 36,016 square miles. How much bigger is Alaska than Rhode Island?

40. The United States Pacific Coast shoreline is 40,298 miles long. If California comprises 3,427 of those miles, how many miles are left over for Alaska, Oregon, and Washington?

Looking Back

41. What is the place value of the digit 6 in the number 24,165,327,449?

42. Write the number 102,044,001 in words.

43. Write the number three million, six thousand, fourteen in standard form.

44. Write the number 4,037,263 in two expanded forms.

45. Round 7,963,554 to the nearest hundred thousand.

PRACTICE-FOR-SUCCESS ANSWERS

1. 600	**2.** 5,501	**3.** 76,271
4. 1,036	**5.** 999,000,000,000	**6.** 3,091

1.3   **MULTIPLICATION AND DIVISION**

OBJECTIVES

□   To multiply whole numbers
□   To divide whole numbers
□   To use multiplication and division to solve word problems

Multiplication of Whole Numbers

Another fundamental operation used with whole numbers is **multiplication.** Imagine you go to the video store four times and rent two videocassettes each time. You could calculate the number of videocassettes rented by adding 2 four times: $2 + 2 + 2 + 2 = 8$ (see Figure 1.6). However, with the operation of multiplication, the same problem is done much more easily. The problem using multiplication is $4 \cdot 2 = 8$.

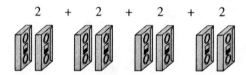

FIGURE 1.6   Multiplication as repeated addition

The raised dot, ·, is used to write the multiplication of two numbers in a horizontal form. Multiplication problems can also be written with the symbol × to indicate multiplication. For example, $4 \cdot 2 = 8$ can also be written as $4 \times 2 = 8$. However, in algebra, x is used to denote a variable, which may be confused with the multiplication symbol ×. So in algebra, the raised dot is preferred to the × symbol when multiplying two numbers. The raised dot is not the same as the decimal point, as in numbers such as 3.14 or 0.065.

Because $2 + 2 + 2 + 2 = 8$ and $4 \cdot 2 = 8$, we can define multiplication to be repeated addition of the same number. If we have the problem $6 \cdot 4$, then we know the answer can be found by adding $4 + 4 + 4 + 4 + 4 + 4 = 24$. However, knowing the multiplication fact $6 \cdot 4 = 24$ gets the job done much faster and keeps us from having to write several 4s.

The following multiplication table (see Figure 1.7) can be constructed using the fact that multiplication is simply repeated addition, as we have seen. By learning this table, our speed and proficiency in doing multiplication problems will increase. Memorizing these facts will make later computations much easier.

We can also illustrate multiplication by using the number line (see Figure 1.8). For example, if we have the problem $5 \cdot 3$, an arrow representing the whole number 3 can be drawn, end to end, 5 times.

The last arrow's tip reaches 15. The numbers that are being multiplied, 5 and 3, are called **factors** and the answer 15 is the **product.**

$$
\begin{array}{r}
5 \quad \leftarrow\text{factor} \\
\times\ \ 3 \quad \leftarrow\text{factor} \\
\hline
15 \quad \leftarrow\text{product}
\end{array}
$$

Multiplication with factors that have more than one digit requires using the multiplication facts several times.

×	1	2	3	4	5	6	7	8	9	10
1	1	2	3	4	5	6	7	8	9	10
2	2	4	6	8	10	12	14	16	18	20
3	3	6	9	12	15	18	21	24	27	30
4	4	8	12	16	20	24	28	32	36	40
5	5	10	15	20	25	30	35	40	45	50
6	6	12	18	24	30	36	42	48	54	60
7	7	14	21	28	35	42	49	56	63	70
8	8	16	24	32	40	48	56	64	72	80
9	9	18	27	36	45	54	63	72	81	90
10	10	20	30	40	50	60	70	80	90	100

FIGURE 1.7   Multiplication table

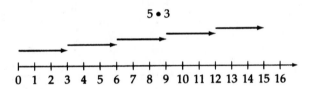

FIGURE 1.8   Number line depicting multiplication

| **EXAMPLE 1** | Multiply $23 \cdot 4$. |

SOLUTION

$$
\begin{array}{r}
\overset{1}{23} \\
\times\ 4 \\
\hline
92
\end{array}
$$

Multiply $4 \cdot 3$ in the ones place first and get 12. Carry the 1 ten, placing it above the 2 in the tens place. Then multiply $4 \cdot 2$ in the tens place and add the 1, which is carried to get a total of 9 in the tens place.   ■

| **EXAMPLE 2** | Multiply $87 \cdot 45$. |

SOLUTION

$$
\begin{array}{r}
87 \\
\times\ 45 \\
\hline
435 \\
3\ 480 \\
\hline
3{,}915
\end{array}
$$

Multiply $87 \cdot 5$ first to get 435. Then multiply $87 \cdot 4 = 348$. Because the 4 is in the tens place, the last digit (8) is lined up in the tens place. A zero can be placed in the ones place as a place holder. We then add the columns.   ■

EXAMPLE 3	An average heart rate for a human is 72 beats per minute. How many times would an average heart beat in an hour (60 minutes)?

SOLUTION

$$
\begin{array}{r}
72 \\
\times \quad 60 \\
\hline
0 \\
432 \\
\hline
4{,}320 \text{ heartbeats}
\end{array}
$$

or the problem can be written:

$$
\begin{array}{r}
72 \\
\times \quad 60 \\
\hline
4{,}320 \text{ heartbeats}
\end{array}
$$

Any number multiplied by 0 is 0, so 72 multiplied by 0 equals 0.   ■

> **MULTIPLYING BY ZERO**
>
> If n represents any number, $n \cdot 0 = 0$

The justification for the principle of multiplication by zero is the fact that multiplication is repeated addition: $5 \cdot 0 = 0 + 0 + 0 + 0 + 0 = 0$. When writing this principle, the letter n is used to represent any whole number. When a letter of the alphabet is used to represent more than one number, that letter is called a **variable.**

EXAMPLE 4	Multiply $423 \cdot 96$.

SOLUTION

$$
\begin{array}{r}
423 \\
\times \quad 96 \\
\hline
2\,538 \\
38\,070 \\
\hline
40{,}608
\end{array}
$$

■

EXAMPLE 5	One hot summer day, Jennie drank 12 glasses of lemonade. If each glass of lemonade had 106 calories, how many calories did she consume?

SOLUTION

$$
\begin{array}{r}
12 \\
\times \quad 106 \\
\hline
72 \\
000 \\
1\,200 \\
\hline
1{,}272 \text{ calories}
\end{array}
$$

or

$$
\begin{array}{r}
106 \\
\times \quad 12 \\
\hline
212 \\
1\,060 \\
\hline
1{,}272 \text{ calories}
\end{array}
$$

■

The second solution contains only two numbers to add. When we put the factor with fewer digits on the lower line of the multiplication, the result is fewer lines of numbers to add.

| **EXAMPLE 6** | A professional basketball team averaged 108 points per game during the season, including the playoff games. If the team played 104 games, how many points did the team score that season? |

SOLUTION

$$
\begin{array}{r}
108 \\
\times \quad 104 \\
\hline
432 \\
0\,000 \\
10\,800 \\
\hline
11{,}232 \text{ points}
\end{array}
$$

■

Division of Whole Numbers

We use division to separate objects into equal groups. For example, Carrie has a collection of 21 videocassettes. She has 3 different types of movies: action adventure films, comedies, and dramas. She discovers after sorting her movies that she has exactly the same amount of each type. In Figure 1.9 we see that Carrie has 7 videocassettes of each type.

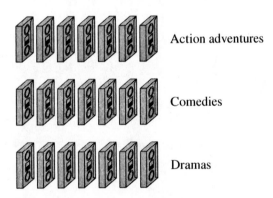

Action adventures

Comedies

Dramas

FIGURE 1.9   **21 divided into 3 equal categories**

Just as multiplication can be thought of as repeated addition, division can be considered to be repeated subtraction of the same number. Suppose 30 athletes in a coed basketball class are to be divided into teams of 5. How many teams can be made? This sample problem might be done in the following way:

$$
\begin{array}{ll}
30 - 5 = 25 & \leftarrow\text{1st subtraction} \\
25 - 5 = 20 & \leftarrow\text{2nd subtraction} \\
20 - 5 = 15 & \leftarrow\text{3rd subtraction} \\
15 - 5 = 10 & \leftarrow\text{4th subtraction} \\
10 - 5 = 5 & \leftarrow\text{5th subtraction} \\
5 - 5 = 0 & \leftarrow\text{6th subtraction}
\end{array}
$$

We see from this demonstration that we needed to do 6 subtractions before every player was placed on a team. This shows that 30 divided into groups of 5 results in 6 groups, or that $30 \div 5 = 6$. The symbol $\div$ is used to indicate division when the numbers are written horizontally on one line. Another notation is shown in the following problem. In this problem, the number being divided (30) is called the **dividend,** the number by which we are dividing (5) is called the **divisor** and the result or answer (6) is called the **quotient.**

$$\text{divisor} \to \quad \underset{5)\overline{30}}{\overset{6}{}} \quad \begin{matrix} \leftarrow\text{quotient} \\ \leftarrow\text{dividend} \end{matrix}$$

We learned in the previous section that addition and subtraction were inverse operations. Similarly, multiplication and division are inverse operations. From $30 \div 5 = 6$, we get the related multiplication fact $5 \cdot 6 = 30$, because the divisor multiplied by the quotient equals the dividend. We can use this fact to check division.

EXAMPLE 7

Divide $119 \div 7$.

Because dividing using repeated subtraction can be tedious, we divide using the following process, called the **division algorithm.**

Step 1:
$$\begin{array}{r} 1 \\ 7)\overline{119} \end{array}$$
Because we cannot divide 7 into 1, we divide 7 into the first two digits (11). Each number into which we divide must be at least as large as the divisor. 11 contains one group of 7, so we put 1 in the quotient above the second 1 (the last digit of the number into which we are dividing).

Step 2:
$$\begin{array}{r} 1 \\ 7)\overline{119} \\ 7 \end{array}$$
We multiply $1 \cdot 7 = 7$ and place the 7 under the 11.

Step 3:
$$\begin{array}{r} 1 \\ 7)\overline{119} \\ -\ 7 \\ \hline 4 \end{array}$$
Subtract 7 from 11. The result of each subtraction must be a number smaller than the divisor.

Step 4:
$$\begin{array}{r} 1 \\ 7)\overline{119} \\ -\ 7 \\ \hline 49 \end{array}$$
Bring down the 9.

Step 5:
$$\begin{array}{r} 17 \\ 7)\overline{119} \\ -\ 7 \\ \hline 49 \\ -49 \\ \hline 0 \end{array}$$
Repeat the process by dividing 49 by 7 and placing the result above the 9. Multiply $7 \cdot 7 = 49$ and subtract $49 - 49 = 0$.

Check
$$\begin{array}{r} 17 \\ \times\ \ 7 \\ \hline 119 \end{array} \quad \sqrt{} \quad \begin{matrix} \leftarrow\text{quotient} \\ \leftarrow\text{divisor} \\ \leftarrow\text{dividend} \end{matrix}$$

■

The algorithm was shown in detail to emphasize the four parts of the process. At each stage we divide, multiply, subtract, and then bring down. We repeat the process until no digits remain to bring down. The result of the final subtraction is called the **remainder.** In the previous example, the remainder was 0, indicating that 119 was divided by 7 evenly.

| **EXAMPLE 8** | Determine the quotient and the remainder when 308 is divided by 9. |

SOLUTION

$$
\begin{array}{r}
34\ \text{R2} \\
9\overline{)308} \\
-\ 27 \\
\hline
38 \\
-\ 36 \\
\hline
2
\end{array}
$$

remainder→ 2

Check

$$
\begin{array}{r}
34 \quad \leftarrow\text{quotient} \\
\times\ \ 9 \quad \leftarrow\text{divisor} \\
\hline
306 \\
+\ \ 2 \quad \leftarrow\text{remainder} \\
\hline
308 \ \surd \quad \leftarrow\text{dividend}
\end{array}
$$

■

In Example 8, 308 is divided by 9 and the result is 34 equal groups with a remainder of 2. In the check we multiply the quotient by the divisor and add the remainder. If our work is correct, our sum is the dividend. The formula for verifying that a division is correct is called the **division check.**

DIVISION CHECK

quotient × divisor + remainder = dividend

| **EXAMPLE 9** | Seven computers have a total combined memory of 7,168 kilobytes. Each computer has the same amount of memory. How much memory does each computer have? |

SOLUTION

$$
\begin{array}{r}
1{,}024 \ \text{kilobytes} \\
7\overline{)7{,}168} \\
-7 \\
\hline
0\ 1 \\
-\ 0 \\
\hline
16 \\
-\ 14 \\
\hline
28 \\
-\ 28 \\
\hline
0
\end{array}
$$

Check

$$
\begin{array}{r}
1{,}024 \\
\times\ \ 7 \\
\hline
7{,}168 \ \ \surd
\end{array}
$$

At one point we attempted to divide 7 into 1 but because 7 is smaller than 1, we needed the place holder 0 in the quotient.   ■

| **EXAMPLE 10** | Divide $923 \div 17$. |

SOLUTION   This example has a two-digit divisor. As our multiplication table (Figure 1.7) stops at $10 \cdot 10$, it is helpful to create our own times table for 17.

$\begin{array}{r} 17 \\ \times\ 1 \\ \hline 17 \end{array}$	$\begin{array}{r} 17 \\ \times\ 2 \\ \hline 34 \end{array}$	$\begin{array}{r} 17 \\ \times\ 3 \\ \hline 51 \end{array}$	$\begin{array}{r} 17 \\ \times\ 4 \\ \hline 68 \end{array}$	$\begin{array}{r} 17 \\ \times\ 5 \\ \hline 85 \end{array}$	$\begin{array}{r} 17 \\ \times\ 6 \\ \hline 102 \end{array}$	$\begin{array}{r} 17 \\ \times\ 7 \\ \hline 119 \end{array}$	$\begin{array}{r} 17 \\ \times\ 8 \\ \hline 136 \end{array}$	$\begin{array}{r} 17 \\ \times\ 9 \\ \hline 153 \end{array}$

$$
\begin{array}{r}
54\ \text{R5} \\
17\overline{)923} \\
-\ 85 \quad \leftarrow \text{Using our table, } 17 \cdot 5 = 85 \\
\hline
73 \\
-\ 68 \quad \leftarrow \text{Using our table again, } 17 \cdot 4 = 68 \\
\hline
5
\end{array}
$$

■

Although making a table for two-digit divisors is an excellent way to increase success, it is time-consuming. Instead, we can do division with two-digit divisors using estimation.

| **EXAMPLE 11** | Find the quotient of 744 divided by 31. |

SOLUTION   **Step 1:**
$$
\begin{array}{r}
2 \\
31\overline{)744} \\
-\ 62 \\
\hline
124
\end{array}
$$
Because 7 is smaller than 31, we divide 31 into 74. We need to find the largest number that, when multiplied by 31, is less than 74. If we ignore for the moment the last digit in each number, we have the problem 3 into 7, which gives us an opening estimate of 2. Multiplying $31 \cdot 2 = 62$, which is close to 74, confirms that our estimate is correct.

Step 2:
$$
\begin{array}{r}
24 \\
31\overline{)744} \\
-\ 62 \\
\hline
124 \\
-\ 124 \\
\hline
0
\end{array}
$$
We are dividing 31 into 124. If we again ignore the last digit in each number, we have the problem 3 into 12, which gives us an opening estimate of 4. Multiplying $31 \cdot 4 = 124$ confirms that our estimate is accurate.

■

EXAMPLE 12	James has an annual income of $10,080. How much is his monthly income?

SOLUTION   Because a year has 12 months, divide the yearly (annual) income by 12.

Step 1:
$$\begin{array}{r} 8 \\ 12\overline{)10{,}080} \\ -96 \\ \hline 48 \end{array}$$

As 12 is larger than 1 or 10, divide 12 into 100, ignoring the last digit in each number. The problem 1 into 10 gives an opening estimate of 10, which does not fit in a one-digit column, so the estimate 10 is too large. $9 \cdot 12 = 108$, which is still too large, but $8 \cdot 12 = 96$, which is less than 100.

Step 2:
$$\begin{array}{r} 84 \\ 12\overline{)10{,}080} \\ -96 \\ \hline 48 \\ -48 \\ \hline 00 \end{array}$$

Divide 12 into 48 and, again, ignore the last digit in each number. The problem 1 into 4 gives an opening guess of 4. Multiplying $4 \cdot 12 = 48$ shows that 4 is a good estimate.

Step 3:
$$\begin{array}{r} 840 \\ 12\overline{)10{,}080} \\ -96 \\ \hline 48 \\ -48 \\ \hline 00 \\ -0 \\ \hline 0 \end{array}$$

Divide 12 into 0. Because 12 goes into 0 zero times, place the digit 0 in the ones column.

James has a monthly income of $840.   ■

PRACTICE FOR SUCCESS

Practice 1.   Multiply $47 \cdot 91$

Practice 2.   Multiply $765 \cdot 23$

Practice 3.   In 1997, the *Los Angeles Times* had a circulation of 1,050,176. How many newspapers were delivered in that year, assuming there are 365 days in a year?

Practice 4.   Divide $5{,}226 \div 3$

Practice 5.   Divide $1{,}000 \div 19$

Practice 6.   The Martinez family took a 6,860-mile trip across the United States and back. They traveled approximately the same number of miles each day. About how many miles did they travel each day if the trip took 2 weeks to complete?

EXERCISES 1.3

In exercises 1–15, perform the indicated multiplications.

1. $2,634 \cdot 8$
2. $487 \cdot 45$
3. $385 \cdot 39$
4. $4,036 \cdot 253$
5. $6,387 \cdot 586$
6. $7,892 \cdot 574$
7. $3,754 \cdot 877$
8. $9,009 \cdot 854$
9. $9,200 \cdot 670$
10. $8,897 \cdot 978$
11. $10,062 \cdot 534$
12. $336 \cdot 1,897$
13. $10,208 \cdot 349$
14. $8,000 \cdot 860$
15. $747 \cdot 1,037$

In exercises 16–30, perform the indicated divisions. Find the quotient, and when the remainder is nonzero, also write the remainder. (For example, 30 ÷ 7 = 4 R2.)

16. $325 \div 8$
17. $673 \div 7$
18. $2,528 \div 9$
19. $13,581 \div 3$
20. $38,136 \div 42$
21. $4,065 \div 39$
22. $305,122 \div 61$
23. $85,660 \div 42$
24. $312,160 \div 39$
25. $2,292 \div 56$
26. $325,620 \div 324$
27. $2,420,032 \div 548$
28. $371,712 \div 528$
29. $156,078 \div 780$
30. $225,225 \div 4,500$

In exercises 31–50, use multiplication or division as required to solve the given word problem.

31. One square foot consists of 144 square inches. How many square inches are in 65 square feet?

32. One gallon is equivalent to 231 cubic inches. How many cubic inches are in 89 gallons?

33. If a mile consists of 5,280 feet and a yard consists of 3 feet, how many yards are in one mile?

34. If 1 ounce of cheddar cheese contains 115 calories, how many total calories are in 85 ounces of the cheese?

35. The total profit from a certain stock is $90,750, and this amount is to be distributed among 375 stockholders. What amount should each stockholder expect to receive?

36. If in the United States 40,248,000 ounces of silver are produced in one year, how many ounces of silver would be expected over a 25-year period?

37. A case of cherry Coke consists of 24 cans. How many cases can be made from a group of 7,296 cans?

38. One year in California the average beginning teacher earned $19,038. What would the total income be for 35 such teachers?

39. If a book publisher takes in $18,360 from the sales of an art book that costs $17 per copy, how many books did the publisher sell?

40. If 12 inches equal one foot and 5,280 feet equal one mile, how many inches are in one mile?

41. If you earn a salary of $3,235 per month, how much money will you have earned after 5 years?

42. While planning a wedding, Joan is responsible for obtaining the catering services. Assuming she is quoted a price of $18 per person, what will the cost be for a wedding with 175 people?

43. One minute is equivalent to 60 seconds, and one hour is equivalent to 60 minutes. How many hours are in 1,807,200 seconds?

44. A regular tetrahedron is a 3-dimensional figure that has four equal faces, each of which is an equilateral triangle. If in one example of a tetrahedron each face has eighty-one square inches of area, how many square inches are there in the surface area of the entire tetrahedron?

45. New Jersey has an area of 7,468 square miles. California has an area of approximately 156,828 square miles. How many times could New Jersey fit inside California?

46. If a professional bowler averages a score of 209 per game, what would be the expected total score for the player over a season of 975 games?

47. A single sheet of computer paper has 44 holes down both sides. If a box of computer paper contains 3,500 sheets, how many individual holes are there in all the sheets in the box?

48. If an interest-free loan for $15,048 is to be paid off in 72 equal monthly payments, how much is each payment?

49. If Nevada has a population of approximately 800,000 people, and New York has a population of 18,000,000 people, approximately how many times bigger is New York compared to Nevada in terms of population?

50. The distance between Boston and New York City is 206 miles. The distance between Philadelphia and San Francisco is 2,866 miles. Driving once from Philadelphia to San Francisco is equivalent to making approximately how many trips between Boston and New York?

Looking Back

51. Subtract 476,997 from 9,436,332.

52. What is the place value of the digit 8 in the number 845,531,996?

53. Europe is approximately 4,017,000 square miles in area. Australia is approximately 2,966,000 square miles in area. How much bigger is Europe compared to Australia?

54. The Pacific Ocean is approximately 64,186,300 square miles in area. The Atlantic Ocean is approximately 33,420,000 square miles in area. How much bigger is the Pacific Ocean compared to the Atlantic Ocean?

PRACTICE-FOR-SUCCESS ANSWERS

1. 4,277   **2.** 17,595   **3.** 383,314,240 newspapers

4. 1,742   **5.** 52 R12   **6.** 490 miles

1.4 EXPONENTS

OBJECTIVES

☐ To distinguish bases and exponents

☐ To read and expand numbers in exponential form

☐ To simplify numbers in exponential form

When learning arithmetic, we commonly study addition before multiplication because multiplication is defined in terms of repeated addition. When we multiply $5 \cdot 6$, we can think of the first number being added to itself several times. The number of times the first number is repeated is indicated by the second number.

$$5 \cdot 6 = 5 + 5 + 5 + 5 + 5 + 5$$

Six 5s are being added, which shows that multiplication can be viewed as repeated addition. This fact corresponds to how students first begin to understand multiplication. Another notation, **exponential notation,** is used to represent a different repeated operation: multiplication.

$$5^6 = 5 \cdot 5 \cdot 5 \cdot 5 \cdot 5 \cdot 5$$

Just as in the preceding multiplication example, the second number (6) tells how many times to write the first number (5). The difference is that the 5s are now multiplied instead of added, and the number 6 is written as a superscript just above and to the right of 5. As another example,

$$8^4 = 8 \cdot 8 \cdot 8 \cdot 8$$

The first number (8) is written as many times as is indicated by the exponent (4). In exponential notation, the first number is called the **base** and the second number, which is written as a superscript, is called the **exponent.** In exponential notation, the exponent tells how many times the base is to be used as a factor.

| **EXAMPLE 1** | Identify the base and exponent of: **a.** 10^{12} **b.** 3^9 **c.** 4^5 |

SOLUTION **a.** In 10^{12}, the base is 10 and the exponent is 12.

b. In 3^9, the base is 3 and the exponent is 9.

c. In 4^5, the base is 4 and the exponent is 5. ■

| **EXAMPLE 2** | Expand: **a.** 7^4 **b.** 3^6 **c.** 8^5 |

SOLUTION **a.** $7^4 = 7 \cdot 7 \cdot 7 \cdot 7$

b. $3^6 = 3 \cdot 3 \cdot 3 \cdot 3 \cdot 3 \cdot 3$

c. $8^5 = 8 \cdot 8 \cdot 8 \cdot 8 \cdot 8$ ■

In arithmetic it does not make any difference if we write $3 \cdot 4$ or $4 \cdot 3$, because the answer turns out to be 12 in both cases. However, if the base and exponent are different numbers and we switch their order, we get entirely different results; 4 raised to the third power is different from 3 raised to the fourth power.

$$4^3 = 4 \cdot 4 \cdot 4$$
$$= 16 \cdot 4$$
$$= 64$$
$$3^4 = 3 \cdot 3 \cdot 3 \cdot 3$$
$$= 9 \cdot 3 \cdot 3$$
$$= 27 \cdot 3$$
$$= 81$$

| **EXAMPLE 3** | Simplify the following exponential forms. **a.** 2^3 **b.** 3^2 **c.** 5^4 |

SOLUTION **a.** $2^3 = 2 \cdot 2 \cdot 2$
$$= 4 \cdot 2$$
$$= 8$$

b. $3^2 = 3 \cdot 3$
$$= 9$$

c. $5^4 = 5 \cdot 5 \cdot 5 \cdot 5$
$$= 25 \cdot 5 \cdot 5$$
$$= 125 \cdot 5$$
$$= 625$$ ■

Exponents are sometimes called *powers* of the base, and numbers in exponential form are read as follows:

5^6 is read as "five to the sixth power" or as "five to the power of six"

3^4 is read as "three to the fourth power" or as "three to the power of four"

Special names related to area and volume are associated with second and third powers.

The formula for the area of a square is

$$\boxed{\text{Area of a square} = \text{side} \cdot \text{side}}$$

Now, if our square measures 4 feet on a side (as shown in Figure 1.10), then the area of the square is $4 \cdot 4 = 4^2 = 16$ square feet. So sometimes second powers are called *square powers* or more simply *squares*, and 4^2 can be read as "four squared."

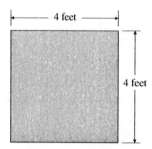

FIGURE 1.10   A square measuring 4 feet on a side

The formula for the volume of a cube is

$$\boxed{\text{Volume of a cube} = \text{side} \cdot \text{side} \cdot \text{side}}$$

If we have a cube that measures 4 feet on a side (as illustrated in Figure 1.11), then the volume of the cube is $4 \cdot 4 \cdot 4 = 4^3 = 64$ cubic feet. Consequently, sometimes third powers are called *cubes*, and a number such as 4^3 may be read as "four cubed."

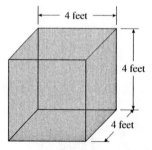

FIGURE 1.11   A cube measuring 4 feet on a side

EXAMPLE 4   Write the following numbers using words. **a.** 7^3 **b.** 9^2 **c.** 4^8

SOLUTION   **a.** 7^3 can be written as "seven cubed."

b. 9^2 can be written as "nine squared."

c. 4^8 can be written as "four to the eighth power."   ■

Sometimes people think 4^3 means to multiply 4 by itself three times. But this is misleading because $4^3 = 4 \cdot 4 \cdot 4$ shows that the number 4 is used as a factor three times but only two multiplications are needed. The actual number of multiplication operations is always one less than the exponent.

It also possible to use 1 as an exponent. When we write 5^1, the exponent 1 tells us how many 5s to write; just one. No multiplications are to be performed, so $5^1 = 5$. Any number to a power of 1 is just that number.

EXAMPLE 5   Expand 2^6 and then simplify to a single number.

SOLUTION   We begin by expanding the exponent and then we rewrite several lines, each time performing one more product with 2, starting on the left.

$$2^6 = 2 \cdot 2 \cdot 2 \cdot 2 \cdot 2 \cdot 2$$
$$= 4 \cdot 2 \cdot 2 \cdot 2 \cdot 2$$
$$= 8 \cdot 2 \cdot 2 \cdot 2$$
$$= 16 \cdot 2 \cdot 2$$
$$= 32 \cdot 2$$
$$= 64$$ ■

EXAMPLE 6   Simplify $3^2 \cdot 5^2 \cdot 7^2$.

SOLUTION   We simplify the three numbers in exponential form to single numbers and then we multiply them.

$$3^2 \cdot 5^2 \cdot 7^2 = 9 \cdot 25 \cdot 49$$
$$= 225 \cdot 49$$
$$= 11,025$$ ■

PRACTICE FOR SUCCESS

Practice 1   Expand 6^3 and then simplify to a single number.

Practice 2   Expand 7^4 and then simplify to a single number.

Practice 3   Expand $3^3 \cdot 5^2$ and then simplify to a single number.

Practice 4   Expand $2^4 \cdot 7^2 \cdot 8^1$ and then simplify to a single number.

EXERCISES 1.4

Compute the powers and products of powers in exercises 1–69. Write your solutions using several lines as necessary before writing the final numerical value.

1. $2^3 =$ 2. $3^4 =$ 3. $3^2 =$

4. $4^3 =$ 5. $4^5 =$ 6. $2^7 =$

7. $5^4 =$ 8. $7^2 =$ 9. $6^3 =$

10. $5^3 =$ 11. $3^6 =$ 12. $3^5 =$

13. $3^7 =$ 14. $2^6 =$ 15. $7^3 =$

16. $2^8 =$ 17. $3^3 =$ 18. $2^{10} =$

19. $4^4 =$ 20. $2^{12} =$ 21. $5^5 =$

22. $2^{14} =$ 23. $6^6 =$ 24. $2^{16} =$

25. $2^{11} =$ 26. $2^{13} =$ 27. $1^{100} =$

28. $0^{10} =$ 29. $0^{100} =$ 30. $0^{1000} =$

31. $1^{1001} =$ 32. $10^5 =$ 33. $10^{10} =$

34. $0^{30} =$ 35. $100^3 =$ 36. $100^5 =$

37. $1,000^3 =$ 38. $1,000^5 =$ 39. $20^3 =$

40. $10,000^2 =$ 41. $1,000,000^2 =$

42. $2^2 \cdot 2^5 =$ (compare this problem with problem 6)

43. $2^4 \cdot 2^6 =$ (compare this problem with problem 18)

44. $3^2 \cdot 3^4 =$ (compare this problem with problem 11)

45. $3^2 \cdot 3^5 =$ (compare this problem with problem 13)

46. $2^2 \cdot 2^5 \cdot 2^7 =$ (compare this problem with problem 22)

47. $2^2 \cdot 2^4 \cdot 2^3 \cdot 2^2 =$ (compare this problem with problem 25)

48. $2^2 \cdot 2^{10} \cdot 2^4 =$ (compare this problem with problem 24)

49. $3^4 \cdot 5^2 =$ 50. $3^1 \cdot 3^3 =$ 51. $2^3 \cdot 2^2 \cdot 2^1 =$

52. $2^4 \cdot 5^2 =$ 53. $2^3 \cdot 5^1 \cdot 7^2 =$ 54. $3^2 \cdot 5^3 \cdot 11^1 =$

55. $541^1 =$ 56. $733^1 =$ 57. $2^2 \cdot 3^1 \cdot 5^2 =$

58. $2^4 \cdot 3^2 \cdot 5^2 =$ 59. $2^1 \cdot 3^3 \cdot 7^2 =$ 60. $3^2 \cdot 5^2 \cdot 7^2 =$

61. $2^3 \cdot 5^1 \cdot 11^2 =$ 62. $2^2 \cdot 3^2 \cdot 5^2 =$ 63. $3^2 \cdot 3^3 \cdot 3^1 =$

64. $2^1 \cdot 3^1 \cdot 5^2 \cdot 7^1 =$ 65. $2^2 \cdot 3^2 \cdot 7^2 \cdot 13^1 =$ 66. $2^3 \cdot 3^2 \cdot 5^1 \cdot 7^2 =$

67. $2^3 \cdot 5^2 \cdot 11^1 =$ 68. $3^4 \cdot 13^2 =$ 69. $2^9 \cdot 3^2 \cdot 7^1 =$

Looking Back

70. What is the place value of 8 in the number 780,455,631?

71. Perform the division $15,050 \div 25$.

72. Write the number 56,783 in two expanded forms.

73. Write the number 504,044,096 in words.

74. The Matterhorn in Switzerland is 14,690 feet high, whereas Mount Kilimanjaro in Tanzania is 19,340 feet high. How much higher is Mount Kilimanjaro compared to the Matterhorn?

75. The Gulf of California has an area of 59,100 square miles, whereas the Hudson Bay covers an area that is 281,900 square miles. Approximately how many times is the Hudson Bay larger than the Gulf of California?

76. Round 989,654,132 to the nearest million.

PRACTICE-FOR-SUCCESS ANSWERS

1. 216   **2.** 2,401   **3.** 675   **4.** 6,272

| **1.5** | **ORDER OF OPERATIONS AND GROUPING SYMBOLS** |

OBJECTIVES

☐ To simplify expressions containing fundamental operations and exponents

☐ To simplify expressions containing grouping symbols

☐ To identify the basic operation for any expression

In this section we will simplify mathematical expressions. We define an **expression** to be a single term or a series of terms that are combined by the operations of addition and/or subtraction. For example, $5 + 8 - 10$ is an example of an expression that contains two operations that connect three terms. In this example each term is a single number, but a **term** can be defined to be either a single number or a series of numbers that are combined by the operations of multiplication and/or division. As an example, $5 \cdot 13 + 84 \div 4 \div 3$ is an expression that consists of one addition operation that connects two terms. The two terms in this case are $5 \cdot 13$ and $84 \div 4 \div 3$.

What happens when we have an expression with more than one operation? We need to know what to do first: add, subtract, multiply, or divide. For example, what is the value of the mathematical expression

$$2 + 3 \cdot 7$$

Some people might think the answer is 35, whereas others might think the answer is 23. People who think the answer is 35 would add 2 and 3 before multiplying by 7, whereas those who arrive at 23 do so by first multiplying 3 and 7 and then adding 2. The correct answer is 23. In this problem we multiply before we add according to the following *order of operations agreement*, which has been adopted by mathematicians worldwide.

> ## ORDER OF OPERATIONS AGREEMENT I
>
> **To simplify mathematical expressions without exponents or grouping symbols:**
>
> 1. **We first do all multiplications or divisions in the problem. When a single term contains more than one multiplication and/or division, we perform these operations as they occur from left to right.**
> 2. **We then do all additions or subtractions in the problem. When an expression contains more than one addition or subtraction of terms, we perform the additions and subtractions as they occur from left to right.**

EXAMPLE 1	Simplify $21 \div 7 + 8 \cdot 4$

SOLUTION

$$
\begin{aligned}
21 \div 7 + 8 \cdot 4 &= 3 + 8 \cdot 4 &&\text{Divide 21 by 7.} \\
&= 3 + 32 &&\text{Multiply 8 times 4.} \\
&= 35 &&\text{Add 3 and 32.} \quad ■
\end{aligned}
$$

EXAMPLE 2	Simplify $100 - 50 - 25 + 45$

SOLUTION

$$
\begin{aligned}
100 - 50 - 25 + 45 &= 50 - 25 + 45 &&\text{Subtract 50 from 100.} \\
&= 25 + 45 &&\text{Subtract 25 from 50.} \\
&= 70 &&\text{Add 25 and 45.}
\end{aligned}
$$

Because no multiplications or divisions occur in this example, we begin by working the additions and subtractions from left to right.   ■

EXAMPLE 3	Simplify $50 \div 10 \div 5 + 36 \div 3 \cdot 2$

SOLUTION

$$
\begin{aligned}
50 \div 10 \div 5 + 36 \div 3 \cdot 2 &= 5 \div 5 + 36 \div 3 \cdot 2 &&\text{Divide 50 by 10.} \\
&= 1 + 36 \div 3 \cdot 2 &&\text{Divide 5 by 5.} \\
&= 1 + 12 \cdot 2 &&\text{Divide 36 by 3.} \\
&= 1 + 24 &&\text{Multiply 12 times 2.} \\
&= 25 &&\text{Add 1 and 24.}
\end{aligned}
$$

In this example, we start with the leftmost division and continue doing divisions from left to right. In the second term, we do the division and then the multiplication, and finally we do the remaining addition.   ■

We simplify mathematical expressions by performing one operation at a time until no more operations are left. We show our work "top down," writing each line under the previous one, making sure to line up the equal signs.

Suppose we have a mathematical expression with more than one operation that contains exponents: for example, $4 + 7^2$. Because **exponentiation** is a higher level operation than any of the four fundamental operations, we do 7^2 first, which equals 49. We then add the 4 to simplify the expression to 53. Now we need to expand our order of operations agreement to include exponents.

ORDER OF OPERATIONS AGREEMENT II

To simplify mathematical expressions without grouping symbols:

1. **We first simplify all exponential expressions.**
2. **Next, we do all multiplications or divisions in the problem. When a single term contains more than one multiplication and/or division, we perform these operations as they occur from left to right.**
3. **Lastly, we do all additions or subtractions in the problem. When an expression contains more than one addition or subtraction of terms, we perform the additions and subtractions as they occur from left to right.**

| **EXAMPLE 4** | Simplify $72 - 2^5$ |

SOLUTION

$$72 - 2^5 = 72 - 32 \qquad \text{Simplify } 2^5.$$
$$= 40 \qquad\qquad \text{Subtract 32 from 72.} \quad ■$$

| **EXAMPLE 5** | Simplify $5^2 + 12^2$ |

SOLUTION

$$5^2 + 12^2 = 25 + 12^2 \qquad 5^2 \text{ simplifies to 25.}$$
$$= 25 + 144 \qquad 12^2 \text{ simplifies to 144.}$$
$$= 169 \qquad\qquad \text{Add 25 and 144.} \quad ■$$

| **EXAMPLE 6** | Simplify $4^2 + 2 \cdot 7 \cdot 4 - 3^3$ |

SOLUTION

$$4^2 + 2 \cdot 7 \cdot 4 - 3^3 = 16 + 2 \cdot 7 \cdot 4 - 3^3 \qquad \text{Simplify } 4^2.$$
$$= 16 + 2 \cdot 7 \cdot 4 - 27 \qquad \text{Simplify } 3^3.$$
$$= 16 + 14 \cdot 4 - 27 \qquad \text{Multiply 2 times 7.}$$
$$= 16 + 56 - 27 \qquad \text{Multiply 14 times 4.}$$
$$= 72 - 27 \qquad\qquad \text{Add 16 and 56.}$$
$$= 45 \qquad\qquad\qquad \text{Subtract 27 from 72.} \quad ■$$

In mathematical expressions, we often find **grouping symbols**. These include parentheses (), square brackets [], and curly braces {}. Grouping symbols are used to change the standard order in which operations are otherwise done using the previously stated rules. Referring back to $2 + 3 \cdot 7$, if we want to add before multiplying, we can change the problem by inserting a pair of parentheses around $2 + 3$. The problem then becomes $(2 + 3) \cdot 7$. Now the final answer will be 35 because whenever we have grouping symbols we perform the operations within the grouping symbols first. Thus,

$$(2 + 3) \cdot 7 = 5 \cdot 7 = 35$$

Again, the order of operations agreement needs to be expanded to include the use of grouping symbols to dictate which operations should be done first.

ORDER OF OPERATIONS AGREEMENT III

To simplify any mathematical expression:

1. **If grouping symbols are used, we simplify within each innermost pair of grouping symbols until no grouping symbols remain.**
2. **Within the innermost pair of grouping symbols, we first simplify all exponential expressions.**
3. **Then, within the innermost grouping symbol pair, we do all multiplications or divisions in the problem. When a single term contains more than one multiplication and/or division, we perform these operations as they occur from left to right.**
4. **Finally, within the innermost grouping symbol pair, we do all additions or subtractions in the problem. When an expression contains more than one addition or subtraction of terms, we perform the additions and subtractions as they occur from left to right.**
5. **When a grouping symbol pair encloses a single number, that pair of grouping symbols can be omitted.**

The Order of Operations Agreement III includes the previous two agreements and can be used to simplify any mathematical expression.

EXAMPLE 7 | Simplify $16 \div (4 - 2)$

SOLUTION | $16 \div (4 - 2) = 16 \div 2$ Simplify $(4 - 2)$.
            $= 8$ Divide 16 by 2. ■

EXAMPLE 8 | Simplify $(35 + 7) \div (18 - 12) \cdot 4$

SOLUTION | $(35 + 7) \div (18 - 12) \cdot 4 = 42 \div (18 - 12) \cdot 4$ Simplify $(35 + 7)$.
                              $= 42 \div 6 \cdot 4$ Simplify $(18 - 12)$.
                              $= 7 \cdot 4$ Divide 42 by 6.
                              $= 28$ Multiply 7 times 4.

The expression given has two separate pairs of parentheses. When an expression has more than one pair of grouping symbols, simplify within each grouping symbol pair. ■

EXAMPLE 9	Simplify $7 + (37 - 3^2)$

SOLUTION

$$
\begin{aligned}
7 + (37 - 3^2) &= 7 + (37 - 9) && \text{Simplify } 3^2. \\
&= 7 + 28 && \text{Simplify } (37 - 9). \\
&= 35 && \text{Add 7 and 28.}
\end{aligned}
$$

The first expression has more than one operation inside of a pair of parentheses. We use Order of Operations Agreement III and simplify the exponent before adding. When multiple operations occur inside a grouping symbol pair, follow Order of Operations Agreement II *inside* the grouping symbol pair. ■

EXAMPLE 10	Simplify $3 \cdot (2 + 5 \cdot 3^2)^2$

SOLUTION

$$
\begin{aligned}
3 \cdot (2 + 5 \cdot 3^2)^2 &= 3 \cdot (2 + 5 \cdot 9)^2 && \text{Simplify } 3^2. \\
&= 3 \cdot (2 + 45)^2 && \text{Multiply 5 times 9.} \\
&= 3 \cdot 47^2 && \text{Add 2 and 45.} \\
&= 3 \cdot 2{,}209 && \text{Simplify } 47^2. \\
&= 6{,}627 && \text{Multiply 3 times 2,209.}
\end{aligned}
$$
■

In mathematical expressions we often find grouping symbols *nested* within other grouping symbols. For a problem such as $13 \cdot [(16 - 8) \div 2]$, mathematicians have agreed to simplify inside the innermost grouping symbol pair first. In this problem we subtract $16 - 8$ first because this operation is inside the innermost grouping symbol pair. We then divide by 2, operating inside the square brackets, and our quotient is 4. Multiplying by 13, we get our final answer, 52.

EXAMPLE 11	Simplify $5 \cdot [(37 - 7 \cdot 2) - 7]$

SOLUTION

$$
\begin{aligned}
5 \cdot [(37 - 7 \cdot 2) - 7] &= 5 \cdot [(37 - 14) - 7] && \text{Multiply 7 times 2.} \\
&= 5 \cdot [23 - 7] && \text{Simplify } (37 - 14). \\
&= 5 \cdot 16 && \text{Simplify } [23 - 7]. \\
&= 80 && \text{Multiply 5 times 16.}
\end{aligned}
$$
■

EXAMPLE 12	Simplify $4 \cdot \{2 + [7 + 9 \cdot (6 + 5)]\}$

SOLUTION

$$
\begin{aligned}
4 \cdot \{2 + [7 + 9 \cdot (6 + 5)]\} &= 4 \cdot \{2 + [7 + 9 \cdot 11]\} \\
&= 4 \cdot \{2 + [7 + 99]\} \\
&= 4 \cdot \{2 + 106\} \\
&= 4 \cdot 108 \\
&= 432
\end{aligned}
$$
■

EXAMPLE 13 | Simplify $12^2 - \{10 - [8 - (6 - (4 - 2))]\}^2$

SOLUTION

$$
\begin{aligned}
12^2 - \{10 - [8 - (6 - (4 - 2))]\}^2 &= 12^2 - \{10 - [8 - (6 - 2)]\}^2 \\
&= 12^2 - \{10 - [8 - 4]\}^2 \\
&= 12^2 - \{10 - 4\}^2 \\
&= 12^2 - 6^2 \\
&= 144 - 6^2 \\
&= 144 - 36 \\
&= 108 \quad\blacksquare
\end{aligned}
$$

The first two order of operations agreements allow us to write expressions with a minimal number of grouping symbols. For example, the following equation has two expressions, one on each side of the = sign.

$$(64 \div 16) \div 2 = 64 \div 16 \div 2$$

Although it is not wrong to write parentheses in the expression on the left side of the equation, the order of operations agreement makes it unnecessary to write parentheses unless we want to deliberately change the order of operations implied by the preceding rules. We want to write as few grouping symbols as possible while maintaining the intended meaning.

The two expressions $2 \cdot (3^4)$ and $(2 \cdot 3)^4$ sound the same if we read them as "two times three to the fourth power." However,

$$2 \cdot (3^4) = 2 \cdot (81) = 162$$

whereas

$$(2 \cdot 3)^4 = (6)^4 = 1{,}296$$

We have shown

$$2 \cdot (3^4) \neq (2 \cdot 3)^4$$

A better way to read the second expression $(2 \cdot 3)^4$ is "the quantity two times three, to the fourth power." By using the words *the quantity*, we are referring to an expression in parentheses.

According to the order of operations agreement, the expression $2 \cdot (3^4)$ is the same as $2 \cdot 3^4$ because we perform exponents before multiplying. The parentheses in $2 \cdot (3^4)$ are not necessary. And since we do what is in parentheses first, the fourth power in $(2 \cdot 3)^4$ cannot be performed until after we calculate the number 6 in parentheses. The parentheses in $(2 \cdot 3)^4$ are necessary to give the expression the intended meaning of multiplying 2 times 3 before applying the exponent 4.

Two points are to be understood from these examples. The first point is that some expressions may seem ambiguous because they sound the same or at least sound very similar when they are read. But when we follow the order of operations agreement, we have only one correct answer. Second, when reading $2 \cdot 3^4$, it may be tempting to think the fourth power applies to both the number 2 and the number 3. But since we do exponents before multiplications, we can say that an exponent only applies to the first number that precedes it.

Basic Operation for an Expression

Every expression, no matter how complex, can be described as having a **basic operation.** The basic operation for an expression is the last operation performed in simplifying the expression.

EXAMPLE 14	What is the basic operation for $2 + 3 \cdot 7$?

SOLUTION   Because we multiply first and add last, the basic operation for this expression is addition. The expression $2 + 3 \cdot 7$ is called a **basic sum.**   ■

EXAMPLE 15	What is the basic operation for $54 \div 9 \cdot 2$?

SOLUTION   Because multiplication and division are on the same level, we work the problem left to right, so the multiplication is the last operation. The basic operation for this expression is multiplication and the expression $54 \div 9 \cdot 2$ is called a **basic product.**   ■

EXAMPLE 16	What is the basic operation for $[16 + (13 + 2 \cdot 5) \div 23] \cdot 7$?

SOLUTION   Because we first perform all the operations within the square brackets, the last operation is to multiply by 7. The basic operation is multiplication and the entire expression is called a **basic product.**   ■

EXAMPLE 17	What is the basic operation for $(3 + 5 \cdot 7)^{(8 \div 4)}$?

SOLUTION   Because we first perform all operations within parentheses, the last operation is exponentiation. The basic operation is exponentiation.   ■

P R A C T I C E   F O R   S U C C E S S

Practice 1.   Simplify $17 - 4 \cdot 2 + 45 \div 5$

Practice 2.   Simplify $10 + 5 \cdot 9^2$

Practice 3.   Simplify $7 \cdot (15 - 8) + 4 \cdot (12 + 2)^2$

Practice 4.   Simplify $6 \cdot \{4 + [17 - (13 - 11)] + 40\}$

Practice 5.   What is the basic operation for the expression in Practice 3?

EXERCISES 1.5

In exercises 1–55, simplify the given expression by applying the rules for the order of operations.

1. $52 - 39 + 1$
2. $42 - 28 + 2 - 1$
3. $1,024 \div 4 \div 2 \div 4 \div 2$
4. $579 - 26 - 48 - 13$
5. $6,561 \div 9 \div 3 - 28 - 15 + 12 - 8$
6. $50 - 24 + 18 \div 3 \cdot 2$
7. $9 \cdot [8 + (5 \cdot 4 - 3) \cdot 6]$
8. $(72 - 5 - 6 \cdot 8) \cdot 12$
9. $(35 + 7) \div (18 - 12) \cdot 4$
10. $2 + 5 \cdot 6^2$
11. $3 \cdot (2 + 5 \cdot 3^2)^2$
12. $48 \div (4^2 + 2^3) \div 2$
13. $5^2 + 3^2$
14. $3^2 - 2^3 + 2^3 - 3^2$
15. $(5 + 3)^2$
16. $(6 + 2 \cdot 3^3)^2$
17. $5^2 + 2 \cdot 5 \cdot 3 + 3^2$
18. $2^4 + 3^4 + (2 + 3)^4$
19. $1,540 - 7 \cdot (2^2 + 8)^2$
20. $1,440 \div 6 \div (3^2 + 24 \div 4)$
21. $(16 \cdot 8 + 3)^2 - (9 \cdot 3 - 4)^2$
22. $(27 - 8 \cdot 3)^3 - (4 \cdot 7 - 3 \cdot 9)^5$
23. $(16 \cdot 8 + 3^2) - (9 \cdot 3 - 4^2)$
24. $(15 \cdot 5 - 150 \div 2)^6 - (6^2 - 2^2 \cdot 3^2)^4$
25. $(23 \cdot 0 + 14) \cdot (13 - 7) \div (3^2 - 5)$
26. $(0 \div 8 \cdot 9 + 2)^5 \div (12 - 8) \div (1 + 1^5)^3$
27. $(19 - 9 \cdot 2)^{34} \cdot (48 - 3 \cdot 4^2)^{16}$
28. $(5 \cdot 9 - 11 \cdot 4)^{17}$
29. $[(6 \cdot 3 + 5) + 2] \cdot 3 - 8$
30. $[(52 \div 13 - 3) + 17] \div 6 - 2$
31. $\{[(5 \cdot 2 - 4) \cdot 2 + 6] \cdot 2 + 7\} \cdot 3 + 8$
32. $\{[(8 \cdot 9 - 4) \div 17 - 2] \cdot 2 + 3\} \cdot 2 - 11$
33. $\{[(6 \cdot 7 - 4) \cdot 7 + 3] \cdot 7 - 5\} \cdot 7 - 13$
34. $\{[(6 \cdot 3^2 - 24) \div 10 + 3] \cdot 5 - 3\} \cdot 2 - 3^3$
35. $\{[(8 \cdot 2^2 + 3) \cdot 2^2 - 9] \cdot 2^2 - 7\} \cdot 2^2 + 13$

36. $\{[(3 \cdot 5^2 - 8 \cdot 9) \cdot 5^2 - 7 \cdot 10] \cdot 5^2 + 1\} \cdot 2$

37. $7 \cdot 10^3 + 5 \cdot 10^2 + 6 \cdot 10^1 + 4$

38. $8 \cdot 10^3 + 9 \cdot 10^2 + 3 \cdot 10^1 + 7$

39. $6 \cdot 10^4 + 2 \cdot 10^3 + 2 \cdot 10^2 + 7 \cdot 10^1 + 5$

40. $3 \cdot 10^4 + 6 \cdot 10^3 + 5 \cdot 10^2 + 2 \cdot 10^1 + 1$

41. $(7 + 4)^2 - (7 + 3)^2$

42. $(18 - 14)^2 + (9 + 3)^2$

43. $4^2 - [6 - (20 - 18)]$

44. $6^3 - [12 - (45 - 3 \cdot 14)]$

45. $12 - \{10 - [8 - (6 - (4 - 2))]\}$

46. $63 - \{70 - [48 - (36 - (14 - 8))]\}$

47. $2 \cdot \{8 - 2 \cdot [6 - 2 \cdot (5 - 3)]\}$

48. $\{140 - 3 \cdot [49 - 3 \cdot (15 - 13)]\} \cdot 2$

49. $3 \cdot \{7 + 3 \cdot [8 + 3 \cdot (16 - 3 \cdot (3 \cdot 5 - 12))]\}$

50. $\{7 + 5 \cdot [50 + 5 \cdot (60 - 5 \cdot (6 \cdot 4 - 14))]\} \cdot 4$

51. $2^2 \cdot \{9 + 2^2 \cdot [17 + 2^2 \cdot (31 + 2^2 \cdot (3^3 - 4))]\}$

52. $3^2 \cdot \{3 + 3^2 \cdot [5 + 3^2 \cdot (4 + 3^2 \cdot (3^3 - 25))]\}$

53. $7 \cdot \{4^2 + 6 \cdot [6 + 8 \cdot (4 + 2 \cdot 3)]\}$

54. $\{7^2 + 10 \cdot [8 + 10 \cdot (10 + 5 \cdot 7)]\} \cdot 10$

55. $6 \cdot \{9^2 - 5 \cdot [27 - 7 \cdot (26 - 3 \cdot 2^3)]\}$

In exercises 56–72, identify the basic operation for the given expression. Do not simplify the given expression.

56. $81 - (15 + 25)$

57. $624 \div 8 + 75$

58. $6 \cdot [20 + 5 \cdot (61 - 5 \cdot 9)]$

59. $90 \div \{60 \div [2,880 \div (24 \cdot 8)] + 2\}$

60. $[7 + 35 \cdot 4] \cdot [15 \cdot 7 - 23]$

61. $6 \cdot 8 \cdot 4 \div 16$

62. $12 \cdot [7 + 3 \cdot (60 - 2 \cdot 16 \div 4)] - 30$

63. $120 - (16 - 13) \cdot 6 \cdot 6$

64. $80 \div \{50 \div [30 \div (12 \div 2)]\} \cdot 5$

65. $100 \div 4 + 36 \cdot 2 - 8 \cdot 9 \div 3$

66. $27 \cdot 3 - 18 \div 6 + 40 \div 10 \cdot 3$

67. $(7 + 4)^2 - (7 + 3)^2$

68. $(9 + 3)^2 \div (4 + 2)^2$

69. $3 \cdot 7^2$

70. $[(16 \cdot 13 + 15) + 12] \cdot 5 - 34$

71. $(2 + 40 \div 20)^{(3+2)}$

72. $[26 \div 13 - 3]^{(4 \div 2)}$

Looking Back

73. Divide 42 into 315,336 and give the quotient and remainder.
74. Compute 5^4.
75. Simplify 0^8.
76. Compute $(12)^3$.
77. Divide 36 into 101,124 and give the quotient and remainder.
78. Simplify 1^{20}.
79. What is the place value of the digit 7 in the number 394,661,457?
80. State the division check.
81. Round 7,285,998 to the nearest ten.

PRACTICE-FOR-SUCCESS ANSWERS

1. 18   2. 415   3. 833   4. 354
5. The basic operation is addition.

1.6   PRIME NUMBERS, DIVISIBILITY TESTS, AND PRIME FACTORIZATIONS

OBJECTIVES

☐ To determine whether a whole number is prime, composite, or neither
☐ To use tests of divisibility for 2, 3, and 5
☐ To find the prime factorization of any composite number

Prime and Composite Numbers

Whole numbers greater than 1 are members of two distinct groups. One of these groups of numbers is the **prime numbers,** which are defined as follows:

DEFINITION	PRIME NUMBER

A prime number is any whole number greater than 1 that is divisible only by itself and the number 1.

A key word in the definition of a prime number is the word *divisible*. To say that a number is divisible by a second number means that the second number divides into the first with a remainder of 0. The number 8 is divisible by 4 because 4 goes into 8 exactly 2 times. We also say 4 and 2 are **divisors** or **factors** of 8.

When the word *factor* is used in mathematics, it is sometimes used as a noun and other times as a verb. When we say 2 is a factor of 6, we are using the word *factor* as a noun. When used as nouns, the terms *factor* and *divisor* can be used interchangeably because multiplication and division are inverse operations. When the word *factor* is used as a verb, it means "to write as a product." When we are asked "to factor" the number 6, the word *factor* is being used as a verb, and in this case, we could write either $6 = 1 \cdot 6$ or $6 = 2 \cdot 3$.

We are going to investigate which of the first few whole numbers are prime. We first factor 2. The only two divisors of 2 are 1 and 2; therefore, the number 2 is a prime number because it has exactly two divisors, 1 and itself. The next prime number is 3 because the only two numbers that divide evenly into 3 are 1 and 3. The number 6, however, is not prime because it can be written as $1 \cdot 6$ or $2 \cdot 3$. It has four divisors: 1, 2, 3, and 6. Every prime number has exactly two divisors, 1 and the prime number itself. Numbers like 6, with more than two divisors, are **composite numbers.**

DEFINITION	**COMPOSITE NUMBER**
	A composite number is any nonzero whole number that has more than two divisors.

Whether a given whole number is considered to be prime, composite, or neither depends on the number of factors the number has. The whole numbers 0 and 1 deserve special consideration. There is only one way to factor the number 1: $1 = 1 \cdot 1$. The number 1 has only one factor, and it is the only whole number that has exactly one factor. The number 1 is sometimes called a **unit.** On the other hand, the number 0 has an infinite number of factors as can be seen from

$$0 = 0 \cdot 1, \quad 0 = 0 \cdot 2, \quad 0 = 0 \cdot 3, \quad 0 = 0 \cdot 4, \quad 0 = 0 \cdot 5, \dots$$

Because prime numbers have exactly two factors, neither the number 1 nor the number 0 qualifies as a prime number. Composite numbers always have more than two factors, but always a finite number of factors. So again, neither the number 1 nor the number 0 qualifies as a composite number. The numbers 0 and 1 are neither prime nor composite and are the only two whole numbers that are not prime and not composite.

EXAMPLE 1 Tell whether each number is a prime number or a composite number.

a. 16 **b.** 29 **c.** 42

SOLUTION **a.** 16 is composite because $16 = 1 \cdot 16$

$16 = 2 \cdot 8$

$16 = 4 \cdot 4$

16 has 5 divisors: 1, 2, 4, 8, and 16.

b. 29 is prime because it has only two divisors, 1 and 29.

c. 42 is composite because $42 = 1 \cdot 42$

$42 = 2 \cdot 21$

$42 = 3 \cdot 14$

$42 = 6 \cdot 7$

42 has 8 factors: 1, 2, 3, 6, 7, 14, 21, and 42. ■

We have seen that the first two prime numbers are 2 and 3. The next prime number is 5 because it has only two divisors, 1 and itself. In fact, the prime numbers continue forever and supercomputers are currently searching for the next greatest prime number. Eratosthenes, a Greek mathematician who lived more than 2,000 years ago, developed the following technique for finding prime numbers called the "Sieve of Eratosthenes." Figure 1.12 illustrates the procedure Eratosthenes followed to identify the first several prime numbers.

	(2)	(3)	~~4~~	(5)	~~6~~	(7)	~~8~~	~~9~~	~~10~~
11	~~12~~	13	~~14~~	~~15~~	~~16~~	17	~~18~~	19	~~20~~
~~21~~	~~22~~	23	~~24~~	~~25~~	~~26~~	~~27~~	~~28~~	29	~~30~~
31	~~32~~	~~33~~	~~34~~	~~35~~	~~36~~	37	~~38~~	~~39~~	~~40~~
41	~~42~~	43	~~44~~	~~45~~	~~46~~	47	~~48~~	~~49~~	~~50~~

FIGURE 1.12 Sieve of Eratosthenes

Eratosthenes first circled 2 because it was a prime number and then crossed out any number in the chart that was divisible by 2 (4, 6, 8, ..., 50). Next, he circled 3 because it was uncrossed and prime and then crossed out any number that was divisible by 3 (6, 9, 12, ..., 48) and hadn't already been crossed out as divisible by 2. The next uncrossed number was 5. Because it was prime, he circled it and again crossed out all numbers divisible by 5 that had not been previously crossed out: 25 and 35. Continuing, he circled 7 because it was uncrossed and prime and eliminated one number on the list divisible by 7 that had not been previously crossed out, 49. He then tested the numbers that remained and found that they were all prime numbers. From the chart, we see that the prime numbers less than 50 are

2, 3, 5, 7, 11, 13, 17, 19, 23, 29, 31, 37, 41, 43, and 47

Divisibility Tests

In math, we have **tests of divisibility** that tell us when a number divides evenly into another.

DIVISIBILITY TESTS FOR 2, 3, AND 5

1. **A whole number is divisible by 2 if the number is an even number, which means that the digit in the ones place is 0, 2, 4, 6, or 8.**
2. **A whole number is divisible by 3 if the sum of its digits is divisible by 3.**
3. **A whole number is divisible by 5 if the digit in the ones place is 0 or 5.**

| **EXAMPLE 2** | Show which of the numbers 2, 3, and 5 divide evenly into the following numbers: |

    a. 51   **b.** 65   **c.** 72   **d.** 120

SOLUTION   **a.** 51 is not divisible by 2 because it is not even.

51 is divisible by 3 because 5 + 1 = 6 and 3 divides evenly into 6.

51 is not divisible by 5 because the last digit is not 0 or 5.

b. 65 is not divisible by 2 because it is not even.

65 is not divisible by 3 because 6 + 5 = 11 and 3 does not divide evenly into 11.

65 is divisible by 5 because the last digit is 5.

c. 72 is divisible by 2 because it is even.

72 is divisible by 3 because 7 + 2 = 9 and 3 divides evenly into 9.

72 is not divisible by 5 because the last digit is not 0 or 5.

d. 120 is divisible by 2 because it is even.

120 is divisible by 3 because 1 + 2 + 0 = 3 and 3 divides evenly into 3.

120 is divisible by 5 because the last digit is 0.   ■

The divisibility test for 3 is different from the divisibility tests for 2 and 5. With the divisibility test for 3, we find the sum of the digits and then check to see if 3 divides evenly into the sum. However, when we do the tests of divisibility for 2 or 5, we simply check the last digit. Tests of divisibility exist for many other numbers, but the three tests presented in this book are the most commonly used. Divisibility tests are simply shortcuts that tell us whether or not our answers will come out even and do not provide the answers to division problems.

Prime Factorizations

We can use divisibility tests to verify the fundamental theorem of arithmetic. (A *theorem* is a mathematical statement that is accepted as true because it can be proved.)

FUNDAMENTAL THEOREM OF ARITHMETIC

Any whole number greater than 1 is prime or can be expressed as a unique product of powers of prime numbers.

For example, 60 is a composite number because it has more than two divisors. The divisors of 60 are 1, 2, 3, 4, 5, 6, 10, 12, 15, 20, 30, and 60. We know the prime number 2 divides evenly into 60, so we start by dividing by 2.

$$\begin{array}{r} 30 \\ 2\overline{)60} \end{array}$$

This computation tells us that $60 = 2 \cdot 30$. We continue to divide 2 into 30 because, from the divisibility test for 2, we know that 2 will go evenly into 30. We keep dividing by the same prime number until that prime no longer divides evenly before we try the next prime.

$$\begin{array}{r} 15 \\ 2\overline{)30} \end{array}$$

This division tells us that $60 = 2 \cdot 2 \cdot 15$. We can no longer divide by 2 because 15 is not even. We can, however, divide by 3 because the sum of the digits of 15 is 6, which is divisible by 3.

$$\begin{array}{r} 5 \\ 3\overline{)15} \end{array}$$

This division tells us that $60 = 2 \cdot 2 \cdot 3 \cdot 5$. We can no longer divide by 3 because 5 is not divisible by 3. We can, however, divide by 5.

$$\begin{array}{r} 1 \\ 5\overline{)5} \end{array}$$

We have found, then, that the product of primes for the composite number 60 is $2 \cdot 2 \cdot 3 \cdot 5$ or, using exponents, $2^2 \cdot 3^1 \cdot 5^1$. We have demonstrated an instance of the fundamental theorem of arithmetic for the number 60. This unique product of powers of prime numbers that equal 60 is called the **prime factorization** of 60.

The preceding divisions to find the prime factorization of 60 could be done more easily in the following manner:

$$\begin{array}{r} 2\overline{)60} \\ 2\overline{)30} \\ 3\overline{)15} \\ 5\overline{)\,5} \\ 1 \end{array}$$

←When we reach a quotient of one, we stop and exclude it from the product because it is not prime.

Again, we see the prime factorization of 60 is $2 \cdot 2 \cdot 3 \cdot 5$ or $2^2 \cdot 3^1 \cdot 5^1$.

| EXAMPLE 3 | Find the prime factorizations of the following numbers: |

a. 39   **b.** 91   **c.** 103   **d.** 221   **e.** 1,100

SOLUTION **a.** To find the prime factorization of 39, we use the divisibility tests. The first prime number that divides into 39 evenly is 3.

$$3)\overline{39}$$
$$13)\overline{13}$$
$$1$$

The only number that divides evenly into a prime number is itself or 1.

The prime factorization of 39 is $3 \cdot 13$ or $3^1 \cdot 13^1$.

b. To find the prime factorization of 91, we use the divisibility tests and find that 2, 3, and 5 do not go evenly into 91. We then divide by 7, because it is the next prime number, and find that 7 divides evenly into 91.

$$7)\overline{91}$$
$$13)\overline{13}$$
$$1$$

The prime factorization of 91 is $7 \cdot 13$ or $7^1 \cdot 13^1$.

c. To find the prime factorization of 103, we use the divisibility tests and find that 2, 3, and 5 do not go evenly into 103. We then divide by 7 and find that 7 does not divide evenly into 103, and then we divide by 11 and find that it also does not divide evenly. However, we interpret the trial quotient in a special way.

$$
\begin{array}{r}
9 \\
11)\overline{103} \\
-\,99 \\
\hline
4
\end{array}
$$

Now, 9 is smaller than 11, and *whenever the trial quotient is smaller than the divisor we can stop.* The reason is that if we attempt to divide by primes larger than 11, for example 13 or 17, the resulting trial quotients will be smaller than 8. Because we have already checked all the primes less than 8, attempting to divide by primes larger than 11 cannot possibly lead to the discovery of other prime factors.

Because 103 has no factors other than 1 and itself, 103 is a prime number. Because 103 is prime, it is written, using powers of primes, as $103 = 103^1$.

d. Using the divisibility tests, we find that 2, 3, and 5 do not go evenly into 221. We then divide and determine that 7 and 11 are not factors. We next divide by 13 and discover that 13 goes into 221 evenly 17 times.

$$13)\overline{221}$$
$$17)\overline{\;17}$$
$$1$$

The prime factorization of 221 is $13 \cdot 17$ or $13^1 \cdot 17^1$.

e. Using the tests of divisibility, we find that 2 goes evenly into 1,100.

$$
\begin{array}{r}
2)\overline{1{,}100} \\
\rightarrow \quad 2)\overline{550} \\
5)\overline{275} \\
5)\overline{55} \\
11)\overline{11} \\
1
\end{array}
$$

The prime factorization of 1,100 is $2 \cdot 2 \cdot 5 \cdot 5 \cdot 11$ or $2^2 \cdot 5^2 \cdot 11^1$.

The arrow in the computation alerts us to the following: when it is possible to divide by the same prime number a second time, we do so to help organize our prime factorization and make it easier to determine the exponents.

■

PRIME FACTORIZATION

To find the prime factorization of any number, select the first prime number and using successively larger primes perform steps 1 through 3.

Step 1. If the currently selected prime number divides evenly, then divide by that prime again to make the number to be factored smaller. Keep dividing by this same prime until step 2 occurs.

Step 2. If the currently selected prime number does not divide evenly, then try the next larger prime.

Step 3. Repeat steps 1 and 2 until the original number becomes the number 1 or until the trial quotient is smaller than the trial prime divisor. When the trial quotient is smaller than the trial prime divisor, the remaining number must be the last prime factor.

Step 4. Write the original number as a product of powers of the prime divisors.

PRACTICE FOR SUCCESS

Practice 1. Tell whether each number is a prime number or a composite number.
 a. 49   **b.** 68   **c.** 71

Practice 2. Show which of the numbers 2, 3, and 5 divide evenly into the following numbers:
 a. 30   **b.** 39   **c.** 61

Practice 3. Find the prime factorizations of the following numbers:
 a. 105   **b.** 300   **c.** 1,001

EXERCISES 1.6

In exercises 1–15, tell whether the given number is prime, composite, or neither.

1. 73	**2.** 91	**3.** 111	**4.** 113
5. 157	**6.** 159	**7.** 161	**8.** 163
9. 201	**10.** 203	**11.** 211	**12.** 317
13. 1	**14.** 403	**15.** 323	

In exercises 16–38, tell whether or not the given number is divisible by 2, 3, or 5. When a number in a problem does pass a divisibility test, factor the number using the corresponding divisor.

16. 4,776	**17.** 5,637	**18.** 5,984	**19.** 3,695
20. 120	**21.** 2,510	**22.** 6,714	**23.** 8,280
24. 35,560	**25.** 243	**26.** 743	**27.** 13,145
28. 31,955	**29.** 4,672	**30.** 221	**31.** 6,000
32. 1,532	**33.** 3,337	**34.** 73,025	**35.** 140,725
36. 170,600	**37.** 252,689,241	**38.** 9,681,849,520	

In exercises 39–75, find all the prime factors of the given number and write the given number as a product of powers of those primes.

39. 1,050	**40.** 200	**41.** 221	**42.** 223
43. 4,500	**44.** 210	**45.** 120	**46.** 900
47. 15,400	**48.** 315	**49.** 2,695	**50.** 1,001
51. 286	**52.** 440	**53.** 442	**54.** 108
55. 500	**56.** 4,851	**57.** 437	**58.** 93
59. 53	**60.** 229	**61.** 178	**62.** 159
63. 34,300	**64.** 13,750	**65.** 5,915	**66.** 21,413
67. 493	**68.** 961	**69.** 1,023	**70.** 1,131
71. 3,451	**72.** 5,491	**73.** 2,691	**74.** 2,088
75. 100,320			

Looking Back

76. Simplify $(2 \cdot 29 + 13) - (7 + 8 \cdot 5)$.

77. Simplify $[4^2 + 5^2] + [4 + 5]^2$.

78. What is the basic operation for the expression $[14 \div 7 + 7] \cdot [2^3 + 3]$?

79. What is the basic operation for the expression $[23 \cdot 0 \div 8] \cdot [11 + 5] \div 6$?

80. Calculate 8^4.

81. Simplify 9^3.

PRACTICE-FOR-SUCCESS ANSWERS

1. **a.** composite   **b.** composite   **c.** prime

2. **a.** 2, 3, and 5   **b.** 3 only   **c.** none of 2, 3, or 5

3. **a.** $105 = 3^1 \cdot 5^1 \cdot 7^1$ **b.** $300 = 2^2 \cdot 3^1 \cdot 5^2$ **c.** $1{,}001 = 7^1 \cdot 11^1 \cdot 13^1$

1.7   ## LCMs AND GCFs USING PRIMES AND EXPONENTS

OBJECTIVES

□ To understand least common multiple (LCM) and greatest common factor (GCF)

□ To distinguish LCMs from GCFs

□ To calculate LCMs and GCFs using primes and exponents

□ To write relationships with number pairs and their LCMs and GCFs

This section applies the prime number factoring skills and the use of exponents learned in previous sections to calculate two important quantities. These two quantities are called **least common multiple (LCM)** and **greatest common factor (GCF).** Both the LCM and GCF concepts will help us to develop a deeper appreciation of the prime factoring process. The skills developed in this section will be applied when we expand and reduce fractions in Chapter 3.

Least Common Multiple

DEFINITION   **LEAST COMMON MULTIPLE (LCM)**

The least common multiple (LCM) of two nonzero whole numbers is the smallest nonzero number into which both whole numbers will divide evenly.

For example, what is the least common multiple of 6 and 8? One method of finding the LCM is to write the multiples of the two numbers. The multiples of 8 begin with $8 \cdot 1$, $8 \cdot 2$, $8 \cdot 3$, and so on.

Multiples of 8:   8, 16, 24, 32, 40, 48, 56, 64, 72, 80, 88, 96, ...

The multiples of 8 continue on forever. However, only certain multiples of 8 listed are also multiples of 6.

Multiples of 6:   6, 12, 18, 24, 30, 36, 42, 48, 54, 60, 66, 72, 78, 84, 90, 96, ...

Comparing the two lists, we can see that some multiples of 8 are not multiples of 6 and vice versa. But we find some special numbers that are multiples of both, called the **common multiples** of 6 and 8.

Common multiples of 6 and 8:   24, 48, 72, 96, ...

The common multiples of 6 and 8 continue forever. The least common multiple of 6 and 8 is 24, the smallest number into which both 6 and 8 divide evenly.

| EXAMPLE 1 | Find the least common multiple of 8 and 10. |

SOLUTION   We list the multiples of the larger number, 10, until we find a number that is also divisible by the smaller number, 8.

Multiples of 10:   10, 20, 30, 40

Because 8 does not divide into 10, 20, or 30, we keep listing the multiples of 10 until we get to 40, which can be divided by 8 five times. 40 is the LCM of 8 and 10.   ■

It is easy to misinterpret the intended meaning of LCM because LCMs can be large numbers and yet the terminology uses the word *least*. When the two numbers are small, we can usually guess the LCM or use the list method to find the LCM. But when the numbers get larger, we use another procedure. The method that follows is used to find the LCM of any two whole numbers.

The LCM of 15 and 18 is 90. We know 90 is a common multiple of 15 and 18 because

$$90 = 15 \cdot 6 \text{ and } 90 = 18 \cdot 5$$

But how do we know both 18 and 15 do not divide evenly into a number smaller than 90? The answer will become clear if we consider the prime factorizations of the numbers 15 and 18.

$$15 = 3^1 \cdot 5^1 \text{ and } 18 = 2^1 \cdot 3^2$$

Every multiple of 15 must contain the numbers 3 and 5 as factors because these are the prime factors of 15. Every multiple of 18 must contain the numbers 2 and 3 as factors because these are the only prime factors of 18. The LCM of 15 and 18 *must contain all the prime factors of both numbers*. The only question is what the exponents on those primes will be.

For each prime, the LCM exponent should be at least as big as either of the exponents of that prime in the two given numbers. In the preceding example, we look at the exponents of each occurrence of the number 3. For the number 15, the exponent above 3 is 1; for the number 18, the exponent above 3 is 2. The exponent associated with 3 in the LCM must therefore be at least as big as the largest of 1 and 2, so the LCM exponent for 3 is 2.

The rule for selecting the LCM exponent for each prime is to choose the larger of the two exponents when we have a choice. The prime number 2 has an exponent 1 in the number 18, but 2 is not a prime factor of 15, so in this case we have no choice between two exponents. We select the LCM exponent to be the only exponent that occurs above the prime number 2. When selecting an exponent for the prime factor 5, our only exponent choice is 1. Now we can understand where the number 90 comes from. We write each prime factor using the choices for the exponents associated with those primes. Thus the LCM of 15 and 18 is $2^1 \cdot 3^2 \cdot 5^1 = 90$.

We can now summarize the procedure illustrated by the preceding example and can apply the summarized steps to find the LCM of any two whole numbers.

FINDING THE LCM OF TWO NUMBERS

1. **Prime factor each of the two numbers and write the two prime factorizations in exponential form.**
2. **Write down each prime number base that occurs in either or both factorizations. A prime base that occurs in both factorizations is written down only once. Write the prime bases in increasing order and leave room for writing exponents.**
3. **Write exponents above each prime base. If the same prime base occurs in both factorizations, then the exponent is the larger of the two exponents. If a prime base occurs in only one factorization, we use the exponent associated with that prime base.**
4. **Evaluate the resulting exponential expression.**

EXAMPLE 2   Use the procedure outlined above to find the LCM of 48 and 54.

SOLUTION   **Step 1:** $48 = 2^4 \cdot 3^1$
$54 = 2^1 \cdot 3^3$

Step 2: $\text{LCM} = 2^? \cdot 3^?$

Step 3: The exponent above 2 is the larger of 4 and 1; 4.
The exponent above 3 is the larger of 1 and 3; 3.
$\text{LCM} = 2^4 \cdot 3^3$

Step 4: $\text{LCM} = 2^4 \cdot 3^3$
$= 16 \cdot 27$
$= 432$

This would be a more difficult problem to solve using multiples.   ■

EXAMPLE 3   Using the answer found in Example 2, write the LCM as a multiple of both 48 and 54.

SOLUTION   To write the LCM as a product involving 48, we compare the prime factorizations of 48 and 432.

$$48 = 2^4 \cdot 3^1$$

$$432 = 2^4 \cdot 3^3$$

Note the difference between the two exponents above the prime base 3.

$$3^{3-1} = 3^2 = 9$$

$$432 = 48 \cdot 9$$

To write the LCM as a product involving 54, we compare the prime factorizations of 54 and 432.

$$54 = 2^1 \cdot 3^3$$

$$432 = 2^4 \cdot 3^3$$

Note the difference between the two exponents above the prime base 2.

$$2^{4-1} = 2^3 = 8$$

$$432 = 54 \cdot 8$$ ■

| **EXAMPLE 4** | Find the LCM of 98 and 360 and then write the LCM as a product involving each of these two numbers. |

SOLUTION   **Step 1:** $98 = 2^1 \cdot 7^2$

$360 = 2^3 \cdot 3^2 \cdot 5^1$

Step 2:   LCM $= 2^? \cdot 3^? \cdot 5^? \cdot 7^?$

Step 3:   The exponent above 2 is the larger of 1 and 3; 3.
There is only one choice for the exponent above 3; 2.
There is only one choice for the exponent above 5; 1.
There is only one choice for the exponent above 7; 2.
LCM $= 2^3 \cdot 3^2 \cdot 5^1 \cdot 7^2$

Step 4:   LCM $= 2^3 \cdot 3^2 \cdot 5^1 \cdot 7^2$
$= 8 \cdot 9 \cdot 5 \cdot 49$
$= 72 \cdot 5 \cdot 49$
$= 360 \cdot 49$
$= 17,640$

Finally, to write the LCM as a product involving 98, we compare the prime factorizations of 98 and 17,640.

$$98 = 2^1 \cdot 7^2$$

$$17,640 = 2^3 \cdot 3^2 \cdot 5^1 \cdot 7^2$$

Note the differences consist of

$$2^2 \cdot 3^2 \cdot 5^1 = 4 \cdot 9 \cdot 5 = 36 \cdot 5 = 180$$

$$17,640 = 98 \cdot 180$$

To write the LCM as a product involving 360, we compare the prime factorizations of 360 and 17,640.

$$360 = 2^3 \cdot 3^2 \cdot 5^1$$

$$17,640 = 2^3 \cdot 3^2 \cdot 5^1 \cdot 7^2$$

Note the difference is $7^2 = 49$.

$$17,640 = 360 \cdot 49$$ ■

Greatest Common Factor

The second quantity to be discussed is called the greatest common factor (GCF). Greatest common factors are also sometimes called greatest common divisors (GCDs), but in this book we will use GCF. GCFs can be used to reduce fractions.

DEFINITION	GREATEST COMMON FACTOR (GCF)
	The greatest common factor (GCF) of two nonzero whole numbers is the largest number that divides evenly into both whole numbers.

The greatest common factor of 6 and 8 is 2. It may seem contradictory, but the greatest common factor of two numbers will always be at least as small as the smaller of the two numbers. This situation is analogous to the LCM being at least as large as the larger of the two numbers. In general, a GCF is small and an LCM is large.

Just as with LCMs, problems with GCFs can sometimes be easy when the numbers are small, but a method of computation is needed when the numbers are large. For example, what is the GCF of 360 and 580? Look at the prime factorizations of both numbers for clues.

$$360 = 2^3 \cdot 3^2 \cdot 5^1$$
$$580 = 2^2 \cdot 5^1 \cdot 29^1$$

Any divisor of 360 must contain only prime powers similar to those found in the prime factorization of 360 but with smaller exponents. Similarly, any divisor of 580 must contain only prime powers similar to those found in the prime factorization of 580, but with smaller exponents.

So why not build the GCF by using those primes common to both 360 and 580? This question then becomes one concerning which exponents should be associated with those primes. The answer is related to the exponents in the two prime factorizations. When finding the LCM, we chose the *larger* of the two exponents whenever we had a choice. With GCFs, we will always have a choice because we are using only prime factors common to both numbers; but the exponent selected should now be the *smaller* of the two exponents.

$$360 = 2^3 \cdot 3^2 \cdot 5^1$$
$$580 = 2^2 \cdot 5^1 \cdot 29^1$$

The only prime bases that are common to both numbers are 2 and 5. So, after selecting the smaller exponents, we have

$$\text{GCF} = 2^2 \cdot 5^1 = 4 \cdot 5 = 20$$

We can now summarize the procedure for finding the GCF of any two whole numbers.

FINDING THE GCF OF TWO NUMBERS

1. **Prime factor each of the two numbers and write the two factorizations in exponential form.**
2. **Write down every prime base that occurs simultaneously in both factorizations. Leave room for writing exponents above the prime bases. If no common prime base exists, the process ends and the GCF in this case is the number 1.**
3. **Write exponents above each prime base, using the smaller of the exponents in the two factorizations. If the two exponents are the same, use that exponent.**
4. **Simplify the resulting exponential expression.**

| **EXAMPLE 5** | Use the preceding procedure to find the GCF of 325 and 585 and then write the numbers as products using the GCF. |

SOLUTION   **Step 1:** $325 = 5^2 \cdot 13^1$
$585 = 3^2 \cdot 5^1 \cdot 13^1$

Step 2: GCF $= 5^? \cdot 13^?$

Step 3: The exponent above 5 is the smaller of 2 and 1; 1.
The exponent above 13 is 1 in both cases.
GCF $= 5^1 \cdot 13^1$

Step 4: GCF $= 5^1 \cdot 13^1$
$= 5 \cdot 13$
$= 65$

Finally, we compare the prime factorizations of the numbers to note the differences that determine how to form the products using the given numbers.

$$325 = 5^2 \cdot 13^1 \qquad 585 = 3^2 \cdot 5^1 \cdot 13^1$$
$$65 = 5^1 \cdot 13^1 \qquad 65 = 5^1 \cdot 13^1$$

The first difference is 5^1, so $325 = 65 \cdot 5$.
The second difference is 3^2, so $585 = 65 \cdot 9$. ■

| **EXAMPLE 6** | Find the GCF of 468 and 385. |

SOLUTION   **Step 1:** $468 = 2^2 \cdot 3^2 \cdot 13^1$
$385 = 5^1 \cdot 7^1 \cdot 11^1$

Step 2: Because no common prime base exists, the GCF is the number 1. In other words, no number larger than 1 divides into both 468 and 385. Numbers that have no common prime always have a GCF of 1 and are said to be **relatively prime.** ■

As a final comment about relationships between numbers, we refer back to the two numbers 6 and 8. The product of these two numbers is 48, their GCF is 2, and their LCM is 24. Note that $48 = 2 \cdot 24$; the product of the GCF and LCM is the product of the two numbers. Let's try another pair of numbers. The product of 10 and 15 is 150. It is not too difficult to guess that the GCF of 10 and 15 is 5, and it is just as easy to guess that the LCM of 10 and 15 is 30. Note that $150 = 5 \cdot 30$. The product of the LCM and the GCF will always equal the product of the two original numbers.

The rules given for finding the LCM and GCF of two numbers can be extended to find these same quantities for three or more numbers. The only change is that when selecting an exponent, the choice will need to be made by considering the multiple occurrences of the prime factor. In the case of three numbers at a time, the same prime must appear in each of the three numbers to count as part of the GCF.

EXAMPLE 7   Find both the GCF and the LCM of the three numbers 90, 108, and 180. Write each number as a product involving the GCF, and write the LCM as a product involving each of the three numbers.

SOLUTION   We will work both the LCM and the GCF at the same time.

Step 1: $90 = 2^1 \cdot 3^2 \cdot 5^1$
$108 = 2^2 \cdot 3^3$
$180 = 2^2 \cdot 3^2 \cdot 5^1$

Step 2: $\text{LCM} = 2^? \cdot 3^? \cdot 5^?$ $\text{GCF} = 2^? \cdot 3^?$
Note that 5 is not common to all three numbers.

Step 3: $\text{LCM} = 2^2 \cdot 3^3 \cdot 5^1$ $\text{GCF} = 2^1 \cdot 3^2$

Step 4: $\text{LCM} = 2^2 \cdot 3^3 \cdot 5^1$ $\text{GCF} = 2^1 \cdot 3^2$
$= 4 \cdot 27 \cdot 5$ $= 2 \cdot 9$
$= 108 \cdot 5$ $= 18$
$= 540$

Finally, we arrive at the following products by first comparing the prime factorizations of all the numbers.

$$540 = 6 \cdot 90 \qquad 90 = 18 \cdot 5$$
$$540 = 5 \cdot 108 \qquad 108 = 18 \cdot 6$$
$$540 = 3 \cdot 180 \qquad 180 = 18 \cdot 10$$ ■

P R A C T I C E   F O R   S U C C E S S

Practice 1.   Find the LCM of 12 and 15.
Practice 2.   Find the LCM of 36 and 66.
Practice 3.   Find the GCF of 45 and 135.
Practice 4.   Find the GCF of 24 and 175.
Practice 5.   Find the LCM and GCF of 36, 60, and 72.

EXERCISES 1.7

In exercises 1–20, calculate the LCM of the pairs of numbers. Write each LCM as a product that involves each number in the given pair.

1. 15 and 35   **2.** 26 and 30   **3.** 36 and 48

4. 44 and 24   **5.** 2,100 and 720   **6.** 48 and 108

7. 28 and 36   **8.** 42 and 56   **9.** 18 and 64

10. 12 and 52   **11.** 24 and 40   **12.** 54 and 30

13. 46 and 20   **14.** 13 and 62   **15.** 360 and 1,500

16. 30 and 24   **17.** 60 and 50   **18.** 40 and 108

19. 120 and 500   **20.** 240 and 480

In exercises 21–40, calculate the GCF of each pair of numbers. Write each number in the given pair as a product that involves the GCF.

21. 1,680 and 4,900   **22.** 1,500 and 360   **23.** 150 and 504

24. 525 and 693   **25.** 2,002 and 2,805   **26.** 2,700 and 2,250

27. 400 and 560   **28.** 104 and 338   **29.** 525 and 2,205

30. 6,125 and 595   **31.** 4,704 and 7,560   **32.** 630 and 1,170

33. 315 and 495   **34.** 560 and 784   **35.** 385 and 605

36. 480 and 672   **37.** 3,500 and 455   **38.** 2,220 and 260

39. 1,680 and 3,696   **40.** 416 and 544

In exercises 41–55, calculate both the LCM and the GCF of each triple of numbers. Write each LCM as a product that involves each number in the given triple, and write each number in the triple as a product that involves the GCF.

41. 12, 24, and 36   **42.** 20, 30, and 90   **43.** 40, 48, and 64

44. 108, 36, and 72   **45.** 120, 245, and 300 **46.** 80, 96, and 128

47. 20, 35, and 55   **48.** 32, 256, and 100 **49.** 7, 11, and 13

50. 40, 77, and 39   **51.** 80, 55, and 91   **52.** 42, 49, and 119

53. 28, 52, and 60   **54.** 130, 52, and 91   **55.** 78, 42, and 104

 ### Looking Back

56. Is the number 117 prime?

57. Is the number 91 prime?

58. Write 9,828 as a product of powers of prime numbers.

59. Write 114,954 as a product of powers of prime numbers.

60. Simplify $3 + 5^2 + (3 + 5)^2 \div [2 + 2^2 + 2]$.

61. Simplify $7 \cdot 10^5 + 4 \cdot 10^4 + 9 \cdot 10^3 + 6 \cdot 10^2 + 3 \cdot 10 + 2$.

62. Compute $(1,001)^2$.

63. Compute $(789)^2$.

64. What does the verb "to factor" mean?

PRACTICE-FOR-SUCCESS ANSWERS

1. LCM = 60   **2.** LCM = 396   **3.** GCF = 45

4. GCF = 1   **5.** LCM = 360   GCF = 12

1.8   FUNDAMENTAL ALGEBRAIC PROPERTIES OF OPERATIONS

OBJECTIVES

□ To identify and use the commutative laws for addition and multiplication

□ To recognize commutative operations

□ To identify and use the associative laws for addition and multiplication

□ To recognize associative operations

□ To identify and use the distributive law

In math, we have a few general laws that apply to operations with numbers. An understanding of these laws based on numerical examples will be beneficial when we see them again in a later chapter, using the language of algebra.

Commutative Law

The first law tells us about the importance of the order in which we write numbers in operations. We know that $3 + 5 = 5 + 3$ because the order in which the two numbers are written in an addition problem does not change the sum. We also know that $3 \cdot 5 = 5 \cdot 3$ because the order in which the two numbers are written does not change the product. The operations of addition and multiplication are said to be **commutative** because the written order of the numbers does not affect the answer. We say the commutative law holds for addition and multiplication and holds for all pairs of numbers.

For example, we can use the numbers 10 and 12 to demonstrate the commutative law for addition and multiplication.

$$10 + 12 = 12 + 10 \qquad 10 \cdot 12 = 12 \cdot 10$$
$$22 = 22 \ \ \surd \qquad\qquad 120 = 120 \ \ \surd$$

The order of the numbers, however, can make a difference in a subtraction problem: $9 - 5 \neq 5 - 9$. The symbol $\neq$ is read "not equals". (In the next section we will learn the meaning of $5 - 9$.) In division, order is also important; $8 \div 4 \neq 4 \div 8$. And order is essential for exponentiation, as $2^3 \neq 3^2$.

> **COMMUTATIVE LAWS**
>
> The commutative law applies to addition and multiplication but does not hold for subtraction, division, or exponentiation.
> Symbolically, if x and y denote any two numbers, then
>
> $$x + y = y + x \quad \textbf{(commutative law for addition)}$$
>
> $$x \cdot y = y \cdot x \quad \textbf{(commutative law for multiplication)}$$
>
> Addition and multiplication are commutative; subtraction, division, and exponentiation are not commutative.

Associative Laws

The commutative law is concerned only with the order in which we *write* a single operation problem. The next laws are concerned with the order in which we *perform* operations. Think of what happens when you put on a pair of pants; as long as you do not put them on backward, it does not make any difference if you start with your left leg or your right leg. But when it comes to putting on your shoes and socks, you find a real difference whether you put on your socks first or your shoes first.

The expression $5 + 8 + 7$, for example, contains two addition operations. If we first perform $5 + 8$ to get 13 and then add 7, we get 20. If we first perform $8 + 7$ to get 15 and then add the first 5, we still get 20. The answer to the problem is the same regardless of which addition we perform first. We make this clear by using parentheses to indicate the two different orders in which the operations can be performed.

$$(5 + 8) + 7 = 5 + (8 + 7)$$

$$13 + 7 = 5 + 15$$

$$20 = 20 \quad \checkmark$$

This is an example of the **associative law for addition.** This law of addition works for any three numbers and a similar law, the **associative law for multiplication,** holds for any three numbers with multiplication.

$$(4 \cdot 2) \cdot 5 = 4 \cdot (2 \cdot 5)$$

$$8 \cdot 5 = 4 \cdot 10$$

$$40 = 40 \quad \checkmark$$

The associative law holds for addition and multiplication. As the following computations show, neither subtraction nor division is associative because we get different answers depending on which operation we perform first. We can demonstrate this in the following two problems.

$$(27 - 13) - 5 \stackrel{?}{=} 27 - (13 - 5)$$

$$14 - 5 \stackrel{?}{=} 27 - 8$$

$$9 \neq 19$$

Thus,

$$(27 - 13) - 5 \neq 27 - (13 - 5)$$

and we say *subtraction is not associative*.
Similarly,

$$(32 \div 8) \div 4 \stackrel{?}{=} 32 \div (8 \div 4)$$

$$4 \div 4 \stackrel{?}{=} 32 \div 2$$

$$1 \neq 16$$

Thus,

$$(32 \div 8) \div 4 \neq 32 \div (8 \div 4)$$

and we say *division is not associative*.

ASSOCIATIVE LAWS

Symbolically, if x, y, and z denote any three numbers, then

$$(x + y) + z = x + (y + z) \quad \text{(associative law for addition)}$$

$$(x \cdot y) \cdot z = x \cdot (y \cdot z) \quad \text{(associative law for multiplication)}$$

Addition and multiplication are associative; subtraction and division are not associative.

The basic difference between the commutative and associative laws is that the commutative law pertains to the physical order in which we write a problem, whereas the associative law refers to the mental order in which we perform the same operation twice. The commutative law always involves a different left-to-right order of the numbers (they are always reversed), whereas the associative law keeps the numbers in the same left-to-right order but involves writing the parentheses in two different ways.

Distributive Law

The *distributive law* is perhaps the most important law in algebra. This law shows a strong connection between multiplication and addition and allows us to multiply the sum of several terms by the same number:

$$7 \cdot (8 + 2) = 7 \cdot 8 + 7 \cdot 2$$

$$7 \cdot 10 = 56 + 14$$

$$70 = 70 \quad \surd$$

The distributive law can be shown visually as well. We can gain a better understanding of the principle by counting the number of dots in the box in Figure 1.13.

The most efficient way to determine the number of dots is to count the number of dots down and then count the number of dots across and multiply to get the total number of dots. Figure 1.14 shows the same number of dots split up into two different boxes.

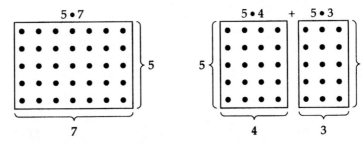

FIGURE 1.13
Depiction of 5 · 7

FIGURE 1.14
Depiction of 5 · 4 + 5 · 3

To find the total, we calculate the number of dots in each box as before and then add the two answers. The distributive law tells us that we will get the same total number of dots regardless of how we box them.

$$5 \cdot (4 + 3) = 5 \cdot 4 + 5 \cdot 3$$
$$5 \cdot 7 = 20 + 15$$
$$35 = 35 \quad \checkmark$$

$5 \cdot (4 + 3)$ is a product that involves a sum and $5 \cdot 4 + 5 \cdot 3$ is a sum of two products. Notice that 5, the number outside the parentheses, is written only once on the left and twice on the right of the = sign.

$$5 \cdot (4 + 3) = 5 \cdot 4 + 5 \cdot 3$$

The following example shows the distributive law as it would apply to a sum of three numbers.

$$6 \cdot (7 + 4 + 3) = 6 \cdot 7 + 6 \cdot 4 + 6 \cdot 3$$
$$= 42 + 24 + 18$$
$$= 66 + 18$$
$$= 84$$

Thus, when we have a sum in parentheses and are multiplying by a number outside the parentheses, we can simply multiply the outside number by each number in the sum and then add all the products.

According to the distributive law, we can switch the left and right sides of the = sign. Our original example would then look like

$$7 \cdot 8 + 7 \cdot 2 = 7 \cdot (8 + 2)$$

In this case, the distributive law is telling us how to rewrite a sum of two products as a single product that involves a sum. We can do this when the two products have a common factor, which in this equation is 7. Depending on how the two sides of the equation are arranged, the distributive law provides a way to change a basic product into a basic sum or vice versa.

$$9 \cdot (3 + 6) = 9 \cdot 3 + 9 \cdot 6 \qquad \text{A basic product becomes a basic sum.}$$
$$9 \cdot 3 + 9 \cdot 6 = 9 \cdot (3 + 6) \qquad \text{A basic sum becomes a basic product.}$$

We can write another example of the distributive law involving a sum of three terms with a common factor of 10 as follows:

$$10 \cdot 9 + 10 \cdot 3 + 10 \cdot 5 = 10 \cdot (9 + 3 + 5)$$

A large part of beginning algebra is concerned with manipulating symbols. In this section so far, we have been manipulating numbers without performing many computations. As we will see in later chapters, the real importance of the distributive law is its ability to manipulate symbols, not its ability to make computations easier.

DISTRIBUTIVE LAW

If x, y, and z denote any three numbers, then

$$x \cdot (y + z) = x \cdot y + x \cdot z$$

and

$$(y + z) \cdot x = y \cdot x + z \cdot x$$

EXAMPLE 1	Compute $8 \cdot (11 + 12)$ using the distributive law.

SOLUTION

$$8 \cdot (11 + 12) = 8 \cdot 11 + 8 \cdot 12$$
$$= 88 + 96$$
$$= 184$$

Using the distributive law as in this example provides an alternative to the usual rules for the order of operations, which would require us to do the operation enclosed in the parentheses first. ■

EXAMPLE 2	Compute $12 \cdot 17 + 12 \cdot 13$ using the distributive law.

SOLUTION

$$12 \cdot 17 + 12 \cdot 13 = 12 \cdot (17 + 13)$$
$$= 12 \cdot 30$$
$$= 360$$

Using the distributive law as in this example, simplifies the computation. ■

In the four examples that follow, the left and right sides of the equations are equal. In each case, we identify whether the change from the left side to the right side illustrates one of the commutative or associative laws, or illustrates the distributive law. In the cases of the commutative and associative laws, we state the corresponding operation (addition or multiplication).

EXAMPLE 3	$5 + (13 + 17) = (5 + 13) + 17$	associative law for addition	■

EXAMPLE 4	$3 \cdot (9 + 11) + 12 = 3 \cdot 9 + 3 \cdot 11 + 12$	distributive law	■

| **EXAMPLE 5** | $9 \cdot (72 + 85 \cdot 12) = 9 \cdot (72 + 12 \cdot 85)$ commutative law for multiplication   ■ |

| **EXAMPLE 6** | $[2 \cdot (4 \cdot 6) + 15 + 11 \cdot 12] = [(2 \cdot 4) \cdot 6 + 15 + 11 \cdot 12]$
associative law for multiplication   ■ |

In the next two examples, an inequality in which the left and right sides are unequal is given. We need to determine which one of the commutative or associative laws or the distributive law has been incorrectly applied in transforming the left side into the right side.

| **EXAMPLE 7** | $(28 \div 7) \div 7 \neq 28 \div (7 \div 7)$ Why? |

SOLUTION   The associative law has been incorrectly applied; it does not hold for division.
■

| **EXAMPLE 8** | $8 \cdot (3 + 7 + 1) \neq 8 \cdot 3 + 7 + 1$ Why? |

SOLUTION   The distributive law has been incorrectly applied; we must multiply each number in the sum by 8, not just the first one.
■

P R A C T I C E   F O R   S U C C E S S

Practice 1.   Compute $8 \cdot (7 + 11 + 13)$ using the distributive law.

Practice 2.   Identify whether the change from the left side to the right side in the following equation illustrates one of the commutative or associative laws, or the distributive law. In the cases of the commutative and associative laws, state the corresponding operation (addition or multiplication).

$$5 \cdot [10 \div (4 + 1)] + 25 = 5 \cdot [10 \div (1 + 4)] + 25$$

Practice 3.   Determine which one of the commutative or associative laws or the distributive law has been incorrectly applied in transforming the left side into the right side of the following inequality.

$$4 \cdot 12 - 24 \div 6 + 39 \div 3 \neq 4 \cdot 12 - 6 \div 24 + 39 \div 3$$

EXERCISES 1.8

In exercises 1–29, an equation is given in which the left and right sides are mathematically the same. A single instance of either the commutative law, associative law, or distributive law has been made in transforming the left side into the right side. Identify which law applies to each given equation, and in the case of the commutative or associative laws state the corresponding operation.

1. $5 + (8 + 6) = (5 + 8) + 6$
2. $32 \div 16 + 9 + 7 = 32 \div 16 + 7 + 9$
3. $48 \cdot (5 + 3) + 20 = 48 \cdot 5 + 48 \cdot 3 + 20$
4. $800 - 5 \cdot (10 + 13 \cdot 15) = 800 - 5 \cdot (10 + 15 \cdot 13)$
5. $[(90 - 23) \cdot 15 + 12 \cdot (10 \cdot 18)] = [(90 - 23) \cdot 15 + (12 \cdot 10) \cdot 18]$
6. $[15 \cdot 3 + 15 \cdot 5 - 38] = [15 \cdot (3 + 5) - 38]$
7. $[(18 + 32) + 50] \cdot 5 = [18 + (32 + 50)] \cdot 5$
8. $[23 \cdot (12 \cdot 13) + 26 \cdot 17] = [(23 \cdot 12) \cdot 13 + 26 \cdot 17]$
9. $5 \cdot [12 + 17 \cdot 19] + 13 - 27 = 5 \cdot [12 + 19 \cdot 17] + 13 - 27$
10. $[6 \cdot 17 + 6 \cdot 12 + 6 \cdot 10] = [6 \cdot (17 + 12 + 10)]$
11. $[9 \cdot (5 + 27 + 13)] - 32 = [9 \cdot 5 + 9 \cdot 27 + 9 \cdot 13] - 32$
12. $(71 \cdot 13 - 26 + 31) = (13 \cdot 71 - 26 + 31)$
13. $[33 + 29 + 48 - 21 - 45] = [33 + 48 + 29 - 21 - 45]$
14. $[28 \div 14 - 32 \cdot 0 + 6 \cdot 18] = [28 \div 14 - 32 \cdot 0 + 18 \cdot 6]$
15. $13 + [26 \div 13 + (5 + 8) + 9] = 13 + [26 \div 13 + 5 + (8 + 9)]$
16. $34 + [27 + 4 \cdot 5 + 9 \div 3] = 34 + [27 + 5 \cdot 4 + 9 \div 3]$
17. $(6 \cdot 10 + 6 \cdot 9 + 6 \cdot 7) = 6 \cdot (10 + 9 + 7)$
18. $[8 \cdot (5 \cdot 10) + 13 + 9 \cdot 8] = [(8 \cdot 5) \cdot 10 + 13 + 9 \cdot 8]$
19. $[6 \cdot (7 \cdot 3) + 7 \cdot (3 + 13)] = [6 \cdot (7 \cdot 3) + 7 \cdot 3 + 7 \cdot 13]$
20. $[5 \cdot (26 - 12) + (5 + 9) + 7] = [5 \cdot (26 - 12) + 5 + (9 + 7)]$
21. $[9 \cdot (4 + 10) + (7 \cdot 5) \cdot 10] = [9 \cdot (4 + 10) + 7 \cdot (5 \cdot 10)]$
22. $[3 \cdot (5 + 9) + (8 \cdot 7) \cdot 6] = [3 \cdot (5 + 9) + (7 \cdot 8) \cdot 6]$
23. $[5 + (5 \cdot 3 + 5 \cdot 7 + 5 \cdot 8)] = [5 + (5 \cdot 3 + 5 \cdot 7 + 8 \cdot 5)]$
24. $[64 \div 16 + 9 + (8 + 7)] = [64 \div 16 + 9 + (7 + 8)]$
25. $[32 \div 8 \div 4 + 7 \cdot 9 + 7 \cdot 8] = [32 \div 8 \div 4 + 7 \cdot (9 + 8)]$
26. $[56 \div 8 + (8 \cdot 7) \cdot 3 + 9] = [56 \div 8 + 8 \cdot (7 \cdot 3) + 9]$
27. $[42 \div 14 - 13 \cdot 5 + 8 \cdot (7 + 3)] = [42 \div 14 - 5 \cdot 13 + 8 \cdot (7 + 3)]$
28. $[8 \cdot 7 + 8 \cdot 5 + 8 \cdot 3 + 8 \cdot 9] = [8 \cdot 7 + 8 \cdot 5 + 8 \cdot (3 + 9)]$
29. $[9 \cdot 7 + 8 \cdot 3 + 4 \cdot (7 + 8)] = [9 \cdot 7 + 8 \cdot 3 + 4 \cdot 7 + 4 \cdot 8]$

In exercises 30–40, an inequality is given in which the left and right sides are mathematically different. A single instance of either the commutative law, associative law, or distributive law has been violated in transforming the left side into the right side. In cases in which the associative or commutative law is involved, identify the corresponding operation.

30. $[64 \div (4 \div 4) + 9 \cdot (3 \cdot 7)] \neq [(64 \div 4) \div 4 + 9 \cdot (3 \cdot 7)]$
31. $[32 - (26 - 2) + 3 \cdot 12] \neq [(32 - 26) - 2 + 3 \cdot 12]$
32. $[6 \cdot 13 - (18 \div 6) + 12 \div 2] \neq [6 \cdot 13 - (6 \div 18) + 12 \div 2]$
33. $52 + 17 - (9 - 2) + 34 \cdot 3 \neq 52 + (17 - 9) - 2 + 34 \cdot 3$
34. $[28 - 19 + 13 \cdot 3 + 7 \cdot (3 \cdot 5)] \neq [19 - 28 + 13 \cdot 3 + 7 \cdot (3 \cdot 5)]$
35. $[23 \cdot 3 - (48 \div 8) \div 2 + 3 \cdot 5] \neq [23 \cdot 3 - 48 \div (8 \div 2) + 3 \cdot 5]$
36. $[52 - 26 - 3 \cdot 8 - (17 - 5)] \neq [52 - 26 - 3 \cdot 8 - (5 - 17)]$

37. $34 - 14 - 11 - 5 \neq 34 - 14 - (11 - 5)$
38. $[96 \div 12 \div 4 + 17 \cdot 5] \neq [96 \div (12 \div 4) + 17 \cdot 5]$
39. $7 \cdot 5 + 7 \cdot 3 + 7 \cdot 9 \neq 7 \cdot (5 + 3) + 9$
40. $[75 \cdot (3 + 4 + 5)] \neq [75 \cdot 3 + 75 \cdot 4 + 5]$

In exercises 41–55, apply the distributive law to rewrite the given expression into a mathematically equivalent expression but do not simplify the resulting expression.

41. $5 \cdot (8 + 6) = ?$
42. $12 \cdot (16 + 9) = ?$
43. $48 \cdot 5 + 48 \cdot 3 = ?$
44. $7 \cdot (8 + 5 + 9) = ?$
45. $9 \cdot 3 + 9 \cdot 5 + 9 \cdot 7 = ?$
46. $13 \cdot (12 + 13 + 5) = ?$
47. $5 \cdot 8 + 5 \cdot 12 + 5 \cdot 20 = ?$
48. $12 \cdot (34 + 17 + 9 + 27) = ?$
49. $24 \cdot 5 + 24 \cdot 9 + 24 \cdot 10 + 24 \cdot 18 = ?$
50. $32 \cdot 7 + 32 \cdot 32 + 32 \cdot 16 = ?$
51. $19 \cdot (8 + 17 + 19 + 23) = ?$
52. $25 \cdot (25 + 24 + 23 + 22) = ?$
53. $15 \cdot 7 + 15 \cdot 23 + 15 \cdot 2 + 15 \cdot 8 = ?$
54. $12 \cdot 13 + 12 \cdot 12 + 12 \cdot 0 + 12 \cdot 5 = ?$
55. $8 \cdot (11 + 32 + 8 + 17) = ?$

Looking Back

56. Find the LCM and the GCF of 168 and 540.
57. Find the LCM and the GCF of 2,184 and 1,404.
58. What is the basic operation for the expression
$12 \cdot [8 + 3 \cdot (58 \div 2 + 3)] \div 4?$
59. What is the basic operation for the expression $(2 + 3)^{(3+4)}$?
60. Is 259 a prime number?
61. Is 119 a prime number?
62. Write the number 1,479 in two expanded forms.
63. Write the number 675,543 in two expanded forms.

PRACTICE-FOR-SUCCESS ANSWERS

1. $8 \cdot (7 + 11 + 13) = 8 \cdot 7 + 8 \cdot 11 + 8 \cdot 13$
$= 56 + 88 + 104$
$= 144 + 104$
$= 248$

2. Commutative law for addition: $4 + 1 = 1 + 4$

3. Commutative law does not hold for division: $24 \div 6 \neq 6 \div 24$

SUMMARY

This chapter has presented all of the fundamental topics related to whole numbers that build a foundation for learning algebra. We examined the place value of digits and found, for example, that the digit 7 in the number 435,728,190 is in the hundred thousands place and that the digit 3 is in the ten millions place. When we round to the nearest ten thousand, 435,728,190 ≈ 435,730,000. Written in words, the original number is four hundred thirty-five million, seven hundred twenty-eight thousand, one hundred ninety. The number 435,728,190 is divisible by 2 because the rightmost digit is an even number, it is divisible by 3 because the sum of the digits is 39, which is divisible by 3, and it is divisible by 5 because the right-most digit is 0. The prime factorization is: $435{,}728{,}190 = 2 \cdot 3 \cdot 5 \cdot 17^2 \cdot 29 \cdot 1{,}733$. In this expression the number 17 is the base, which appears with an exponent of 2.

We reviewed the four fundamental operations and the order of operations for expressions that contain several operations and/or grouping symbols. The terminology we encountered included the division check—that is, divisor × quotient + remainder = dividend. To find the least common multiple (LCM) and the greatest common factor (GCF) of the numbers 200 and 300, we consider their prime factorizations: $200 = 2^3 \cdot 5^2$ and $300 = 2^2 \cdot 3^1 \cdot 5^2$. The LCM includes all the prime bases and the largest exponent found on each of the bases. The GCF includes only the common primes as bases and uses the smallest exponent found on these bases. The $\text{LCM} = 2^3 \cdot 3^1 \cdot 5^2 = 600$. The $\text{GCF} = 2^2 \cdot 5^2 = 100$.

In the fundamental properties of expressions, the basic operation for an expression is the last operation performed according to the rules for the order of operations. For example, the basic operation for $7 \cdot [(12 + 3) \div 5 - 2]$ is multiplication. Other fundamental properties are the commutative, associative, and distributive laws.

Commutative laws: $x + y = y + x$ $x \cdot y = y \cdot x$

Associative laws: $(x + y) + z = x + (y + z)$ $(x \cdot y) \cdot z = x \cdot (y \cdot z)$

Distributive law: $x \cdot (y + z) = x \cdot y + x \cdot z$

CHAPTER 1 REVIEW PROBLEMS

In problems 1–8, write the place value of the given digit in the given number.

1. The digit 7 in 45,732
2. The digit 3 in 34,802
3. The digit 5 in 5,461,202
4. The digit 8 in 18,735,119
5. The digit 2 in 724,391
6. The digit 6 in 6,793,451,237
7. The digit 9 in 954,613,204,821
8. The digit 7 in 32,782,561

In problems 9–14, write each number in two expanded forms.

9. 96,127

10. 8,744

11. 79,548

12. 764,149

13. 203,080

14. 85,501

In problems 15–20, write each number in words.

15. 454,407

16. 82,050

17. 55,660

18. 37,397,855,013

19. 22,332,222,239

20. 219,161,274,076

In problems 21–25, write the number described in standard form.

21. Two million, nine hundred thirty-four thousand, five hundred twenty-seven.

22. Five hundred three thousand, sixty-nine.

23. Seventeen thousand, five.

24. Four hundred ninety-eight thousand, five hundred seventeen.

25. Six million, seventy-two thousand, fifteen.

In problems 26–35, solve each problem using addition, subtraction, multiplication, or division, as required.

26. In a baseball 3-game series, the attendance figures for the Tigers were 54,692, 34,985, and 44,758. What was the total attendance for all three games?

27. The balance in a checkbook was $5,672 before three checks were written for $1,286, $567, and $2,986, respectively. What was the final balance in the account after these three checks were paid?

28. If a copy machine can reproduce 525 pages in 5 minutes, how many pages can it reproduce in 1 hour?

29. If a bus can carry 48 passengers in 1 trip from Los Angeles to Santa Barbara, how many total passengers can it transport in a week if it makes 3 trips a day?

30. If a radio station plays 187 records in 1 day, how many records would it play starting on September 12 and continuing through September 29?

31. If a soup company can pack 36 cans in 1 crate, how many crates would be needed to hold 5,940 cans?

32. On a recent cross-country trip of 2,268 miles, a person used 81 gallons of gasoline. This is equivalent to how many miles per gallon?

33. A land speculator owns 480 acres of land, which is valued at $2,025 per acre. What is the total value of this land?

34. If an oil well produces 38 barrels per day, how many days will it take to produce 3,990 barrels?

35. A nationwide motel chain is planning to purchase televisions that cost $276 a set. How many sets can the chain buy if it has budgeted $41,400 for this purpose?

In problems 36–48, simplify each expression using the rules for the order of operations.

36. $5 + 3^2 \cdot 4$

37. $(2 + 7)^2 + 2^2 + 7^2$

38. $(113 - 2 \cdot 4)^2 - (2 + 4 \cdot 5)^2$

39. $(72 \div 12 \cdot 6)^2 - (7 + 3 \cdot 9)^2$

40. $(17 \cdot 0 + 3) \cdot (15 - 2) \div (4^2 - 3)$

41. $(9^2 - 8^2)^2 \div (13 \cdot 0 + 17) \cdot (8^2 + 8 \div 4 \div 2)$

42. $5 \cdot 12^2 \div 16 + 14$

43. $5 \cdot 6^2 \div 15 - 9^2 \div 3^3$

44. $\{[(3 \cdot 2 - 4) \cdot 2 + 5] \cdot 2 + 6\}$

45. $4 \cdot [8 + 2 \cdot 2^3 \cdot (13 + 2)^2]$

46. $20 \cdot [38 - 3 \cdot 3^4 \div (24 - 5 \cdot 4 - 1)^2]$

47. $3 \cdot [17 + 2 \cdot (4 + 3 \cdot 6) \div 4]$

48. $5 \cdot [29 + 3 \cdot (14 + 33 \div 11) \div 3]$

In problems 49–57, write each number as a product of powers of primes.

49. 200   **50.** 2,475   **51.** 5,746

52. 67,375   **53.** 5,005   **54.** 29,536

55. 341   **56.** 2,160   **57.** 637

In problems 58–66, find both the LCM and the GCF of the given numbers. Then write the LCM using multiples of the given numbers and write each given number as the result of a product that uses the GCF.

58. 360 and 1,200   **59.** 900 and 240   **60.** 1,323 and 294

61. 1,925 and 455   **62.** 672 and 1,155   **63.** 680 and 952

64. 1,764 and 390   **65.** 48 and 64 and 96   **66.** 200 and 48 and 600

In problems 67–78, an equation is given in which a single application of one of the commutative laws, associative laws, or the distributive law connects the left and right sides of the equation. Identify which law is used and, in the case of the commutative or associative laws, identify the corresponding operation.

67. $44 \div 11 + 5 + 3 = 44 \div 11 + 3 + 5$

68. $26 \cdot (9 + 16) + 17 = 26 \cdot 9 + 26 \cdot 16 + 17$

69. $[(9 - 3) \cdot 8 - 3 \cdot (9 \cdot 5)] = [(9 - 3) \cdot 8 - (3 \cdot 9) \cdot 5]$

70. $[8 \cdot 7 + 8 \cdot 4 - 45] = [8 \cdot (7 + 4) - 45]$

71. $[(20 + 19) + 18] \cdot 23 = [20 + (19 + 18)] \cdot 23$

72. $[42 \cdot (13 \cdot 8) + 31 \cdot 7] = [(42 \cdot 13) \cdot 8 + 31 \cdot 7]$

73. $9 \cdot [73 + 32 \cdot 44] + 77 - 62 = 9 \cdot [73 + 44 \cdot 32] + 77 - 62$

74. $[19 \cdot 27 + 19 \cdot 62 + 19 \cdot 75] = [19 \cdot (27 + 62 + 75)]$

75. $[8 \cdot (3 + 52 + 41)] - 56 = [8 \cdot 3 + 8 \cdot 52 + 8 \cdot 41] - 56$

76. $[75 \div 15 - 42 \cdot 0 + 7 \cdot 19] = [75 \div 15 - 42 \cdot 0 + 19 \cdot 7]$

77. $40 + [18 \div 6 + (7 + 2) + 59] = 40 + [18 \div 6 + 7 + (2 + 59)]$

78. $(22 \cdot 38 + 22 \cdot 15 + 22 \cdot 27) = 22 \cdot (38 + 15 + 27)$

In problems 79–88, use the distributive law to transform the given left side into a correct equation.

79. $6 \cdot (7 + 5) = ?$

80. $14 \cdot (2 + 8) = ?$

81. $7 \cdot 3 + 7 \cdot 17 = ?$

82. $13 \cdot 2 + 13 \cdot 18 = ?$

83. $5 \cdot 2 + 5 \cdot 21 + 5 \cdot 7 = ?$

84. $4 \cdot (3 + 11 + 13) = ?$

85. $23 \cdot 7 + 23 \cdot 5 + 23 \cdot 18 = ?$

86. $8 \cdot (9 + 13 + 8) = ?$

87. $56 \cdot 23 + 56 \cdot 17 + 56 \cdot 20 = ?$

88. $92 \cdot (13 + 30 + 17) = ?$

In problems 89–98, an expression is given. Give the basic operation for the expression but do not evaluate the expressions.

89. $945 \div 5 - 19 \cdot 7 + 26$

90. $(36 \div 9 + 3)^2$

91. $(2 + 7)^2 + 2^2 + 7^2$

92. $(113 - 2 \cdot 4)^2 - (2 + 4 \cdot 5)^2$

93. $(72 \div 12 \cdot 6)^4 \div (36 - 3 \cdot 9)^3$

94. $(17 \cdot 0 + 3) \cdot (15 - 2) \div (4^2 - 3)$

95. $5 \cdot 6^2 \div 15 - 9^2 \div 3^3$

96. $\{[(7 \cdot 9 + 5) \cdot 7 - 13] \cdot 7 - 28\}$

97. $4 \cdot [8 + 2 \cdot 2^3 \cdot (13 + 2)^2]$

98. $[4 \cdot 17 - 23]^2 \cdot (67 - 32 \div 8)^3$

CHAPTER 1 PRACTICE TEST

1. Give the place values of the digits 1, 4, and 8 in the number 85,495,216,239.

2. Write the number 56,198 in two expanded forms.

3. Write the number 63,154,044,909 in words.

4. The three most prolific scorers in NBA history are Kareem Abdul-Jabbar, Wilt Chamberlain, and Michael Jordan. If Kareem scored 38,387 points, Wilt scored 31,419 points, and Michael scored 29,277 points, what is the total number of points scored by all three players?

5. If 28 oranges can be packed in one crate, how many crates will be required to hold 8,008 oranges?

In problems 6–10, simplify each expression using the rules for the order of operations.

6. $5 \cdot 3^2 + (12 + 120 \div 4 \div 3)^2$

7. $\{[(5 \cdot 6 + 8) \cdot 6 - 220] \cdot 6 + 7\} \cdot 6 - 13$

8. $\{[(4 \cdot 2^2 + 10) \cdot 2^2 - 100] \cdot 2^2 + 13\} \cdot 2^2 - 21$

9. $4 \cdot \{10 + 4 \cdot [4 \cdot (10 + 3 \cdot 4) - 80]\} - 13$

10. $(19 + 7^2 - 6 \cdot 3)^2 - [2^3 + 64 \div 2]^2$

11. Give the definition for a prime number.

12. Write 837 as a product of powers of prime numbers.

13. Write 8,352 as a product of powers of prime numbers.

14. Give the meaning of the acronyms LCM and GCF and then give the definitions of these terms.

15. Find the LCM of the numbers 3,500 and 2,800. Then write the LCM as a multiple of each number.

16. Find the GCF of the numbers 1,674 and 4,176 and write each number as a product that uses the GCF.

In problems 17–21, identify the fundamental law that makes each equation true. In cases of the associative or commutative laws, name the corresponding operation.

17. $[34 \div 17 - 13 \cdot 9 + 10 \cdot 5] = [34 \div 17 - 13 \cdot 9 + 5 \cdot 10]$

18. $[7 \cdot (6 \cdot 2) - 25 + 68 \div 4] = [(7 \cdot 6) \cdot 2 - 25 + 68 \div 4]$

19. $[8 \cdot (7 + 3 + 9) + 8 + 3] = [8 \cdot (7 + 3 + 9) + 3 + 8]$

20. $[12 \cdot 6 \cdot 10 + 12 \cdot 7 + 12 \cdot 3 + 7 \cdot 9] = [12 \cdot 6 \cdot 10 + 12 \cdot (7 + 3) + 7 \cdot 9]$

21. $[8 \cdot (7 + 9) - (3 \cdot 8) \cdot 5 - 5^2] = [8 \cdot (7 + 9) - 3 \cdot (8 \cdot 5) - 5^2]$

In problems 22–25, identify the basic operation for the given expression.

22. $20 \div 4 + 3^2 \cdot 8$

23. $8 \cdot 12^2 \div 16 - 10^2 \div 5^2$

24. $140,088 \div [20 + 2 \cdot 3^4 \cdot (5 + 7)^2]$

25. $[9 \cdot 6^2 + 52^2 \div 13 - 6 \cdot (3 + 2)]$

INTEGERS

This chapter covers signed whole numbers, or integers, including the adding, subtracting, multiplying, and dividing of positive and negative whole numbers. Concepts related to opposites, absolute value, and the ordering of signed numbers are explored, as is the use of these concepts to calculate the distance between two points on a number line. Special properties of the number zero are examined, and signed numbers are used to solve word problems and to work problems with mixed operations, including exponents and grouping symbols.

2.1 THE NUMBER LINE

OBJECTIVES

- To express a quantity as an integer
- To find the opposite of an integer
- To find the absolute value of an integer
- To find the absolute value of expressions
- To compare any two integers

The set of numbers that we have used so far has consisted of the set of whole numbers {0, 1, 2, 3, ...}. In this section, we expand the set of numbers to include **negative numbers.**

Expanding the Number Line

In the last chapter we used a number line to depict the whole numbers beginning at 0 and continuing forever to the right, with the numbers getting progressively larger (see Figure 2.1). However, whole numbers cannot be

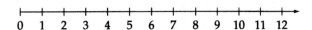

Figure 2.1 Number line depicting whole numbers

used in every situation. For example, in some places the temperature may drop to 3° (three degrees) below 0° Fahrenheit. The temperature cannot be expressed as 3° because the number 3 indicates three units to the right of 0. Instead, the negative sign − is used to indicate that the number is to the left of 0. In this instance, the temperature would be −3°. Negative numbers are shown on the number line as depicted in Figure 2.2.

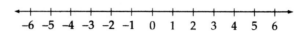

FIGURE 2.2   **Number line depicting negative numbers to the left of 0**

On the number line the numbers to the left of 0 are designated by a negative sign and progress from right to left: −1, −2, −3, …. The left arrow indicates that the negative numbers, like the positive numbers, continue forever, but to the left. The number −5 is read as "negative five" and −15 is read as "negative fifteen." Although −15 is not shown in Figure 2.2, if the line were extended, −15 would lie ten marks to the left of −5. To further distinguish the positive from the negative numbers, the positive sign + is used to denote the numbers to the right of 0. For example +3 is read as "positive three." The number line with positive and negative signs in place is shown in Figure 2.3.

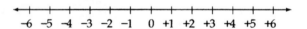

FIGURE 2.3   **Number line with signed integers**

The whole numbers together with the negative numbers, as presented in Figure 2.3, are called the **integers.** The word *integer* is a name for a signed whole number. The numbers to the right of 0 are called the **positive integers** and the numbers to the left of 0 are called the **negative integers**. Because 0 is a neutral integer and is neither positive nor negative, it is not necessary to write any sign in front of it: 0 = −0 = +0. Further, because the whole numbers covered in Chapter 1 are the positive integers just introduced, it is not necessary to write a positive sign in front of a positive number: +4 = 4. Unless it is being emphasized that a number is positive, positive signs will be omitted in this book whenever they are not needed. However if a number is negative, then the negative sign must be used in front of the number.

Although the positive sign and the negative sign look like the symbols used for addition and subtraction, they are not used to add or subtract on the number line. The positive sign is used with a number to indicate a number of units to the right of 0: +4 indicates four units to the right of 0. The negative sign is used with a number to indicate a number of units to the left of 0: −4 indicates four units to the left of 0.

Positive and negative integers can also be used to represent different quantities. A profit of $1,000 can be represented by 1,000 or +1,000; a gambling loss of $20 can be represented by the integer −20.

EXAMPLE 1	Express the following as integers:

a. 70° above 0

b. a loss of $1,000

c. the number of brothers and sisters in a family of one child

d. a 20-point gain in the value of a stock

e. the elevation of the Salton Sea at 280 feet below sea level

SOLUTION   **a.** 70 or +70   **b.** −1,000   **c.** 0   **d.** 20 or +20   **e.** −280   ■

Opposites

As we can see in Figure 2.3, the positive and negative integers are evenly distributed on both sides of the number 0. +2 and −2 are on opposite sides of 0; therefore, the opposite of +2 is −2 and the opposite of −2 is +2. **Opposites** are any two numbers that have opposite signs and are equidistant from 0.

In math the − symbol is used for three different purposes: for subtraction, to show that a number is negative, and to indicate the opposite of a number. Because −(−2) is read as "the opposite of negative two," −(−2) = +2. On the other hand, −(+2) = −2. In both cases, the sign for "the opposite of" looks similar to the subtraction sign or the sign used to indicate that a number is negative. How the − symbol is interpreted depends on the context in which it is used. For example:

50 − 25   In this case the − symbol indicates subtraction. If we have numbers on both sides of the − symbol, it indicates subtraction.

−12   Here the − symbol indicates that the number is negative and is read "negative 12." No number is in front of the − symbol, so the symbol does not indicate subtraction.

−(−76)   This time the first − symbol indicates that we are finding the opposite of a number. The second − symbol indicates that the number is negative. This expression is read "the opposite of negative 76."

Only integers will be used in this chapter, so wherever the variable x appears, it represents an integer. The notation $-x$ will denote "the opposite of x." Therefore $-x$ is not necessarily a negative quantity and in fact, may be positive, 0, or negative. If $x = -13$, then $-x = -(-13) = 13$.

EXAMPLE 2	Find the opposite of the following integers:

a. 77   **b.** −3,500   **c.** 0

SOLUTION   **a.** −(77) = −77   **b.** −(−3,500) = 3,500   **c.** −(0) = 0   ■

Absolute Value

Sometimes it is useful to know the value of a number regardless of its sign. This is called the **absolute value** of the number. We use the concept of distance to define absolute value. What is meant by *distance* in the definition is the number of units without regard to direction. Distance is never negative. If your best friend lives 5 miles away from you, you both live 5 miles away from each other; neither of you lives −5 miles from the other. In fact, distance is nonnegative. The word *nonnegative* means "not a negative," which implies that the number could be either 0 or positive.

DEFINITION	ABSOLUTE VALUE
	The absolute value of a number is the distance between the point on the number line that corresponds to the given number and the point on the number line that corresponds to 0.

The notation $|x|$ is read as "the absolute value of x." $|x|$ is the distance between the point on the number line that corresponds to 0 and the point that corresponds to x. For example, $|3|$ means that the number 3 is three units away from 0, so $|3| = 3$. $|−3|$ also means that the number −3 is three units away from 0, so $|−3| = 3$, as we can see in Figure 2.4.

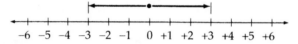

FIGURE 2.4   Depiction of $|−3| = 3$ and $|3| = 3$

EXAMPLE 3	Find the absolute value of the following numbers:

    a. −32   **b.** 8   **c.** 0

SOLUTION   **a.** $|−32| = 32$

    b. $|8| = 8$

    c. $|0| = 0$ since 0 is 0 units away from itself. Zero is the only distance that is nonpositive and also nonnegative.   ■

Absolute value bars also act as grouping symbols. When more than one number appears between the vertical bars, all operations inside them are performed to obtain a single number. Then the absolute value of that number is written as nonnegative number.

EXAMPLE 4	Simplify the following expressions:

    a. $−|−52|$

    b. $|−(+75)| − |−(−44)|$

    c. $|−(4^3 − 2^5)|$

    d. $−|12 \cdot 12 \cdot 0|$

    e. $|−(−13)| + |89 − 32| − |169 \div 13|$

SOLUTION   **a.** $-|-52| = -(+52)$ The absolute value of -52 is $+52$.
                    $= -52$ The opposite of $+52$ is -52.

b. $|-(+75)| - |-(-44)| = |-75| - |+44|$
                                $= 75 - 44$
                                $= 31$

c. $|-(4^3 - 2^5)| = |-(64 - 32)|$ Operate inside the absolute value bars first.
                      $= |-(32)|$
                      $= |-32|$
                      $= 32$

d. $-|12 \cdot 12 \cdot 0| = -|144 \cdot 0|$
                            $= -|0|$
                            $= -0$ The absolute value of 0 is 0.
                            $= 0$ The opposite of 0 is 0.

e. $|-(-13)| + |89 - 32| - |169 \div 13| = |+13| + |57| - |13|$
                                          $= 13 + 57 - 13$
                                          $= 70 - 13$
                                          $= 57$ ■

Order

Numbers are used to compare quantities. For example, everyone knows that a 3-day weekend is longer (or greater) than a 2-day weekend. In mathematics the symbol $>$ stands for "greater than" and the symbol $<$ stands for "less than." Instead of writing "3 is greater than 2," we can write $3 > 2$, and instead of writing "2 is less than 3," we can write $2 < 3$. We can always tell which number is larger and which is smaller in such expressions because the symbols $<$ and $>$ point in the direction of the smaller number, and the open part faces the larger number.

$4 < 7$ is read as "4 is less than 7" and $7 > 4$ is read "7 is greater than 4." Both mathematical statements convey the same message. On a number line the larger number 7 lies to the right of the smaller number 4. We can also say the smaller number 4 lies to the left of the larger number 7.

From the preceding figures we can see that the integers decrease as the corresponding points on the number line lie farther to the left. According to the definition of ordering integers, $-1 < 4$ because -1 lies to the left of 4. This becomes clear if we think in terms of money; it is better to have \$4 than to owe a fellow student \$1. Also according to the definition, $-6 < -2$, which may seem incorrect because $6 > 2$. However, the relative locations of -6 and -2 on the number line show that -6 is farther to the left, and, therefore, -6 is less than -2. Again, stating it in monetary terms, it is better to lose \$2 than \$6.

DEFINITION   **ORDERING OF INTEGERS**

The number x is defined to be less than the number y if, on the number line, the point corresponding to x lies to the left of the point corresponding to y.

| EXAMPLE 5 | Replace the ? with the appropriate symbol < or >. |

a. 5 ? 22   **b.** −4 ? −9   **c.** −32 ? 20   **d.** 0 ? $|-9|$ **e.** $|-8|$? $|5|$

SOLUTION   **a.** 5 < 22; 5 is farther to the left than 22 on the number line.

b. −4 > −9; −4 is farther to the right than −9 on the number line.

c. −32 < 20; −32 is farther to the left than 20 on the number line.

d. Since $|-9|$ = 9, then 0 < $|-9|$; 0 is farther to the left on the number line.

e. Since $|-8|$ = 8 and $|5|$ = 5, then $|-8|$ > $|5|$; 8 is farther to the right than 5 on the number line. ■

Whenever in doubt as to how to make the comparison of two integers, think of a picture of the number line and make the symbol point toward the integer that is to the left on the number line.

PRACTICE FOR SUCCESS

Practice 1.   Express as an integer the elevation of the bottom of an abyss in the Atlantic Ocean 9,200 feet below sea level.

Practice 2.   Find the opposite of −15.

Practice 3.   Find $|-(+36)|$.

Practice 4.   Evaluate the expression $|72 - 3^2| - |-(88 \div 22)|$.

Practice 5.   Replace the ? with the appropriate symbol < or > in the expression −13 ? −10.

EXERCISES 2.1

In exercises 1–18, express the quantity described using integers.

1. The temperature is seventeen degrees below zero.
2. You have just incurred a debt of eighteen dollars.
3. A submarine is at a depth of three hundred fifty feet below sea level.
4. In the first quarter of a football game, the USC Trojans lost fifteen yards rushing.
5. The UCLA Bruins have just made a first down with a 45-yard pass.
6. In a golf match, your score is six below par.
7. A certain stock on the New York Stock Exchange went down two points in one day.
8. You have just won $1,000 in the New York lottery.
9. In a game of gin rummy, you have just lost thirty-five points.
10. Your bathroom scales are properly calibrated three pounds to the left of the true zero mark.

11. The 4-digit tape counter on a VCR has passed 0 and shows the number 9,987.

12. The water level in a swimming pool after an earthquake is two feet below normal.

13. The oil dipstick in your car shows you are down one quart of oil.

14. Bay Horse, Idaho, became a ghost town after its two hundred fifty citizens abandoned it.

15. Your boss just asked you to make 500 copies of her mother's favorite recipe.

16. After returning from a strenuous camping trip, you notice you dropped twelve pounds in weight.

17. In an oil well blow-out in the Gulf of Mexico in 1979, six hundred thousand tons of oil were lost.

18. In Charleston, South Carolina, the ocean tide can drop as much as sixty-three inches.

In exercises 19–33, simplify the given expressions to a single integer without parentheses.

19. $-(+7)$	20. $-(-5)$	21. $-(+12)$
22. $-(-16)$	23. $-(+16)$	24. $-(50)$
25. $-(-50)$	26. $-(+0)$	27. $-(+2)$
28. -0	29. $-(7)$	30. $-(-0)$
31. $+(7)$	32. $+0$	33. $-(+7)$

In exercises 34–51, calculate the value of the given expressions.

34. $\lvert -3 \rvert$	35. $\lvert +9 \rvert$	36. $\lvert -(+3) \rvert$
37. $\lvert -(+9) \rvert$	38. $\lvert -(-3) \rvert$	39. $\lvert -(+5) \rvert$
40. $\lvert -0 \rvert$	41. $\lvert 0 \rvert$	42. $\lvert -(-12) \rvert$
43. $\lvert -16 \rvert$	44. $\lvert +0 \rvert$	45. $\lvert -(+84) \rvert$
46. $\lvert 827 \rvert$	47. $\lvert -(-0) \rvert$	48. $\lvert -(+0) \rvert$
49. $\lvert -(+62) \rvert$	50. $\lvert -(-62) \rvert$	51. $\lvert -(+524) \rvert$

In exercises 52–66, write the correct comparison symbol $<$ or $>$ between the integers to make the resulting statement true.

52. $-35\ ?\ -45$	53. $0\ ?\ -7$	54. $-7\ ?\ 0$
55. $16\ ?\ 0$	56. $-0\ ?\ 6$	57. $-82\ ?\ -93$
58. $+0\ ?\ -112$	59. $-134\ ?\ -135$	60. $-256\ ?\ -257$
61. $353\ ?\ \lvert -352 \rvert$	62. $-257\ ?\ -256$	63. $85\ ?\ +93$
64. $\lvert -25 \rvert\ ?\ 36$	65. $18\ ?\ -27$	66. $45\ ?\ -3$

In exercises 67–81, perform the indicated operations and simplify each expression to a single integer without parentheses or absolute value bars.

67. $-(+62)$

68. $\lvert -(-62) \rvert$

$-73 + -73$

69. $\left|-(+73)\right| + \left|-(+73)\right|$

70. $\left|-(-102)\right| + \left|-(+48)\right|$

71. $\left|-(+691)\right| - \left|-(+53)\right|$

72. $\left|-(+231)\right| - \left|-137\right|$

73. $\left|-(-336)\right| + 735$

74. $\left|-(+0)\right| + 58$

75. $\left|-(2^5 - 3^2)\right|$

76. $\left|-(4^2 - 2^4)\right|$ $+ -2$

77. $\left|-(7 \cdot 0 \cdot 7)\right| + \left|-(3^3)\right|$

78. $\left|-(+74)\right| - \left|-(+53)\right| - \left|-(+11)\right|$

79. $\left|-(+543)\right| - \left|-(+87)\right| - \left|-(-275)\right|$

80. $\left|-(-387)\right| + \left|-(+35)\right| - \left|-(+265)\right|$

81. $\left|-(+7,581)\right| - \left|-(-3,638)\right| - \left|-(-1,709)\right|$

👁 Looking Back

82. Find the prime factorization of 1,105.

83. Find the LCM and GCF of 845 and 962.

84. What is the basic operation for the expression
$$\{50 \cdot [9 + 6 \cdot 3^2 \cdot (93 - 27 \cdot 3)] \div 2\}$$

85. Name two operations that are commutative and name two operations that are *not* commutative.

86. Name two operations that are associative and name two operations that are *not* associative.

87. What number is the product of the LCM and GCF of 12 and 16? How is this answer related to the product 12 · 16?

PRACTICE-FOR-SUCCESS ANSWERS

1. −9,200   **2.** +15   **3.** +36   **4.** +59   **5.** −13 < −10

2.2	**ADDITION OF INTEGERS**

OBJECTIVES

- ☐ To add any two integers
- ☐ To simplify expressions using addition
- ☐ To solve word problems using addition

In this section, we will develop rules for the addition of integers. Again, the number line will be used as a way of visualizing what happens when integers are added. Imagine that the halfback from your favorite football team carries the ball and gains 4 yards and then 3 yards. How many total yards have been gained on the two running plays? Starting at 0, draw an arrow representing 4, going 4 units to the right. Next, draw another arrow starting at 4, going 3 units farther to the right. The tip of the second arrow reaches 7, which is the sum of the two numbers added together. 4 + 3 = 7. The halfback has gained 7 yards. From Figure 2.5, the rule for adding any two positive integers can be developed.

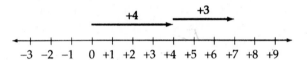

FIGURE 2.5   Depiction of the addition of 4 and 3

ADDING TWO POSITIVE INTEGERS

To add a positive integer to another positive integer, perform ordinary addition. The sum is positive.

An arrow representing a positive number is drawn to the right on the number line, so it follows logically that an arrow representing a negative number is drawn to the left on the number line. Imagine that the halfback from your favorite football team loses 2 yards and then loses an additional 3 yards. How many yards does the halfback lose? To solve this problem we add $-2 + (-3)$. The second integer is placed in parentheses when it is negative to emphasize that the symbol $-$ is not being used for subtraction and to avoid unnecessary confusion about which operation is being done. The problem is read "negative 2 plus negative 3." It is not necessary to place parentheses around the first integer -2, because in this case the symbol $-$ can only indicate a negative number.

Using a number line we draw an arrow representing -2 starting at 0 and going 2 units to the left. Next, starting at the tip of the first arrow, we draw another arrow to represent -3. This second arrow also points left on the number line because it represents a negative number. The sum of the two numbers is at the end of the second arrow $-2 + (-3) = -5$. The halfback has lost 5 yards. Figure 2.6 shows that when both integers are negative, the answer is negative and its numerical value is the ordinary sum of the integers, or just the sum of the integers without their signs.

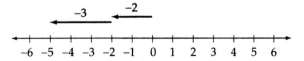

FIGURE 2.6   Depiction of the addition of −2 and −3

ADDING TWO NEGATIVE INTEGERS

To add a negative integer to another negative integer, disregard the negative signs, perform ordinary addition, and attach a negative sign to the result.

Another way to show that the sum of two negative integers is itself a negative integer is to imagine being in Atlantic City playing video poker and losing $2 worth of quarters in one machine and $3 worth of quarters in another machine. In one instance the loss is $2 ($-2$) and in the other instance the loss is $3 ($-3$); because $-2 + (-3) = -5$, $5 were lost.

| EXAMPLE 1 | Add the following integers: |

a. $-7 + (-17)$ **b.** $-88 + (-12) + (-100)$

c. $-15 + [-8 + (-7)]$ **d.** $14 + \{7 + [22 + (6 + 2)]\}$

SOLUTION

a. $-7 + (-17) = -24$

b. $-88 + (-12) + (-100) = -100 + (-100)$
$$= -200$$

c. $-15 + [-8 + (-7)] = -15 + [-15]$
$$= -30$$

d. $14 + \{7 + [22 + (6 + 2)]\} = 14 + \{7 + [22 + 8]\}$
$$= 14 + \{7 + 30\}$$
$$= 14 + 37$$
$$= 51 \qquad ■$$

Often, we want to add positive integers to negative integers, or vice versa. Imagine that the fullback gets to carry the ball. On one running play he gains 4 yards, and on the next play he loses 3 yards. How many yards did the fullback gain on the two running plays? On the number line draw an arrow representing 4, starting at 0 and going 4 units to the right. Next, starting at 4, draw an arrow 3 units to the left representing -3. The sum of the two numbers is at the end of the second arrow as shown in Figure 2.7, $4 + (-3) = 1$. The fullback only gained one yard.

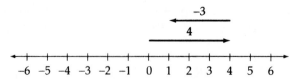

FIGURE 2.7   **Depiction of 4 + (−3)**

Now consider adding a negative integer to a positive integer. Imagine that the fullback gets two more chances to carry the ball. The first time he is dropped for a loss of 6 yards, and on the second play he gains back 3 yards. As before draw an arrow to the left representing -6 and then draw an arrow to the right representing 3. The sum is at the end of the second arrow, as shown in Figure 2.8: $-6 + 3 = -3$. The fullback had a net loss of 3 yards.

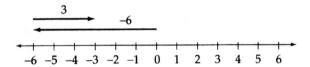

FIGURE 2.8   **Depiction of $-6 + 3$**

Adding positive integers to negative integers can be shown visually on a number line when the numbers are relatively small. However, a number line is not practical for adding large numbers, such as 273 to -584. Instead, we can develop a rule using the concept of absolute value that offers an alternative to drawing number lines to add positive and negative integers.

Going back to the problem $4 + (-3)$, we can see that the same result is obtained if we take the absolute value of each of the numbers and *subtract* the smaller absolute value from the larger. The sign of the number whose absolute value is larger is then attached to the difference. Since $|4| = 4$ and $|-3| = 3$, we subtract $4 - 3 = 1$. The sum is $+1$ and not -1 because 4, the number with the larger absolute value, is positive. For the problem $-6 + 3$, $|-6| = 6$ and $|3| = 3$; we subtract $6 - 3 = 3$. The sum is -3 because -6, the number having the larger absolute value, is negative.

ADDING A POSITIVE AND A NEGATIVE INTEGER

To add integers with opposite signs, take the absolute value of each integer and subtract the smaller absolute value from the larger. The sign of the result is the sign of the number whose absolute value is larger.

EXAMPLE 2   Add the following integers:

    a. $-175 + 144$ **b.** $362 + (-18)$ **c.** $-44 + (-61)$ **d.** $-29 + 29$

SOLUTION   **a.** $-175 + 144 = -31$
        $|-175| = 175$ and $|144| = 144$

        Taking the ordinary difference, $175 - 144 = 31$. The answer is -31 because -175 has the larger absolute value.

    b. $362 + (-18) = 344$
        $|362| = 362$ and $|-18| = 18$

        Taking the ordinary difference, $362 - 18 = 344$. The answer is $+344$ because 362 has the larger absolute value.

c. $-44 + (-61) = -105$

In this example, both integers are negative, and the rule for adding two negative integers is used.

d. $-29 + 29 = 0$
$|-29| = 29$ and $|29| = 29$

Taking the ordinary difference, $29 - 29 = 0$. Of course, 0 does not need a sign. This example illustrates an important idea in algebra; *the sum of opposites is always zero.*   ■

Now suppose we want to add more than two integers. Imagine that the quarterback passes the ball on three consecutive plays. On the first play the receiver who catches the ball loses 2 yards. The next play a receiver gains 8 yards, and on the third play a receiver gains 2 yards. The problem $-2 + 8 + 2$ could be done adding from left to right as follows:

$$-2 + 8 + 2 = 6 + 2$$
$$= 8$$

The problem could also be done by using the commutative law for addition, which allows us to change the order of any two numbers in a sum. The same problem could be written as follows:

$$-2 + 8 + 2 = -2 + 2 + 8$$
$$= 0 + 8$$
$$= 8$$

Although an extra step is needed, using the commutative law made the calculations easier because the sum of opposites is always 0, and the sum of any number and 0 is that number.

Another problem we might add from left to right is $-3 + 6 + (-9) + 4$.

$$-3 + 6 + (-9) + 4 = 3 + (-9) + 4$$
$$= -6 + 4$$
$$= -2$$

The same problem can also be done using both the commutative law and the associative law. Using the commutative law for addition, the integers can be rearranged so that the negative integers appear first and the positive integers appear second. Using the associative law for addition, the integers with like signs are then grouped together and added. Finally, the two partial sums with opposite signs are added to obtain the final answer.

$$-3 + 6 + (-9) + 4 = [-3 + (-9)] + [6 + 4]$$
$$= -12 + 10$$
$$= -2$$

This is a useful method because problems may have several integers to add and reorganizing the data allows the problem to be done more efficiently than adding from left to right. Adding integers of like signs (two positive integers or two negative integers) is easier than adding positive and negative integers several times.

| **EXAMPLE 3** | Add the following integers: |

a. $-10 + (-12) + 22$ **b.** $-23 + 46 + (-69)$

c. $28 + (-33) + (-68) + 55$ **d.** $-5 + \{22 + [-8 + (-9)]\}$

SOLUTION   **a.** $-10 + (-12) + 22 = -22 + 22$
$$= 0$$

Since the negative integers are together and the one positive integer follows directly after, the commutative law is not used and we add from left to right.

b. $-23 + 46 + (-69) = -23 + (-69) + 46$
$$= -92 + 46$$
$$= -46$$

Since the negative integers are not together, the commutative law is used to change the order of the integers so that the negative integers are together. Then the negative integers are added, giving a partial sum. The partial sum is added to the positive integer, resulting in the answer.

c. $28 + (-33) + (-68) + 55 = (-33) + (-68) + 28 + 55$
$$= [-33 + (-68] + [28 + 55]$$
$$= -101 + 83$$
$$= -18$$

Since neither the negative integers nor the positive integers are together, the commutative law is first used to organize the integers so that the integers of like signs are together. Then the associative law is used to group together the integers of like signs and the integers of like signs are added together to get our partial sums. The resulting negative and positive integers are added together.

d. $-5 + \{22 + [-8 + (-9)]\} = -5 + \{22 + (-17)\}$
$$= -5 + 5$$
$$= 0$$

Since this problem contains grouping symbols, the order of operations agreement is used. Operate inside the square brackets, and then operate inside the curly braces. The rules for adding integers are then used.

■

The rules for adding integers can be used to help solve word problems. Quantities in a word problem can be written using integers, and those integers can be added to determine the solution to the problem.

| **EXAMPLE 4** | Russ decided to go to Pounds 'R' Us, a local weight reduction center. At the center, he was weighed every week to figure his weight loss. At the end of the first week, Russ lost 6 pounds. At the end of the second week, he lost an additional 4 pounds. At the end of the third week, he gained back 2 pounds. |

If his initial weight was 225 pounds, how much did Russ weigh at the end of three weeks?

SOLUTION   In this problem losses are represented by negative integers and gains by positive integers. All operations are represented by addition: Russ's weight + 6 lb loss + 4 lb loss + 2 lb gain = Russ's new weight.

$$225 + (-6) + (-4) + 2 = [225 + 2] + [-6 + (-4)]$$
$$= 227 + [-10]$$
$$= 217 \text{ pounds}$$

Russ weighed 217 pounds at the end of three weeks.   ■

EXAMPLE 5   Maritza deposited $550 in a new checking account. She then wrote checks for $82 and $66 and then deposited $50. A week later she wrote checks for $420 and $96. Did Maritza need to deposit more money into her account to cover the checks she wrote?

SOLUTION   In this problem checks are represented by negative integers and deposits by positive integers. All transactions are represented by addition.

$$550 + (-82) + (-66) + 50 + (-420) + (-96)$$
$$= [550 + 50] + [-82 + (-66) + (-420) + (-96)]$$
$$= 600 + (-664)$$
$$= -64 \text{ dollars}$$

Since Maritza wrote checks for $64 more than she had deposited in her account, she needed to deposit at least $64 into her account to ensure that her checks would not bounce.   ■

Other problems containing a mixture of grouping symbols and absolute values can be solved using the order of operations agreement.

EXAMPLE 6 $[-(-23) + (-14) + 60] \div (-28 + |11 + (-62)|)$

SOLUTION $[-(-23) + (-14) + 60] \div (-28 + |11 + (-62)|)$
$$= [+23 + (-14) + 60] \div (-28 + |-51|)$$
$$= [9 + 60] \div (-28 + 51)$$
$$= [69] \div (23)$$
$$= 3$$ ■

P R A C T I C E   F O R   S U C C E S S

Practice 1. $-22 + (-967)$

Practice 2. $94 + (-220)$

Practice 3. $32 + (-44) + (-21) + 87 + (-103)$

Practice 4. $[-(-14) + 64 + 8 + (-2)] + [-13 + |{-13} + (-13 + (-(-56)))|]$

Practice 5. A bellhop in Hotel Ritz picks up some suitcases in the lobby to be delivered. She then goes up 7 floors, down 2 floors, up 16 floors, and then down 9 floors, each time stopping to deliver suitcases. Before returning to the lobby, what was the last floor the bellhop was on? (*Hint:* Write an expression using integer addition to represent the problem and consider the lobby to be floor 0.)

EXERCISES 2.2

In exercises 1–75, perform the indicated operations and simplify all expressions to a single integer.

1. $16 + (-37)$	**2.** $-37 + 5$
3. $-10 + 7$	**4.** $-3 + 15$
5. $25 + (-4)$	**6.** $-43 + (-46)$
7. $12 + (-12)$	**8.** $9 + (-41)$
9. $-15 + 45$	**10.** $-46 + (-10)$
11. $4 + (-3)$	**12.** $75 + (-15)$
13. $34 + (-4)$	**14.** $-12 + (-28)$
15. $-15 + (-3)$	**16.** $8 + (-13)$
17. $43 + (-36)$	**18.** $-46 + 31$
19. $36 + (-24)$	**20.** $-47 + (-33)$
21. $27 + (-3)$	**22.** $-9 + 25$
23. $27 + (-14)$	**24.** $49 + (-31)$
25. $38 + (-44)$	**26.** $8 + (-42)$
27. $-44 + 15$	**28.** $7 + (-7)$
29. $-35 + 0$	**30.** $36 + 0$
31. $-15 + 43 + (-10)$	**32.** $23 + (-15) + (-39)$
33. $39 + (-65) + 83$	**34.** $-19 + (-2) + 52$
35. $-36 + 19 + |{-8}|$	**36.** $63 + (-82) + |{-38}|$
37. $-25 + |{-18}| + (-73)$	**38.** $-90 + |19 + (-48)|$
39. $|{-49} + 130 + 38|$	**40.** $|{-36} + (-44) + 85|$
41. $|{-70} + 28| + (-128)$	**42.** $|253 + (-519)| + (-827)$
43. $-255 + (-719) + |{-436}|$	**44.** $-367 + 519 + |{-329}|$

45. $[13 + (-42) + 59] + |{-56} + 47|$

46. $[-4 + (-14) + |{-86}|] + |{-15} + (-2)|$

47. $|{-52} + 26 + (-78)| + (-24 + 18 + 8)$

48. $[-(-26) + (-16) + 72] + (-18 + |{-13} + (-46)|)$

49. $[-(73) + [-(-95)] + (-22)] + (|{-17} + (-14)| + (-25))$

50. $\{-32 + [-(-16)] + 2\} + [|{-18} + (-13)| + (-46)]$

51. $[-(-20) + 4 + (-10)] + \{|-18 + 11| + (-9) + (-(-9))\}$
52. $[-(-16) + 54 + (-6) + (-80)] + (-37 + |-23 + (-(-85))|)$
53. $[28 + \{3 + (-3)\} + (-9)] + (|-7 + 1|)$
54. $-(-8) + \{8 + 11 + [-19 + (-200)]\}$
55. $|-(-12) + (-36)| + (-18 + |-9 + (-15)|)$
56. $-(-7) + [-(-3)] + [-5 + |-50| + (-5)]$
57. $-(|-(-14)|)$
58. $\{-1 + [-(-11) + 196 + |-14|]\} + (-210)$
59. $[23 + (-2) + (-15)] + (-19 + |-39 + 7|)$
60. $\{1 + [-(-42 + 3)]\} + \{-(-1 + (-2))\} + |-5| + \{-(-2)\}$
61. $-141 + |-10 + (-9)| + \{-(-4)\} + |-9| + |-(-9)|$
62. $|-5| + |-12| + (10 + 0) + \{3 + |-5| + (-13)\}$
63. $|-(-12) + 9 + \{0 + (-3)\} + (-78)| + \{-(-30)\}$
64. $-\{|-(-33)|\}$
65. $-(-8) + [-(-5)] + [-13 + |-842| + (-421) + (-(-18))]$
66. $[-25 + |-625| + (-625)] + \{-12 + [-(-38)]\}$
67. $|-9 + [-(-6)] + [-8 + |-80| + (-4)]|$
68. $|-36 + |-78|| + \{-(-34)\}$
69. $|-(-31) + (-309) + |-91| + (-7) + |-27||$
70. $|-26 + 13 + (-17) + [-(|-13|)] + |-7| + 19|$
71. $-117 + (-13) + (-28) + |-27| + \{-[-|-6|]\} + 7$
72. $-92 + 73 + (-26) + |0| + (-63) + 154 + (-147)$
73. $[-(-52) + |-520| + (-52)] + \{-21 + [-(-83)]\}$
74. $[-17 + |-550| + (-538)] + \{-79 + [-(-565)]\}$
75. $|-159 + |-115| + (-92)| + \{-99 + |-129|\}$

In exercises 76–85, solve by first writing an expression that represents the problem using addition operations with integers. Add a positive number to make an increase in a given quantity; add a negative number to make a decrease in the same quantity. Then solve the problem using the rules for addition of integers.

76. On a planet in a science fiction novel, one day the temperature began at $-160°$, then fell $20°$, and then went up $15°$ before it dropped another $8°$. What is the final temperature?

77. A gambler began a poker game with $250 and played four hands. On the first hand he lost $25 and on the second hand he lost another $30 before winning $18 on the third hand. On the fourth hand he lost another $25. After the four hands, what was the gambler's gain or loss?

78. A submarine is under water at a depth of 100 feet when it changes course and descends another 75 feet. It then rises 90 feet before making a deep plunge of 220 feet. What is the final depth of the submarine?

79. A golfer begins a round of golf at even par. On the first hole she makes a birdie (1 below par), and on the second hole she makes an eagle (2 below par). On the next two holes she makes two bogies (each 1 above par). How far above or below par is she after playing these four holes?

80. On the Pacific Stock Exchange, Ticky Tack Paper Clip stock starts the day at a value of $85 per share. During the day of trading, the stock value per share drops $1 and then drops another $2 before making late day gains of $3 and $4. What is the value of the stock at the end of the day?

81. In a game of gin rummy you first score 42 points before losing 15 points and gaining another 35 points. Then you lose again, this time 20 points, and in the last hand you score 32 points. What is your final score?

82. Your car burns oil badly. During a 6-month period of driving, you lose 1 pint each month but you add 1 full quart every two months. If you start with five quarts of oil, how much oil do you end up with at the end of six months?

83. Otis got tired of health food so he discontinued his membership in the Healthy Eater's Weight Clinic. His initial weight was 175 pounds, but then his weight started going up and down like an elevator. First, he lost 8 pounds, then gained 10 pounds, then lost another 12 pounds, gained 7 pounds, and finally lost 7 pounds. How much does Otis weigh?

84. The number of barrels of oil carried by an oil tanker varies greatly as the tanker picks up and deposits oil at various tanker stations. Assume a full tanker begins with a load of 564,700 barrels and makes deposits of 123,200 and 234,500 barrels at two ports before loading 115,800 barrels and 185,600 barrels at two offshore oil wells. How many barrels of oil remain in the tanker?

85. At a swimming pool party the water level in the swimming pool is at 5 feet when no one is in the pool. For every 3 people that jump in the pool, the water level rises 1 inch. The water level also goes down 2 inches every time 3 people get out of the pool. Assume a dozen people jump in the pool at the start of the party, and then they are joined by another dozen and finally by another 9. On two separate occasions 6 people get out of the pool. What is the final water level in the pool?

Looking Back

86. Find the prime factorization of 546.

87. Find the LCM and GCF of 56 and 182.

88. What is the basic operation for the expression
$-(-7) + -(-3) \cdot [-5 + |-50| \div 5]$?

89. Use the distributive law to expand the product $13 \cdot (14 + 82)$ into a basic sum.

90. Use the distributive law to transform the basic sum $17 \cdot 23 + 17 \cdot 41$ into a basic product.

PRACTICE-FOR-SUCCESS ANSWERS

---

1. −989
2. −126
3. −49
4. 101
5. $0 + (+7) + (−2) + (+16) + (−9) = (+12) = 12$
    She was on the 12th floor before she returned to the lobby.

2.3	**SUBTRACTION OF INTEGERS**

OBJECTIVES

☐   To subtract any two integers
☐   To simplify expressions using subtraction
☐   To use absolute values to find the distance between two points
☐   To solve word problems using subtraction

To understand subtraction of integers, imagine that you have $5 and you spend $3 on lunch. How much money do you still have? This problem is illustrated on a number line in Figure 2.9. To subtract a positive integer, go to the left on the number line a distance equal to the positive integer being subtracted: $5 − 3 = 2$. You have $2 left for dinner.

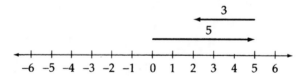

FIGURE 2.9   Depiction of 5 − 3

In the previous section we added integers with different signs, such as $5 + (−3)$. This problem is illustrated with a number line in Figure 2.10.

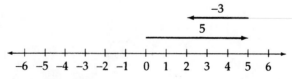

FIGURE 2.10   Depiction of 5 + (−3)

In Figure 2.10 the number line shows that $5 + (-3) = 2$. Because the number lines in Figures 2.9 and 2.10 are identical, $5 - 3 = 2$ can be rewritten as $5 + (-3) = 2$. We can change the operation from subtraction to addition and then change the second number to its opposite.

Another problem will help to develop a rule that can be used to subtract any integer from another. The problem $-1 - 4$ is shown on the number line in Figure 2.11. The arrow representing the number 4 is drawn pointing to the left because a positive integer is being *subtracted*.

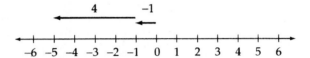

FIGURE 2.11   **Depiction of $-1 - 4$**

The problem $-1 + (-4)$ can also be done using a number line. Now the arrow representing -4 points to the left because the operation is addition and the number is negative. In Figure 2.12 the number line shows that $-1 + (-4) = -5$, which is identical to Figure 2.11. The problem $-1 - 4 = -5$ can be rewritten as $-1 + (-4) = -5$ by changing the operation from subtraction to addition and then changing the second number to its opposite.

FIGURE 2.12 Depiction of $-1 + (-4)$

In all of the preceding problems the direction of the second arrow is determined by both the operation preceding the number and the sign of the number. When the operation is addition, the direction is determined by the sign of the second number, but when the operation is subtraction, the direction is opposite to the sign of the second number. The easiest way to determine the direction of the second arrow is to convert subtractions to addition of the opposite of the second number, as given by the rule for subtracting integers.

SUBTRACTING INTEGERS

To subtract one integer from another, keep the first integer the same. Change the subtraction operation to addition and change the second number to its opposite. Then apply the rules for addition of integers. The rule for changing subtraction to adding the opposite can be expressed using variables a and b, which represent integers.

$$a - b = a + (-b)$$

| EXAMPLE 1 | Perform the following subtractions: |

a. $-36 - 48$ **b.** $72 - 100$ **c.** $200 - 96$

SOLUTION   **a.** $-36 - 48 = -36 + (-48)$ Change to adding the opposite.
$= -84$ Use the rule for adding two negative integers.

b. $72 - 100 = 72 + (-100)$ Change to adding the opposite.
$= -28$ Use the rule for adding positive and negative integers.

c. $200 - 96 = 200 + (-96)$ Change to adding the opposite.
$= 104$ Use the rule for adding positive and negative integers.

In part c, $200 - 96$ is an ordinary subtraction problem; a smaller whole number is subtracted from a larger one. We could get the same result without changing to adding the opposite.   ■

When a positive integer is subtracted, the second arrow will point left on the number line, as illustrated in Figures 2.9 and 2.11. When a negative integer is subtracted the second arrow points right. The problem $2 - (-4)$ is shown on the number line in Figure 2.13.

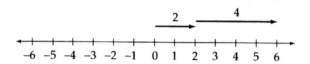

FIGURE 2.13 Depiction of 2 − (−4) − = 2 + (+4)

Recall that when a positive integer is subtracted, the second arrow points left. When a negative integer is subtracted, the second arrow points opposite to the direction used when subtracting a positive integer. *When a negative number is subtracted, the second arrow will always point to the right.*

Following the rule for changing subtraction to addition of the opposite:

$2 - (-4) = 2 + (+4)$ Change subtraction to addition and change the sign of
$= 6$ the second number. We have written $(+4)$ to emphasize that (-4) changes to $(+4)$.

| EXAMPLE 2 | Perform the following subtractions: |

a. $27 - (-66)$ **b.** $-69 - (-82)$ **c.** $-528 - 324$

SOLUTION   **a.** $27 - (-66) = 27 + (+66)$ Change to adding the opposite.
$= 93$ Use the rule for adding two positive integers.

b. $-69 - (-82) = -69 + (+82)$ Change to adding the opposite.
$= 13$ Use the rule for adding positive and negative integers.

c. $-528 - 324 = -528 + (-324)$ Change to adding the opposite.
$= -852$ Use the rule for adding two negative integers.   ■

In word problems it may be necessary to find the difference between two integers: for example, the difference between -5 and -15. Because the difference is the answer to a subtraction problem, we subtract $-5 - (-15) = -5 + 15 = 10$. The order of the integers being subtracted is exactly the same as the order in which the integers occur in this type of word problem.

EXAMPLE 3	Find the difference between -28 and 166.

SOLUTION $-28 - 166 = -28 + (-166)$ Change to adding the opposite.
$ = -194$ Use the rule for adding two negative integers.   ■

In a word problem that says to subtract one number from another, the number to be subtracted comes after the word *subtract* and is written second in the expression. "Subtract 4 from 8" means that we write the problem $8 - 4$. Order is critical in subtraction because subtraction is not commutative, and if the problem is incorrectly written as $4 - 8$, the answer will be wrong.

EXAMPLE 4	Subtract 169 from 81.

SOLUTION   Recall that the number following the word *subtract* is written after the subtraction operation.

$81 - 169 = 81 + (-169)$ Change to adding the opposite.
$ = -88$ Use the rule for adding positive and negative integers.   ■

Sometimes we need to simplify expressions that involve only the operation of subtraction but that have more than two integers.

EXAMPLE 5	Perform the following subtractions:

a. $4 - 8 - 12 - 16$

b. $-10 - (-20) - 30$

SOLUTION   **a.** $4 - 8 - 12 - 16$
$= 4 + (-8) + (-12) + (-16)$ Change to adding the opposite.
$= 4 + [-8 + (-12) + (-16)]$ Regroup using the associative law.
$= 4 + [-20 + (-16)]$ Simplify within the square brackets.
$= 4 + (-36)$
$= -32$

b. $-10 - (-20) - 30$
$= -10 + (+20) + (-30)$ Change to adding the opposite.
$= (+20) + (-10) + (-30)$ Use the commutative law for addition.
$= 20 + [-10 + (-30)]$ Regroup using the associative law.
$= 20 + [-40]$ Simplify within the square brackets.
$= -20$ ■

Grouping symbols are used to change the usual order in which operations are performed. Our understanding of grouping symbols and subtraction of integers can now be used to simplify algebraic expressions that contain subtractions.

| **EXAMPLE 6** | Simplify the following expressions: |

a. $27 - [13 - 19]$

b. $546 - \{938 - [589 - 597]\}$

c. $266 - \{-741 - [-235 - (-458)]\}$

SOLUTION   **a.** $27 - [13 - 19] = 27 - [13 + (-19)]$
$= 27 - [-6]$
$= 27 + [+6]$
$= 33$

b. $546 - \{938 - [589 - 597]\} = 546 - \{938 - [589 + (-597)]\}$
$= 546 - \{938 - [-8]\}$
$= 546 - \{938 + [+8]\}$
$= 546 - 946$
$= 546 + (-946)$
$= -400$

c. $266 - \{-741 - [-235 - (-458)]\} = 266 - \{-741 - [-235 + (+458)]\}$
$= 266 - \{-741 - [223]\}$
$= 266 - \{-741 + [-223]\}$
$= 266 - \{-964\}$
$= 266 + \{+964\}$
$= 1,230$ ■

| **EXAMPLE 7** | Dan's checking account had a balance of $109 before he wrote checks for $19, $32, $45, and $37. What was his final balance? Should he get a checking account with overdraft protection? |

SOLUTION   Each check transaction is represented by subtracting positive integers that correspond to each check amount.

$109 - 19 - 32 - 45 - 37 = 109 + (-19) + (-32) + (-45) + (-37)$
$= 109 + [-19 + (-32) + (-45) + (-37)]$
$= 109 + [-51 + (-45) + (-37)]$
$= 109 + [-96 + (-37)]$
$= 109 + [-133]$
$= -24$

Yes, Dan needs overdraft protection; his account was $24 overdrawn.   ■

Distance Between Two Points

The ability to subtract integers can be used to determine the distance between any two points on the number line. For example, on the number line, the distance between -2 and 4 can be drawn with an arrow from -2 to

4 or with one from 4 to −2 (see Figure 2.14). Because distance is never negative, the answer should be the same no matter which arrow is used.

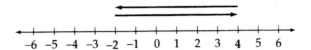

FIGURE 2.14   **Depiction of the distance between −2 and 4**

To find the distance between −2 and 4, subtract −2 from 4: $4 − (−2) = 4 + (+2) = 6$. To find the distance between 4 and −2, subtract 4 from −2: $−2 − 4 = −2 + (−4) = −6$. It appears that we have two different answers for the distance, 6 and −6. Since the distance between two points is independent of the starting point, we can remedy the situation by using the absolute value of either difference and thereby avoid negative answers for distances.

$$|4 − (−2)| = |4 + 2| = |6| = 6$$

and

$$|−2 − 4| = |−2 + (−4)| = |−6| = 6$$

Because both absolute values are equal, we may subtract in either order as long as we take the absolute value afterward.

DISTANCE BETWEEN TWO POINTS

If a and b are the coordinates of two points A and B on a number line, then the distance between A and B is $|a − b|$ or $|b − a|$.

EXAMPLE 8 | What is the distance between the points corresponding to −19 and −6?

SOLUTION $|−19 − (−6)| = |−19 + 6|$ or $|−6 − (−19)| = |−6 + 19|$
$= |−13|$ $= |13|$
$= 13$ $= 13$ ■

P R A C T I C E   F O R   S U C C E S S

Practice 1.   Subtract $−47 − (−99)$.
Practice 2.   Subtract 25 from −116.
Practice 3.   Subtract $22 − (−16) − 56$.
Practice 4.   Subtract $57 − [−27 + 44]$.

Practice 5.   The highest temperature in Bemidji, Minnesota, one cold winter day was −12°F. The lowest temperature that same day was −39°F. What was the difference between the highest temperature and the lowest temperature that day?

Practice 6.   What is the distance between the points corresponding to −5 and 6?

EXERCISES 2.3

In exercises 1–72, perform the indicated operations and simplify all expressions to a single integer.

1. $16 - (-37)$
2. $-37 - 5$
3. $-10 - 7$
4. $-3 - 15$
5. $25 - (-4)$
6. $-43 + (-76)$
7. $12 - (+12)$
8. $9 - (+41)$
9. $-15 - 45$
10. $-46 - (-10)$
11. $39 + (-3)$
12. $75 - (-15)$
13. $34 - (-4)$
14. $-12 - (-28)$
15. $-75 + (-3)$
16. $8 - 13$
17. $43 - (-36)$
18. $-46 - 31$
19. $36 - (-24)$
20. $-47 - 33$
21. $27 - (+3)$
22. $-9 - 25$
23. $27 - (-14)$
24. $49 - (-31)$
25. $7 - (-7)$
26. $-35 - 0$
27. $36 - 0$
28. Subtract -7 from $+16$.
29. Subtract $+19$ from -57.
30. What is 109 subtract -32?
31. Subtract -73 from 93.
32. What is -537 subtract 423?
33. What is 39 subtract -59?
34. Subtract $+765$ from -228.
35. What is -431 subtract $+369$?
36. $-15 - 43 - (-10)$
37. $23 - (-15) - (-39)$
38. $39 - (-65) - 83$
39. $-19 - (-2) - 52$
40. $-36 - 19 - |-8|$
41. $63 - (-82) - |-38|$
42. $|-59 - 420 - 38|$
43. $|-36 - (-44) - 85|$
44. $|-80 - 26| - (-328)$
45. $|253 - (-519)| - (-827)$
46. $-255 - (-719) - |-436|$
47. $-367 - 519 - |-329|$
48. $[13 - (-42 - 59)] - |-56 - (-47)|$
49. $[-4 + (-14) - |-86|] - |-11 - 2|$
50. $|-52 + 26 - (-78)| - (-24 - 18 - 8)$
51. $[-(-26) - (-16) - 72] - (-18 - |-34 - (-46)|)$
52. $[-(73) - (+12) - (-22)] - (|-17 - (+14)| - (-25))$
53. $\{-32 - [-(-16)] - 2\} - [-18 - |-13 - (-46)|]$
54. $\{-(-20) - [-(-4)] - (-10)\} - \{|-15 - 11| - (-9) - [-(-9)]\}$

55. $[-(-16) - 54 - 6 - 3] - \{-37 - |-23 - [-(-85)]|\}$

56. $-(-8) - [8 - 11 - (-14 - 20)]$

57. $|-(-12) - (-36)| - (-18 - |-9 - (-15)|)$

58. $-(-7) - [-(-3)] - [-5 - |-50| -5]$

59. $84 - \{-(| - (-14)|)\}$

60. $\{-1 - [-(-11) - 196 - |-14|]\} - [- (-2)]$

61. $\{1 - [-(42 - 3)]\} - \{- [-1 - (-2)]\} - |-3| - \{-(-2)\}$

62. $14 - |-10 - (-9)| - \{-(-4)\} - |-9| - | - (-9)|$

63. $|-5| - |-12| - (10 - 0) - [3 - |-5| - (-13)]$

64. $|-(-12) - 9 - \{0 - (-3)\} - (-78)| - \{-(-42)\}$

65. $379 - \{- |- (-33)|\}$

66. $[-25 - |-625| -25] - \{-12 - [- (-38)]\}$

67. $|-9 - \{-(-6)\} - \{-8 - | -80| -4\}|$

68. $|-36 - |-78| | - \{- (-34)\}$

69. $|-(-31) - (-309) - |-91| - 7 - |-27| |$

70. $117 - 13 - (-28) - |-27| - |-6| - 7$

71. $[-(-52) - |-520| - 52] - \{-21 - [- (-83)]\}$

72. $|-159 - |-115| -5| - \{99 - |-129|\}$

In exercises 73–84, two points called A and B are assumed to be on the same number line with their coordinates given. Use subtraction of signed numbers and absolute value to calculate the straight line distance between A and B.

	A	B			A	B
73.	−15	+20		**74.**	+16	−39
75.	+39	−65		**76.**	−23	0
77.	−68	+69		**78.**	+6	−6
79.	−9	+9		**80.**	−102	−102
81.	−23	−35		**82.**	62	−117
83.	−754	592		**84.**	+57	+291

In exercises 85–93, solve by first writing an expression that represents the problem using subtraction and addition of positive integers. Subtract a positive integer to make a decrease in a given quantity, or add a positive integer to make an increase in the same quantity. Then, solve the problem using the rules for subtraction and addition of integers.

85. On a planet in a science fiction novel, one day the temperature began at 180°, then went up 39°, and then fell 113° before it went up another 56°. What is the final temperature?

86. A gambler began a poker game with $125 and played four hands. On the first hand he won $40, on the second hand he won another $18, but he lost $33 on the third hand. On the fourth hand he lost another $25. What amount did the gambler end up with?

87. A submarine is underwater at a depth of 250 feet when it changes course and ascends 80 feet. Then it dives down 110 feet and then makes a deep plunge of 220 feet. What is the depth of the submarine?

88. A golfer begins a round of golf at even par. On the first hole she makes a birdie (1 below par) and on the second hole makes an eagle (2 below par). On the next two holes she makes two bogies (each 1 above par). How far above or below par is she after playing these four holes?

89. On the Pacific Stock Exchange, Ticky Tack Paper Clip stock starts the day at a value of $85 per share. During the day of trading the stock value per share drops $1 and then drops another $2 before making late day gains of $3 and $4. What is the value of the stock at the end of the day?

90. In a game of gin rummy you first score 58 points, then lose 12 points, and then gain 46 points. Then you lose again, this time 34 points, and finally you score 52 points. What is your final score?

91. Your car burns oil. During a 6-month period of driving, you lose 1 pint each month but you add 1 full quart every two months. If you start with six quarts of oil, how much oil do you end up with at the end of six months?

92. Otis tires of health food so he discontinues his membership in the Healthy Eater's Weight Clinic. His initial weight is 175 pounds but then his weight starts going up and down like an elevator. At first he loses 8 pounds but then he gains 10 pounds. Then he loses another 12 pounds and then gains 7 pounds and loses 7 pounds. How much does Otis weigh?

93. The number of barrels of oil carried by an oil tanker varies greatly as the tanker picks up and deposits oil at various tanker stations. Assume a full tanker begins with a load of 564,700 barrels and makes deposits of 123,200 and 234,500 barrels at two ports before loading 115,800 barrels and 185,600 barrels at two offshore oil wells. How many barrels of oil remain in the tanker?

 Looking Back

94. Find the prime factorization of 7,429.

95. Find the LCM and GCF of 82 and 908.

96. What is the basic operation for the expression

$$- (-50) \div (+5) \cdot [-200 \div \left| -40 \right| + 87]?$$

97. What does the verb *to factor* mean?

98. Write in words the check for a division problem.

99. Does the number 0 have a sign? If so, is it positive or negative?

PRACTICE-FOR-SUCCESS ANSWERS

1. 52   2. -141

3. -18 4. 40

5. $-12 - (-39) = 27$ degrees difference   6. $\left| -5 - 6 \right| = \left| -11 \right| = +11$

OBJECTIVES

☐ To multiply two or more integers

☐ To divide two or more integers

☐ To solve word problems using multiplication and division

Multiplication of Integers

We learned to multiply whole numbers in Chapter 1. In this chapter that knowledge will be used to multiply integers. Imagine that your favorite football team gains 2 yards on three consecutive running plays, and you want to know if they have made a first down. (It takes 10 yards to make a first down in football.) Multiply 3, the number of plays, times 2, the number of yards gained on each play, to determine the total yardage. Because multiplication is repeated addition, $3 \cdot 2$ equals three twos or $2 + 2 + 2 = 6$, and the team needs 4 more yards to get a first down. This example can be illustrated using a number line, as in Figure 2.15, which suggests the rule for multiplying integers.

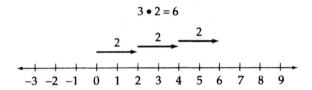

FIGURE 2.15 Depiction of $3 \cdot 2 = 6$

MULTIPLYING TWO POSITIVE INTEGERS

To multiply a positive integer times another positive integer, perform ordinary multiplication. The product is positive.

Multiplication is indicated by either a raised dot or parentheses, so 3 multiplied by 2 can be written

$$3 \cdot 2 \qquad (3)(2) \qquad 3(2) \qquad (3)2 \qquad (3) \cdot (2) \qquad 3 \cdot (2) \qquad (3) \cdot 2$$

We try to avoid writing unnecessary parentheses; however, parentheses are always placed around a negative integer. The parentheses are helpful when multiplying negative integers, as in the problem $7 \cdot (-2)$, because then we know that the symbol $-$ is being used to indicate that an integer is negative.

Imagine that your favorite football team has the ball again. The quarterback goes back to pass three consecutive times and each time loses three yards. To calculate the total yardage lost, multiply $3 \cdot (-3)$. Because multiplication is repeated addition, $3 \cdot (-3)$ can be rewritten as

$$(-3) + (-3) + (-3) = -9$$

The quarterback has lost 9 yards. This example can also be illustrated using a number line. Figure 2.16 illustrates a positive integer multiplied times a negative integer; the product is negative.

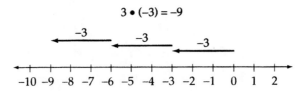

FIGURE 2.16   Depiction of $3 \cdot (-3) = -9$

Let's see if it is always true that the product will be negative when multiplying a positive integer times a negative integer. The following pattern can be used to help us determine the product of integers of unlike signs.

$$6 \cdot 4 = 24$$
$$6 \cdot 3 = 18$$
$$6 \cdot 2 = 12$$
$$6 \cdot 1 = 6$$
$$6 \cdot 0 = 0$$
$$6 \cdot (-1) = -6$$

The pattern begins with the multiplication fact $6 \cdot 4 = 24$. Each time the second factor is decreased by 1 the product decreases correspondingly by 6. In other words, each product is 6 less than the previous product. In the case of $6 \cdot (-1)$ the answer must be 6 less than the product $6 \cdot 0 = 0$. Since $0 - 6 = -6$, $6 \cdot (-1) = -6$. This pattern can be illustrated on a number line, as in Figure 2.17. The prior two examples suggest the rule for multiplying a positive and a negative integer.

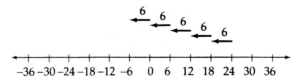

FIGURE 2.17   Number line showing smaller multiples of 6

MULTIPLYING A POSITIVE INTEGER AND A NEGATIVE INTEGER

To multiply a positive integer times a negative integer, perform ordinary multiplication on the two integers, disregarding their signs. The product is negative.

In Chapter 1 we learned that the commutative law holds for whole numbers. If any two whole numbers are multiplied, the product remains the same regardless of the order of the two numbers: $7 \cdot 8 = 8 \cdot 7 = 56$. We can determine if the commutative law also holds for the set of integers by considering whether $9 \cdot (-1)$ has the same product as $(-1) \cdot 9$. We know $9 \cdot (-1) = -9$ by the rule for multiplying a positive and negative integer. For $(-1) \cdot 9$, we use a pattern again to determine the product.

$$4 \cdot 9 = 36$$
$$3 \cdot 9 = 27$$
$$2 \cdot 9 = 18$$
$$1 \cdot 9 = 9$$
$$0 \cdot 9 = 0$$
$$(-1) \cdot 9 = -9$$

The pattern demonstrates that $(-1) \cdot 9 = -9$, since each product was 9 less than the previous product. The commutative law for multiplication thus holds for the set of integers and suggests the following rule.

MULTIPLYING A NEGATIVE INTEGER AND A POSITIVE INTEGER

To multiply a negative integer times a positive integer, perform ordinary multiplication on the two integers, disregarding their signs. The product is negative.

Two integers being multiplied also could both be negative, such as $(-7) \cdot (-9)$. We can solve this problem by creating another problem, $(-7) \cdot [9 + (-9)]$, and then using some of the laws already presented.

$(-7) \cdot [9 + (-9)] = (-7) \cdot [0]$ Opposites add up to 0.
$ = 0$ Any number multiplied by 0 is 0.

The same problem can also be worked using the distributive law.

$(-7) \cdot [9 + (-9)] = (-7) \cdot 9 + (-7) \cdot (-9)$ Distribute -7.
$ = -63 + (-7) \cdot (-9)$

Because the two problems are identical, the following is logical.

$$-63 + (-7) \cdot (-9) = 0$$

We also know that the number to add to -63 to make 0 is its opposite, 63. Therefore, $(-7) \cdot (-9) = 63$ suggests the rule for multiplying two negative integers. The rules for multiplying integers can be condensed to make them easier to remember.

MULTIPLYING TWO NEGATIVE INTEGERS

To multiply a negative integer times another negative integer, perform ordinary multiplication on the two integers disregarding their signs. The product is positive.

MULTIPLYING ANY TWO NONZERO INTEGERS

To multiply two nonzero integers, perform ordinary multiplication without regard to the signs. If the two integers have like signs, the product is positive. If the integers have different signs, the product is negative.

EXAMPLE 1

Multiply the following integers:

   a. $9 \cdot (-13)$ **b.** $(-11) \cdot (-17)$ **c.** $(-20) \cdot 15$ **d.** $18 \cdot 18$

SOLUTION   **a.** $9 \cdot (-13) = -117$

           (Positive Integer) $\cdot$ (Negative Integer) = Negative Product

    b. $(-11) \cdot (-17) = 187$

           (Negative Integer) $\cdot$ (Negative Integer) = Positive Product

    c. $(-20) \cdot 15 = -300$

           (Negative Integer) $\cdot$ (Positive Integer) = Negative Product

    d. $18 \cdot 18 = 324$

           (Positive Integer) $\cdot$ (Positive Integer) = Positive Product   ■

Three or more integers are often multiplied in the same expression. To find the value, multiply the integers from left to right as follows.

$$(-3) \cdot (-5) \cdot 8 = 15 \cdot 8 \qquad \text{Multiply } (-3) \cdot (-5) = 15.$$
$$= 120 \qquad \text{Multiply } 15 \cdot 8 = 120.$$

The problem with two negative signs suggests that when an even number of negative signs is present in an expression, the product is positive.

$$(-2) \cdot (-4) \cdot (-7) = 8 \cdot (-7) \qquad \text{Multiply } (-2) \cdot (-4) = 8.$$
$$= -56 \qquad \text{Multiply } 8 \cdot (-7) = -56.$$

The problem with three negative signs suggests that when an odd number of negative signs is present in an expression, the product is negative.

DETERMINING THE SIGN OF TWO OR MORE FACTORS

To determine the sign of a product of two or more nonzero numbers, count the number of negative signs. If the expression has an even number of negative signs, the product is positive. If the expression has an odd number of negative signs, the product is negative.

EXAMPLE 2

Multiply the following integers:

   a. $(-4) \cdot (-8) \cdot (-2) \cdot 5$

   b. $(-3) \cdot 4 \cdot (-5) \cdot 10$

   c. $(-7) \cdot (-6) \cdot (-2) \cdot (-11)$

   d. $(-9) \cdot (-5) \cdot (-4) \cdot (-3) \cdot (-2)$

SOLUTION   **a.** $(-4) \cdot (-8) \cdot (-2) \cdot 5 = (32) \cdot (-2) \cdot 5$
$$= (-64) \cdot 5$$
$$= -320$$

To check that the product is negative, count the number of negative signs (3).

b. $(-3) \cdot 4 \cdot (-5) \cdot 10 = (-12) \cdot (-5) \cdot 10$
$$= 60 \cdot 10$$
$$= 600$$

To check that the product is positive, count the number of negative signs (2).

c. $(-7) \cdot (-6) \cdot (-2) \cdot (-11) = 42 \cdot (-2) \cdot (-11)$
$$= (-84) \cdot (-11)$$
$$= 924$$

To check the sign of the product, count the number of negative signs (4).

d. $(-9) \cdot (-5) \cdot (-4) \cdot (-3) \cdot (-2) = (45) \cdot (-4) \cdot (-3) \cdot (-2)$
$$= (-180) \cdot (-3) \cdot (-2)$$
$$= (540) \cdot (-2)$$
$$= -1,080$$

To check the sign of the product, count the number of negative signs (5).   ■

EXAMPLE 3   Find the product of -10, -11, and 3.

SOLUTION   To find a product, multiply the integers.

$$(-10) \cdot (-11) \cdot 3 = [(-10) \cdot (-11)] \cdot 3$$
$$= [110] \cdot 3$$
$$= 330$$ ■

EXAMPLE 4   During a cold snap, the temperature dropped 3° every eight minutes. If the temperature began at 39°, what was the temperature after two hours?

SOLUTION   First, we determine the number of 8-minute periods in two hours. Two hours consists of 120 minutes and $120 \div 8 = 15$, so there are 15 temperature drops at 3° each. We use the number -3 to represent a temperature drop of 3°.

$$39 + 15 \cdot (-3) = 39 + (-45) = -6$$

After two hours, the temperature is 6° below zero.   ■

Division of Integers

Imagine that you and four friends invest $6,000 in real estate, only to find out later that the property that you purchased was worthless swamp land. You will never receive a return on your investment, so the $6,000 is gone.

How much money has each of you lost? Since the total lost is $6,000 and the number of investors is 5, we divide $(-6,000) \div 5 = -1,200$; each investor lost $1,200. Common sense tells us that the quotient should be negative, but we use the division check to verify the quotient. The division check states that quotient · divisor + remainder = dividend: $-1,200 \cdot 5 + 0 = -6,000$.

This example verifies that when a negative integer is divided by a positive integer, the quotient is negative. This parallels the rule for multiplication that a negative integer multiplied by a positive integer equals a negative product. We can illustrate how the other division rules also parallel the multiplication rules as follows:

$$28 \div 7 = 4 \qquad \text{since } 4 \cdot 7 = 28 \text{ using the division check.}$$

$$28 \div (-7) = -4 \qquad \text{since } (-4) \cdot (-7) = 28 \text{ using the division check.}$$

$$(-28) \div 7 = -4 \qquad \text{since } (-4) \cdot 7 = -28 \text{ using the division check.}$$

$$(-28) \div (-7) = 4 \qquad \text{since } 4 \cdot (-7) = -28 \text{ using the division check.}$$

We can now state the rule for division of integers.

DIVIDING ANY TWO NONZERO INTEGERS

To divide two nonzero integers, perform ordinary division without regard to the signs. If the two integers have like signs, the quotient is positive. If the integers have different signs, the quotient is negative.

EXAMPLE 5   Perform the following divisions:

   a. $56 \div (-8)$ **b.** $132 \div 11$ **c.** $(-294) \div (-7)$ **d.** $(-2,052) \div 3$

SOLUTION   **a.** $56 \div (-8) = -7$
                (Positive Integer) ÷ (Negative Integer) = Negative Quotient

   b. $132 \div 11 = 12$
                (Positive Integer) ÷ (Positive Integer) = Positive Quotient

   c. $(-294) \div (-7) = 42$
                (Negative Integer) ÷ (Negative Integer) = Positive Quotient

   d. $(-2,052) \div 3 = -684$
                (Negative Integer) ÷ (Positive Integer) = Negative Quotient   ■

Division is also shown in another format. The problem $30 \div 5 = 6$ is also expressed

$$\frac{30}{5} = 6$$

The dividend is written as the top number, the bar indicates "divided by," and the divisor is written as the bottom number.

EXAMPLE 6   Perform the following divisions:

a. $\dfrac{48}{-6}$ b. $\dfrac{175}{5}$ c. $\dfrac{-1,080}{-45}$ d. $\dfrac{-625}{25}$

SOLUTION   a. $\dfrac{48}{-6} = -8$ $\dfrac{\text{(Positive Integer)}}{\text{(Negative Integer)}} = \text{Negative Quotient}$

b. $\dfrac{175}{5} = 35$ $\dfrac{\text{(Positive Integer)}}{\text{(Positive Integer)}} = \text{Positive Quotient}$

c. $\dfrac{-1,080}{-45} = 24$ $\dfrac{\text{(Negative Integer)}}{\text{(Negative Integer)}} = \text{Positive Quotient}$

d. $\dfrac{-625}{25} = -25$ $\dfrac{\text{(Negative Integer)}}{\text{(Positive Integer)}} = \text{Negative Quotient}$ ■

A division problem of the form $\dfrac{a}{b}$, where either a or b or both may be 0, requires a careful explanation. If $\dfrac{a}{b} = c$, then the number a is the dividend, the number b is the divisor, and the number c is the quotient. According to the division check, if $\dfrac{a}{b} = c$, then we should be able to verify that $a = b \cdot c$. As we will see there are three cases for which the answers for c result in either a unique answer, an impossible answer, or an infinite number of possible answers. Because we desire mathematical answers that both exist and are unique, in the latter two cases, where $b = 0$, we will say the division $\dfrac{a}{b}$ is undefined.

Case 1 $\dfrac{a}{b}$, where $a = 0$ and $b \neq 0$.

For example, $\dfrac{0}{3} = 0$, since according to the division check, $0 = 3 \cdot 0$. The division check verifies the unique answer, $c = 0$.

Case 2 $\dfrac{a}{b}$, where $a \neq 0$ and $b = 0$.

For example, if $\dfrac{3}{0} = c$, then by the division check we should be able to verify that $3 = 0 \cdot c$. But no matter what number is chosen for c, $3 \neq 0 \cdot c$. In this case no answer is possible.

Case 3 $\dfrac{a}{b}$, where $a = 0$ and $b = 0$.

In this case the problem is $\dfrac{0}{0}$. Since $0 = 0 \cdot c$ no matter what the value is for c, the division check will work. For example, we could have $\dfrac{0}{0} = 1$, or $\dfrac{0}{0} = 3$, or $\dfrac{0}{0} = 100$, or even $\dfrac{0}{0} = 0$.

There are an infinite number of possible correct answers for c and there is no reason for us to prefer one answer over any of the others. Since we desire a unique answer we conclude that $\dfrac{0}{0}$ is undefined.

Cases 2 and 3 can be combined into one statement: *division by 0 is undefined*. Case 1 shows that dividing a nonzero number into 0 is defined and the answer is 0: you can divide *into* 0 but you cannot divide *by* 0. The number 0 can be used as a dividend but it can never be a divisor.

DIVIDING INTO 0

If x is a nonzero number, then $\dfrac{0}{x} = 0$ $x \neq 0$.

DIVIDING BY 0

If x is any number (including zero), $\dfrac{x}{0}$ is undefined.

EXAMPLE 7	Perform the following divisions:

$$\textbf{a.} \ \frac{-22}{0} \qquad \textbf{b.} \ \frac{0}{1{,}001} \qquad \textbf{c.} \ \frac{0}{-25} \qquad \textbf{d.} \ \frac{4}{0}$$

SOLUTION

a. $\dfrac{-22}{0} = $ undefined   Division by 0 is undefined.

b. $\dfrac{0}{1{,}001} = 0$ Using the division check, $0 \cdot 1{,}001 = 0$.

c. $\dfrac{0}{-25} = 0$ Using the division check, $0 \cdot (-25) = 0$.

d. $\dfrac{4}{0} = $ undefined   Division by 0 is undefined.   ■

EXAMPLE 8	Simplify the following expressions:

$$\textbf{a.} \ 32 \div 8 \div 4 \qquad\qquad \textbf{b.} \ 100 \div [40 \div (-10)]$$

$$\textbf{c.} \ \frac{(-125) \div 5}{(-30) \div (-6)} \qquad\qquad \textbf{d.} \ \frac{(-343) \div 7}{[448 \div (-8)] \div 8}$$

SOLUTION

a. $32 \div 8 \div 4 = 4 \div 4$ Use the order of operations agreement.
$\qquad\qquad\qquad = 1$ Divide $4 \div 4$.

b. $100 \div [40 \div (-10)] = 100 \div [-4]$ Simplify inside the brackets.
$\qquad\qquad\qquad\qquad\quad = -25$ Divide $100 \div [-4]$.

c. $\dfrac{(-125) \div 5}{(-30) \div (-6)} = \dfrac{-25}{5}$

$\qquad\qquad\qquad = -5$ The division bar acts as a grouping symbol for the expressions above and below the bar.

d. $\dfrac{(-343) \div 7}{[448 \div (-8)] \div 8} = \dfrac{-49}{(-56) \div 8}$ Simplify the expressions above and below the bar before performing the division represented by the bar.

$$= \dfrac{-49}{-7}$$

$$= 7$$ ■

EXAMPLE 9	Find the quotient of 1,728 and -12.

SOLUTION $\dfrac{1,728}{-12} = -144$.

In this type of problem the dividend appears after the word *of* and the divisor appears after the word *and*. This type of problem is similar to finding the "difference" because the order of the integers remains the same.   ■

EXAMPLE 10	Divide -5 into 335.

SOLUTION $\dfrac{335}{-5} = -67$

In this type of problem the dividend appears after the word *into* and the divisor appears after the word *Divide*. This type of problem is similar to those of the form "Subtract ... from ..." because the order of the integers is reversed.   ■

EXAMPLE 11	A high-stakes gambler goes to Las Vegas with $60,000. She plays roulette and loses all of her money in 12 consecutive games. What was her average loss per game?

SOLUTION $60,000 was lost, represented by the integer $-60,000$. To find the average loss per game, the loss ($-60,000$) is divided by the number of games played (12).

$$\dfrac{-60,000}{12} = -5,000$$

She lost $5,000 per game of roulette.   ■

P R A C T I C E   F O R   S U C C E S S

Practice 1.   Multiply $(-19) \cdot (-21)$.

Practice 2.   Multiply $6 \cdot (-4) \cdot (-11) \cdot (-3)$.

Practice 3.   Find the product of 17, 5, and -3.

Practice 4. Ashley started a company that sold oat bran cookies. The first week she lost $225 each day. How much money did she lose by the end of the first week?

Practice 5. Divide $264 \div (-3)$.

Practice 6. Divide $\dfrac{-27}{0}$.

Practice 7. Simplify $\dfrac{(-36) \div (-6)}{51 \div 17}$.

Practice 8. The temperature dropped 39° over a 13-hour period in Nome, Alaska. Find the average temperature drop per hour.

EXERCISES 2.4

In exercises 1–76, perform the indicated operations and simplify each expression to a single signed number.

1. $-210 \div 15$	**2.** $182 \div (-13)$	**3.** $84 \div (-12)$
4. $-13 \cdot 3$	**5.** $-117 \div 9$	**6.** $-14 \cdot (-4)$
7. $-5 \cdot 15$	**8.** $14 \cdot (-11)$	**9.** $0 \cdot (-13)$
10. $-14 \cdot 12$	**11.** $-169 \div 13$	**12.** $0 \cdot 6$
13. $-7 \cdot (-12)$	**14.** $-182 \div 13$	**15.** $-11 \cdot (-9)$
16. $-144 \div (-12)$	**17.** $11 \cdot (-12)$	**18.** $-3 \cdot (-13)$
19. $-192 \div (-6)$	**20.** $8 \cdot (-13)$	**21.** $-11 \cdot (-10)$
22. $182 \div (-13)$	**23.** $-11 \cdot 14$	**24.** $-13 \cdot (-9)$
25. $-56 \div (-4)$	**26.** $0 \div 9$	**27.** $-13 \cdot 14$
28. $-110 \div 10$	**29.** $-12 \cdot 13$	**30.** $-112 \div 14$
31. $13 \cdot (-9)$	**32.** $-78 \div 13$	**33.** $0 \div (-9)$
34. $126 \div (-14)$	**35.** $-13 \cdot (-9)$	**36.** $-13 \cdot 14$

37. $7 \cdot [\,|-112| \div (-8)]$

38. $\{-(-3)\} \cdot [-2 \cdot (-9) \div 3]$

39. $-4 \cdot [-(-2) \cdot 140 \div (-14)]$

40. $-3 \cdot [\,|-(-2)| \cdot (-21) \div 7]$

41. $-(-7) \cdot (4 \cdot (-5) \cdot 6)$

42. $2 \cdot \{-4 \div [-20 \div (-10)]\}$

43. $-8 \cdot \{-(-210) \div [-1 \cdot (-14)]\}$

44. $12 \cdot (-9) \div |-2 \cdot 27|$

45. $[28 \div (-14)] \cdot (-35 \div 5)$

46. $15 \cdot [-130 \div (-5) \cdot (-13)]$

47. $-13 \cdot (-4 \cdot (-180) \div 12)$

48. $|-14 \cdot (-112) \div 16| \div \{-(-7)\}$

49. $-5 \cdot [-2 \cdot (-91) \div (-7)]$

50. $-(-196) \div [(-2) \cdot 7]$

51. $-5 \cdot [-4 \cdot |-15 \div (-3)|]$

52. $0 \cdot [- (-11) \cdot (-36) \div |-12|]$

53. $-(-10) \cdot \{-8 \cdot [- (-2) \cdot (-63) \div 7]\}$

54. $[0 \div (-1) \cdot |12 \div (-3)|] \div [-2 \div (-1)]$

55. $-(-13) \cdot [- (-88) \div (-22) \times (-11)]$

56. $-1{,}400 \div (-10) \cdot [- (-5) \cdot (-210) \div 15]$

57. $-(-12) \cdot \{-(-1)\} \cdot |-400 \div (-50) \cdot 2|$

58. $(-165) \div [(-3) \cdot (-5) \cdot (-11)]$

59. $[-7 \div (-7) \cdot \{7 \cdot |-15|\}] \div [-98 \div (-14)]$

60. $-(-1{,}920) \div \{- (-4)\} \cdot [12 \cdot (-2) \cdot |-10|]$

61. $[91 \div (-7) \cdot \{13 \cdot (-14)\}] \cdot 11 \div [-13 \cdot 1]$

62. $216 \div \{- |-8|\} \cdot \{- (-3) \cdot [(-45) \div 15]\}$

63. $-(-5) \cdot [-144 \div (-24) \div (-6)]$

64. $\{[- (-10)] \cdot [- (-9)]\} \cdot (-5) \div [(-2) \cdot (-25)]$

65. $-(-16) \cdot [- (-288) \div |24| \div (- (-12)]$

66. $\{[-18 \div |-3| \div (-2)] \cdot (9 \div (-3)) \cdot [(-72) \div 8]\} \cdot (-1)$

67. $\{|-154 \div (-11) \div (2 \cdot (-7))| \cdot |- (-1)|\} \cdot [-4 \cdot 1]$

68. $[-150 \div 10 \div \{-3 \cdot (-5)\}] \cdot \{- (-8)\}$

69. Find the product of -7, -8, -9, and -10.

70. Find the product of -3, -5, -7, and -9.

71. Find the product of -6, -8, -10, and 12.

72. Find the product of -8, -11, -13, and 20.

73. Find the quotient of -150 and 0.

74. Find the quotient of 0 and -150.

75. Find the quotient of 0 and 4.

76. Find the quotient of 4 and 0.

In exercises 77–87, solve each word problem using the operations of multiplication and division with positive and/or negative numbers as required.

77. If the temperature in a science experiment drops $2°$ every minute, what is the temperature change after an hour and a half?

78. A submarine descends at a constant rate of 15 feet every 4 seconds. What is the change in depth after 7 minutes and 20 seconds?

79. Every week on the Pacific Stock Exchange a certain stock gains $3 per share in value. What is the gain in value between June 1 and August 17?

80. As a swimming pool is being drained, the water level decreases by 3 inches every minute. What is the change in water level after 26 minutes?

81. If the *Queen Mary* passenger ship uses 13 gallons of fuel to travel one foot, how many gallons of fuel will it consume traveling between Los Angeles and San Francisco, which is approximately 377 nautical miles? (Assume one nautical mile equals 6,076 feet.)

82. If the average person consumes 8 pounds of coffee in a year, how many pounds of coffee would the average person consume between the ages of 18 and 27?

83. If sound travels at 1,088 feet per second, how long would it take for a sonic boom to travel between Los Angeles and San Francisco? (Assume the distance is 442 miles and assume one mile is 5,280 feet. Also assume the sonic boom is strong enough to really travel that far.)

84. One of the world's fastest freight ships crossed the Atlantic Ocean in 3 days and 16 hours. How many feet per second did this ship average? (Assume the distance was 3,360 miles with 5,280 feet per mile.)

85. When lumber is cut in a lumber yard, a small amount of waste is produced in the form of sawdust. The amount of sawdust is equivalent to the volume of a cut, which is determined by the thickness of the saw blade. If the waste from one cut of an average-size tree is 56 cubic inches of sawdust, and if each tree requires 6 cuts, how much waste is produced by cutting 2,400 trees?

86. If the temperature is rising 3° every 15 minutes, what is the temperature change after two and a quarter hours?

87. A submarine ascends at a constant rate of 18 feet every 6 seconds. What is the change in depth after 5 minutes and 30 seconds?

 **Looking Back**

88. What is −7 subtracted from 15?

89. What is −18 subtract 43?

90. The concept of the *opposite* of a number is relative to what number on a number line?

91. Describe the difference between the noun *factor* and the verb *to factor*.

92. What difference, if any, exists between the set of nonnegative numbers and the set of positive numbers?

93. How many numbers can be classified as simultaneously being nonpositive and nonnegative?

94. What is the basic operation for the expression

$$-(-10) - (-11) \cdot [12 + (-117) \div (-13)]$$

PRACTICE-FOR-SUCCESS ANSWERS

1. 399   2. −792
3. −255   4. She lost $1,575.
5. −88   6. undefined
7. 2   8. The temperature dropped 3° per hour.

| 2.5 | **MIXED OPERATIONS AND GROUPING SYMBOLS** |

OBJECTIVES

_____

□   To simplify expressions with mixed operations, exponentiation, and grouping symbols

□   To solve word problems using mixed operations and grouping symbols

_____

In this section many of the skills learned in Chapters 1 and 2 will be helpful. This section will use the order of operations agreement as well as the ability to add, subtract, multiply, and divide integers to simplify expressions. Knowledge of exponents and the concept of absolute value will come in handy also.

| **EXAMPLE 1** | Simplify $-7 - [-32 + (-25 + 48)]$. |

SOLUTION $-7 - [-32 + (-25 + 48)] = -7 - [-32 + 23]$ Start inside the innermost grouping symbol pair and drop the parentheses: $-25 + 48 = 23$.

$$= -7 - [-9]$$ Simplify inside the square brackets.

$$= -7 + [+9]$$ Change subtraction to adding the opposite.

$$= 2$$ ■

| **EXAMPLE 2** | Simplify $|-44| \cdot (-5) - (-3) \cdot |-12|$. |

SOLUTION $|-44| \cdot (-5) - (-3) \cdot |-12| = 44 \cdot (-5) - (-3) \cdot 12$ Simplify the absolute value parts first.

$$= -220 - (-36)$$ Perform multiplications before the subtraction.

$$= -220 + (+36)$$ Convert subtraction to adding the opposite.

$$= -184$$ ■

| **EXAMPLE 3** | Simplify $(-3) \cdot [-7 + 13 - (-22)]$. |

SOLUTION $(-3) \cdot [-7 + 13 - (-22)] = (-3) \cdot [-7 + 13 + (+22)]$

Convert subtraction to adding the opposite.

$$= (-3) \cdot [6 + 22]$$ Continue to simplify inside the square brackets.

$$= (-3) \cdot [28]$$
$$= -84$$ ■

EXAMPLE 4	Simplify $-8 \cdot (-7 + 2^2) + 4 \cdot \{12 \div [6 \div (-2)]\}$.

SOLUTION

$-8 \cdot (-7 + 2^2) + 4 \cdot \{12 \div [6 \div (-2)]\}$

$= -8 \cdot (-7 + 4) + 4 \cdot \{12 \div [6 \div (-2)]\}$ Perform exponentiation first.

$= -8 \cdot (-7 + 4) + 4 \cdot \{12 \div [-3]\}$ Divide inside the square brackets.

$= -8 \cdot (-3) + 4 \cdot \{-4\}$ Simplify inside parentheses and curly braces.

$= 24 + \{-16\}$ Multiply before adding.

$= 8$ ■

EXAMPLE 5	Simplify -7^2.

SOLUTION   As there are no parentheses, we simplify the exponent before finding the opposite. This problem should be read as "the opposite of the square of seven" or "the opposite of seven raised to the second power."

$-7^2 = -(7^2)$

$\quad = -(49)$

$\quad = -49$ ■

When a negative integer is raised to a power, the negative integer must be contained inside parentheses.

EXAMPLE 6	Simplify $(-7)^2$.

SOLUTION   Given parentheses, we simplify the exponent first. This problem should be read as "the square of negative seven" or "negative seven raised to the second power."

$(-7)^2 = (-7) \cdot (-7)$

$\quad = 49$ ■

EXAMPLE 7	Simplify $-3^2 - 4^2 - (3 - 5)^2$.

SOLUTION

$-3^2 - 4^2 - (3 - 5)^2 = -3^2 - 4^2 - (-2)^2$ Simplify inside the parentheses.

$= -9 - 4^2 - (-2)^2$ Simplify the leftmost exponent.

$= -9 - 16 - (-2)^2$ Simplify the leftmost exponent.

$= -9 - 16 - 4$ Simplify the remaining exponent.

$= -9 + (-16) - 4$ Change the leftmost subtraction to adding the opposite.

$= -25 - 4$ Add $-9 + (-16)$.

$= -25 + (-4)$ Change to adding the opposite.

$= -29$ ■

EXAMPLE 8   Simplify $\dfrac{-3 \cdot [8 - (-12 + 6)]}{-4 \cdot [4 - (-2)] - (-5) \cdot (6)}$.

SOLUTION $\dfrac{-3 \cdot [8 - (-12 + 6)]}{-4 \cdot [4 - (-2)] - (-5) \cdot (6)} = \dfrac{-3 \cdot [8 - (-6)]}{-4 \cdot [4 + (+2)] - (-30)}$ Simplify above and below the division bar.

$$= \dfrac{-3 \cdot [8 + (+6)]}{-4 \cdot [6] - (-30)}$$

$$= \dfrac{-3 \cdot [14]}{-24 + (+30)}$$

$$= \dfrac{-42}{6}$$

$$= -7$$ ■

EXAMPLE 9   Simplify $\dfrac{-2^4 - 6^2 + (-4)^2}{3^2 - (5 - 8)^3}$.

SOLUTION $\dfrac{-2^4 - 6^2 + (-4)^2}{3^2 - (5 - 8)^3} = \dfrac{-16 - 36 + 16}{9 - (-3)^3}$ Simplify the exponents in the top part and simplify inside the parentheses in the bottom.

$$= \dfrac{-16 + (-36) + 16}{9 - (-27)}$$ Perform the cube of -3.

$$= \dfrac{-52 + 16}{9 + (+27)}$$

$$= \dfrac{-36}{36}$$

$$= -1$$ ■

EXAMPLE 10   What is -5 times the difference of -7 and -10?

SOLUTION $-5 \cdot [-7 - (-10)] = -5 \cdot [-7 + (+10)]$

$$= -5 \cdot [3]$$

$$= -15$$ ■

EXAMPLE 11   What is the opposite of the absolute value of -15 divided by the product of 6 and 0?

SOLUTION $\dfrac{-|-15|}{6 \cdot 0} = \dfrac{-15}{0}$ Simplify the absolute value first.

= undefined   Division by 0 is undefined.

Whenever a problem results in an undefined operation the correct answer to the problem is "undefined."   ■

EXAMPLE 12	Find eight less than twice the difference between forty-seven and negative ten.

SOLUTION   In this example we must translate the English description into a mathematical expression and then simplify that expression to a single number. The phrase "eight less than" means subtract 8 from a quantity. Which quantity? The quantity that is 2 times the difference between 47 and -10. So we begin by writing the difference between 47 and -10 and placing this quantity in brackets because it will be multiplied by 2. Then we subtract 8.

$$2 \cdot [47 - (-10)] - 8 = 2 \cdot [47 + (+10)] - 8$$ Change the subtraction to adding the opposite.

$$= 2 \cdot [57] - 8$$ Simplify inside the square brackets.

$$= 114 - 8$$
$$= 106$$ ■

P R A C T I C E   F O R   S U C C E S S

Practice 1.   Simplify $|-66| \cdot (-7) - (-5) \cdot |-10|$.

Practice 2.   Simplify $(-9) \cdot [-8 + 12 - (-26)]$.

Practice 3.   Simplify $-10 \cdot (-7 + 3^2) + -5 \cdot \{-32 \div [-8 \div (-2)]\}$.

Practice 4.   Simplify $-7^2 - 6^2 - (4 - 13)^2$.

Practice 5.   Simplify $\dfrac{-7 \cdot [4 - (-8 + 16)]}{-7 \cdot [3 - (-5)] - (-7) \cdot (6)}$.

Practice 6.   Write a mathematical expression that corresponds to the English description, then simplify the expression to a single number:

The difference between the product of negative eight and positive thirteen and the quotient of two hundred five and negative forty-one.

EXERCISES 2.5

In exercises 1–51, simplify each expression according to the rules for signed numbers and the order of operations to arrive at a single signed number for each problem answer.

1. $3 - 13 \cdot [-(-13) - (-8) \div 1]$
2. $9 - (-8) \cdot [- (-5) + (-70) \div 10]$
3. $12 - 5 \cdot [-11 + (-9) \cdot (-1)]$
4. $-(-14) \cdot [- (-9) + 0 \cdot (-10)]$
5. $-11 \cdot [-(-6) - (-130) \div 10]$
6. $(-2)^3$

7. $(-2)^7$

8. $(-1)^{100}$

9. $(-3)^3$

10. $(-2)^4 + (2)^4$

11. $(-2)^5 + (2)^5$

12. $-(-5) \cdot [-(-2) - 3 \cdot (-9)^2]$

13. $-(-7) \cdot [-(-14)^2 - (-52) \div 4]$

14. $-(-5) \cdot [-(-12) + (-13) \cdot (-6)]$

15. $5 + 4 \cdot [-(-9) - (-8) \cdot 15]$

16. $-(-9) - (-6) \cdot [11 - (-1) \cdot (-1)^5]$

17. $|-5| + (-13)^2 \cdot [-14 + (-10) \div 2]$

18. $-(-3) \cdot [-(-11) - (-98) \div 14]$

19. $14 + (-5) \cdot [-12 + 14 \cdot (-12)]$

20. $4 + |-12| \cdot [-6 - (-48) \div (-2)^3]$

21. $-13 - |-9| \cdot [-(-11) - (-98) \div (-7)^2]$

22. $-14 + |-4| \cdot \left[-2 - \dfrac{84}{(-12)} \right]$

23. $-(-7) - |-12| \cdot [-(-3) - (-6) \cdot 6]$

24. $|-5| - |-3| \cdot [-6 + (-9) \cdot (-5)^2]$

25. $-14 - |-10| \cdot [-(-12) - 0 \cdot 12]$

26. $[63 \div (-7) + \{11 - (-7)\}] \cdot (-13 \div 1)$

27. $[50 \div (-10) + \{7 - (-5)\}] \cdot [-14 \cdot (-3)^2]$

28. $[-8 \cdot 14 + \{-14 + (-7)^3\}] \cdot (-6) - (-7) \cdot 14$

29. $[-3 \cdot 15 - \{5 + (-7)\}] \cdot \left[-5 \cdot \dfrac{85 - 13}{(-3) \cdot |-3|} \right] + (-6)$

30. $[-10 \cdot (-4) + \{4 + (-7)\}] \cdot |-(-8)| - \dfrac{(-24)}{4}$

31. $[\{0 - 0\} \cdot (8 \cdot (-7)) - [11 - (-14)]] \cdot \{-3 \cdot 7\}$

32. $[-99 \div (-11) - \{-2 - 4\}] \cdot (-4 \cdot 14) - (-5)$

33. $\left[\{10 - 0\} \cdot \dfrac{(-5)^3 + (5)^2}{20} - [6 + (-9)] \right] \cdot \{-2 \div 1\}$

34. $[\{|-13| - (-3)\} \cdot (-12 \div 6) - [|-11| - (-6)]] \cdot \{0 \div 15\} - 15$

35. $\left[52 \div (-13) + \left\{ -13 + \dfrac{(-2)^3 - 60 - 12}{(-2)^3} \right\} \right] \cdot |-13| - (-40) \div 4$

36. $[\{8 - (-10)\} \cdot (-9 \cdot 6) + [9 - |-14|]] \cdot \{-33 \div 3\}$

37. $[\{-6 \div (-3) + 9\} \cdot (11 - (-9)) - |-5|^2] \cdot [0 \cdot (-2)]$

38. $[\{-12 + (-10)\} \cdot (-9 \cdot |-7|) - [7 - 13]] \cdot \{14 \div (-7)\} - (-2)$

39. $[\{1 + (-10)\} \cdot (-15 \div (-3)) - [(-2)^2 - 13]] \cdot (-(-2)) - 0 \cdot 1$

40. $[\{12 - (-9)\} \cdot (-30 \div 15) + [-4 - (-3)^2]] \cdot \{-7 \cdot (-10)\}$

41. $[\{-11 - 0\} \cdot (-2 \cdot 8) - [0 + 15]] \cdot \{15 \cdot (-11)\}$

42. $[\{-6 \cdot 6 - 13\} \cdot (-10 - (-3)^2) - (-(-5))] \cdot [0 \div 14]$

43. $\left[\{0 + (-4)\} \cdot \dfrac{(-6)^2 + (-\,|-57|)}{(-2)^2 - 1} - [-7 - (-1)] \right] \cdot \{14 \cdot 0\}$

44. $[\{-48 \div 4 + (-13 + 9)\} \cdot [-6 \div 6] - \{0 + (-7)\}] \cdot (-3 \cdot 0)$

45. $[\{6 - 11\} \cdot ((-2)^3 \cdot (-12)) + [-5 + (-11)]] \cdot \{-10 \cdot 3\} - 6$

46. $[\{-3 + 11\} \cdot (-7 \cdot |-10|) - [6 + (-1)]] \cdot \{-156 \div (-12)\}$

47. $\left[\{0 + (-5)\} \cdot \dfrac{-67 + 7}{-12 + 7} - [6 + (-7)] \right] \cdot 13 - (-3) \cdot 12$

48. $[\{-20 \div (-10) + |-6|\} \cdot (13 + (-1)^{21}) - (-36) \div 9] \cdot 11$

49. $[\{10 + (-8)\} \cdot (-7 \cdot (-9)) - [-9 + (-3)^2]] \cdot \{-3 \cdot 10\} - (-(-9))$

50. $[\{14 \cdot (-11) - (-1 - 2)\} \cdot [-10 \cdot 15] + \{13 + (-7)\}] \cdot (-9 \cdot 0) - (-11)$

51. $\left[\left\{ \dfrac{(-3)^3 - 33}{(-2)^4 - 36} - (3 - (-12)) \right\} \cdot [-12 \cdot 0] + \{13 + (-10)\} \right] \cdot (-6 \cdot 7)$

In exercises 52–62, first formulate an expression corresponding to the expression described and then simplify the expression to a single number.

52. The difference between negative thirteen and the quotient of negative fifty and positive ten.

53. The product of the sum of negative sixty-eight and ninety-two with the sum of seventy-three and negative seventy-eight.

54. Six less than twice the difference between fifty-eight and negative six.

55. Negative one hundred thirty-two divided by negative twelve plus the quotient of negative fifty-four and positive twenty-seven.

56. Twenty-seven less than twice the product of negative seven and positive nine.

57. Eighteen more than the quotient of negative one hundred forty and negative twenty-eight.

58. The difference between the product of negative nine and positive fourteen and the quotient of one hundred five and negative thirty-five.

59. Five times the sum of the quotient of negative sixty-eight and positive seventeen and the product of negative twelve and positive fifteen.

60. Three less than twice the product of the sum of negative forty-two and six and the quotient of negative eighteen and negative nine.

61. Twenty-five more than the sum of the quotient of negative forty-eight and positive sixteen and the product of the absolute value of negative twelve and positive four.

62. The number of this problem less negative fifteen times negative twenty-two divided by the absolute value of negative eleven.

Looking Back

63. Define the absolute value of a number.

64. How is absolute value used to find the distance between two points on a number line?

65. Find the GCF and LCM of 328 and 472.

66. State the test for divisibility by 3.

67. What is the test for divisibility by 5?

68. Give an example of the distributive law.

PRACTICE-FOR-SUCCESS ANSWERS

1. -412 **2.** -270 **3.** 20

4. -166 **5.** -2 **6.** $(-8)(13) - 205 \div (-41) = -99$

SUMMARY

Chapter 2 has laid the foundation for working with positive and negative numbers, which can be indicated by the signs $+$ and $-$. Signed whole numbers are called integers. While the use of the positive sign $+$ to indicate that a number is positive is optional, the negative sign $-$ must be used to indicate that a number is negative. The number 0 is neutral and does not have any sign associated with it. The negative sign can have three different interpretations, depending on the context in which it is used: It can indicate that a number is negative, it can refer to subtraction, or it can mean the opposite — for example, we would read the expression $5 - [-(-7)]$ as *subtract the opposite of negative seven from five*.

Negative and positive numbers correspond to signed distances on a number line. The concept of absolute value is used to measure the distance between any two points on the number line. In this case, the distance concept refers to a nonnegative number. The expression $|a - b|$ refers to the distance between the two points corresponding to a and b. As an example, $|3 - 9| = |-6| = 6$. For a single number, $|x|$ refers to the distance on a number line between 0 and the point corresponding to x. As examples, $|-5| = 5$, $|0| = 0$, and $|16| = 16$.

The ordering of integers is determined by the rule that smaller numbers lie to the left and larger numbers lie to the right, relative to one another on a number line. Thus, because -6 lies to the left of -2 on a number line, we can write $-6 < -2$ or $-2 > -6$. The symbols for both less than $<$ and greater than $>$ are always used so that they point to the smaller number.

We covered the four standard operations for integers. When adding, if the two integers have like signs their sum will have the same sign and the numerical value can be calculated using ordinary addition — for example, $-8 + (-10) = -18$. When adding numbers of unlike signs, the sign of the answer is the sign of the number with the larger absolute value and the numerical value is calculated using ordinary subtraction — for example, $35 + (-52) = -17$. Regardless of the combination of signs, we usually convert a subtraction problem into the addition of the opposite — for example, $-23 - (-33) = -23 + (+33) = 10$.

The rule of signs for multiplication and division are the same. When multiplying or dividing two numbers, their product or quotient is positive when they have like signs and is negative when they have unlike signs. The numerical values are always calculated using ordinary multiplication or division — for example, $(+7) \cdot (-9) = -63$ and $(-88) \div (-11) = 8$. Division by zero is impossible.

CHAPTER 2 REVIEW PROBLEMS

In problems 1–56, perform the indicated operations and simplify each expression to a single signed number without parentheses or absolute value bars.

1. $-5-(-10) \div 10$
2. $6 \cdot [0 - (-14) \cdot 13]$
3. What is -25 subtracted from -17?
4. $-9 \cdot [2 + (-45) \div 15]$
5. $11 \cdot [3 + (-165) \div 15]$
6. $7 \cdot [-(-10)^2 + (-8) \cdot 9]$
7. Subtract -5 from -17.
8. $15 \cdot [6 - 0 \cdot (-7)]$
9. $0 \cdot [-(-12) + 0 \div (-3)]$
10. $1 - 8 \cdot [-8 + |-11| \cdot (-1)]$
11. Subtract 12 from 8.
12. $5 \cdot [-12 - |-132| \div (-12)]$
13. What is 52 subtract -12?
14. $9 \cdot [-14 - |-33| \div (-11)]$
15. What is -34 subtracted from -81?
16. $-(-13) \cdot [(-2)^3 + (-22) \div 11]$
17. $-(-7) \cdot [6 + (-72) \div (-3)^2]$
18. Subtract 23 from -89.
19. $-6 \cdot [11 - (-8) \cdot (-2)^3]$
20. $-(-3) \cdot [-(-4) + (-9) \cdot (-1)^{11}]$
21. $-(-8) \cdot [-11 - (-63) \div (-7)]$
22. $-4 \cdot [-(-12) + 0 \div (-3)^5]$
23. What is -70 subtracted from 70?
24. $-10 \cdot [-(-5) + (-44) \div (-2)^2]$
25. $-(-9) \cdot [-6 + (-30) \div |-3|]$
26. $8 - (-2) \cdot [-7 - 12 \cdot (-11)]$
27. $14 + (-4) \cdot [3 + (-9) \cdot 7]$
28. $-(-2) \cdot [-(-6) - 3 \cdot (-3)]$
29. $14 \cdot [-7 - (-10) \cdot (-6)]$
30. $-(-9) \cdot [-13 - (-3)^3 \div (-9)]$
31. $-(-2)^4 \cdot [(-1)^9 - (-6) \cdot (-3)]$
32. $-(-8) \cdot [-(-8) - (-112) \div 14]$

33. $\dfrac{-6 - (-5) \cdot [-(-5) - 13 \cdot (-4)]}{4^3 - 3 \cdot 2^3 - (-\,|-53|)}$

34. $12 - |-2| \cdot [-13 - (-2) \cdot (-7)^2 \div 14]$

35. $-(-10) \cdot [-(-8) + 7 \cdot (-2)^3 \div (-7)]$

36. $10 - (-(-6)) \cdot [-(-1) - (-35) \div |-7|]$

37. $\dfrac{-(-4) - (-1) \cdot [14 - (-60) \div 6]}{(-5)^3 + 3^4 - (-5) \cdot (+6)}$

38. $[0 \div (-7) - \{(-2)^5 - 11\}] \cdot (0 \div (-12))$

39. $-(-8) - (-1)^9 \cdot [-(-5) + (-108) \div (-9)]$

40. $(-2)^4 + |-6| \cdot [-(-6) - (-72) \div |-8|]$

41. $-(-14) \cdot [-(-15) + (-168) \div (-14)]$

42. $[8 \cdot (-5) - \{-1 + |-6|^2\}] \cdot (0 \cdot 1) + -(-5)$

43. $\dfrac{-(-6) - |-12| \cdot [-2 - (-120) \div 15]}{-7^2 + |-8| \cdot |7| - (-2)^5 - 6}$

44. $-(-12) - (-2) \cdot [-(-14) - (-10) \div (-5)]$

45. $-(-9) - |-6| \cdot [-(-7) + (-8) \cdot 12]$

46. $[-12 \div 6 + \{13 - (-3)\}] \cdot (-1) + (-1) \cdot 12$

47. $[-99 \div 9 - \{-13 - (-11)\}] \cdot (-4) - 6 \cdot (-6)$

48. $\dfrac{[-13 \cdot 13 - \{-8 + (-8)\}] \cdot -(-2) - (-2) \cdot 23}{-7 \cdot [3 - (-5)] - (-9) \cdot (5) + |-7|}$

49. $[42 \div (-6) - \{-1 + 11\}] \cdot (-210 \div (-14))$

50. $[\{3 + (-3)\} \cdot (-6 \cdot 1) - (|-8| - 15)] \cdot \{-144 \div 12\}$

51. $[\{-10 \div (-2) + (12 - 14)\} \cdot 8 - 63 \div (-9)] \cdot 5$

52. $[\{-96 \div 8 - [0 + (-1)]\} \cdot (-4) - (-8) \cdot (-7)] \cdot (-3)$

53. $[\{-4 + 15\} \cdot (-16 \div 4) + [|-13| + (-2)]] \cdot \{-40 \div 8\}$

54. $[\{-99 \div 11 - 8\} \cdot (0 - 5) - |-6|] \cdot [-98 \div (-7)]$

55. $[\{-169 \div 13 + (13 - 14)\} \cdot (-9) - (-14)] \cdot [-132 \div 12]$

56. $[\{-91 \div (-13) - (10 + (-1))\} \cdot -(-5) + -8 \cdot 8] \cdot |-5|$

In problems 57–68, write the correct comparison symbol, < or >, between the integers to make the resulting statement true.

57. $-28 \,?\, 27$ **58.** $61 \,?\, -61$ **59.** $43 \,?\, 44$ **60.** $-23 \,?\, 23$

61. $-18 \,?\, -19$ **62.** $0 \,?\, -15$ **63.** $78 \,?\, -2$ **64.** $89 \,?\, -91$

65. $-51 \,?\, -49$ **66.** $-9 \,?\, -8$ **67.** $-7 \,?\, 0$ **68.** $-5 \,?\, 0$

In problems 69–82, you are given the coordinates of two points called A and B that are assumed to be on the same number line. Use subtraction of signed numbers and absolute values to calculate the straight line distance between A and B.

	A	B		A	B		A	B		A	B
69.	−56	22	**70.**	−26	−15	**71.**	40	−90	**72.**	−46	−64
73.	−39	−74	**74.**	75	15	**75.**	−60	50	**76.**	−75	−15
77.	−893	−528	**78.**	−45	−46	**79.**	−225	0	**80.**	0	−71
81.	0	31	**82.**	−93	−89						

In problems 83–93, write an expression corresponding to the description in the problem, and then simplify your expression to a single number.

83. Two more than three times the quotient of seventy-five and the sum of negative ten and positive thirty-five.

84. The cube of four plus the opposite of the square of seventeen all divided by two hundred twenty-five.

85. Seven less than the product of the absolute value of negative ten and the square of negative three.

86. Negative nine times the sum of two and the quotient of negative forty-five and fifteen.

87. Seven times the sum of the opposite of negative ten and the product of negative eight and nine.

88. One minus eight times the sum of negative eight and the product of eleven and negative one.

89. Nine times the difference of negative fourteen and the quotient of thirty-three and negative eleven.

90. The opposite of negative seven times the sum of six and the quotient of negative seventy-two and negative nine.

91. Negative six times the difference between eleven and the product of negative eleven and negative eight.

92. The opposite of negative three times the sum of the opposite of negative four and the product of negative nine and one.

93. The absolute value of the difference between negative eighty and twenty-six minus negative three hundred twenty-eight.

CHAPTER 2 PRACTICE TEST

In problems 1–6, write the correct comparison symbol, $<$ or $>$, between the integers to make the resulting statement true.

1. $-67 \, ? \, 22$	2. $-44 \, ? \, -63$	3. $90 \, ? \, -99$
4. $-64 \, ? \, 81$	5. $-700 \, ? \, -816$	6. $-318 \, ? \, -319$

In problems 7–12, you are given the coordinates of two points called A and B, which are assumed to be on the same number line. Use subtraction of signed numbers and absolute values to calculate the straight line distance between A and B.

	A	B		A	B		A	B
7.	-46	91	8.	72	277	9.	-79	-91
10.	-94	-81	11.	78	-19	12.	87	0

In problems 13–28, perform the indicated operations and simplify each expression to a single signed number without parentheses or absolute value bars.

13. $-4 + (-3)^2 \cdot (-1 - |-60| \div 4)$

14. $-(-2) \cdot [-4 + (-8) \cdot (-4)^2]$

15. What is -67 subtracted from -31?

16. $(-2)^3 \cdot [-(-12) - 5 \cdot (-5)]$

17. $[56 \div (-7) - \{-7 + (-6)\}] \cdot 14 - (-12) \cdot 13$

18. $-(-14) \cdot [-(-8) - 11 \cdot (-1)]$

19. Subtract -13 from -23.

20. $-4 + -8 \cdot [-(-2)^4 + (-18) \div 9]$

21. $\dfrac{-(-11) + (-8) \cdot [-(-10) - |-77| \div 11]}{1 - (-2)^5 + (-34 \div 17) + (-6) \cdot 3}$

22. $-14 - (-3) \cdot [-10 - (-10) \cdot (-2)]$

23. $\dfrac{-13 - (-(-9)) \cdot [-14 - (-9) \div 9]}{(-6)^2 - |-50| \div 5}$

24. $[-98 \div (-7) + \{4 + 0\}] \cdot (-6) + (-5) \cdot 13$

25. $\dfrac{14 - (-(-6)) \cdot [-(-1) - (-9) \cdot |-12|]}{|(-3)^3| + 3 \cdot (-5)^2 - (-4)^3 - 6}$

26. $\dfrac{9 \cdot \{-14 - 33 \div (-11)\}}{(-6) \cdot (-3) + -|3 \cdot (-5)|}$

27. $[-7 \cdot 10 - \{-6 + (-8)\}] \cdot (168 \div (-14))$

28. $[\{-7 + 9\} \cdot (-65 \div (-5)) - [-1 + (-9)]] \cdot \{-11 \cdot 8\}$

In problems 29–32, write an expression corresponding to the given description. Then simplify your expression to a single number.

29. Fourteen times the sum of negative three and the quotient of seventy-two and negative eight.

30. Negative seven times the difference between negative six and the product of negative eight and thirteen.

31. Ten times the difference of the opposite of negative 12 and the quotient of thirty-three and negative three.

32. The opposite of negative fourteen times the difference between the opposite of negative five and the product of negative eleven and fourteen.

CHAPTER THREE

FRACTIONS

Chapter 3 expands the signed number concept to include fractions, or rational numbers. The topics covered are expanding, reducing, adding, subtracting, multiplying, and dividing positive and negative fractions. Some of the prime factoring techniques from Chapter 1 are applied to create equivalent fractions. Also covered are the methods for converting between mixed numbers and improper fractions and for ordering signed fractions. Some special properties of the number 1 are introduced, with use being made of the reciprocal of a number. We continue to work word problems and to simplify expressions with mixed operations including fractions, exponents, and grouping symbols. The chapter concludes by showing how to use a fundamental property of fractions and the distributive law to simplify complex fractions.

3.1   EXPANSION AND REDUCTION OF FRACTIONS

OBJECTIVES

☐   To expand a fraction to an equivalent fraction

☐   To reduce a fraction to lowest terms

In the first chapter we explored the set of whole numbers $\{0, 1, 2, 3, ...\}$ and in the second chapter, the set of integers $\{..., -3, -2, -1, 0, 1, 2, 3, ...\}$. This chapter deals with fractions, such as $\frac{1}{2}$, $\frac{7}{10}$, and $\frac{-17}{31}$, which fill in the gaps between the integers on the number line. Fractions are also called **rational numbers.**

A number written as a quotient in the form $\frac{m}{n}$, where m and n denote integers and $n \neq 0$, is called a **fraction.** The top number m is called the **numerator,** and the bottom number n is called the **denominator.** The dividing line between the numerator and denominator is called a **fraction bar.** The denominator of a fraction can never be zero, because it represents division by zero, which is undefined.

Fractions can represent parts of a whole or a whole amount; $\frac{90}{6}$ represents the whole number 15, because $90 \div 6 = 15$. However, fractions are usually used to represent a smaller part of a whole amount. If a person eats $\frac{3}{8}$ of a pizza, then the person has eaten 3 of the possible 8 equal parts that make up the whole pizza, as illustrated in Figure 3.1.

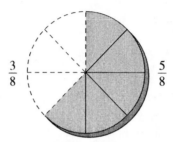

FIGURE 3.1   Circular pizza with the missing $\frac{3}{8}$ portion

More than one fraction can be used to represent the same number. Figure 3.2 shows several fractions, all equivalent to $\frac{2}{3}$. Fractions that represent the same number and are thus equal are called *equivalent fractions.*

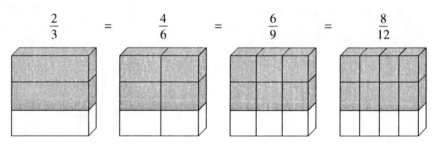

FIGURE 3.2   Depiction of $\frac{2}{3} = \frac{4}{6} = \frac{6}{9} = \frac{8}{12}$

DEFINITION	EQUIVALENT FRACTIONS
	Two fractions are called equivalent if they represent the same number.

One set of equivalent fractions is $\frac{1}{1} = \frac{2}{2} = \frac{3}{3} = \frac{4}{4} = \frac{5}{5}$, and so on. All of these fractions are equal to 1 because $\frac{1}{1} = 1 \div 1 = 1, \frac{2}{2} = 2 \div 2 = 1$, and so on. Any fraction whose nonzero denominator is equal to its numerator is equal to 1, or the *whole unit.*

DIVIDING A NONZERO NUMBER BY ITSELF

For any number $x \neq 0$, $\dfrac{x}{x} = 1$.

CREATING EQUIVALENT FRACTIONS

To make fractions that are equivalent, both the numerator and denominator are either multiplied or divided by the same nonzero number. The following three fractions are all equivalent, provided b and x are nonzero.

$$\frac{a}{b} = \frac{a \cdot x}{b \cdot x} = \frac{a \div x}{b \div x} \qquad b \neq 0, \quad x \neq 0$$

According to the rules for creating equivalent fractions, $\dfrac{3}{5} = \dfrac{3 \cdot 4}{5 \cdot 4} = \dfrac{12}{20}$ or $\dfrac{12}{20} = \dfrac{12 \div 4}{20 \div 4} = \dfrac{3}{5}$. Multiplication or division are the operations used to expand or reduce a fraction to an equivalent fraction.

Expansion of Fractions

Multiplication by whole numbers is used to expand a fraction, and division by whole numbers is used to reduce a fraction. For example, to expand $\dfrac{2}{3}$ to obtain a fraction whose denominator is 24, multiply both the numerator and denominator by 8 because 3 multiplied by 8 equals 24.

$$\frac{2}{3} = \frac{2 \cdot 8}{3 \cdot 8} = \frac{16}{24}$$

Knowing how to expand fractions to equivalent forms will be necessary later in this chapter when we discuss addition and subtraction with unlike denominators.

EXAMPLE 1	Expand $\dfrac{7}{10}$ to an equivalent fraction with a denominator of 60.

SOLUTION   Because $10 \cdot 6 = 60$, multiply the numerator and denominator of $\dfrac{7}{10}$ by 6.

$$\frac{7}{10} = \frac{7 \cdot 6}{10 \cdot 6} = \frac{42}{60}$$

■

| EXAMPLE 2 | Expand $\frac{11}{8}$ to an equivalent fraction with a denominator of 168. |

SOLUTION   To determine what number to multiply by 8 to make the denominator equal to 168, divide 168 by 8.

$$\begin{array}{r} 21 \\ 8\overline{)168} \end{array}$$

Because $8 \cdot 21 = 168$, multiply the numerator and denominator of $\frac{11}{8}$ by 21.

$$\frac{11}{8} = \frac{11 \cdot 21}{8 \cdot 21} = \frac{231}{168}$$ ■

| EXAMPLE 3 | Expand $\frac{25}{32}$ to an equivalent fraction with a numerator of 100. |

SOLUTION   Because $25 \cdot 4 = 100$, multiply the numerator and denominator of $\frac{25}{32}$ by 4.

$$\frac{25}{32} = \frac{25 \cdot 4}{32 \cdot 4} = \frac{100}{128}$$ ■

Reduction of Fractions

Fractions are easier to use when the numerator and denominator are as small as possible, or are expressed in lowest terms.

DEFINITION   **FRACTION IN LOWEST TERMS**

A fraction is in lowest terms when the only common factor of the numerator and the denominator is 1.

Is the fraction $\frac{4}{9}$ in lowest terms according to the definition? The whole number factors of 4 are 1, 2, and 4, and the whole number factors of 9 are 1, 3, and 9. Since the numerator and the denominator of the fraction $\frac{4}{9}$ have no common factors other than 1, the fraction $\frac{4}{9}$ is in lowest terms. A fraction is completely reduced whenever its numerator and denominator are relatively prime. Because the nouns *factor* and *divisor* can be interchanged, another way to check if the fraction $\frac{4}{9}$ is in lowest terms is to see if 1 is the only whole number divisor of both the numerator and denominator.

To partially reduce a fraction, the numerator and denominator can be divided by the same nonzero number. The fraction $\frac{10}{15}$, which is not in lowest terms, reduces to $\frac{2}{3}$ when both the numerator and denominator are divided by 5.

$$\frac{10}{15} = \frac{10 \div 5}{15 \div 5} = \frac{2}{3}$$

The fraction $\frac{2}{3}$ is in lowest terms because the only common factor of both the numerator and denominator is 1. In fact, since 5 is the greatest common factor of 10 and 15, when we divide both the numerator and denominator by 5 we completely reduce $\frac{10}{15}$.

Another method to reduce a fraction to lowest terms is to write the prime factorizations of both the numerator and the denominator and then divide by the common factors.

$$\frac{10}{15} = \frac{2 \cdot 5}{3 \cdot 5} = \frac{2 \cdot \cancel{5}}{3 \cdot \cancel{5}} = \frac{2}{3}$$

The 5s can be canceled because $\frac{5}{5}$ equals 1. The real operation is division since canceling or crossing out the 5s in pairs is really performing the operation $5 \div 5$, which is the same as writing the fraction $\frac{5}{5}$. Reducing the fraction in this manner is equivalent to multiplying by 1.

$$\frac{10}{15} = \frac{10 \div 5}{15 \div 5} = \frac{2}{3} \quad \text{is the same as} \quad \frac{10}{15} = \frac{2 \cdot \cancel{5}}{3 \cdot \cancel{5}} = \frac{2}{3}$$

Factoring both numerator and denominator with the same common factor and canceling the common factor is equivalent to dividing both numerator and denominator by the same factor.

EXAMPLE 4

Reduce $\frac{6}{21}$ to lowest terms.

SOLUTION

Because 6 and 21 are both divisible by 3, divide both the numerator and denominator by 3.

$$\frac{6}{21} = \frac{6 \div 3}{21 \div 3} = \frac{2}{7} \quad \text{or} \quad \frac{6}{21} = \frac{2 \cdot \cancel{3}}{\cancel{3} \cdot 7} = \frac{2}{7}$$

The only requirement for canceling is that the two numbers must be factors and must be the same number. The common factors do not have to be vertically aligned to be divided or canceled. The fraction $\frac{2}{7}$ is in lowest terms because now the only common factor of both 2 and 7 is 1. ■

In example 4 the greatest common divisor, 3, was divided into the numerator and denominator. Often, however, it may be difficult to recognize the greatest common divisor of a fraction's numerator and denominator. When the greatest common divisor is not readily apparent, it is easier to write the prime factorizations of the numerator and denominator first. For example, $\frac{45}{60}$ can be written using primes as $\frac{3 \cdot 3 \cdot 5}{2 \cdot 2 \cdot 3 \cdot 5}$. Because 3 and 5 are common factors of both the numerator and the denominator, they can both be divided or canceled because $\frac{3}{3} = 1$ and $\frac{5}{5} = 1$. The problem can be then be then shown as follows.

$$\frac{45}{60} = \frac{3 \cdot \cancel{3} \cdot \cancel{5}}{2 \cdot 2 \cdot \cancel{3} \cdot \cancel{5}} = \frac{3}{2 \cdot 2} = \frac{3}{4}$$

Another method to reduce $\frac{45}{60}$ is to first find any common factor of the numerator and denominator that is greater than 1. Since 45 and 60 are divisible by 3, $\frac{45}{60}$ is written $\frac{\cancel{3} \cdot 15}{\cancel{3} \cdot 20}$ or as $\frac{15}{20}$. The fraction $\frac{45}{60}$ has thus been only partially reduced because 1 is not the only common factor of 15 and 20. Because 15 and 20 are divisible by 5, $\frac{15}{20}$ is written $\frac{\cancel{5} \cdot 3}{\cancel{5} \cdot 4}$ or as $\frac{3}{4}$, the form in lowest terms. The whole method can be shown horizontally as follows.

$$\frac{45}{60} = \frac{\cancel{3} \cdot 15}{\cancel{3} \cdot 20} = \frac{\cancel{5} \cdot 3}{\cancel{5} \cdot 4} = \frac{3}{4}$$

Multiplying the common factor of 3 times the common factor of 5 gives us the greatest common factor 15, which can then also be divided into both the numerator and denominator. The same problem could be shown a third way as follows.

$$\frac{45}{60} = \frac{45 \div 15}{60 \div 15} = \frac{3}{4}$$

EXAMPLE 5	Reduce $\frac{81}{243}$ to lowest terms.

SOLUTION
a. Using prime factorizations:

$$\frac{81}{243} = \frac{\cancel{3} \cdot \cancel{3} \cdot \cancel{3} \cdot \cancel{3}}{\cancel{3} \cdot \cancel{3} \cdot \cancel{3} \cdot \cancel{3} \cdot 3} = \frac{1}{3}$$

When every factor is crossed out in either the numerator or the denominator, the number 1 is placed in that part of the fraction. The justification for doing this is the principle of dividing a nonzero number by itself.

$$\frac{3}{3} = \frac{\cancel{3}}{\cancel{3}} = 1 \qquad \frac{3 \cdot 3 \cdot 3 \cdot 3}{3 \cdot 3 \cdot 3 \cdot 3} = \frac{81}{81} = \frac{\cancel{81}}{\cancel{81}} = 1$$

b. Using common factors:

$$\frac{81}{243} = \frac{\cancel{3} \cdot 27}{\cancel{3} \cdot 81} = \frac{\cancel{3} \cdot 9}{\cancel{3} \cdot 27} = \frac{\cancel{3} \cdot 3}{\cancel{3} \cdot 9} = \frac{\cancel{3} \cdot 1}{\cancel{3} \cdot 3} = \frac{1}{3}$$

c. Using division by the greatest common factor:

$$\frac{81}{243} = \frac{81 \div 81}{243 \div 81} = \frac{1}{3}$$

The fraction $\frac{1}{3}$ is in lowest terms because the only common factor of both the numerator and denominator is 1.   ■

| **EXAMPLE 6** | Reduce $\frac{280}{210}$ to lowest terms. |

SOLUTION   **a.** Using prime factorizations:

$$\frac{280}{210} = \frac{\cancel{2} \cdot 2 \cdot 2 \cdot \cancel{5} \cdot \cancel{7}}{\cancel{2} \cdot 3 \cdot \cancel{5} \cdot \cancel{7}} = \frac{4}{3}$$

The remaining factors in the numerator $2 \cdot 2$ are multiplied.

b. Using common factors:

$$\frac{280}{210} = \frac{\cancel{10} \cdot 28}{\cancel{10} \cdot 21} = \frac{\cancel{7} \cdot 4}{\cancel{7} \cdot 3} = \frac{4}{3}$$

Notice that 280 and 210 are both divisible by 10, so the first factor that is chosen is 10.

c. Using division by the greatest common factor:

$$\frac{280}{210} = \frac{280 \div 70}{210 \div 70} = \frac{4}{3}$$

The fraction $\frac{4}{3}$ is in lowest terms because the only common factor of both the numerator and denominator is 1.   ■

| **EXAMPLE 7** | Rori completes 70 of 105 math problems. Express the amount of problems completed as a fraction in lowest terms. |

SOLUTION   Rori has completed 70 out of the total amount 105, or $\frac{70}{105}$ of the problems.

The fraction $\frac{70}{105}$ needs to be reduced to lowest terms.

Using prime factorizations:

$$\frac{70}{105} = \frac{2 \cdot \cancel{5} \cdot \cancel{7}}{3 \cdot \cancel{5} \cdot \cancel{7}} = \frac{2}{3}$$

The fraction $\frac{2}{3}$ is in lowest terms because the only common factor of both the numerator and denominator is 1. Rori has completed $\frac{2}{3}$ of the problems.   ■

REDUCING A FRACTION TO LOWEST TERMS

Method A

1. Write the prime factorizations of the numerator and denominator.
2. Divide out their common factors.
3. Multiply the factors that remain in the numerator and then multiply the factors that remain in the denominator.

Method B

1. Write factorizations of the numerator and denominator with a common factor greater than 1 in each.
2. Divide out their common factors.
3. Continue the process until the fraction is reduced to lowest terms.

Method C

1. Find the greatest common factor.
2. Divide the numerator and denominator by the greatest common factor.

In the following example, either the numerator or the denominator of the second fraction is missing. To find the missing quantity, the first fraction must be either expanded or reduced.

EXAMPLE 8

Find the missing number.

a. $\dfrac{36}{48} = \dfrac{3}{?}$ **b.** $\dfrac{7}{10} = \dfrac{?}{120}$ **c.** $\dfrac{54}{?} = \dfrac{18}{25}$ **d.** $\dfrac{?}{42} = \dfrac{13}{6}$

SOLUTION

a. The numerator in the second fraction is smaller than the numerator in the first fraction, so the first fraction needs to be reduced. Because the first numerator (36) divided by 12 gives the second numerator (3), the common divisor is 12.

$$\frac{36}{48} = \frac{36 \div 12}{48 \div 12} = \frac{3}{4} \qquad \text{The missing denominator is 4.}$$

b. The denominator of the second fraction is larger than the denominator of the first fraction, so the first fraction needs to be expanded. The common multiplier is 12.

$$\frac{7}{10} = \frac{7 \cdot 12}{10 \cdot 12} = \frac{84}{120} \qquad \text{The missing numerator is 84.}$$

c. The numerator in the first fraction is larger than the numerator in the second fraction, so the second fraction needs to be expanded. Because the second numerator (18) multiplied by 3 gives the first numerator (54), the desired common multiplier is 3.

$$\frac{18}{25} = \frac{18 \cdot 3}{25 \cdot 3} = \frac{54}{75} \qquad \text{The missing denominator is 75.}$$

d. The denominator of the first fraction is larger than the denominator of the second fraction so the second fraction needs to be expanded. The common multiplier is 7.

$$\frac{13}{6} = \frac{13 \cdot 7}{6 \cdot 7} = \frac{91}{42} \qquad \text{The missing numerator is 91.} \qquad ■$$

PRACTICE FOR SUCCESS

Practice 1. Expand $\dfrac{13}{15}$ to an equivalent fraction with denominator 75.

Practice 2. Expand $\dfrac{23}{20}$ to an equivalent fraction with numerator 92.

Practice 3. Reduce $\dfrac{84}{96}$ to lowest terms.

Practice 4. Reduce $\dfrac{150}{600}$ to lowest terms.

Practice 5. If the total enrollment of a community college is 8,000 and 5,500 students are male, what fraction of the student population is female?

Practice 6. Find the missing number: $\dfrac{20}{28} = \dfrac{5}{?}$.

Practice 7. Find the missing number: $\dfrac{?}{108} = \dfrac{11}{12}$.

EXERCISES 3.1

In exercises 1–24, reduce each fraction to lowest terms. Use any one of the three methods given in examples 5 through 9.

1. $\dfrac{15}{35}$		**2.** $\dfrac{18}{39}$
3. $\dfrac{34}{48}$		**4.** $\dfrac{47}{94}$
5. $\dfrac{43}{86}$		**6.** $\dfrac{4}{52}$
7. $\dfrac{10}{46}$		**8.** $\dfrac{14}{98}$
9. $\dfrac{65}{78}$		**10.** $\dfrac{38}{95}$
11. $\dfrac{57}{76}$		**12.** $\dfrac{26}{91}$

13. $\dfrac{91}{364}$

14. $\dfrac{92}{115}$

15. $\dfrac{85}{102}$

16. $\dfrac{28}{119}$

17. $\dfrac{49}{147}$

18. $\dfrac{85}{748}$

19. $\dfrac{167}{501}$

20. $\dfrac{51}{867}$

21. $\dfrac{118}{295}$

22. $\dfrac{217}{620}$

23. $\dfrac{73}{219}$

24. $\dfrac{248}{512}$

In exercises 25–36, expand each fraction so that the new fraction has the given numerator or denominator.

25. $\dfrac{1}{2}$ denominator = 34

26. $\dfrac{3}{4}$ numerator = 21

27. $\dfrac{4}{7}$ denominator = 84

28. $\dfrac{5}{8}$ numerator = 55

29. $\dfrac{13}{29}$ denominator = 116

30. $\dfrac{85}{78}$ denominator = 312

31. $\dfrac{13}{56}$ numerator = 104

32. $\dfrac{3}{19}$ denominator = 95

33. $\dfrac{7}{13}$ denominator = 91

34. $\dfrac{8}{15}$ denominator = 120

35. $\dfrac{5}{37}$ denominator = 185

36. $\dfrac{7}{43}$ denominator = 301

In exercises 37–57, find the missing number, assuming the two given fractions are equivalent.

37. $\dfrac{?}{45} = \dfrac{4}{3}$

38. $\dfrac{30}{?} = \dfrac{5}{12}$

39. $\dfrac{65}{80} = \dfrac{?}{16}$

40. $\dfrac{6}{81} = \dfrac{2}{?}$

41. $\dfrac{?}{22} = \dfrac{32}{11}$

42. $\dfrac{14}{?} = \dfrac{7}{26}$

43. $\dfrac{80}{64} = \dfrac{?}{4}$

44. $\dfrac{70}{42} = \dfrac{5}{?}$

45. $\dfrac{?}{63} = \dfrac{8}{7}$

46. $\dfrac{?}{92} = \dfrac{9}{23}$

47. $\dfrac{212}{?} = \dfrac{53}{59}$

48. $\dfrac{144}{390} = \dfrac{?}{65}$

49. $\dfrac{328}{568} = \dfrac{?}{71}$

50. $\dfrac{408}{616} = \dfrac{51}{?}$

51. $\dfrac{?}{406} = \dfrac{69}{203}$

52. $\dfrac{99}{?} = \dfrac{11}{34}$

53. $\dfrac{96}{513} = \dfrac{?}{171}$

54. $\dfrac{370}{644} = \dfrac{185}{?}$

55. $\dfrac{?}{176} = \dfrac{13}{44}$

56. $\dfrac{486}{?} = \dfrac{81}{106}$

57. $\dfrac{360}{185} = \dfrac{?}{37}$

In exercises 58–65, reduce each fraction to lowest terms after first finding all the prime factors of the numerator and denominator.

58. $\dfrac{60}{350}$

59. $\dfrac{517}{564}$

60. $\dfrac{76}{624}$

61. $\dfrac{324}{322}$

62. $\dfrac{134}{316}$

63. $\dfrac{68}{650}$

64. $\dfrac{164}{205}$

65. $\dfrac{106}{344}$

In exercises 66–77, reduce each fraction to lowest terms after first checking, in order, whether 2, 3, 5, or 7 is a common factor of both the numerator and denominator. Keep reducing by the same prime number factor until that prime number is no longer a common factor of both numerator and denominator. For all of the fractions in these problems you may assume that the only common prime factors will be one or more of 2, 3, 5, or 7.

66. $\dfrac{48}{72}$

67. $\dfrac{70}{280}$

68. $\dfrac{150}{240}$

69. $\dfrac{45}{105}$

70. $\dfrac{119}{231}$

71. $\dfrac{96}{176}$

72. $\dfrac{1,875}{5,000}$

73. $\dfrac{162}{567}$

74. $\dfrac{1,050}{1,470}$

75. $\dfrac{216}{504}$

76. $\dfrac{1,890}{2,730}$

77. $\dfrac{1,260}{2,310}$

In exercises 78–87, write a fraction that corresponds to the description of the given quantity and then reduce that fraction to lowest terms.

78. An office worker works Monday through Friday but does not work on the weekend (Saturday and Sunday). Over a 6-week period, what fractional number of days is the worker in the office compared to the total number of days?

79. A car worth $12,000 was assessed a value of $8,000 for tax purposes. What fractional part of the total value of the car was used for tax purposes?

80. A family of five is planning to vacation in Hawaii. If the family has 3 children (in addition to the mother and father) and if the air fare for each person is $150, what fraction of the total cost is represented by the children's total fare?

81. If a carpenter spends 3 hours and 20 minutes framing a room in a house, and if 50 minutes of that time is spent cutting boards while the remaining time is spent carrying and nailing boards, what fractional part of the total minutes does she spend carrying and nailing?

82. The mathematical number π is a decimal number that is a little larger than 3. The number π can be approximated using a fraction made out of the two numbers 710 and 226. Write the fraction that approximates π and then reduce it.

83. Albert went on a diet and dropped his weight down from 235 pounds to 185 pounds. What fractional part of his original weight did Albert lose?

84. When 20 pounds of ground turkey are cooked and the resulting waste grease is drained, the remaining weight is 18 pounds. What fractional part of the original weight is wasted?

85. Gasoline mileage for a car is calculated by dividing the number of miles traveled by the number of gallons of gasoline consumed driving those miles. What fraction represents the miles per gallon if you travel 185 miles on 15 gallons of gasoline?

86. If your net paycheck is for $756 while your gross pay is $945 what fractional part of your gross pay represents the amount taken out for taxes?

87. If the birth rate is such that for every 100 girls that are born, 106 boys are born, what fraction represents the comparison of boys to girls?

Looking Back

88. In evaluating the exponential expression 5^6, how many multiplications would be performed?

89. What is the reason for calling third powers *cubes*?

90. Explain in your own words what is meant by the basic operation for an expression.

91. What is the difference between a *term* and an *expression*?

92. State the division check.

93. What is the definition of a composite number?

94. Name two whole numbers that are neither prime nor composite.

PRACTICE-FOR-SUCCESS ANSWERS

1. $\dfrac{65}{75}$ 2. $\dfrac{92}{80}$ 3. $\dfrac{7}{8}$ 4. $\dfrac{1}{4}$ 5. $\dfrac{5}{16}$ 6. 7   7. 99

<table>
<tr><td>**3.2**</td><td># SIGNED FRACTIONS, MIXED NUMBERS, AND INEQUALITIES</td></tr>
</table>

OBJECTIVES

- □ To change mixed numbers to improper fractions
- □ To change improper fractions to mixed numbers
- □ To compare any two fractions

In the first section of this chapter we learned how to expand and reduce fractions. All of the problems in that section used only 0 or positive numerators and denominators. In Figure 3.3 a few fractions of the type used in the first section are shown on a number line.

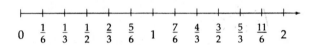

FIGURE 3.3 **Number line showing positive fractions in increments of $\dfrac{1}{6}$**

Signed Fractions

This section will introduce fractions with a mixture of positive and negative numerators and denominators. Just as every positive integer has an opposite negative integer to the left of 0, so every positive fraction has an opposite negative fraction on the opposite side of 0. For example, the opposite of $\dfrac{1}{2}$ is $-\dfrac{1}{2}$; the opposite of $\dfrac{5}{6}$ is $-\dfrac{5}{6}$. In Figure 3.4 some fractions and their opposites are shown on the number line.

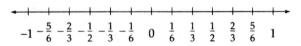

FIGURE 3.4 **Number line showing signed fractions in increments of $\dfrac{1}{6}$**

The positive fractions together with the negative fractions are called **signed fractions.** As with integers, positive fractions usually do not have a $+$ sign in front of them, whereas negative fractions always have a $-$ sign in front of them. This rule of signs is exactly the same as the one used for positive and negative integers, with the number of signs used to be kept to a minimum.

In a signed fraction both the numerator and denominator might be positive or negative. If they are both positive, as with 5 divided by 7, the fractional form is $\dfrac{5}{7}$. If the numerator and denominator are both negative, as with -5 divided by -7, the fractional form can be written $\dfrac{-5}{-7}$. However, $\dfrac{-5}{-7} = \dfrac{-1 \cdot 5}{-1 \cdot 7} = \dfrac{\cancel{-1} \cdot 5}{\cancel{-1} \cdot 7} = \dfrac{5}{7}$. Because negative signs are to be kept to a minimum, the preferred form for $\dfrac{-5}{-7}$ is $\dfrac{5}{7}$.

The following argument is a way to show $-\dfrac{2}{3}$ and $\dfrac{-2}{3}$ represent the same point on a number line. With integers a number and its opposite add up to 0; for example, $5 + (-5) = 0$. If we apply this same principle for signed fractions, we can show that the opposite of $\dfrac{2}{3}$ is $\dfrac{-2}{3}$. When we add these two fractions, which have the same denominator, we get

$$\frac{2}{3} + \frac{-2}{3} = \frac{2 + (-2)}{3} = \frac{0}{3} = 0.$$

Therefore, the opposite of $\dfrac{2}{3}$ must be $\dfrac{-2}{3}$, and the way to write the opposite of $\dfrac{2}{3}$ is $-\dfrac{2}{3}$.

The same fraction can be written with a positive numerator and a negative denominator. Two divided by -3 is written in fractional form as $\dfrac{2}{-3}$. Because a positive integer divided by a negative integer yields a negative quotient,

$$\frac{2}{-3} = -\frac{2}{3}.$$

Signed fractions are rarely left in the form with a negative denominator, so the preferred fractional form for 2 divided by -3 is $-\dfrac{2}{3}$.

We have seen that a negative signed fraction can be written in one of three forms:

$$\frac{-2}{3} = \frac{2}{-3} = -\frac{2}{3}.$$

The first form is sometimes used, the second form is rarely used, and the third form is the one most commonly used to indicate that a fraction is negative.

Proper Fractions

When the absolute value of the numerator is smaller than the absolute value of the denominator, the fraction is called a **proper fraction.** $\dfrac{11}{12}, \dfrac{20}{27},$ and $\dfrac{3}{40}$

are examples of proper fractions. $-\frac{4}{5}$ is also an example of a proper fraction because $-\frac{4}{5} = \frac{-4}{5}$ and the absolute value of -4 is less than the absolute value of 5.

DEFINITION	PROPER FRACTION
	A proper fraction is one in which the absolute value of the numerator is smaller than the absolute value of the denominator.

Improper Fractions

The fraction $\frac{22}{7}$ is an example of an improper fraction. In an **improper fraction** the absolute value of the numerator is greater than or equal to the absolute value of the denominator. $-\frac{4}{4}$ is also an example of an improper fraction because $-\frac{4}{4} = \frac{-4}{4}$ and the absolute value of -4 is equal to the absolute value of 4.

DEFINITION	IMPROPER FRACTION
	An improper fraction is one in which the absolute value of the numerator is greater than or equal to the absolute value of the denominator.

Mixed Numbers

Integers can be combined together with proper fractions to form **mixed numbers:** for example, $2\frac{2}{3}$.

$$2\frac{2}{3} = 2 \text{ (an integer)} + \frac{2}{3} \text{ (a proper fraction)}$$

Similarly, $-5\frac{1}{8}$ is also a mixed number.

$$-5\frac{1}{8} = -\left(5 + \frac{1}{8}\right) = -5 \text{ (an integer)} + \left(-\frac{1}{8}\right) \text{ (a proper fraction)}$$

DEFINITION	MIXED NUMBER
	A mixed number is the sum of an integer and a proper fraction.

Converting Mixed Numbers to Improper Fractions

To see that mixed numbers can be converted to improper fractions, imagine you have 2 candy bars and you eat $1\frac{3}{8}$ of those candy bars (see Figure 3.5). The shaded areas in Figure 3.5 indicate the amount of candy you ate. You ate $\frac{8}{8} + \frac{3}{8} = \frac{11}{8}$; therefore, $1 + \frac{3}{8}$ or $1\frac{3}{8} = \frac{11}{8}$. Rather than draw a picture every time we want to convert a mixed number into an improper fraction, we multiply the denominator by the integer part of the mixed number and add that to the numerator of the fraction part. The original denominator of the fraction part of the mixed number remains the denominator of the improper fraction.

$$\frac{8}{8} \qquad + \qquad \frac{3}{8}$$

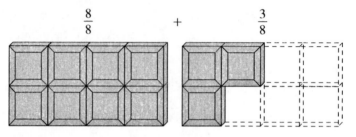

FIGURE 3.5   Depiction of $1 + \frac{3}{8} = \frac{8}{8} + \frac{3}{8}$

CONVERTING A MIXED NUMBER TO AN IMPROPER FRACTION

1. **Multiply the integer part by the denominator of the fraction part of the mixed number.**
2. **Add the answer from step 1 to the numerator of the fraction part of the mixed number; this sum is the numerator of the improper fraction.**
3. **The original denominator of the fraction part of the mixed number is the denominator of the improper fraction.**

EXAMPLE 1   Convert the following mixed numbers to improper fractions.

　　　　　　　a. $5\frac{4}{7}$　　　　**b.** $-18\frac{9}{10}$

SOLUTION　　**a.** $5\frac{4}{7} = \frac{5 \cdot 7 + 4}{7} = \frac{35 + 4}{7} = \frac{39}{7}$

　　　　　　b. $-18\frac{9}{10} = -\left(18 + \frac{9}{10}\right) = -\left(\frac{18 \cdot 10 + 9}{10}\right) = -\left(\frac{180 + 9}{10}\right) = -\frac{189}{10}$　　■

Converting Improper Fractions to Mixed Numbers

Figure 3.6 illustrates that $\frac{15}{8} = \frac{8}{8} + \frac{7}{8}$ or $1 + \frac{7}{8}$ or $1\frac{7}{8}$. Rather than drawing pictures to convert $\frac{15}{8}$, the numerator can be divided by the denominator to get the same result much more quickly.

$$\frac{15}{8} = 15 \div 8 \qquad \text{or in long division form} \qquad 8\overline{)15}^{\displaystyle 1}$$

$$\begin{array}{r} \underline{-8} \\ 7 \end{array}$$

$$\frac{15}{8} = 1\frac{7}{8}$$

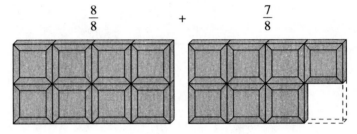

$$\frac{8}{8} \qquad + \qquad \frac{7}{8}$$

FIGURE 3.6   Depiction of $\frac{15}{8}$ as $\frac{8}{8} + \frac{7}{8}$ or $1\frac{7}{8}$

The division check is closely related to the process of converting between an improper fraction and a mixed number, as illustrated by the following:

$$3\frac{5}{9} = \frac{3 \cdot 9 + 5}{9} = \frac{27 + 5}{9} = \frac{32}{9}$$

When 32 is divided by 9 using long division, the quotient is 3 and the remainder is 5.

$$9\overline{)32}^{\displaystyle 3} \qquad \text{divisor} \cdot \text{quotient} + \text{remainder} = \text{dividend}$$

$$\begin{array}{r} \underline{-27} \\ 5 \end{array}$$

$$9 \cdot 3 + 5 = 32$$

$$\frac{32}{9} = \frac{9 \cdot 3 + 5}{9} = \frac{\cancel{9} \cdot 3}{\cancel{9}} + \frac{5}{9} = 3 + \frac{5}{9} = 3\frac{5}{9}$$

> ## CONVERTING AN IMPROPER FRACTION TO A MIXED NUMBER
>
> 1. **Divide the numerator by the denominator.**
> 2. **The quotient is the integer part of the mixed number; the remainder is the numerator of the proper fraction portion of the mixed number; the divisor is the denominator of the proper fraction portion of the mixed number.**

EXAMPLE 2	Convert the following improper fractions to mixed numbers.

$$\textbf{a.}\ \frac{105}{11} \qquad \textbf{b.}\ \frac{64}{6} \qquad \textbf{c.}\ -\frac{76}{16}$$

SOLUTION   **a.** $\dfrac{105}{11}$ $11\overline{)105}$ The division check shows $105 = 11 \cdot 9 + 6$.
$$\underline{-\ 99}$$
$$6$$

$$\frac{105}{11} = \frac{11 \cdot 9 + 6}{11} = \frac{\cancel{11} \cdot 9}{\cancel{11}} + \frac{6}{11} = 9 + \frac{6}{11} = 9\frac{6}{11}$$

b. $\dfrac{64}{6}$ $6\overline{)64}$ $\dfrac{64}{6} = 10\dfrac{4}{6} = 10\dfrac{2}{3}$
$$\underline{-\ 60}$$
$$4$$

Note that the fractional part of the mixed number must be reduced to lowest terms whenever it is possible to do so: $10\dfrac{4}{6}$ becomes $10\dfrac{2}{3}$. This conversion also could have been done by first reducing $\dfrac{64}{6}$ to $\dfrac{32}{3}$:

$$\frac{32}{3} \qquad 3\overline{)32} \qquad \frac{32}{3} = 10\frac{2}{3}$$
$$\underline{-\ 30}$$
$$2$$

c. $-\dfrac{76}{16} = \dfrac{-76}{16}$ $16\overline{)76}$ $-4\dfrac{12}{16} = -4\dfrac{3}{4}$
$$\underline{-\ 64}$$
$$12$$

The fractional part of the mixed number must always be reduced to lowest terms. This conversion also could have been done by first reducing $\dfrac{-76}{16}$ to $\dfrac{-19}{4}$: $\dfrac{-19}{4} = -4\dfrac{3}{4}$ ▪

Comparing Fractions and Mixed Numbers

It is often valuable to be able to compare fractions and decide which is the larger of the two: for example between $\dfrac{7}{8}$ or $\dfrac{13}{16}$. One student might argue that $\dfrac{13}{16}$ is larger because it has the larger numerator or denominator, and another student might argue that $\dfrac{7}{8}$ is larger because 7 is closer to 8 than 13 is to 16. One way to accurately compare fractions is to draw pictures of each, as in Figure 3.7. The shaded areas in Figure 3.7 show that $\dfrac{7}{8}$ is slightly larger than $\dfrac{13}{16}$. This comparison can be stated using an inequality symbol;

$$\frac{7}{8} > \frac{13}{16}.$$

$$\frac{7}{8} \qquad\qquad \frac{13}{16}$$

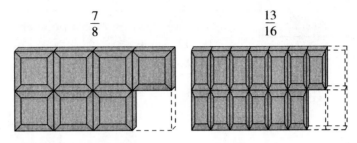

FIGURE 3.7   Depiction of $\frac{7}{8}$ and $\frac{13}{16}$

Another way to compare two fractions without drawing pictures is to expand them so that both fractions have the same denominator. In this example $\frac{7}{8}$ can be expanded to $\frac{14}{16}$ to help compare the two fractions.

$$\frac{7}{8} \, ? \, \frac{13}{16}$$

$$\frac{14}{16} > \frac{13}{16} \quad \text{because } 14 > 13, \text{ so}$$

$$\frac{7}{8} > \frac{13}{16}$$

COMPARING TWO FRACTIONS

1. **If necessary expand either or both fractions so that both fractions have the same denominator.**
2. **When the fractions have the same denominator, compare the numerators.**

EXAMPLE 3	Compare the following fractions. Replace the ? symbol with either the $>$ or the $<$ symbol.

a. $\dfrac{9}{10} \, ? \, \dfrac{13}{15}$ **b.** $-\dfrac{3}{4} \, ? \, -\dfrac{17}{25}$

SOLUTION   **a.**

$$\frac{9}{10} \, ? \, \frac{13}{15}$$

$$\frac{9 \cdot 3}{10 \cdot 3} \, ? \, \frac{13 \cdot 2}{15 \cdot 2}$$

$$\frac{27}{30} > \frac{26}{30}$$

The LCM of 10 and 15 is 30, so each fraction is expanded to have a denominator of 30.

Because $27 > 26$; thus, $\dfrac{9}{10} > \dfrac{13}{15}$.

b.

$$-\frac{3}{4} \, ? \, -\frac{17}{25}$$

$$-\frac{3 \cdot 25}{4 \cdot 25} \, ? \, -\frac{17 \cdot 4}{25 \cdot 4}$$

$$\frac{-75}{100} < \frac{-68}{100}$$

The LCM of 4 and 25 is 100 so each fraction is expanded to have a denominator of 100.

Because $-75 < -68$; thus, $-\dfrac{3}{4} < -\dfrac{17}{25}$.   ■

EXAMPLE 4	Compare the following mixed numbers. Replace the ? symbol with either the $>$ or the $<$ symbol.

$$\text{a. } 5\frac{1}{2} \text{ ? } 4\frac{5}{6} \qquad \text{b. } -2\frac{1}{4} \text{ ? } -2\frac{1}{3}$$

SOLUTION   a. $5\frac{1}{2} \text{ ? } 4\frac{5}{6}$ Comparing the whole number parts is sufficient to determine the answer.

$$5\frac{1}{2} > 4\frac{5}{6}$$

b. $-2\frac{1}{4} \text{ ? } -2\frac{1}{3}$ Because the whole number parts are the same, we need only compare the fractional parts, but we must include the negative signs.

$$\frac{-1}{4} \text{ ? } \frac{-1}{3}$$ Expand the fractions to have the same denominator, 12.

$$\frac{-1 \cdot 3}{4 \cdot 3} \text{ ? } \frac{-1 \cdot 4}{3 \cdot 4}$$

$$\frac{-3}{12} > \frac{-4}{12}$$ Because $-3 > -4$; thus, $-2\frac{1}{4} > -2\frac{1}{3}$.   ▪

P R A C T I C E   F O R   S U C C E S S

Practice 1.   Reduce $\dfrac{-15}{-60}$ to lowest terms using a minimum number of negative signs in the answer.

Practice 2.   Reduce $-\dfrac{-48}{-80}$ to lowest terms using a minimum number of negative signs in the answer.

Practice 3.   Convert $3\dfrac{4}{21}$ to an improper fraction.

Practice 4.   Convert $-7\dfrac{1}{7}$ to an improper fraction.

Practice 5.   Convert $\dfrac{-28}{5}$ to a mixed number.

Practice 6.   Convert $\dfrac{84}{18}$ to a mixed number.

Practice 7.   Compare $\dfrac{11}{12}$ and $\dfrac{13}{15}$ using either the $<$ or the $>$ symbol.

Practice 8.   Compare $-1\dfrac{11}{12}$ and $-1\dfrac{5}{6}$ using either the $<$ or the $>$ symbol.

EXERCISES 3.2

In exercises 1–24, reduce each fraction to lowest terms and write each answer using a minimum number of negative signs.

1. $\dfrac{-24}{42}$
2. $\dfrac{-78}{116}$
3. $\dfrac{32}{-76}$

4. $\dfrac{28}{-150}$
5. $\dfrac{-10}{-154}$
6. $\dfrac{4}{-58}$

7. $\dfrac{123}{-159}$
8. $\dfrac{-124}{-38}$
9. $-\dfrac{-134}{32}$

10. $-\dfrac{76}{-104}$
11. $-\dfrac{-154}{-150}$
12. $-\dfrac{-76}{-150}$

13. $\dfrac{-96}{-172}$
14. $\dfrac{-77}{66}$
15. $\dfrac{-74}{-114}$

16. $-\dfrac{46}{-80}$
17. $-\dfrac{18}{-134}$
18. $-\dfrac{-75}{-130}$

19. $-\dfrac{-205}{-180}$
20. $-\dfrac{-182}{-343}$
21. $\dfrac{-338}{-260}$

22. $\dfrac{195}{-480}$
23. $-\dfrac{-168}{117}$
24. $\dfrac{-165}{-154}$

In exercises 25–44, convert each improper fraction to a mixed number and, if possible, reduce the resulting fractional part.

25. $\dfrac{49}{5}$
26. $\dfrac{38}{4}$
27. $\dfrac{-50}{15}$

28. $\dfrac{54}{-8}$
29. $\dfrac{130}{-40}$
30. $\dfrac{-85}{20}$

31. $\dfrac{-260}{-12}$
32. $\dfrac{-38}{-29}$
33. $-\dfrac{-78}{16}$

34. $-\dfrac{80}{-15}$
35. $-\dfrac{-93}{-12}$
36. $\dfrac{77}{-19}$

37. $-\dfrac{-91}{-13}$
38. $\dfrac{-83}{-23}$
39. $\dfrac{-67}{-13}$

40. $\dfrac{-70}{25}$
41. $-\dfrac{-48}{-17}$
42. $\dfrac{-64}{-19}$

43. $\dfrac{-76}{-5}$
44. $\dfrac{-199}{30}$

In exercises 45–62, convert each mixed number to an improper fraction.

45. $7\dfrac{1}{2}$
46. $8\dfrac{2}{3}$
47. $-9\dfrac{1}{3}$

48. $-16\dfrac{2}{5}$
49. $10\dfrac{3}{4}$
50. $-5\dfrac{3}{7}$

51. $-3\dfrac{5}{9}$ **52.** $-25\dfrac{1}{2}$ **53.** $8\dfrac{9}{13}$

54. $-4\dfrac{3}{29}$ **55.** $5\dfrac{1}{15}$ **56.** $-7\dfrac{3}{8}$

57. $11\dfrac{1}{3}$ **58.** $-12\dfrac{4}{11}$ **59.** $-14\dfrac{1}{7}$

60. $16\dfrac{3}{4}$ **61.** $18\dfrac{3}{5}$ **62.** $-12\dfrac{1}{7}$

In exercises 63–76, write the correct comparison symbol between each pair of fractions. Use only the > or < symbols.

63. $\dfrac{1}{2}$? $-\dfrac{1}{4}$ **64.** $\dfrac{3}{4}$? $\dfrac{4}{7}$ **65.** $\dfrac{-5}{8}$? $\dfrac{-4}{9}$

66. $2\dfrac{5}{13}$? $2\dfrac{5}{12}$ **67.** $2\dfrac{3}{14}$? $\dfrac{5}{-15}$ **68.** $-3\dfrac{2}{7}$? $-3\dfrac{3}{8}$

69. $\dfrac{2}{-13}$? $\dfrac{-3}{12}$ **70.** $\dfrac{16}{-56}$? $\dfrac{-14}{58}$ **71.** $\dfrac{-8}{-21}$? $\dfrac{-3}{-7}$

72. $\dfrac{-5}{-16}$? $\dfrac{-19}{-64}$ **73.** $\dfrac{-9}{31}$? $\dfrac{4}{15}$ **74.** $\dfrac{-20}{-36}$? $1\dfrac{7}{12}$

75. $\dfrac{-55}{80}$? $\dfrac{28}{-41}$ **76.** $1\dfrac{3}{50}$? $-1\dfrac{2}{49}$

Looking Back

77. Describe the difference between using the word *factor* as a noun and a verb.

78. State the divisibility test for 3.

79. State the fundamental theorem of arithmetic.

80. Give an example of the associative law for addition.

81. How do you find the distance between any two points on a number line?

82. Give an example of an undefined operation.

83. What does it mean for two fractions to be equivalent?

PRACTICE-FOR-SUCCESS ANSWERS

1. $\dfrac{1}{4}$ **2.** $-\dfrac{3}{5}$ **3.** $\dfrac{67}{21}$ **4.** $-\dfrac{50}{7}$

5. $-5\dfrac{3}{5}$ **6.** $4\dfrac{2}{3}$ **7.** $\dfrac{11}{12} > \dfrac{13}{15}$ **8.** $-1\dfrac{11}{12} < -1\dfrac{5}{6}$

| 3.3 | **ADDITION OF SIGNED FRACTIONS** |

OBJECTIVES

☐ To find the LCD of two or more signed fractions

☐ To add signed fractions

☐ To add signed mixed numbers

In Chapter 1 we discussed how to perform the four fundamental operations on whole numbers, and in Chapter 2 we discussed how to use them on integers. In the next three sections we will learn how to use them with signed fractions and signed mixed numbers.

Addition of Signed Fractions with Like Denominators

Imagine you have a candy bar that has 8 equal sections. If you eat $\frac{5}{8}$ of the candy bar and then $\frac{1}{8}$ of the candy bar, Figure 3.8 shows that you have eaten $\frac{6}{8}$ or $\frac{3}{4}$ of the candy bar.

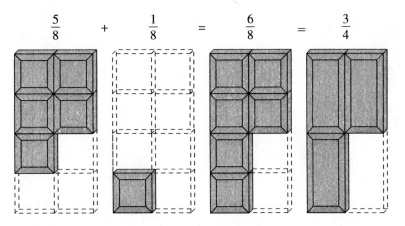

FIGURE 3.8   **Depiction of $\frac{5}{8} + \frac{1}{8} = \frac{6}{8} = \frac{3}{4}$**

Figure 3.8 thus illustrates that signed fractions can be added when the denominators are identical. The sum of the numerators is placed over the common denominator and the resulting fraction is reduced, whenever possible.

Using a, b, and c to represent any integers, except that b cannot equal 0, we can write the rule for addition of signed fractions with like denominators.

ADDING FRACTIONS WITH LIKE DENOMINATORS

$$\frac{a}{b} + \frac{c}{b} = \frac{a+c}{b} \qquad \text{provided } b \neq 0$$

EXAMPLE 1   Add the following signed fractions and reduce the resulting fraction when possible.

$$\textbf{a. } \frac{13}{45} + \frac{22}{45} \qquad \textbf{b. } \frac{-16}{49} + \frac{9}{49}$$

SOLUTION   **a.** $\dfrac{13}{45} + \dfrac{22}{45} = \dfrac{13+22}{45}$ Use the rule $\dfrac{a}{b} + \dfrac{c}{b} = \dfrac{a+c}{b}$.

$\qquad\qquad\quad = \dfrac{35}{45}$ Add the terms in the numerator and place the sum over the common denominator.

$\qquad\qquad\quad = \dfrac{\cancel{5} \cdot 7}{3 \cdot 3 \cdot \cancel{5}}$ Reduce by dividing out common factors.

$\qquad\qquad\quad = \dfrac{7}{3 \cdot 3}$ Multiply the remaining factors.

$\qquad\qquad\quad = \dfrac{7}{9}$

b. $\dfrac{-16}{49} + \dfrac{9}{49} = \dfrac{-16+9}{49}$ Use the rule $\dfrac{a}{b} + \dfrac{c}{b} = \dfrac{a+c}{b}$.

$\qquad\qquad\quad = \dfrac{-7}{49}$ Add the terms in the numerator and place the sum over the common denominator.

$\qquad\qquad\quad = \dfrac{-7 \div 7}{49 \div 7}$ Reduce by dividing the numerator and denominator by the GCF.

$\qquad\qquad\quad = \dfrac{-1}{7} = -\dfrac{1}{7}$ Place the negative sign in front of the fraction bar.

■

Many signed fractions that are to be added do not have the same denominator. Imagine that you have another candy bar and that first you eat $\frac{1}{2}$ of the candy bar and then you eat $\frac{1}{5}$ of it. How much of the candy bar have you eaten?

Using Figure 3.9 it is difficult to visually interpret how much of the candy bar you have eaten because the two depictions are not divided into equally sized sections. When each of the candy bars is divided into 10 equal sections, you can see that $\frac{1}{2}$ is equivalent to $\frac{5}{10}$ and that $\frac{1}{5}$ is equivalent to $\frac{2}{10}$; you have eaten $\frac{5}{10} + \frac{2}{10} = \frac{7}{10}$ of the candy bar (Figure 3.10).

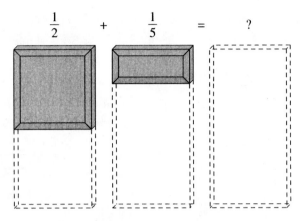

FIGURE 3.9   **Depiction of $\dfrac{1}{2} + \dfrac{1}{5} = ?$**

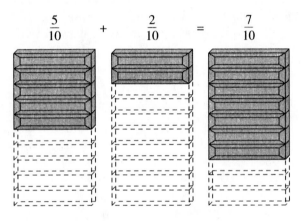

FIGURE 3.10   **Depiction of $\dfrac{1}{2} + \dfrac{1}{5} = \dfrac{5}{10} + \dfrac{2}{10} = \dfrac{7}{10}$**

Finding the Least Common Denominator (LCD)

Figure 3.10 illustrates again that signed fractions can be added when they have common denominators. Any common denominator would be satisfactory to add two signed fractions, but to keep the numbers as small as possible and thus make the calculations easier, the least common denominator (LCD) of the fractions is chosen to be the common denominator. For example, to find the least common denominator of $\dfrac{7}{12}$ and $\dfrac{11}{15}$, the least common multiple of 12 and 15 is determined by the following procedure, first explained in Section 1.7.

Step 1 $12 = 2^2 \cdot 3^1$ Prime factor the denominator of each fraction.
                 $15 = 3^1 \cdot 5^1$

Step 2 $LCM = 2^? \cdot 3^? \cdot 5^?$ Write the prime bases.

Step 3   The exponent above 2 is the only choice, 2.
                 The exponent above 3 is 1 because both prime bases have an exponent of 1.
                 The exponent above 5 is the only choice, 1.

Step 4 $LCM = 2^2 \cdot 3^1 \cdot 5^1$ Place the correct exponents above the prime bases
    $= 4 \cdot 3 \cdot 5$ and simplify.
    $= 12 \cdot 5$
    $= 60$

The least common multiple (LCM) of 12 and 15 is 60, so the least common denominator (LCD) of the signed fractions $\dfrac{7}{12}$ and $\dfrac{9}{10}$ is 60.

FINDING THE LCD OF SIGNED FRACTIONS

To find the least common denominator (LCD) of two or more signed fractions, find the least common multiple (LCM) of their denominators.

EXAMPLE 1

Find the least common denominator (LCD) of the following signed fractions and expand them so they have that same denominator.

a. $\dfrac{-13}{48}$ and $\dfrac{29}{96}$ **b.** $\dfrac{-5}{18}$ and $\dfrac{4}{9}$ and $\dfrac{2}{21}$

SOLUTION   **a.** To find the least common denominator of $\dfrac{-13}{48}$ and $\dfrac{29}{96}$, we first determine the least common multiple of 48 and 96. As $96 = 2 \cdot 48$, 96 is the LCM. When the smaller denominator divides evenly into the larger denominator, the larger denominator is the LCD. Expanding the signed fractions so that they have the same LCD, 96:

$$\frac{-13}{48} = \frac{-13 \cdot 2}{48 \cdot 2} = \frac{-26}{96} \text{ and } \frac{29}{96} = \frac{29}{96}$$

b. $\dfrac{-5}{18}$ and $\dfrac{4}{9}$ and $\dfrac{2}{21}$

To find the least common denominator of $\dfrac{-5}{18}, \dfrac{4}{9}$, and $\dfrac{2}{21}$, we determine the least common multiple of 18, 9, and 21 by finding the prime factors of each denominator.

$$18 = 2^1 \cdot 3^2 \qquad 9 = 3^2 \qquad 21 = 3^1 \cdot 7^1$$

$$LCM = 2^1 \cdot 3^2 \cdot 7^1 = 2 \cdot 9 \cdot 7 = 18 \cdot 7 = 126$$

Next, we show the numbers that make 126 a multiple of each denominator.

$$126 = 18 \cdot 7 \qquad 126 = 9 \cdot 14 \qquad 126 = 21 \cdot 6$$

Finally, we expand the fractions to equivalent fractions with the LCD.

$$\frac{-5}{18} = \frac{-5 \cdot 7}{18 \cdot 7} = \frac{-35}{126}$$
$$\frac{4}{9} = \frac{4 \cdot 14}{9 \cdot 14} = \frac{56}{126}$$
$$\frac{2}{21} = \frac{2 \cdot 6}{21 \cdot 6} = \frac{12}{126}$$

■

Addition of Signed Fractions with Unlike Denominators

Now that we know how to find the LCD of two or more signed fractions, we can add fractions with unlike denominators. For example, to add $\frac{3}{4}$ and $\frac{1}{10}$, first find the LCD. Because the numbers are small we find the LCD, 20, by listing multiples of 10. We then expand both fractions to equivalent fractions having the same denominator, 20. The problem can then be written horizontally as follows.

$$\frac{3}{4} + \frac{1}{10} = \frac{3 \cdot 5}{4 \cdot 5} + \frac{1 \cdot 2}{10 \cdot 2}$$

$$= \frac{15}{20} + \frac{2}{20}$$

$$= \frac{15 + 2}{20} \qquad \text{Use the rule } \frac{a}{b} + \frac{c}{b} = \frac{a + c}{b}.$$

$$= \frac{17}{20} \qquad \begin{array}{l}\text{Add the numerators and place} \\ \text{the sum over the LCD.}\end{array}$$

The distributive law can be used to justify the procedure for adding fractions with unlike denominators. We can see that a common denominator is always required by slightly changing the preceding example.

$$\frac{3}{4} + \frac{1}{10} = \frac{15}{20} + \frac{2}{20}$$

$$= 15 \cdot \frac{1}{20} + 2 \cdot \frac{1}{20} \quad \begin{array}{l}\text{Write } \frac{1}{20} \text{ as a common} \\ \text{factor.}\end{array}$$

$$= (15 + 2) \cdot \frac{1}{20} \quad \begin{array}{l}\text{Apply the distributive} \\ \text{law:} \\ a \cdot c + b \cdot c = (a + b) \cdot c\end{array}$$

$$= 17 \cdot \frac{1}{20}$$

$$= \frac{17}{20}$$

The distributive law cannot be applied to the two fractions $\frac{3}{4}$ and $\frac{1}{10}$ until they are expanded to have the same denominator.

> **ADDING SIGNED FRACTIONS WITH UNLIKE DENOMINATORS**
>
> 1. **Find the least common denominator of the fractions.**
> 2. **Expand the fractions to equivalent fractions that each have the LCD as their denominator.**
> 3. **Add the numerators of the expanded fractions from step 2 and reduce if possible.**
> 4. **If the sum is an improper fraction, it may be converted to a mixed number. However, in algebra, improper fractions are usually acceptable except when the answer is part of a word problem; then a mixed number answer may be more meaningful.**

EXAMPLE 3 Add and reduce the following signed fractions.

$$\textbf{a.}\ \frac{-7}{36} + \frac{-25}{27} \qquad \textbf{b.}\ -\frac{5}{24} + \frac{8}{9}$$

SOLUTION **a.** The least common denominator is found using prime factorizations.

$36 = 2^2 \cdot 3^2$ and $27 = 3^3$. The LCD $= 2^2 \cdot 3^3 = 4 \cdot 27 = 108$.

$$\frac{-7}{36} + \frac{-25}{27} = \frac{-7 \cdot 3}{36 \cdot 3} + \frac{-25 \cdot 4}{27 \cdot 4}$$
Expand the fractions so they have the same denominator, 108.

$$= \frac{-21}{108} + \frac{-100}{108}$$

$$= \frac{-21 + (-100)}{108}$$
Use the rule $\frac{a}{b} + \frac{c}{b} = \frac{a+c}{b}$.

$$= \frac{-121}{108}$$
Add the terms in the numerator.

$$= -\frac{121}{108}$$
Place the negative sign in front of the fraction bar.

b. The least common denominator is found using prime factorizations.

$24 = 2^3 \cdot 3^1 \qquad 9 = 3^2 \qquad$ LCD $= 2^3 \cdot 3^2 = 8 \cdot 9 = 72$

$$\frac{-5}{24} + \frac{8}{9} = \frac{-5 \cdot 3}{24 \cdot 3} + \frac{8 \cdot 8}{9 \cdot 8}$$
Expand the fractions so they have the same denominator, 72.

$$= \frac{-15}{72} + \frac{64}{72}$$

$$= \frac{-15 + 64}{72}$$
Use the rule $\frac{a}{b} + \frac{c}{b} = \frac{a+c}{b}$.

$$= \frac{49}{72}$$
Add the terms in the numerator and place the sum over the LCD. ■

Fractions can be added using a vertical format but in algebra fractions are normally added using a horizontal format; that will be the format used in this book. Signed mixed numbers will be added horizontally as well. To accomplish this, the mixed numbers are converted to improper fractions and the rule $\dfrac{a}{b} + \dfrac{c}{b} = \dfrac{a+c}{b}$ is then used to add them.

EXAMPLE 4	Add the following signed mixed numbers. Convert any improper fraction answers back to mixed numbers.

$$\textbf{a. } 6\frac{1}{2} + \left(-\frac{7}{8}\right) \qquad \textbf{b. } -2\frac{7}{16} + \left(-1\frac{5}{40}\right)$$

SOLUTION

$\textbf{a. } 6\dfrac{1}{2} + \left(-\dfrac{7}{8}\right) = \dfrac{13}{2} + \left(-\dfrac{7}{8}\right)$ Convert $6\dfrac{1}{2}$ to an improper fraction.

$\qquad\qquad = \dfrac{13 \cdot 4}{2 \cdot 4} + \left(-\dfrac{7}{8}\right)$ Expand to fractions with LCD = 8.

$\qquad\qquad = \dfrac{52}{8} + \left(\dfrac{-7}{8}\right)$ Move the negative sign in front of the numerator of the second fraction.

$\qquad\qquad = \dfrac{52 + (-7)}{8}$ Use the rule $\dfrac{a}{b} + \dfrac{c}{b} = \dfrac{a+c}{b}$.

$\qquad\qquad = \dfrac{45}{8}$ Simplify the numerator.

$\textbf{b. } -2\dfrac{7}{16} + \left(-1\dfrac{5}{40}\right) = -\dfrac{39}{16} + \left(-\dfrac{45}{40}\right)$ Change to improper fractions.

$\qquad\qquad = -\dfrac{39 \cdot 5}{16 \cdot 5} + \left(-\dfrac{45 \cdot 2}{40 \cdot 2}\right)$ Expand to fractions with LCD = 80.

$\qquad\qquad = -\dfrac{195}{80} + \left(-\dfrac{90}{80}\right)$

$\qquad\qquad = \dfrac{-195}{80} + \left(\dfrac{-90}{80}\right)$ Place the negative sign in front of the numerator of both fractions.

$\qquad\qquad = \dfrac{-195 + (-90)}{80}$ Use the rule $\dfrac{a}{b} + \dfrac{c}{b} = \dfrac{a+c}{b}$.

$\qquad\qquad = \dfrac{-285}{80}$ Simplify the numerator.

$\qquad\qquad = -\dfrac{57}{16}$ Reduce and leave the sign in front. ■

EXAMPLE 5	Simplify $-\dfrac{13}{28} + 1\dfrac{7}{10} + \dfrac{-11}{14}$.

SOLUTION $-\dfrac{13}{28} + 1\dfrac{7}{10} + \dfrac{-11}{14} = -\dfrac{13}{28} + \dfrac{17}{10} + \dfrac{-11}{14}$ Change the mixed number to an improper fraction.

$$= \dfrac{-13}{28} + \dfrac{17}{10} + \dfrac{-11}{14}$$ Move the negative sign in front of the numerator of the first fraction.

$$= \dfrac{-13 \cdot 5}{28 \cdot 5} + \dfrac{17 \cdot 14}{10 \cdot 14} + \dfrac{-11 \cdot 10}{14 \cdot 10}$$ Expand to fractions with LCD = 140.

$$= \dfrac{-65}{140} + \dfrac{238}{140} + \dfrac{-110}{140}$$

$$= \dfrac{-65 + 238 + (-110)}{140}$$ Add the numerators when all the fractions have the same denominator.

$$= \dfrac{63}{140}$$ Simplify the numerator.

$$= \dfrac{3 \cdot 3 \cdot \cancel{7}}{2 \cdot 2 \cdot 5 \cdot \cancel{7}}$$ Prime factor to reduce.

$$= \dfrac{9}{20}$$ Multiply the remaining factors.   ■

EXAMPLE 6	Oatbrania, Inc. stock opens at $\$17\dfrac{7}{8}$ per share and goes up $\$4\dfrac{1}{2}$ one day on the stock exchange when word spreads about the company's new chocolate-chip oat bran muffin. At what price per share does the stock close?

SOLUTION Because the stock went up in price, add the amount the stock went up to the original price per share.

$$17\dfrac{7}{8} + 4\dfrac{1}{2} = \dfrac{143}{8} + \dfrac{9}{2}$$ Convert to improper fractions.

$$= \dfrac{143}{8} + \dfrac{9 \cdot 4}{2 \cdot 4}$$ Expand the fractions so they have LCD = 8.

$$= \dfrac{143}{8} + \dfrac{36}{8}$$

$$= \dfrac{143 + 36}{8}$$ Use the rule $\dfrac{a}{b} + \dfrac{c}{b} = \dfrac{a + c}{b}$.

$$= \dfrac{179}{8}$$

$$= 22\dfrac{3}{8}$$ Convert improper fractions in a word problem to a mixed number answer.

Oatbrania, Inc. stock closed that day at $\$22\dfrac{3}{8}$ per share.   ■

PRACTICE FOR SUCCESS

Practice 1. Find the least common denominator of $-\dfrac{3}{4}$, $\dfrac{7}{9}$, and $\dfrac{1}{12}$.

Practice 2. Add and reduce, if necessary, $\dfrac{11}{12} + \left(-\dfrac{7}{12}\right)$.

Practice 3. Add and reduce, if necessary, $-\dfrac{1}{12} + \dfrac{8}{45}$.

Practice 4. Add and reduce, if necessary, $4\dfrac{7}{8} + \left(-5\dfrac{1}{10}\right)$.

Practice 5. Simplify $5\dfrac{2}{3} + \left(-4\dfrac{1}{6}\right) + 3\dfrac{1}{10}$.

Practice 6. A baby named Rhonda weighed $7\dfrac{13}{16}$ pounds at birth. When she was weighed 13 months later at the doctor's office, records show she gained $10\dfrac{13}{16}$ pounds. What was Rhonda's weight at 13 months?

EXERCISES 3.3

In exercises 1–22, find the least common denominator (LCD) for each set of fractions. Then convert each fraction to an equivalent fraction with the LCD as the new denominator. Where necessary make each new fraction's denominator a positive number.

1. $\dfrac{1}{2}$ and $\dfrac{2}{3}$ 2. $\dfrac{3}{4}$ and $\dfrac{1}{6}$

3. $\dfrac{-5}{14}$ and $\dfrac{5}{4}$ 4. $\dfrac{7}{-20}$ and $\dfrac{9}{30}$

5. $-\dfrac{85}{66}$ and $\dfrac{17}{4}$ 6. $\dfrac{-9}{-74}$ and $\dfrac{11}{-4}$

7. $-\dfrac{108}{-78}$ and $\dfrac{5}{6}$ 8. $-\dfrac{8}{54}$ and $\dfrac{111}{-108}$

9. $-\dfrac{-21}{-24}$ and $\dfrac{39}{-40}$ 10. $\dfrac{56}{-27}$ and $\dfrac{-11}{18}$

11. $-\dfrac{65}{-24}$ and $\dfrac{-21}{16}$ 12. $\dfrac{-18}{13}$ and $\dfrac{1}{-5}$

13. $-\dfrac{17}{15}$ and $\dfrac{91}{-4}$ 14. $-\dfrac{18}{-5}$ and $\dfrac{-7}{9}$

15. $\dfrac{-75}{18}$ and $\dfrac{19}{-24}$ 16. $\dfrac{5}{-27}$ and $\dfrac{11}{-36}$

17. $-\dfrac{25}{18}$ and $\dfrac{7}{9}$ and $\dfrac{32}{21}$ 18. $\dfrac{-33}{-16}$ and $\dfrac{5}{36}$ and $\dfrac{7}{8}$

19. $-\dfrac{46}{-39}$ and $\dfrac{1}{6}$ and $\dfrac{7}{-13}$ 20. $-\dfrac{19}{-28}$ and $\dfrac{1}{21}$ and $\dfrac{13}{12}$

21. $\dfrac{-75}{-32}$ and $\dfrac{-31}{10}$ and $\dfrac{79}{-80}$ 22. $-\dfrac{-51}{40}$ and $\dfrac{29}{24}$ and $\dfrac{13}{12}$

In exercises 23–44, perform addition of the signed fractions. Reduce when possible.

23. $\dfrac{49}{5} + \dfrac{-7}{15}$ 24. $\dfrac{-8}{17} + \dfrac{9}{5}$

25. $\dfrac{-1}{6} + \dfrac{1}{39}$ 26. $\dfrac{-13}{6} + \dfrac{-11}{10}$

27. $\dfrac{-19}{12} + \dfrac{3}{20}$ 28. $\dfrac{8}{5} + \dfrac{2}{19}$

29. $\dfrac{49}{45} + \dfrac{-1}{12}$ 30. $\dfrac{7}{4} + \dfrac{4}{15}$

31. $\dfrac{-5}{36} + \dfrac{-1}{27}$ 32. $\dfrac{54}{-8} + \dfrac{-7}{15}$

33. $\dfrac{3}{-40} + \dfrac{8}{25}$ 34. $\dfrac{-2}{45} + \dfrac{-11}{10}$

35. $\dfrac{-3}{-10} + \dfrac{3}{32}$ 36. $\dfrac{-1}{63} + \dfrac{3}{5}$

37. $-\dfrac{-7}{58} + \dfrac{-3}{29}$ 38. $-\dfrac{8}{-9} + \dfrac{2}{33}$

39. $-\dfrac{91}{-45} + \dfrac{11}{10}$ 40. $\dfrac{-8}{-21} + \dfrac{1}{18}$

41. $-\dfrac{-11}{-24} + \dfrac{-1}{9}$ 42. $\dfrac{-6}{5} + \dfrac{6}{11}$

43. $\dfrac{-7}{-40} + \dfrac{-9}{50}$ 44. $\dfrac{-99}{32} + \dfrac{-7}{-6}$

In exercises 45–72, perform addition of the fractions and mixed numbers as indicated. Reduce when possible.

45. $5\dfrac{1}{2} + \left(-\dfrac{1}{4}\right)$ 46. $2\dfrac{3}{4} + 3\dfrac{4}{7}$

47. $-1\dfrac{5}{8} + \dfrac{-4}{9}$ 48. $2\dfrac{5}{13} + 1\dfrac{1}{12}$

49. $1\dfrac{5}{28} + \dfrac{9}{-10}$ 50. $-2\dfrac{23}{26} + \left(-\dfrac{1}{39}\right)$

51. $-\dfrac{9}{10} + \dfrac{-3}{55}$ 52. $-\dfrac{7}{16} + \dfrac{-5}{18}$

53. $1\dfrac{7}{42} + \dfrac{-3}{4}$ 54. $\dfrac{-5}{22} + \dfrac{19}{55}$

55. $\dfrac{-7}{6} + 1\dfrac{4}{45}$ 56. $\dfrac{-23}{14} + 2\dfrac{5}{6}$

57. $-\dfrac{55}{6} + \left(-\dfrac{41}{22}\right)$ **58.** $-\dfrac{5}{44} + 1\dfrac{5}{12}$

59. $2\dfrac{14}{30} + \dfrac{-11}{12}$ **60.** $-3\dfrac{13}{20} + \dfrac{-5}{6}$

61. $1\dfrac{1}{15} + \left(-\dfrac{1}{40}\right)$ **62.** $3\dfrac{3}{25} + \dfrac{4}{35}$

63. $4\dfrac{5}{8} + \dfrac{-9}{10}$ **64.** $1\dfrac{3}{14} + \dfrac{-19}{40}$

65. $\dfrac{-3}{28} + 1\dfrac{3}{10} + \dfrac{-3}{14}$ **66.** $\dfrac{16}{13} + \left(-2\dfrac{13}{26}\right) + \dfrac{-1}{39}$

67. $\dfrac{-8}{9} + \dfrac{-5}{18} + 2\dfrac{5}{16}$ **68.** $\dfrac{-5}{4} + \dfrac{-19}{7} + \dfrac{-3}{42}$

69. $\dfrac{-9}{22} + 1\dfrac{4}{55} + \dfrac{-3}{11}$ **70.** $\dfrac{-11}{6} + 2\dfrac{7}{45} + \dfrac{-3}{10}$

71. $\dfrac{-55}{14} + \dfrac{7}{-6} + 3\dfrac{5}{21}$ **72.** $-\dfrac{50}{12} + 1\dfrac{29}{30} + \dfrac{-11}{15}$

In exercises 73–78, perform addition of signed fractions to solve each word problem. Reduce all answers and convert any improper fraction answers to mixed numbers.

73. During a normal 5-day work week, assume you put in the following hours on the days as shown in the table.

Day of the Week	Number of Hours
Monday	$5\dfrac{1}{2}$
Tuesday	$7\dfrac{1}{3}$
Wednesday	$6\dfrac{1}{4}$
Thursday	$7\dfrac{1}{5}$
Friday	$4\dfrac{1}{6}$

What is your total number of hours for the week?

74. A rectangular room in a house measures $24\dfrac{2}{3}$ feet on one side and $18\dfrac{3}{4}$ feet on another side. What is the distance in feet around the perimeter of the room?

75. A housing tract has been subdivided into three lots that consist of $2\dfrac{1}{5}$, $3\dfrac{1}{8}$, and $2\dfrac{5}{6}$ acres each, respectively. How many total acres are in the three lots?

76. A fourth-grade class is taking a bicycle trip that has been divided into three sections that are $1\dfrac{1}{2}$, $1\dfrac{2}{3}$, and $2\dfrac{5}{8}$ miles long, respectively. What is the length in miles of the entire trip?

77. A recipe calls for $2\frac{1}{2}$ cups of rice, $\frac{3}{4}$ cup of olive oil, $\frac{5}{6}$ cup of milk, $\frac{3}{8}$ cup of onions, and $2\frac{1}{4}$ cups of water. How many total cups of ingredients are in this recipe?

78. Three Christmas packages must be shipped from New York to Los Angeles. The first package weighs $3\frac{2}{3}$ pounds, the second package weighs $5\frac{8}{15}$ pounds, and the third package weighs $8\frac{17}{30}$ pounds. What is the total weight of all three packages?

Looking Back

79. Reduce the fraction $\frac{1,870}{4,180}$ by the prime factorization method.

80. Reduce the fraction $\frac{1,547}{3,757}$ by the greatest common factor method.

81. Simplify the following expression to a single signed number.

$$(-2) \cdot [8 + (-2) \cdot \{9 + (-2) \cdot (17 - (-2) \cdot (5 - 11))\}]$$

82. What is the basic operation for the expression in exercise 81?

83. Find the least common multiple of 198 and 270.

84. What power of 2 equals 128?

85. If in a division problem the divisor is 17, the dividend is 1,155, and the quotient is 67, what is the remainder?

PRACTICE-FOR-SUCCESS ANSWERS

1. 36   2. $\frac{1}{3}$ 3. $\frac{17}{180}$ 4. $\frac{-9}{40}$ 5. $4\frac{3}{5}$ 6. $18\frac{5}{8}$ pounds

---

| 3.4 | SUBTRACTION OF SIGNED FRACTIONS |

OBJECTIVES

□ To subtract signed fractions
□ To subtract signed mixed numbers

In this section we will learn to subtract signed fractions and signed mixed numbers.

Subtraction of Signed Fractions with Like Denominators

Imagine you have $\frac{3}{8}$ of a candy bar left to eat and you eat $\frac{1}{8}$ of the candy bar. How much of the candy bar do you have left? Figure 3.11 shows that you have $\frac{2}{8}$, or $\frac{1}{4}$, of the candy bar left. Figure 3.11 also shows that fractions can be subtracted when the denominators are identical. The numerators are subtracted and that difference is placed over the common denominator. The resulting fraction is reduced whenever it is possible to do so.

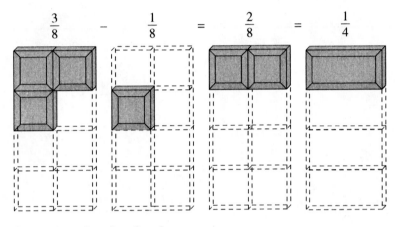

FIGURE 3.11   **Depiction of** $\dfrac{3}{8} - \dfrac{1}{8} = \dfrac{2}{8} = \dfrac{1}{4}$

Sometimes the fractions being subtracted are negative or the second fraction is larger than the first fraction: for example, $\frac{1}{8} - \frac{3}{8}$. This problem can be changed to an addition problem in the same way as was done with integers using the rule $a - b = a + (-b)$.

$$\frac{1}{8} - \frac{3}{8} = \frac{1}{8} + \left(-\frac{3}{8}\right)$$

$$= \frac{1}{8} + \left(\frac{-3}{8}\right) \qquad \text{Write the sign in the numerator.}$$

$$= \frac{1 + (-3)}{8} \qquad \text{Use the rule } \frac{a}{b} + \frac{c}{b} = \frac{a+c}{b}.$$

$$= \frac{-2}{8} \qquad \text{Add the terms in the numerator.}$$

$$= \frac{-2 \div 2}{8 \div 2} \qquad \text{Reduce by dividing by 2.}$$

$$= \frac{-1}{4} = -\frac{1}{4} \qquad \begin{array}{l}\text{Place the negative sign in front of}\\ \text{the fraction bar.}\end{array}$$

Using a, b, and c to represent any integers, except that b cannot equal 0, we can write a rule for subtraction of fractions with like denominators.

SUBTRACTING FRACTIONS WITH LIKE DENOMINATORS

1. **Change the subtraction operation to addition and change the sign of the second fraction.**
2. **Add the fractions using the rule for addition of fractions.**
3. **Reduce the final answer when possible.**

$$\frac{a}{b} - \frac{c}{b} = \frac{a}{b} + \left(-\frac{c}{b}\right) = \frac{a}{b} + \frac{-c}{b} = \frac{a + (-c)}{b} \qquad b \neq 0.$$

EXAMPLE 1

Subtract the following fractions and reduce the resulting fraction when possible.

a. $\dfrac{33}{56} - \dfrac{45}{56}$ b. $-\dfrac{1}{6} - \left(-\dfrac{5}{6}\right)$

SOLUTION   a. $\dfrac{33}{56} - \dfrac{45}{56} = \dfrac{33}{56} + \left(-\dfrac{45}{56}\right)$ Change subtraction to adding the opposite.

$= \dfrac{33}{56} + \dfrac{-45}{56}$ Place the negative sign in the numerator.

$= \dfrac{33 + (-45)}{56}$ Use the rule $\dfrac{a}{b} + \dfrac{c}{b} = \dfrac{a + c}{b}$.

$= \dfrac{-12}{56}$ Add the terms in the numerator.

$= -\dfrac{2 \cdot 2 \cdot 3}{2 \cdot 2 \cdot 2 \cdot 7}$ Reduce using prime factors.

$= -\dfrac{3}{14}$ Simplify.

b. $-\dfrac{1}{6} - \left(-\dfrac{5}{6}\right) = -\dfrac{1}{6} + \left(+\dfrac{5}{6}\right)$ Change subtraction to adding the opposite.

$= \dfrac{-1 + 5}{6}$ Use the rule for adding fractions.

$= \dfrac{4}{6}$ Add the terms in the numerator.

$= \dfrac{2}{3}$ Reduce to lowest terms.   ■

Subtraction of Signed Fractions with Unlike Denominators

When fractions with unlike denominators are subtracted, we still convert the subtraction operation into addition of the opposite. The only modification occurs in the step for adding fractions; before adding, the fractions must be converted to have a common denominator.

EXAMPLE 2   Subtract the following fractions and reduce the resulting fraction when possible.

a. $\dfrac{17}{30} - \dfrac{9}{10}$ **b.** $\dfrac{5}{8} - \left(-\dfrac{11}{15}\right)$

SOLUTION   **a.** $\dfrac{17}{30} - \dfrac{9}{10}$

$\dfrac{17}{30} + \left(-\dfrac{9}{10}\right) = \dfrac{17}{30} + \dfrac{-9}{10}$ Convert subtraction to adding the opposite, and place the sign in the numerator.

$= \dfrac{17}{30} + \dfrac{(-9)\cdot 3}{10 \cdot 3}$ Convert to a common denominator of 30.

$= \dfrac{17}{30} + \dfrac{-27}{30}$ Simplify the products in the second fraction.

$= \dfrac{17 + (-27)}{30}$ Apply the rule for adding fractions with the same denominator.

$= \dfrac{-10}{30}$ Simplify the numerator.

$= -\dfrac{1}{3}$ Reduce the fraction and leave the sign in front.

b. $\dfrac{5}{8} - \left(-\dfrac{11}{15}\right) = \dfrac{5}{8} + \left(+\dfrac{11}{15}\right)$ Change subtraction to adding the opposite.

$= \dfrac{5 \cdot 15}{8 \cdot 15} + \dfrac{11 \cdot 8}{15 \cdot 8}$ Convert to the LCD of 120.

$= \dfrac{75}{120} + \dfrac{88}{120}$ Simplify the products.

$= \dfrac{75 + 88}{120}$ Apply the rule for adding fractions with the same denominator.

$= \dfrac{163}{120}$ Simplify the numerator.   ■

Mixed numbers can also be subtracted by converting them to improper fractions and then using the subtraction rules. For example, the difference $2\dfrac{1}{2} - 1\dfrac{3}{4}$ can be found as follows.

$2\dfrac{1}{2} - 1\dfrac{3}{4} = \dfrac{5}{2} - \dfrac{7}{4}$ Convert the mixed numbers to improper fractions.

$= \dfrac{5}{2} + \left(-\dfrac{7}{4}\right)$ Convert subtraction to adding the opposite.

$= \dfrac{5 \cdot 2}{2 \cdot 2} + \left(\dfrac{-7}{4}\right)$ Change the first fraction to have the common denominator 4.

$$= \frac{10}{4} + \left(\frac{-7}{4}\right) \qquad \text{Simplify the products in the first fraction.}$$

$$= \frac{10 + (-7)}{4} \qquad \text{Add the fractions.}$$

$$= \frac{3}{4} \qquad \text{Simplify.}$$

| **EXAMPLE 3** | Subtract the following mixed numbers. |

$$\textbf{a. } 7 - 5\frac{7}{11} \qquad \textbf{b. } -2\frac{7}{10} - \left(-1\frac{1}{15}\right)$$

SOLUTION   **a.** $7 - 5\dfrac{7}{11} = \dfrac{7}{1} - \dfrac{62}{11}$ Convert to improper fractions.

$$= \frac{7}{1} + \left(-\frac{62}{11}\right) \qquad \text{Change subtraction to adding the opposite.}$$

$$= \frac{7 \cdot 11}{1 \cdot 11} + \frac{-62}{11} \qquad \text{Expand the first fraction to the common denominator.}$$

$$= \frac{77 + (-62)}{11} \qquad \text{Add the fractions.}$$

$$= \frac{15}{11}$$

b. $-2\dfrac{7}{10} - \left(-1\dfrac{1}{15}\right) = -\dfrac{27}{10} - \left(-\dfrac{16}{15}\right)$ Convert the mixed numbers to improper fractions.

$$= -\frac{27}{10} + \left(+\frac{16}{15}\right) \qquad \text{Change subtraction to adding the opposite.}$$

$$= \frac{-27 \cdot 3}{10 \cdot 3} + \frac{16 \cdot 2}{15 \cdot 2} \qquad \text{Expand the fractions to a common denominator.}$$

$$= \frac{-81}{30} + \frac{32}{30} \qquad \text{Simplify the products.}$$

$$= \frac{-81 + 32}{30} \qquad \text{Add the fractions.}$$

$$= -\frac{49}{30} \qquad \text{Simplify.} \qquad ■$$

<table>
<tr><td>**EXAMPLE 4**</td><td>Simplify the expression $3\frac{1}{5} - 2\frac{1}{3} - 5\frac{7}{10}$.</td></tr>
</table>

SOLUTION $\quad 3\frac{1}{5} - 2\frac{1}{3} - 5\frac{7}{10} = \frac{16}{5} - \frac{7}{3} - \frac{57}{10}\qquad$ Convert the mixed numbers to improper fractions.

$$= \frac{16}{5} + \left(-\frac{7}{3}\right) + \left(-\frac{57}{10}\right)\qquad \text{Change subtraction to adding the opposite.}$$

$$= \frac{16 \cdot 6}{5 \cdot 6} + \left(\frac{-7 \cdot 10}{3 \cdot 10}\right) + \left(\frac{-57 \cdot 3}{10 \cdot 3}\right)\qquad \text{Make a common denominator.}$$

$$= \frac{96}{30} + \left(\frac{-70}{30}\right) + \left(\frac{-171}{30}\right)\qquad \text{Simplify the products.}$$

$$= \frac{96 + (-70) + (-171)}{30}\qquad \text{Add the fractions.}$$

$$= \frac{-145}{30}\qquad \text{Simplify the numerator.}$$

$$= -\frac{29}{6}\qquad \text{Reduce the fraction and place the sign in front.}\qquad ■$$

<table>
<tr><td>**EXAMPLE 5**</td><td>In a swim-a-thon Terry swims $2\frac{1}{12}$ miles whereas Annie swims $\frac{5}{18}$ miles. How much farther does Terry swim than Annie?</td></tr>
</table>

SOLUTION Because we want to calculate the difference between the two amounts, we subtract Annie's distance from Terry's. Recall that in a word problem it may be desirable to make the final answer a mixed number.

$$2\frac{1}{12} - \frac{5}{18} = \frac{25}{12} - \frac{5}{18}\qquad \text{Convert to improper fractions.}$$

$$= \frac{25}{12} + \left(-\frac{5}{18}\right)\qquad \text{Change subtraction to adding the opposite.}$$

$$= \frac{25 \cdot 3}{12 \cdot 3} + \frac{-5 \cdot 2}{18 \cdot 2}\qquad \text{Expand to a common denominator.}$$

$$= \frac{75}{36} + \frac{-10}{36}\qquad \text{Simplify the products.}$$

$$= \frac{75 + (-10)}{36}\qquad \text{Add the fractions.}$$

$$= \frac{65}{36}\qquad \text{Simplify.}$$

$$= 1\frac{29}{36}\qquad \text{Convert to a mixed number.}$$

Terry swam $1\frac{29}{36}$ miles more than Annie.   ■

P R A C T I C E   F O R   S U C C E S S

Practice 1. Subtract and reduce, if necessary, $\dfrac{13}{42} - \left(-\dfrac{23}{42}\right)$.

Practice 2. Subtract and reduce, if necessary, $-\dfrac{7}{9} - \left(-\dfrac{25}{33}\right)$.

Practice 3. Subtract and reduce, if necessary, $7\dfrac{1}{4} - 2\dfrac{1}{3}$.

Practice 4. Simplify $1\dfrac{1}{10} - 2\dfrac{5}{12} - \left(-1\dfrac{11}{15}\right)$.

Practice 5. $3\dfrac{3}{4}$ meters of wire is cut from a piece of wire 10 meters long. How long is the remaining piece of wire?

Practice 6. Find the difference between $5\dfrac{8}{9}$ and $2\dfrac{13}{27}$.

EXERCISES 3.4

In exercises 1–30, perform subtraction of the signed fractions. Reduce when possible.

1. $\dfrac{5}{4} - \dfrac{7}{10}$

2. $\dfrac{-3}{8} - \dfrac{8}{5}$

3. $\dfrac{-1}{15} - \dfrac{4}{9}$

4. $\dfrac{3}{10} - \dfrac{-7}{25}$

5. $\dfrac{-19}{6} - \dfrac{-5}{8}$

6. $\dfrac{11}{12} - \dfrac{5}{8}$

7. $\dfrac{7}{20} - \dfrac{-8}{25}$

8. $\dfrac{-7}{9} - \dfrac{5}{21}$

9. $\dfrac{-5}{7} - \dfrac{-5}{28}$

10. $\dfrac{54}{72} - \dfrac{7}{9}$

11. $\dfrac{3}{-80} - \dfrac{9}{10}$

12. $\dfrac{-2}{25} - \dfrac{-11}{10}$

13. $\dfrac{11}{-45} - \dfrac{3}{-10}$

14. $\dfrac{-1}{6} - \dfrac{13}{15}$

15. $-\dfrac{7}{6} - \dfrac{-5}{39}$

16. $-\dfrac{7}{-24} - \dfrac{17}{36}$

17. $-\dfrac{4}{21} - \dfrac{1}{6}$

18. $\dfrac{5}{4} - \dfrac{-21}{26}$

19. $-\dfrac{31}{69} - \dfrac{11}{23}$

20. $\dfrac{-17}{12} - \dfrac{1}{20}$

21. $\dfrac{1}{3} - \dfrac{-29}{40}$

22. $\dfrac{-9}{26} - \dfrac{9}{4}$

23. $\dfrac{-1}{6} - \dfrac{-10}{21}$

24. $\dfrac{-17}{6} - \dfrac{-8}{33}$

25. $\dfrac{-3}{14} - \dfrac{19}{6}$

26. $\dfrac{5}{18} - \dfrac{2}{27}$

27. $\dfrac{49}{14} - \dfrac{14}{49}$

28. $\dfrac{36}{35} - \dfrac{15}{14}$

29. $\dfrac{-36}{55} - \dfrac{-1}{10}$

30. $\dfrac{13}{72} - \dfrac{-7}{15}$

In exercises 31–52, perform subtraction of the fractions and mixed numbers as indicated. Reduce when possible.

31. $2\dfrac{3}{7} - \dfrac{11}{30}$

32. $1\dfrac{2}{45} - \dfrac{9}{10}$

33. $5\dfrac{4}{33} - 2\dfrac{7}{9}$

34. $3\dfrac{1}{15} - 4\dfrac{1}{12}$

35. $-\dfrac{7}{28} - 2\dfrac{5}{12}$

36. $2\dfrac{7}{42} - \dfrac{-3}{14}$

37. $-\dfrac{5}{16} - 1\dfrac{7}{40}$

38. $-\dfrac{7}{10} - 3\dfrac{5}{14}$

39. $-1\dfrac{3}{95} - 2\dfrac{11}{10}$

40. $2\dfrac{1}{45} - 3\dfrac{1}{6}$

41. $-\dfrac{7}{21} - 3\dfrac{1}{12}$

42. $\dfrac{-5}{14} - 5\dfrac{1}{6}$

43. $\dfrac{-11}{-63} - 1\dfrac{1}{6}$

44. $1\dfrac{5}{36} - 2\dfrac{3}{10}$

45. $\dfrac{-1}{28} - 1\dfrac{5}{12}$

46. $\dfrac{-12}{33} - 1\dfrac{1}{22}$

47. $-\dfrac{1}{12} - 1\dfrac{1}{54} - \dfrac{-1}{6}$

48. $\dfrac{-7}{8} - \dfrac{3}{50} - \dfrac{-4}{25}$

49. $\dfrac{-1}{27} - \dfrac{-7}{36} - 1\dfrac{1}{18}$

50. $-\dfrac{13}{30} - 1\dfrac{1}{18} - \dfrac{-11}{10}$

51. $\dfrac{-14}{-51} - \left(-2\dfrac{5}{6}\right) - \dfrac{-4}{17}$

52. $\dfrac{-9}{28} - \dfrac{-17}{6} - 2\dfrac{3}{21}$

In exercises 53–60, perform subtraction of signed fractions to solve each word problem. Reduce when possible and convert any improper fraction answers to mixed numbers.

53. In planning a political campaign poster, a graphics artist must make a border that is $3\dfrac{7}{12}$ inches wide on each side of the poster. If the background cardboard measures $24\dfrac{5}{8}$ inches across, how many inches will be left over for a picture that is to fit in between the side margins?

54. A machinist must cut two pieces from a metal rod that is $87\frac{5}{8}$ inches long. The first piece is to be $15\frac{9}{16}$ inches long and the second should be $17\frac{5}{32}$ inches long. Neglecting the waste material from each cut, how many inches of metal rod will remain after the two pieces are cut from the original rod?

55. If a recipe requires $2\frac{5}{8}$ cups of sugar and you have only $1\frac{2}{3}$ cups left, how many more cups of sugar do you need?

56. If a container that holds a VCR weighs $8\frac{8}{15}$ pounds total, and if the shell of the container weighs only one third of a pound, what does the VCR weigh?

57. If a stock on the Pacific Coast Stock Exchange was trading at $56\frac{5}{8}$ and then the stock dropped $2\frac{1}{3}$ points, what was the new trading value of the stock?

58. If a steak in a meat market weighs $1\frac{7}{16}$ pounds before $\frac{1}{3}$ of a pound of fat is cut off, what is the new weight of the steak?

59. During an earthquake, the supports on a bridge move $3\frac{2}{3}$ inches away from what should be their normal position. The bridge will be declared unsafe if the supports are more than $4\frac{1}{2}$ inches out of alignment. If either an aftershock or another earthquake occurs, what further distance can the bridge move before it is declared unsafe?

60. If you are supposed to work $5\frac{1}{2}$ hours on a job, but you actually work $6\frac{1}{7}$ hours, how many hours of overtime did you work?

Looking Back

61. Given the mixed number $13\frac{51}{75}$, what are the quotient, divisor, dividend, and remainder?

62. Simplify $[127 - (-3)^3] \div 14 + [5 \cdot 2^3]^2$.

63. What is the basic operation for the expression in exercise 62?

64. If a and b represent the coordinates of two points A and B on a number line, of what significance is the expression $|a - b|$?

65. What is the first prime number that is larger than 1,000?

66. Find the LCM and GCF of the three numbers, 375, 625, and 875.

67. Identify which law (distributive, commutative, or associative) justifies the equality between the two expressions:

$$[8 \cdot (5 \cdot 3) + 6 \cdot 9 + 6 \cdot 8] = [8 \cdot (5 \cdot 3) + 6 \cdot (9 + 8)]$$

68. What number is the opposite of the number that lies fifteen units to the left of zero on a number line?

69. Use the distributive law to transform the basic sum $9 \cdot 97 + 9 \cdot 3$ into a basic product.

PRACTICE-FOR-SUCCESS ANSWERS

1. $\dfrac{6}{7}$ **2.** $-\dfrac{2}{99}$ **3.** $4\dfrac{11}{12}$ **4.** $\dfrac{5}{12}$ **5.** $6\dfrac{1}{4}$ meters   **6.** $3\dfrac{11}{27}$

3.5   MULTIPLICATION AND DIVISION OF SIGNED FRACTIONS AND SIGNED MIXED NUMBERS

OBJECTIVES

- ☐ To multiply signed fractions and signed mixed numbers
- ☐ To divide signed fractions and signed mixed numbers
- ☐ To simplify expressions with multiplication and/or division of signed fractions and signed mixed numbers

In this section we will learn to multiply and divide using signed fractions and signed mixed numbers. These operations are easier than addition and subtraction because when we multiply or divide we do not have to find the least common denominator.

Multiplication of Signed Fractions

To justify the multiplication rule for fractions, consider the problem of finding the area of a rectangle that measures $\dfrac{5}{6}$ inches long by $\dfrac{2}{3}$ of an inch wide, as shown in Figure 3.12. The shaded parts of the rectangle show 5 out of 6 parts for the length and 4 out of 6 parts for the width. $\left(\text{Note that } \dfrac{2}{3} = \dfrac{4}{6}.\right)$

To find the area, we multiply the length times the width, which should give the same answer as counting the number of shaded squares.

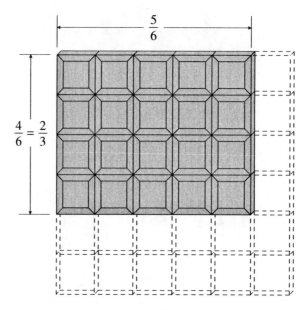

FIGURE 3.12   Depiction of the product of $\dfrac{5}{6} \times \dfrac{2}{3}$

There are 5 shaded squares across and 4 shaded squares down, so there are 20 shaded squares out of a total of 36 squares.

$$\text{Area} = \text{length} \times \text{width} = \frac{5}{6} \times \frac{2}{3} = \frac{20}{36} = \frac{20 \div 4}{36 \div 4} = \frac{5}{9}$$

We arrive at the same answer if we just multiply the numerators and denominators of the two fractions separately and then reduce the resulting fraction.

$$\frac{5}{6} \times \frac{2}{3} = \frac{5 \times 2}{6 \times 3} = \frac{10}{18} = \frac{10 \div 2}{18 \div 2} = \frac{5}{9}$$

By multiplying the numerators of the fractions, we get the numerator of the product, and by multiplying the denominators of the fractions, we get the denominator of the product. Using a, b, c, and d to represent any integers, except that b and d cannot equal 0, the rule for multiplication of signed fractions is written as follows:

MULTIPLICATION OF FRACTIONS

$$\frac{a}{b} \cdot \frac{c}{d} = \frac{a \cdot c}{b \cdot d} \qquad b \neq 0, d \neq 0.$$

EXAMPLE 1 Multiply the signed fractions $\dfrac{2}{5} \cdot \left(-\dfrac{10}{13}\right)$.

SOLUTION Using the rule for multiplication, $\dfrac{a}{b} \cdot \dfrac{c}{d} = \dfrac{a \cdot c}{b \cdot d}$, multiply the numerators and denominators. Then use the rules for multiplication of integers to determine the sign of the product.

$$\frac{2}{5} \cdot \left(-\frac{10}{13}\right) = -\left(\frac{2}{5} \cdot \frac{10}{13}\right)$$
  Because a positive fraction is being multiplied by a negative fraction, the product is negative.

$$= -\frac{20}{65}$$
  Multiply.

$$= -\frac{4}{13}$$ ■

Often, it is more work to multiply the fractions together and then reduce the resulting fraction. For example, find the product of $\dfrac{25}{64}$ and $\dfrac{54}{175}$.

$$\frac{25}{64} \cdot \frac{54}{175} = \frac{25 \cdot 54}{64 \cdot 175} = \frac{1{,}350}{11{,}200}$$

Multiplying the numerators and the denominators of the two fractions results in relatively large numbers. The difficulty in reducing the fraction $\dfrac{1{,}350}{11{,}200}$ is that the numbers to be prime factored are large.

One method that will avoid such large numbers is to first prime factor the numbers in the numerator and denominator that are to be multiplied and then divide out their common factors. The remaining factors in the numerator and the denominator are multiplied to get the product. This alternate method can be done as follows.

$$\frac{25}{64} \cdot \frac{54}{175} = \frac{25 \cdot 54}{64 \cdot 175}$$

$$= \frac{\cancel{5} \cdot \cancel{5} \cdot \cancel{2} \cdot 3 \cdot 3 \cdot 3}{\cancel{2} \cdot 2 \cdot 2 \cdot 2 \cdot 2 \cdot 2 \cdot \cancel{5} \cdot \cancel{5} \cdot 7}$$

$$= \frac{27}{224}$$

Another method depends on the combination of numbers. Since 25 and 175 have a greatest common factor larger than 1 and 54 and 64 also have a greatest common factor larger than 1, we can find the GCF of each pair of numbers.

$$\frac{25}{64} \cdot \frac{54}{175} = \frac{25 \cdot 54}{64 \cdot 175}$$

Factoring 54 and 64 using their greatest common factor, 2, we get $54 = 2 \cdot 27$ and $64 = 2 \cdot 32$. Factoring 25 and 175 using their greatest common factor, 25, we get $25 = 25 \cdot 1$ and $175 = 25 \cdot 7$.

$$\frac{25 \cdot 54}{64 \cdot 175} = \frac{25 \cdot 1 \cdot 2 \cdot 27}{2 \cdot 32 \cdot 25 \cdot 7} = \frac{\cancel{25} \cdot 1 \cdot \cancel{2} \cdot 27}{\cancel{2} \cdot 32 \cdot \cancel{25} \cdot 7} = \frac{27 \cdot 1}{32 \cdot 7} = \frac{27}{224}$$

EXAMPLE 2　Multiply the signed fractions $\dfrac{-7}{24} \cdot \dfrac{36}{49}$.

SOLUTION　We can multiply fractions using prime factorizations.

$$\frac{-7}{24} \cdot \frac{36}{49} = \frac{-7 \cdot 36}{24 \cdot 49}$$ 　　Apply the rule for multiplying fractions.

$$= \frac{-7 \cdot 2 \cdot 2 \cdot 3 \cdot 3}{2 \cdot 2 \cdot 2 \cdot 3 \cdot 7 \cdot 7}$$ 　　Change the numbers into their prime factorizations.

$$= -\frac{\cancel{7} \cdot \cancel{2} \cdot \cancel{2} \cdot \cancel{3} \cdot 3}{\cancel{2} \cdot \cancel{2} \cdot 2 \cdot \cancel{3} \cdot \cancel{7} \cdot 7}$$ 　　Divide out the common prime factors.

$$= -\frac{3}{14}$$ 　　Multiply the remaining factors.

We can also multiply fractions by factoring, using the GCF of 24 and 36 and the GCF of 7 and 49.

$$\frac{-7}{24} \cdot \frac{36}{49} = \frac{-7 \cdot 36}{24 \cdot 49}$$ 　　Apply the rule for multiplying fractions.

$$= -\frac{7 \cdot 3 \cdot 12}{2 \cdot 12 \cdot 7 \cdot 7}$$ 　　Write the numbers as products using 12 and 7, which are the GCFs of 24 and 36, and of 7 and 49.

$$= \frac{-\cancel{7} \cdot 3 \cdot \cancel{12}}{2 \cdot \cancel{12} \cdot \cancel{7} \cdot 7}$$ 　　Divide out the common GCF factors and place the $-$ sign in front.

$$= -\frac{3}{14}$$ 　　Multiply the remaining factors. ■

EXAMPLE 3　Multiply $\dfrac{-8}{11} \cdot \dfrac{23}{56} \cdot \dfrac{-33}{92}$ and reduce if necessary.

SOLUTION　$\dfrac{-8}{11} \cdot \dfrac{23}{56} \cdot \dfrac{-33}{92} = \dfrac{(-8) \cdot 23 \cdot (-33)}{11 \cdot 56 \cdot 92}$ 　　Apply the rule for multiplying fractions, twice.

$$= \frac{8 \cdot 23 \cdot 33}{11 \cdot 56 \cdot 92}$$ 　　Because the expression has an even number of negative signs, the product is positive.

$$= \frac{2 \cdot 2 \cdot 2 \cdot 23 \cdot 3 \cdot 11}{11 \cdot 2 \cdot 2 \cdot 2 \cdot 7 \cdot 2 \cdot 2 \cdot 23}$$ 　　Prime factor each number.

$$= \frac{\cancel{2} \cdot \cancel{2} \cdot \cancel{2} \cdot \cancel{23} \cdot 3 \cdot \cancel{11}}{\cancel{11} \cdot \cancel{2} \cdot \cancel{2} \cdot \cancel{2} \cdot 7 \cdot 2 \cdot 2 \cdot \cancel{23}}$$ 　　Divide out the common prime factors.

$$= \frac{3}{28}$$

The multiplication could also be done by factoring using the greatest common factors.

$$\frac{-8}{11} \cdot \frac{23}{56} \cdot \frac{-33}{92} = \frac{(-8) \cdot 23 \cdot (-33)}{11 \cdot 56 \cdot 92}$$ Apply the rule for multiplying fractions, twice.

$$= \frac{8 \cdot 23 \cdot 33}{11 \cdot 56 \cdot 92}$$ Because the expression has an even number of negative signs, the product is positive.

$$= \frac{8 \cdot 23 \cdot 11 \cdot 3}{11 \cdot 8 \cdot 7 \cdot 23 \cdot 4}$$ Write the numbers as products using 8, 23, and 11, which are the GCFs of 8 and 56, of 23 and 92, and of 33 and 11.

$$= \frac{\not{8} \cdot \not{23} \cdot \not{11} \cdot 3}{\not{11} \cdot \not{8} \cdot 7 \cdot \not{23} \cdot 4}$$ Divide out the common factors.

$$= \frac{3}{28}$$ ■

Multiplication of Signed Mixed Numbers

Sometimes we want to multiply signed mixed numbers and signed fractions together. Imagine you are working 20 hours a week and you are paid $\$7\frac{1}{2}$ per hour. How much money are you making each week? To determine your weekly salary, multiply 20 by $7\frac{1}{2}$.

$$20 \cdot \left(7\frac{1}{2}\right) = \frac{20}{1} \cdot \frac{15}{2}$$ Both numbers are converted to improper fractions.

$$= \frac{20 \cdot 15}{1 \cdot 2}$$ Use the rule $\frac{a}{b} \cdot \frac{c}{d} = \frac{a \cdot c}{b \cdot d}$.

$$= \frac{2 \cdot 10 \cdot 15}{1 \cdot 2}$$ Factor $20 = 2 \cdot 10$.

$$= \frac{\not{2} \cdot 10 \cdot 15}{1 \cdot \not{2}}$$ Divide out the common factor.

$$= \frac{150}{1}$$ Multiply the remaining factors.

$$= 150$$ Convert to an integer.

By converting the mixed numbers to improper fractions and then multiplying, we find that your weekly salary for working 20 hours at $\$7\frac{1}{2}$ per hour would be $150.

When a mixed number is multiplied by another number, the mixed number should be enclosed in parentheses. In the preceding example if we were to write $20 \cdot 7\frac{1}{2}$, it might be misinterpreted to mean that only 7 is being multiplied by 20. The true intention is that both the whole number part, 7, and the fractional part, $\frac{1}{2}$, are to be multiplied by 20. This is best expressed by writing $20 \cdot (7\frac{1}{2})$.

MULTIPLYING SIGNED MIXED NUMBERS

1. **Convert each signed mixed number to an improper fraction.**
2. **Use the rule $\frac{a}{b} \cdot \frac{c}{d} = \frac{a \cdot c}{b \cdot d}$ $b \neq 0, d \neq 0$.**
3. **Reduce when possible.**

EXAMPLE 4   Multiply $(-30) \cdot \left(-\frac{5}{24}\right) \cdot \left(-2\frac{4}{7}\right)$.

SOLUTION $(-30) \cdot \left(-\frac{5}{24}\right) \cdot \left(-2\frac{4}{7}\right) = \left(\frac{-30}{1}\right) \cdot \left(\frac{-5}{24}\right) \cdot \left(\frac{-18}{7}\right)$

Convert to improper fractions.

$= \dfrac{(-30) \cdot (-5) \cdot (-18)}{1 \cdot 24 \cdot 7}$

Apply the rule for multiplying fractions, twice.

$= -\dfrac{30 \cdot 5 \cdot 18}{24 \cdot 7}$

Because the expression has an odd number of negative signs, the product is negative.

$= -\dfrac{2 \cdot 3 \cdot 5 \cdot 5 \cdot 2 \cdot 3 \cdot 3}{2 \cdot 2 \cdot 2 \cdot 3 \cdot 7}$

Prime factor each number.

$= -\dfrac{\cancel{2} \cdot \cancel{3} \cdot 5 \cdot 5 \cdot \cancel{2} \cdot 3 \cdot 3}{\cancel{2} \cdot \cancel{2} \cdot 2 \cdot \cancel{3} \cdot 7}$

Divide out common prime factors.

$= -\dfrac{225}{14}$ Multiply the remaining factors.   ■

Division of Signed Fractions

To explain the rule for division of signed fractions, we first need to include some key mathematical ideas. When we multiply or divide any number by 1, the answer is that number, as expressed in the rules for multiplying and dividing by 1.

MULTIPLYING BY 1

For any number x, $x \cdot 1 = x.$

> ## DIVIDING BY 1
> **For any number x,** $\qquad\qquad \dfrac{x}{1} = x.$

Another important idea concerns multiplying a signed fraction by the same signed fraction but with the numerator and denominator interchanged. For example, $\dfrac{7}{9} \cdot \dfrac{9}{7}$ or $\left(-\dfrac{3}{5}\right) \cdot \left(-\dfrac{5}{3}\right)$.

$$\frac{7}{9} \cdot \frac{9}{7} = \frac{63}{63} = 1 \qquad \left(-\frac{3}{5}\right) \cdot \left(-\frac{5}{3}\right) = +\frac{15}{15} = 1$$

Two numbers whose product is 1 are called **reciprocals** of each other. The reciprocal of $\dfrac{7}{9}$ is $\dfrac{9}{7}$ and the reciprocal of $\dfrac{9}{7}$ is $\dfrac{7}{9}$. Similarly, the reciprocal of $-\dfrac{3}{5}$ is $-\dfrac{5}{3}$ and the reciprocal of $-\dfrac{5}{3}$ is $-\dfrac{3}{5}$. What is the reciprocal of the integer 10? Because $10 = \dfrac{10}{1}$, the reciprocal of 10 is $\dfrac{1}{10}$.

> **DEFINITION** | **RECIPROCAL**
>
> If $x \neq 0$, then the reciprocal of x is the number denoted by $\dfrac{1}{x}$.

In general if x and y are any two nonzero numbers, we say x and y are reciprocals of one another if $x \cdot y = 1$. Since

$$x \cdot \frac{1}{x} = \frac{x}{1} \cdot \frac{1}{x} = \frac{x \cdot 1}{1 \cdot x} = \frac{x}{x} = 1$$

we can not only say that $\dfrac{1}{x}$ is the reciprocal of x, we can also say that the reciprocal of $\dfrac{1}{x}$ is x. Because $\dfrac{a}{b} \cdot \dfrac{b}{a} = 1$, the fractions $\dfrac{a}{b}$ and $\dfrac{b}{a}$ are reciprocals of one another.

> **DEFINITION** | **RECIPROCAL OF A FRACTION**
>
> The reciprocal of $\dfrac{a}{b}$ is $\dfrac{b}{a}$, provided both $a \neq 0$ and $b \neq 0$.

With the mathernatical ideas we've just discussed, we have the tools to demonstrate division of signed numbers. For example:

$$\frac{3}{11} \div \frac{5}{6} = \frac{\dfrac{3}{11}}{\dfrac{5}{6}}$$ Rewrite the division problem using a fraction bar in place of the ÷ symbol.

$$= \frac{\dfrac{3}{11}}{\dfrac{5}{6}} \cdot 1$$ Multiply by 1. (Recall that $x \cdot 1 = x$.)

$$= \frac{\dfrac{3}{11} \cdot \dfrac{6}{5}}{\dfrac{5}{6} \cdot \dfrac{6}{5}}$$ Substitute $\dfrac{\dfrac{6}{5}}{\dfrac{6}{5}}$ for 1. (Recall that any number divided by itself equals 1.)

$$= \frac{\dfrac{3}{11} \cdot \dfrac{6}{5}}{\dfrac{5}{6} \cdot \dfrac{6}{5}}$$ Use the rule $\dfrac{a}{b} \cdot \dfrac{c}{d} = \dfrac{a \cdot c}{b \cdot d}$, with $a = \dfrac{3}{11}$, $b = \dfrac{6}{5}$, $c = \dfrac{5}{6}$, and $d = \dfrac{6}{5}$.

$$= \frac{\dfrac{3}{11} \cdot \dfrac{6}{5}}{1}$$ In the denominator, the product of the reciprocals equals 1.

$$= \frac{3}{11} \cdot \frac{6}{5}$$ Any number divided by 1 equals that number. $\left(\text{Recall that } \dfrac{x}{1} = x.\right)$ We have $x = \dfrac{3}{11} \cdot \dfrac{6}{5}$, therefore; $\dfrac{3}{11} \div \dfrac{5}{6} = \dfrac{3}{11} \cdot \dfrac{6}{5}$.

We have shown that to divide signed fractions we can find the answer by multiplying by the reciprocal of the second fraction. The rule using a, b, c, and d as integers, with none of b, c, or d equal to 0, is expressed in the rule for division of signed fractions.

DIVISION OF SIGNED FRACTIONS

$$\frac{a}{b} \div \frac{c}{d} = \frac{a}{b} \cdot \frac{d}{c} = \frac{a \cdot d}{b \cdot c} \qquad b \neq 0, c \neq 0, d \neq 0.$$

EXAMPLE 5   Divide the following signed fractions and reduce if necessary.

a. $\dfrac{-36}{-51} \div \left(\dfrac{-45}{68}\right)$ b. $-\dfrac{7}{30} \div \dfrac{98}{75}$

SOLUTION   To divide signed fractions, multiply the first fraction by the reciprocal of the second fraction.

a. $\dfrac{-36}{-51} \div \left(\dfrac{-45}{68}\right) = \dfrac{36}{51} \div \left(\dfrac{-45}{68}\right)$ Simplify the signs in the first fraction.

$\qquad = \dfrac{36}{51} \cdot \left(\dfrac{68}{-45}\right)$ Use the rule $\dfrac{a}{b} \div \dfrac{c}{d} = \dfrac{a}{b} \cdot \dfrac{d}{c}$.

$\qquad = \dfrac{36 \cdot 68}{51 \cdot (-45)}$ Use the rule $\dfrac{a}{b} \cdot \dfrac{d}{c} = \dfrac{a \cdot d}{b \cdot c}$.

$\qquad = -\dfrac{9 \cdot 4 \cdot 17 \cdot 4}{17 \cdot 3 \cdot 9 \cdot 5}$ Factor the numbers and write the $-$ sign in front.

$\qquad = -\dfrac{\cancel{9} \cdot 4 \cdot \cancel{17} \cdot 4}{\cancel{17} \cdot 3 \cdot \cancel{9} \cdot 5}$ Divide the common factors.

$\qquad = -\dfrac{16}{15}$

b. $-\dfrac{-7}{30} \div \dfrac{98}{75} = \dfrac{7}{30} \div \dfrac{98}{75}$ Simplify the two negative signs in the first fraction.

$\qquad = \dfrac{7}{30} \cdot \dfrac{75}{98}$ Use the rule $\dfrac{a}{b} \div \dfrac{c}{d} = \dfrac{a}{b} \cdot \dfrac{d}{c}$.

$\qquad = \dfrac{7 \cdot 75}{30 \cdot 98}$ Use the rule $\dfrac{a}{b} \cdot \dfrac{d}{c} = \dfrac{a \cdot d}{b \cdot c}$.

$\qquad = \dfrac{\cancel{7} \cdot \cancel{3} \cdot \cancel{5} \cdot 5}{2 \cdot \cancel{3} \cdot \cancel{5} \cdot 2 \cdot \cancel{7} \cdot 7}$ After prime factoring, divide out the common factors.

$\qquad = \dfrac{5}{28}$ ■

Division of Signed Mixed Numbers

To divide signed mixed numbers, you first need to convert them to improper fractions. The first improper fraction is then multiplied by the reciprocal of the second fraction. For example:

$$\left(-2\dfrac{5}{8}\right) \div \left(2\dfrac{1}{3}\right) = \dfrac{-21}{8} \div \dfrac{7}{3} = \dfrac{-21}{8} \cdot \dfrac{3}{7} = \dfrac{(-21) \cdot 3}{8 \cdot 7} = -\dfrac{3 \cdot \cancel{7} \cdot 3}{8 \cdot \cancel{7}} = -\dfrac{9}{8}$$

DIVIDING SIGNED MIXED NUMBERS

1. **Convert each signed mixed number to an improper fraction.**

2. **Use the rule $\dfrac{a}{b} \div \dfrac{c}{d} = \dfrac{a}{b} \cdot \dfrac{d}{c} = \dfrac{a \cdot d}{b \cdot c}$ provided $b \neq 0, c \neq 0, d \neq 0$.**

3. **When possible, reduce to lowest terms.**

EXAMPLE 6   Divide the signed mixed numbers $\left(8\frac{2}{5}\right) \div \left(-1\frac{3}{4}\right)$.

SOLUTION $\left(8\frac{2}{5}\right) \div \left(-1\frac{3}{4}\right) = \frac{42}{5} \div \left(\frac{-7}{4}\right)$ Convert the mixed numbers to improper fractions.

$$= \frac{42}{5} \cdot \left(\frac{4}{-7}\right)$$ Use the rule $\frac{a}{b} \div \frac{c}{d} = \frac{a}{b} \cdot \frac{d}{c}$.

$$= \frac{42 \cdot 4}{5 \cdot (-7)}$$ Use the rule $\frac{a}{b} \cdot \frac{d}{c} = \frac{a \cdot d}{b \cdot c}$.

$$= -\frac{\cancel{7} \cdot 6 \cdot 4}{5 \cdot \cancel{7}}$$ After factoring using GCFs, divide out the common factors.

$$= -\frac{24}{5}$$ ■

EXAMPLE 7   Simplify the expression $\left(\frac{-50}{-51}\right) \div \left(\frac{-25}{19}\right) \cdot \frac{119}{76}$.

SOLUTION $\left(\frac{-50}{-51}\right) \div \left(\frac{-25}{19}\right) \cdot \frac{119}{76} = \frac{50}{51} \div \left(\frac{-25}{19}\right) \cdot \frac{119}{76}$ Simplify the signs in the first fraction.

$$= \frac{50}{51} \cdot \left(\frac{19}{-25}\right) \cdot \frac{119}{76}$$ Change division to multiplying by the reciprocal.

$$= -\frac{50 \cdot 19 \cdot 119}{51 \cdot 25 \cdot 76}$$ Apply the rule for multiplying fractions, twice.

$$= -\frac{2 \cdot \cancel{5} \cdot \cancel{5} \cdot \cancel{19} \cdot 7 \cdot \cancel{17}}{3 \cdot \cancel{17} \cdot \cancel{5} \cdot \cancel{5} \cdot 2 \cdot 2 \cdot \cancel{19}}$$ Prime factor and then reduce.

$$= -\frac{7}{6}$$ ■

EXAMPLE 8   What is $\frac{2}{3}$ of an hour in minutes?

SOLUTION   Because 1 hour equals 60 minutes, we need to determine what number is $\frac{2}{3}$ of 60. The word *of* in this context indicates the operation to be used is multiplication.

$$\frac{2}{3} \cdot 60 = \frac{2}{3} \cdot \frac{60}{1}$$

$$= \frac{2 \cdot 60}{3 \cdot 1}$$

$$= \frac{2 \cdot \cancel{3} \cdot 20}{\cancel{3} \cdot 1}$$

$$= 40$$

$\frac{2}{3}$ of an hour equals 40 minutes.   ■

Practice 1. Multiply and reduce, if necessary, $\dfrac{13}{7} \cdot \left(-\dfrac{3}{11}\right)$.

Practice 2. Multiply and reduce, if necessary, $\dfrac{-43}{-50} \cdot \left(\dfrac{-125}{129}\right)$.

Practice 3. Multiply and reduce, if necessary, $\left(-6\dfrac{1}{4}\right) \cdot \left(-2\dfrac{2}{5}\right)$.

Practice 4. Divide and reduce, if necessary, $-\dfrac{-14}{29} \div \dfrac{49}{87}$.

Practice 5. Divide and reduce, if necessary, $\left(1\dfrac{45}{95}\right) \div \left(2\dfrac{4}{5}\right)$.

Practice 6. Simplify $\left(\dfrac{-8}{-148}\right) \cdot \left(\dfrac{112}{16}\right) \div \left(\dfrac{-2}{37}\right)$.

Practice 7. Divide $12\dfrac{1}{2}$ into 210.

EXERCISES 3.5

In exercises 1–62, perform the indicated multiplications and divisions. When possible, reduce.

1. $\dfrac{3}{4} \cdot \dfrac{6}{5}$

2. $\dfrac{5}{8} \cdot \dfrac{16}{35}$

3. $\dfrac{-9}{24} \cdot \dfrac{60}{45}$

4. $\dfrac{15}{-28} \cdot \dfrac{49}{30}$

5. $-\dfrac{102}{66} \div \dfrac{17}{4}$

6. $\dfrac{-39}{-74} \div \left(\dfrac{13}{-4}\right)$

7. $-\dfrac{105}{-82} \div \dfrac{5}{6}$

8. $-\dfrac{185}{54} \div \left(\dfrac{50}{-270}\right)$

9. $-\dfrac{-30}{-146} \cdot \left(\dfrac{22}{-2}\right)$

10. $\dfrac{168}{-117} \div \left(\dfrac{-112}{78}\right)$

11. $-\dfrac{36}{-369} \div \dfrac{28}{287}$

12. $\dfrac{-165}{7} \cdot \left(\dfrac{28}{-154}\right)$

13. $-\dfrac{142}{350} \cdot \left(\dfrac{525}{-213}\right)$

14. $-\dfrac{24}{-474} \div \left(\dfrac{-4}{79}\right)$

15. $\dfrac{-144}{171} \div \left(\dfrac{24}{-38}\right)$

16. $\dfrac{66}{-86} \div \left(\dfrac{48}{-36}\right)$

17. $-\dfrac{12}{20} \cdot \dfrac{44}{2} \div \dfrac{30}{25}$

18. $\dfrac{-70}{-9} \div \dfrac{160}{34} \cdot \dfrac{72}{119}$

19. $-\dfrac{5}{-93} \div \dfrac{10}{14} \div \left(\dfrac{21}{-31}\right)$

20. $-\dfrac{15}{-30} \div \dfrac{44}{158} \div \dfrac{79}{33}$

21. $\dfrac{-76}{-14} \div \left(\dfrac{-40}{15}\right) \cdot \left(\dfrac{56}{-21}\right)$

22. $-\dfrac{-2}{21} \div \dfrac{43}{168} \cdot \dfrac{43}{32}$

23. $\dfrac{6}{36} \div \left(\dfrac{-7}{148}\right)$

24. $\dfrac{-132}{3} \cdot \dfrac{22}{48}$

25. $\dfrac{-64}{25} \cdot \dfrac{24}{48}$

26. $\dfrac{-38}{5} \cdot \left(\dfrac{-8}{133}\right)$

27. $\dfrac{-13}{26} \div \dfrac{59}{54}$

28. $\dfrac{65}{91} \div \dfrac{6}{52}$

29. $\dfrac{12}{80} \div \left(\dfrac{-15}{78}\right)$

30. $\dfrac{20}{28} \cdot \dfrac{105}{13}$

31. $\dfrac{6}{108} \cdot \left(\dfrac{-116}{8}\right)$

32. $\dfrac{-70}{12} \cdot \left(\dfrac{-6}{73}\right)$

33. $\dfrac{-12}{80} \div \left(\dfrac{-15}{78}\right)$

34. $\dfrac{10}{-16} \div \left(\dfrac{-2}{9}\right)$

35. $\dfrac{-99}{-27} \div \dfrac{32}{39}$

36. $\dfrac{-9}{49} \div \dfrac{9}{173}$

37. $-\dfrac{4}{-28} \div \dfrac{60}{76}$

38. $\dfrac{3}{-25} \div \dfrac{34}{165}$

39. $-\dfrac{44}{-3} \cdot \dfrac{90}{64}$

40. $\dfrac{-9}{-174} \div \dfrac{1}{13}$

41. $\dfrac{-54}{-28} \div \left(\dfrac{-118}{70}\right)$

42. $\dfrac{-73}{16} \cdot \dfrac{4}{13}$

43. $-\dfrac{-49}{-12} \cdot \left(\dfrac{-2}{42}\right)$

44. $\dfrac{-32}{21} \div \dfrac{20}{56}$

45. $\dfrac{-39}{-45} \div \left(\dfrac{-11}{1}\right)$

46. $\dfrac{-9}{171} \cdot \left(\dfrac{-170}{-16}\right)$

47. $\left(2\dfrac{13}{16}\right) \cdot \left(-\dfrac{4}{12}\right)$

48. $\left(1\dfrac{69}{96}\right) \cdot \left(\dfrac{2}{40}\right)$

49. $\left(14\dfrac{4}{5}\right) \div \left(\dfrac{-2}{84}\right)$

50. $\left(1\dfrac{35}{95}\right) \div \left(1\dfrac{5}{13}\right)$

51. $\left(4\dfrac{1}{3}\right) \div \left(8\dfrac{1}{12}\right)$

52. $\left(\dfrac{26}{-20}\right) \div \left(\dfrac{-2}{90}\right)$

53. $\left(\dfrac{-28}{10}\right) \div \left(4\dfrac{3}{4}\right)$

54. $\left(\dfrac{-49}{-35}\right) \cdot \left(\dfrac{75}{76}\right)$

55. $\left(\dfrac{-68}{80}\right) \cdot \left(\dfrac{-8}{3}\right)$

56. $\dfrac{12}{15} \cdot \left(\dfrac{-39}{114}\right)$

57. $\left(\dfrac{58}{-44}\right) \div \left(\dfrac{102}{17}\right) \cdot \left(\dfrac{-64}{29}\right)$ **58.** $\dfrac{115}{50} \cdot \left(-\dfrac{3}{16}\right) \div \left(\dfrac{-69}{80}\right)$

59. $\left(\dfrac{-96}{-160}\right) \div \left(\dfrac{-23}{19}\right) \cdot \left(\dfrac{230}{104}\right)$ **60.** $\left(\dfrac{35}{-42}\right) \div \left(\dfrac{-56}{38}\right) \cdot \left(\dfrac{-82}{25}\right)$

61. $\left(\dfrac{-11}{24}\right) \div \left(\dfrac{113}{72}\right) \cdot \left(\dfrac{-113}{11}\right)$ **62.** $\left(\dfrac{-8}{-138}\right) \cdot \left(\dfrac{96}{6}\right) \div \left(\dfrac{-8}{23}\right)$

In exercises 63–74 perform multiplication or division with fractions to solve each. Reduce all answers and convert any improper fraction answers to mixed numbers.

63. What is $\dfrac{1}{2}$ of $\dfrac{5}{6}$?   **64.** What is $\dfrac{3}{4}$ of $\dfrac{5}{8}$?

65. What is $\dfrac{17}{5}$ divided by $\dfrac{3}{4}$?   **66.** What is $\dfrac{32}{9}$ divided by $\dfrac{1}{2}$?

67. What is 20 divided by $\dfrac{1}{4}$?   **68.** What number is $\dfrac{2}{3}$ of 60?

69. What number is $\dfrac{3}{5}$ of 95?   **70.** What is $\dfrac{1}{2}$ divided by $\dfrac{1}{2}$?

71. What is $\dfrac{1}{4}$ divided by $\dfrac{1}{4}$?   **72.** What is 8 divided by $\dfrac{1}{2}$?

73. What is $\dfrac{5}{6}$ of $\dfrac{7}{8}$?   **74.** What is $\dfrac{2}{3}$ divided by $\dfrac{15}{9}$?

 Looking Back

75. The word *period* was explained in the discussion about whole numbers. What is a period and how does it relate to the description of a whole number?

76. Write a symbolic formula using variables a and b that shows how to convert a subtraction problem into an addition problem.

77. Is this statement true or false: The absolute value of a number is always positive.

78. Describe a number that is neither positive nor negative.

79. Write the fraction that is the opposite of $\dfrac{4}{5}$ in three different ways.

80. Is this statement true or false: The fraction $\dfrac{5}{-7}$ is an improper fraction.

PRACTICE-FOR-SUCCESS ANSWERS

1. $-\dfrac{39}{77}$ **2.** $-\dfrac{5}{6}$ **3.** 15   **4.** $\dfrac{6}{7}$ **5.** $\dfrac{10}{19}$ **6.** -7 **7.** $16\dfrac{4}{5}$

| 3.6 | **MIXED OPERATIONS AND GROUPING SYMBOLS** |

OBJECTIVES

❑ To simplify expressions with mixed basic operations and grouping symbols
❑ To simplify expressions with exponentiation
❑ To solve word problems using mixed operations and grouping symbols

In this section we will apply all of the skills learned in previous sections of this chapter. We will use the order of operations along with the ability to add, subtract, multiply, and divide signed fractions and signed mixed numbers to simplify various expressions. We will use exponentiation in many of the expressions as well.

EXAMPLE 1   Simplify $\dfrac{-3}{70} + \dfrac{4}{5} \cdot \dfrac{1}{2}$.

SOLUTION   Perform the multiplication before the addition according to the order of operations agreement.

$$\frac{-3}{70} + \frac{4}{5} \cdot \frac{1}{2} = \frac{-3}{70} + \frac{4 \cdot 1}{5 \cdot 2}$$ Multiply the last two fractions.

$$= \frac{-3}{70} + \frac{2}{5}$$ Simplify the product of the fractions.

$$= \frac{-3}{70} + \frac{2 \cdot 14}{5 \cdot 14}$$ Expand the second fraction to the common denominator, 70.

$$= \frac{-3}{70} + \frac{28}{70}$$

$$= \frac{-3 + 28}{70}$$ Add the fractions.

$$= \frac{25}{70}$$

$$= \frac{5}{14}$$ Reduce to lowest terms.   ■

EXAMPLE 2   Simplify $\dfrac{1}{3} - 4 \cdot \left(\dfrac{4}{3} \div \dfrac{8}{39} \right)$.

SOLUTION   To simplify an expression with grouping symbols, perform the operations within the grouping symbols first.

$$\frac{1}{3} - 4 \cdot \left(\frac{4}{3} \div \frac{8}{39}\right) = \frac{1}{3} - 4 \cdot \left(\frac{4}{3} \cdot \frac{39}{8}\right)$$

Change division to multiplying by the reciprocal.

$$= \frac{1}{3} - 4 \cdot \left(\frac{4 \cdot 39}{3 \cdot 8}\right)$$

Apply the rule for multiplying fractions.

$$= \frac{1}{3} - 4 \cdot \left(\frac{\cancel{4} \cdot \cancel{3} \cdot 13}{\cancel{3} \cdot 2 \cdot \cancel{4}}\right)$$

Factor and then reduce.

$$= \frac{1}{3} - \frac{4}{1} \cdot \left(\frac{13}{2}\right)$$

Simplify and convert 4 to an improper fraction, $\frac{4}{1}$.

$$= \frac{1}{3} - \frac{4 \cdot 13}{1 \cdot 2}$$

Multiply the fractions.

$$= \frac{1}{3} - \frac{\cancel{2} \cdot 2 \cdot 13}{\cancel{2}}$$

Factor and then divide the common factors.

$$= \frac{1}{3} - \frac{26}{1}$$

$$= \frac{1}{3} - \frac{26 \cdot 3}{1 \cdot 3}$$

Expand the second fraction so it has LCD = 3.

$$= \frac{1}{3} - \frac{78}{3}$$

$$= \frac{1}{3} + \left(\frac{-78}{3}\right)$$

Change subtraction to adding the opposite.

$$= \frac{1 + (-78)}{3}$$

$$= -\frac{77}{3}$$ ■

EXAMPLE 3   Simplify $\dfrac{11}{16} \div \left(\dfrac{1}{6}\right)^2 - \left(\dfrac{-1}{8}\right)$.

SOLUTION   To simplify an expression with exponents, perform the exponentiation before other operations.

$$\frac{11}{16} \div \left(\frac{1}{6}\right)^2 - \left(\frac{-1}{8}\right) = \frac{11}{16} \div \left(\frac{1}{6} \cdot \frac{1}{6}\right) - \left(\frac{-1}{8}\right)$$

$$= \frac{11}{16} \div \frac{1}{36} - \left(\frac{-1}{8}\right)$$

$$= \frac{11}{16} \cdot \left(\frac{36}{1}\right) - \left(\frac{-1}{8}\right)$$

Use the rule $\dfrac{a}{b} \div \dfrac{c}{d} = \dfrac{a}{b} \cdot \dfrac{d}{c}$.

$$= \frac{11 \cdot 36}{16 \cdot 1} - \left(\frac{-1}{8}\right)$$

Use the rule $\dfrac{a}{b} \cdot \dfrac{c}{d} = \dfrac{a \cdot c}{b \cdot d}$.

$$= \frac{11 \cdot \cancel{4} \cdot 9}{4 \cdot \cancel{4} \cdot 1} - \left(\frac{-1}{8}\right)$$

Factor and then reduce.

$$= \frac{99}{4} - \left(\frac{-1}{8}\right)$$

$$= \frac{99}{4} + \left(\frac{+1}{8}\right) \qquad \text{Change subtraction to adding the opposite.}$$

$$= \frac{99 \cdot 2}{4 \cdot 2} + \frac{1}{8} \qquad \text{Expand the first fraction to make the LCD = 8.}$$

$$= \frac{198}{8} + \frac{1}{8}$$

$$= \frac{198 + 1}{8} \qquad \text{Use the rule } \frac{a}{b} + \frac{c}{b} = \frac{a + c}{b}.$$

$$= \frac{199}{8} \qquad\qquad\qquad\qquad\qquad ■$$

EXAMPLE 4   Simplify $\left(2\frac{1}{4}\right) \div \left(3\frac{1}{2}\right) - \left(1\frac{1}{2}\right)^2 + \frac{5}{7}$.

SOLUTION   To simplify an expression with signed mixed numbers, first convert mixed numbers to improper fractions.

$$\left(2\frac{1}{4}\right) \div \left(3\frac{1}{2}\right) - \left(1\frac{1}{2}\right)^2 + \frac{5}{7} = \frac{9}{4} \div \frac{7}{2} - \left(\frac{3}{2}\right)^2 + \frac{5}{7}$$

$$= \frac{9}{4} \div \frac{7}{2} - \frac{9}{4} + \frac{5}{7}$$

Perform exponentiation first.

$$= \frac{9}{4} \cdot \frac{2}{7} - \frac{9}{4} + \frac{5}{7}$$

Perform division before subtraction or addition.

$$= \frac{9 \cdot 2}{4 \cdot 7} - \frac{9}{4} + \frac{5}{7}$$

Use the rule for multiplying fractions.

$$= \frac{9 \cdot \cancel{2}}{\cancel{2} \cdot 2 \cdot 7} - \frac{9}{4} + \frac{5}{7}$$

Factor and reduce.

$$= \frac{9}{14} + \left(\frac{-9}{4}\right) + \frac{5}{7}$$

Change the subtraction to adding the opposite.

$$= \frac{9 \cdot 2}{14 \cdot 2} + \left(\frac{-9 \cdot 7}{4 \cdot 7}\right) + \frac{5 \cdot 4}{7 \cdot 4}$$

Expand: LCD = 28.

$$= \frac{18}{28} + \left(\frac{-63}{28}\right) + \frac{20}{28}$$

$$= \frac{18 + (-63) + 20}{28}$$

Apply the rule for adding fractions, twice.

$$= -\frac{25}{28}$$ ■

EXAMPLE 5   Simplify $20 \cdot \left[\left(\dfrac{3}{4} - \dfrac{9}{10}\right) \div \left(\dfrac{-1}{5}\right)\right]$.

SOLUTION   In an expression with more than one grouping symbol pair, perform the operation inside the innermost grouping symbol pair first.

$$20 \cdot \left[\left(\frac{3}{4} - \frac{9}{10}\right) \div \left(\frac{-1}{5}\right)\right] = 20 \cdot \left[\left(\frac{3}{4} + \frac{-9}{10}\right) \div \left(\frac{-1}{5}\right)\right]$$

$$= 20 \cdot \left[\left(\frac{3 \cdot 5}{4 \cdot 5} + \frac{-9 \cdot 2}{10 \cdot 2}\right) \div \left(\frac{-1}{5}\right)\right]$$

Expand: LCD = 20.

$$= 20 \cdot \left[\left(\frac{15}{20} + \frac{-18}{20}\right) \div \left(\frac{-1}{5}\right)\right]$$

$$= 20 \cdot \left[\left(\frac{15 + (-18)}{20}\right) \div \left(\frac{-1}{5}\right)\right]$$

Add the fractions.

$$= 20 \cdot \left[\left(\frac{-3}{20}\right) \div \left(\frac{-1}{5}\right)\right]$$

$$= 20 \cdot \left[\left(\frac{-3}{20}\right) \cdot \left(\frac{5}{-1}\right)\right]$$

Change division to multiplying by the reciprocal.

$$= 20 \cdot \left[\frac{3 \cdot 5}{20}\right]$$

Simplify, but do not multiply $3 \cdot 5$.

$$= 3 \cdot 5 = 15$$

Divide the common factor of 20 to simplify.   ■

EXAMPLE 6   Arturo drinks Zip diet cola, which has $\dfrac{5}{6}$ calories per serving, and Zip regular cola, which has 95 calories per serving. One day Arturo drinks 6 servings of both colas. How many more calories does he intake drinking Zip regular cola than he does drinking Zip diet cola that day?

SOLUTION   To determine how many calories Arturo consumes drinking Zip regular cola, multiply 6 times 95. To determine how many calories he consumes drinking Zip diet cola, multiply 6 times $\dfrac{5}{6}$. To find out how many more calories he intakes drinking six servings of the regular cola versus 6 servings of the diet cola, write the expression $6 \cdot 95 - 6 \cdot \dfrac{5}{6}$ and then simplify it.

$$6 \cdot 95 - 6 \cdot \frac{5}{6} = 570 - 5 \qquad \text{Multiply.}$$

$$= 565 \qquad \text{Subtract.}$$

Arturo intakes 565 more calories drinking 6 servings of Zip regular cola than drinking 6 servings of Zip diet cola. ■

PRACTICE FOR SUCCESS

Practice 1. Simplify $\dfrac{3}{10} - \dfrac{2}{5} \cdot \dfrac{5}{6}$.

Practice 2. Simplify $7 \cdot \left(\dfrac{-5}{14}\right) \cdot \left(\dfrac{-1}{3}\right) - \dfrac{11}{12}$.

Practice 3. Simplify $\dfrac{8}{27} - \left(\dfrac{2}{9}\right)^2 \div \left(\dfrac{-1}{18}\right)$.

Practice 4. Simplify $\dfrac{5}{18} - 2\left[2\dfrac{1}{2} - \left(4\dfrac{1}{3} \div 2\dfrac{1}{6}\right)\right]$.

Practice 5. Bonnie rides her bicycle for $3\dfrac{1}{2}$ hours at 20 miles per hour. Rodney rides his bicycle for $4\dfrac{1}{2}$ hours at 15 miles per hour. How many more miles does Bonnie travel than Rodney? (*Hint:* rate × time = distance.)

EXERCISES 3.6

In exercises 1–40, perform the indicated operations and simplify each expression to a single signed fraction. When possible, reduce.

1. $\dfrac{1}{90} + \dfrac{3}{5} \cdot \dfrac{1}{2}$

2. $\dfrac{7}{15} - \dfrac{5}{12} \cdot \dfrac{2}{3}$

3. $\dfrac{5}{9} + \dfrac{-80}{78} \cdot \dfrac{13}{24}$

4. $\dfrac{23}{64} + \dfrac{-21}{6} \cdot \dfrac{9}{96}$

5. $\dfrac{23}{49} - \left(-\dfrac{6}{21}\right) \div \dfrac{7}{62}$

6. $\dfrac{-13}{44} + \left(\dfrac{-27}{-22}\right) \div \left(\dfrac{18}{-19}\right)$

7. $\dfrac{21}{35} \div \dfrac{10}{13} - \left(\dfrac{-7}{10}\right) + \dfrac{6}{25}$

8. $\dfrac{42}{36} - \dfrac{32}{15} + \left(\dfrac{-5}{3}\right) \cdot \dfrac{1}{2}$

9. $\dfrac{40}{25} \cdot \dfrac{22}{28} - \left(\dfrac{-1}{7}\right) - \left(\dfrac{-3}{5}\right)$

10. $\dfrac{21}{9} - \dfrac{46}{14} + \dfrac{8}{1} \div \dfrac{56}{5}$

11. $\dfrac{45}{6} \div \left(-\dfrac{2}{3}\right)^2 \cdot \dfrac{3}{4}$

12. $-\left(\dfrac{-3}{4}\right)^2 \cdot \dfrac{32}{54} + \left(\dfrac{-7}{8}\right)$

13. $-\left(\dfrac{-5}{6}\right)^2 \div \dfrac{5}{18} - \left(\dfrac{-1}{2}\right)$

14. $-\left(\dfrac{2}{3}\right)^3 \div \left(\dfrac{-4}{21}\right) - \left(\dfrac{-5}{9}\right)$

15. $14 \cdot \left[\dfrac{-13}{56} \cdot \dfrac{8}{3}\right] - \dfrac{26}{3}$

16. $\dfrac{1}{2} - 36 \cdot \left(\dfrac{3}{58} \div \dfrac{54}{29}\right)$

17. $-\dfrac{57}{14} \div \dfrac{19}{2} \div \left(\dfrac{-7}{3}\right) + 2$

18. $10 \cdot \left[\dfrac{24}{75} \div \left(\dfrac{-4}{5}\right)^2\right]$

19. $-\dfrac{-9}{8} + \dfrac{5}{12} \div 6$

20. $\left\{\left[-\dfrac{7}{3} + \dfrac{52}{42}\right] \div \dfrac{23}{21}\right\}^5$

21. $8 \div \dfrac{4}{3} \div 16 \cdot \left(\dfrac{56}{-3}\right)$

22. $32 \cdot \left[-\dfrac{-9}{3} - \dfrac{45}{16}\right]$

23. $\left\{\left(\dfrac{-1}{2}\right)^5 \div \left(\dfrac{-7}{152}\right)\right\} \cdot (-10)$

24. $26 \div \left(\dfrac{-104}{3}\right) \cdot \left(\dfrac{-1}{3}\right)^3$

25. $\dfrac{1}{2} \div \left[\dfrac{-33}{24} \div \dfrac{13}{10} \div \dfrac{11}{104}\right]$

26. $\dfrac{56}{43} \cdot \left\{\dfrac{-43}{6} \div \left(\dfrac{-42}{9}\right)\right\}$

27. $9 \cdot \left[\dfrac{-3}{38} \div \dfrac{9}{22} \cdot \dfrac{57}{11}\right]^3$

28. $24 \div \dfrac{-3}{4} + \left(\dfrac{-3}{4}\right)^3 \div \dfrac{3}{32}$

29. $\left(2\dfrac{2}{3}\right)^2 \cdot \dfrac{21}{40} \div \left(\dfrac{-28}{25}\right)$

30. $\left(-2\dfrac{1}{2}\right) \cdot \left(3\dfrac{2}{3}\right) \div \left(2\dfrac{14}{15}\right)$

31. $\left(6\dfrac{1}{8}\right) \div \left(5\dfrac{3}{4}\right) - \left(2\dfrac{1}{2}\right)^2 + \dfrac{1}{2}$

32. $\dfrac{7}{12} - \left[\dfrac{3}{4} - \dfrac{-1}{3}\right]^2 + \left(\dfrac{-3}{2}\right)^2$

33. $\left(8 - 6\dfrac{2}{3} + \dfrac{1}{3}\right)^2 \div \left(\dfrac{-50}{27}\right) \cdot \dfrac{-2}{3}$

34. $\dfrac{-5}{8} \div \left(2\dfrac{5}{8}\right) - \left(\dfrac{-2}{7}\right)^2$

35. $\dfrac{3}{4} + \left(3\dfrac{1}{6}\right) \cdot \left(\dfrac{4}{3}\right)^2 + \dfrac{-5}{8}$

36. $\left(6\dfrac{2}{7}\right) \div \left(2\dfrac{5}{14}\right) - \dfrac{3}{8} + \dfrac{1}{5}$

37. $\dfrac{6}{7} + \dfrac{2}{3} - \left(\dfrac{3}{7}\right) \cdot \left(\dfrac{1}{2}\right)^2 \div \left(1\dfrac{1}{2}\right)^2$

38. $\left(3\dfrac{1}{2}\right) \cdot \left(5\dfrac{1}{3}\right) + \left(\dfrac{5}{12}\right) \div \left(\dfrac{15}{16}\right)$

39. $\dfrac{1}{38} + \left(1\dfrac{2}{19}\right) \cdot \left(1\dfrac{1}{6}\right) \div \left(\dfrac{7}{8}\right)$

40. $\dfrac{3}{4} + \left(4\dfrac{1}{2}\right) \cdot \left(\dfrac{1}{3}\right) \div \left(\dfrac{5}{6}\right)^2$

In exercises 41–54, solve each by first writing an expression that represents the problem. Some exercises may require more than one operation for their solution. Then use the rules for the order of operations to calculate the answer. Reduce all answers and convert any improper fraction answers to mixed numbers.

41. A used car that normally sells for $5,200 has been advertised for a special sale in which the price will be reduced by $\frac{1}{5}$. What is the equivalent dollar value of the reduction amount and what is the final selling price?

42. A case holds 24 cans of a beverage in which each can contains $\frac{7}{8}$ of a liter. How many liters of the beverage are in the entire case?

43. A piece of carpet that is $24\frac{5}{8}$ feet long is to be cut into strips that are $1\frac{1}{3}$ feet long. How many such strips can be made?

44. If $5\frac{1}{3}$ pizzas are to be equally shared among 9 people, what fractional part of a pizza should each person expect to receive?

45. If John's annual income is $32,040 and each year he spends approximately $\frac{4}{15}$ of his annual income on miscellaneous items, what amount does he spend on miscellaneous items in one month?

46. How many square feet are in a window that measures $5\frac{1}{3}$ feet by $2\frac{1}{2}$ feet? (*Hint:* area = length × width.)

47. In a survey of 6,000 workers it was found that $\frac{4}{15}$ of them were absent for 5 or more days during the year due to sickness. How many workers were sufficiently healthy that they missed no more than 4 days in that same year?

48. Finding the average of two numbers requires dividing their sum by the number 2. What is the average of $5\frac{1}{2}$ and $7\frac{1}{3}$?

49. Mary received a gift of $6,000. She put $\frac{1}{4}$ of this gift in a savings account and bought some stocks with $\frac{2}{5}$ of the original gift. The rest she used for the downpayment on a new car. What amount was the downpayment on the car?

50. A swimming pool immediately springs two leaks after an earthquake. The first leak loses $2\frac{1}{18}$ gallons per minute and the second leak loses $3\frac{1}{6}$ gallons per minute. How much water has leaked out of the pool after an hour and a half?

51. Two ocean liners leave the same port at the same time. The first ship traveled at $40\frac{1}{2}$ miles per hour for $6\frac{1}{4}$ hours and then stopped. The second ship traveled at $35\frac{1}{2}$ miles per hour for 8 hours and then stopped. At the end of 8 hours, how many miles apart are the two ships if they travel in the same direction? (*Hint:* distance = rate × time.)

52. Many times in medicine it is desirable to compute the amount of a drug dosage based on body weight. If a wrestler weighs 288 pounds and if the dosage of the medicine he is taking requires $\frac{5}{8}$ of an ounce for each 30 pounds of body weight, how many ounces of that particular drug does he require?

53. A parking lot charges $2 for the first two hours and then charges $\frac{3}{5}$ of a dollar for each additional hour (or fractional part thereof). If a person paid $11 for parking, how many hours was he parked?

54. According to the pay schedule in a hospital, workers are entitled to overtime pay that is $1\frac{1}{2}$ times their normal wage whenever they work more than 40 hours in one week. In addition, workers on the graveyard shift (12 midnight to 8 AM) receive compensation that makes their wage $\frac{6}{5}$ times the regular wage. If the hourly wage for a daytime orderly is $20 and an orderly on the graveyard shift was paid $1,176 in one week, how many hours of overtime did the orderly work that week?

🜂 Looking Back

55. Name one mathematical operation that *cannot* be performed using the number 0.

56. What are the numbers connected by multiplication in the product $3 \cdot 5$ called?

57. Name three different mathematical ideas that are normally expressed using the − symbol.

58. Name two different mathematical ideas that are normally expressed using the + symbol.

59. Characterize the relationship between two integers whose sum is 0.

60. What is the least common multiple of the three numbers 63, 105, and 15?

61. What is the basic operation for the expression
    $[(-10 \div 5 - 16) + 3^3 + 20] \div 2$?

62. Think of the division check as it relates to the equation $322 = 17 \cdot 18 + 16$ and then name the remainder and dividend. Is more than one choice possible for each of the divisor and quotient?

63. Think of the division check as it relates to the conversion of the improper fraction $\frac{68}{15}$ to the mixed number $4\frac{8}{15}$ and then name the dividend, remainder, divisor, and quotient. Is more than one choice possible for each of the divisor and quotient?

PRACTICE-FOR-SUCCESS ANSWERS

1. $-\dfrac{1}{30}$　　2. $-\dfrac{1}{12}$　　3. $1\dfrac{5}{27}$　　4. $-\dfrac{13}{18}$　　5. $2\dfrac{1}{2}$ miles

3.7　COMPLEX FRACTIONS

OBJECTIVES

☐　To recognize a complex fraction

☐　To find the multiplier to simplify a complex fraction

☐　To simplify complex fractions

In this section we will introduce the concept of a complex fraction and explain a technique that can be used to simplify complex fractions.

In addition to the symbol ÷ we can also use the fraction bar to indicate division. Thus, the problem to divide the fraction $\dfrac{2}{3}$ by the fraction $\dfrac{4}{5}$ can be written using two notations.

$$\frac{2}{3} \div \frac{4}{5} = \frac{\dfrac{2}{3}}{\dfrac{4}{5}}$$

The expression to the right of the equal sign is called a **complex fraction.** The longer fraction bar is the dividing line between the numerator and denominator. In a simple fraction the numerator and denominator are single integers, but in a complex fraction, either the numerator, the denominator, or both numerator and denominator may contain other fractions. The numerator of the complex fraction $\dfrac{\dfrac{2}{3}}{\dfrac{4}{5}}$ is the fraction $\dfrac{2}{3}$ and the denominator is the fraction $\dfrac{4}{5}$.

Another example of a complex fraction is the expression

$$\frac{\dfrac{1}{2} + \dfrac{2}{3}}{\dfrac{3}{4} + \dfrac{5}{6}}$$

The numerator of this complex fraction is the sum of two fractions, $\frac{1}{2} + \frac{2}{3}$

and the denominator of the fraction is also a sum of two fractions, $\frac{3}{4} + \frac{5}{6}$.

DEFINITION   **COMPLEX FRACTION**

A fraction is called a complex fraction if either its numerator, or denominator, or both contain other fractions or mixed numbers.

Here are six examples of complex fractions.

$$\frac{3\frac{1}{2}}{5} \qquad\qquad \frac{\frac{1}{2}}{5\frac{5}{6}} \qquad\qquad \frac{-4\frac{3}{7}}{2\frac{1}{4}}$$

$$\frac{\frac{2}{3}}{\frac{5}{7} - \frac{1}{8}} \qquad\qquad \frac{-\frac{9}{10} + \frac{1}{3}}{\frac{5}{13}} \qquad\qquad \frac{3\frac{1}{2} - \frac{1}{5}}{5\frac{1}{8} + 7\frac{1}{2}}$$

We know that the longer fraction bars are another notation for division, and we have already covered the operation of division by fractions as well as addition, subtraction, and multiplication. We now have the ability to simplify any of the preceding complex fractions.

For example, one way to simplify the complex fraction $\dfrac{\frac{1}{2}}{5\frac{5}{6}}$ is to con-

vert the mixed number $5\frac{5}{6}$ in the denominator into the improper fraction $\dfrac{35}{6}$ and then apply the rule for dividing one fraction by another.

$$\frac{\frac{1}{2}}{5\frac{5}{6}} = \frac{\frac{1}{2}}{\frac{35}{6}} = \frac{1}{2} \div \frac{35}{6} = \frac{1}{2} \cdot \frac{6}{35} = \frac{3}{35}$$

Two different methods can be used to simplify the complex fraction

$$\frac{\frac{1}{2} + \frac{2}{3}}{\frac{3}{4} + \frac{5}{6}}$$

One technique is to perform the additions in the numerator and denominator first and then divide the two resulting fractions. Remember we cannot add fractions unless they have the same denominator, so we must first select LCDs. The LCD for the two fractions in the numerator is 6 and the LCD for the two fractions in the denominator is 12. The operations are as follows.

$$\frac{\dfrac{1}{2}+\dfrac{2}{3}}{\dfrac{3}{4}+\dfrac{5}{6}}=\frac{\dfrac{3}{6}+\dfrac{4}{6}}{\dfrac{9}{12}+\dfrac{10}{12}}=\frac{\dfrac{7}{6}}{\dfrac{19}{12}}=\frac{7}{6}\cdot\frac{12}{19}=\frac{14}{19}$$

Although the steps just presented are a straightforward way to simplify the complex fraction, another technique using the principle of multiplying by 1 and the distributive law allows us to arrive at the same answer in only two steps. Rather than work with the fractions two at a time, we can operate on all four fractions by first selecting the LCD for all four of the fractions that make up the entire complex fraction. Since the least common multiple of 2, 3, 4, and 6 is 12, we select 12 as a number with which we can multiply to simplify the complex fraction.

Two properties are very helpful in explaining why we can simplify a complex fraction by multiplying by the LCD. The first property states that multiplying a number by 1 does not change the value of the number.

$$a \cdot 1 = a$$

The second property states that any nonzero number divided by itself equals 1.

$$\frac{b}{b} = 1 \qquad \text{provided } b \neq 0$$

It is how we put these two properties together that makes a useful technique for simplifying complex fractions. If $\dfrac{M}{N}$ represents a complex fraction, and if the number b is the appropriately selected multiplier, then we can simplify the complex fraction by writing

$$\frac{M}{N} = \frac{M}{N} \cdot 1 = \frac{M}{N} \cdot \frac{b}{b} = \frac{M \cdot b}{N \cdot b}$$

SIMPLIFYING A COMPLEX FRACTION

1. **Find the least common denominator (LCD) of all the denominators of the fractions that make up the larger complex fraction.**
2. **Write grouping symbols around the numerator and denominator of the complex fraction.**
3. **Multiply both the numerator and the denominator of the large complex fraction by the LCD number found in step 1.**
4. **Simplify the numerator and denominator products. Apply the distributive law as needed whenever a numerator or denominator is a sum or difference or contains a mixed number.**
5. **Reduce the resulting fraction.**

In the complex fraction $\dfrac{\frac{1}{2}+\frac{2}{3}}{\frac{3}{4}+\frac{5}{6}}$ we have sums in both the numerator

and denominator, so we first place grouping symbols around the numerator and denominator before we multiply them by the number 12.

$$\frac{\frac{1}{2}+\frac{2}{3}}{\frac{3}{4}+\frac{5}{6}}=\frac{\left(\frac{1}{2}+\frac{2}{3}\right)\cdot 12}{\left(\frac{3}{4}+\frac{5}{6}\right)\cdot 12}\qquad\text{Multiply by }1=\frac{12}{12}.$$

$$=\frac{\frac{1}{2}\cdot 12+\frac{2}{3}\cdot 12}{\frac{3}{4}\cdot 12+\frac{5}{6}\cdot 12}\qquad\begin{array}{l}\text{Apply the distributive law twice, once in the numer-}\\\text{ator and once in the denominator.}\end{array}$$

$$=\frac{6+8}{9+10}\qquad\begin{array}{l}\text{Simplify the multiplications with the fractions. This}\\\text{step eliminates all the original fractions.}\end{array}$$

$$=\frac{14}{19}\qquad\text{Simplify.}$$

EXAMPLE 1 For each of the following complex fractions determine the multiplier that can be used to simplify the fraction.

$$\textbf{a.}\ \frac{\frac{3}{8}}{\frac{5}{6}+\frac{1}{3}}\qquad\textbf{b.}\ \frac{3\frac{1}{9}}{\frac{11}{18}-\frac{3}{4}}$$

SOLUTION **a.** $\dfrac{\frac{3}{8}}{\frac{5}{6}+\frac{1}{3}}$ The multiplier is the LCD of the denominators of the three fractions that make up the complex fraction. The LCM of 8, 6, and 3 is 24: the multiplier is 24.

b. $\dfrac{3\frac{1}{9}}{\frac{11}{18}-\frac{3}{4}}$ The multiplier is the LCD of the denominators of the three fractions that make up the complex fraction. The LCM of 9, 18, and 4 is 36: the multiplier is 36. ■

EXAMPLE 2 Simplify each of the following complex fractions by first finding the proper multiplier and then distributing that multiplier across both numerator and denominator, thereby simplifying the complex fraction.

$$\textbf{a.}\ \frac{\frac{1}{10}+\frac{5}{12}}{\frac{11}{20}-\frac{4}{15}}\qquad\textbf{b.}\ \frac{2\frac{4}{9}}{3\frac{11}{15}+2\frac{1}{45}}$$

SOLUTION   **a.** The multiplier is the LCM of the denominators of the four fractions that make up the complex fraction. The LCM of 10, 12, 20, and 15 is 60, so the multiplier is 60.

$$\frac{\dfrac{1}{10}+\dfrac{5}{12}}{\dfrac{11}{20}-\dfrac{4}{15}}=\frac{\left(\dfrac{1}{10}+\dfrac{5}{12}\right)\cdot 60}{\left(\dfrac{11}{20}-\dfrac{4}{15}\right)\cdot 60}$$
Multiply by $\dfrac{60}{60}=1$.

$$=\frac{\dfrac{1}{10}\cdot 60+\dfrac{5}{12}\cdot 60}{\dfrac{11}{20}\cdot 60-\dfrac{4}{15}\cdot 60}$$
Apply the distributive law.

$$=\frac{6+25}{33-16}$$
Simplify the products with the original fractions.

$$=\frac{31}{17}$$
Perform the operations that remain in the fraction.

b. In this part, we show how the distributive law is applied when a mixed number is multiplied by the LCD. The multiplier is the LCM of 9, 15, and 45, which is 45.

$$\frac{2\dfrac{4}{9}}{3\dfrac{11}{15}+2\dfrac{1}{45}}=\frac{\left(2\dfrac{4}{9}\right)\cdot 45}{\left(3\dfrac{11}{15}+2\dfrac{1}{45}\right)\cdot 45}$$
Multiply by $\dfrac{45}{45}=1$.

Apply the distributive law across each sum and across each mixed number.

$$=\frac{2\cdot 45+\dfrac{4}{9}\cdot 45}{3\cdot 45+\dfrac{11}{15}\cdot 45+2\cdot 45+\dfrac{1}{45}\cdot 45}$$

$$=\frac{90+20}{135+33+90+1}$$
Perform the multiplications.

$$=\frac{110}{259}$$
Perform the additions.   ■

EXAMPLE 3

Simplify the complex fraction $\dfrac{2\dfrac{3}{5}}{3\dfrac{4}{25}-5\dfrac{1}{10}}$.

SOLUTION   The multiplier is 50, which is the LCD of 5, 25, and 10.

$$\frac{2\frac{3}{5}}{3\frac{4}{25} - 5\frac{1}{10}} = \frac{\left(2\frac{3}{5}\right) \cdot 50}{\left(3\frac{4}{25} - 5\frac{1}{10}\right) \cdot 50} \qquad \text{Multiply by } \frac{50}{50} = 1.$$

$$= \frac{\left(2\frac{3}{5}\right) \cdot 50}{\left(3\frac{4}{25}\right) \cdot 50 - \left(5\frac{1}{10}\right) \cdot 50}$$

Apply the distributive law but keep parentheses around each mixed number.

$$= \frac{\left(2 \cdot 50 + \frac{3}{5} \cdot 50\right)}{\left(3 \cdot 50 + \frac{4}{25} \cdot 50\right) - \left(5 \cdot 50 + \frac{1}{10} \cdot 50\right)}$$

Because the denominator contains a subtraction, we keep parentheses around the terms being subtracted.

$$= \frac{(100 + 30)}{(150 + 8) - (250 + 5)} \qquad \text{Simplify the products.}$$

$$= \frac{130}{158 - 255} \qquad\qquad \text{Simplify the additions and subtractions.}$$

$$= \frac{130}{-97}$$

$$= -\frac{130}{97} \qquad\qquad \text{Write the negative sign in front of the fraction.} \qquad ■$$

P R A C T I C E   F O R   S U C C E S S

Practice 1. Find the multiplier that will eliminate the two fractions in the complex fraction.

$$\frac{\frac{2}{3}}{\frac{3}{5}}$$

Practice 2. Find the multiplier that will eliminate the two fractions in the complex fraction.

$$\frac{3\frac{1}{6}}{2\frac{4}{9}}$$

Practice 3. Find the multiplier that will eliminate the three fractions in the complex fraction.

$$\frac{\dfrac{1}{5} + \dfrac{3}{4}}{5\dfrac{1}{2}}$$

Practice 4. Simplify the complex fraction.

$$\frac{3\dfrac{3}{8}}{\dfrac{3}{10} - \dfrac{1}{5}}$$

Practice 5. Simplify the complex fraction.

$$\frac{\dfrac{1}{10} + 2\dfrac{1}{12}}{1\dfrac{5}{6}}$$

Practice 6. Simplify the complex fraction.

$$\frac{2\dfrac{3}{8} - 1\dfrac{1}{16}}{3\dfrac{1}{4} - 5\dfrac{1}{2}}$$

EXERCISES 3.7

In exercises 1–34, simplify the complex fractions to single fractions. When possible, reduce.

1. $\dfrac{\dfrac{2}{3}}{\dfrac{3}{4}}$ 2. $\dfrac{\dfrac{5}{8}}{\dfrac{7}{20}}$ 3. $\dfrac{\dfrac{7}{36}}{\dfrac{11}{24}}$

4. $\dfrac{\dfrac{11}{30}}{\dfrac{7}{12}}$ 5. $\dfrac{2\dfrac{1}{3}}{\dfrac{1}{4} + \dfrac{1}{3}}$ 6. $\dfrac{\dfrac{1}{3} - \dfrac{6}{5}}{\dfrac{1}{2} + \dfrac{1}{5}}$

7. $\dfrac{\dfrac{2}{3} + \dfrac{1}{5}}{4\dfrac{1}{2}}$ 8. $\dfrac{-7\dfrac{2}{5}}{-2\dfrac{1}{15}}$ 9. $\dfrac{\dfrac{3}{5} + \dfrac{2}{3}}{\dfrac{5}{6} - \dfrac{2}{5}}$

10. $\dfrac{\dfrac{3}{4} + \dfrac{2}{3}}{\dfrac{51}{6}}$

11. $\dfrac{\dfrac{11}{8}}{1\dfrac{2}{7} - 6}$

12. $\dfrac{\dfrac{1}{6} - \dfrac{2}{3}}{\dfrac{17}{8} - \dfrac{1}{4}}$

13. $\dfrac{\dfrac{3}{20} + \dfrac{1}{30}}{\dfrac{2}{3} - \dfrac{11}{12}}$

14. $\dfrac{\dfrac{39}{10}}{\dfrac{2}{5} + \dfrac{1}{4}}$

15. $\dfrac{\dfrac{7}{4} - \dfrac{5}{9}}{\dfrac{11}{18} + \dfrac{17}{36}}$

16. $\dfrac{\dfrac{17}{4}}{\dfrac{1}{2} - \dfrac{3}{8}}$

17. $\dfrac{\dfrac{7}{100} - \dfrac{28}{50}}{\dfrac{189}{25}}$

18. $\dfrac{\dfrac{2}{3} - \dfrac{5}{6}}{\dfrac{5}{8} - \dfrac{1}{16}}$

19. $\dfrac{\dfrac{4}{15} + \dfrac{6}{25}}{\dfrac{3}{5} + \dfrac{3}{15}}$

20. $\dfrac{2\dfrac{4}{9} + 1\dfrac{1}{18}}{1\dfrac{2}{9} - \dfrac{1}{6}}$

21. $\dfrac{2\dfrac{1}{2} - 7\dfrac{1}{10}}{3\dfrac{5}{8} + 2\dfrac{1}{2}}$

22. $\dfrac{\dfrac{1}{16} + \dfrac{1}{48}}{\dfrac{3}{32} + \dfrac{7}{12}}$

23. $\dfrac{\dfrac{1}{9} + \dfrac{2}{15}}{\dfrac{3}{4} - 4\dfrac{1}{3}}$

24. $\dfrac{2\dfrac{1}{3} + 1\dfrac{5}{6}}{1\dfrac{3}{4} - 3\dfrac{7}{12}}$

25. $\dfrac{\dfrac{1}{4} + \dfrac{2}{5}}{\dfrac{3}{10} - 4\dfrac{1}{5}}$

26. $\dfrac{\dfrac{5}{8} - \dfrac{3}{2}}{4\dfrac{2}{3}}$

27. $\dfrac{\dfrac{2}{18} + \dfrac{32}{27}}{\dfrac{40}{9} - \dfrac{31}{18}}$

28. $\dfrac{\dfrac{5}{36} - \dfrac{5}{18}}{\dfrac{7}{18} - \dfrac{7}{5}}$

29. $\dfrac{\dfrac{1}{24} + \dfrac{5}{9}}{\dfrac{3}{8} - \dfrac{1}{6}}$

30. $\dfrac{\dfrac{5}{6} - \dfrac{11}{42}}{\dfrac{1}{4} + \dfrac{1}{12}}$

31. $\dfrac{2\dfrac{1}{3} - 4\dfrac{5}{9} + \dfrac{5}{6}}{1\dfrac{1}{2} + 3\dfrac{7}{18} - 4\dfrac{2}{3}}$

32. $\dfrac{5\dfrac{1}{10} + 4\dfrac{1}{2}}{\dfrac{3}{4} + \dfrac{7}{10} + \dfrac{1}{5}}$

33. $\dfrac{1\dfrac{1}{5} - 2\dfrac{1}{2} - 3\dfrac{1}{6}}{2\dfrac{1}{3} - 1\dfrac{7}{10} - 3\dfrac{2}{15}}$

34. $\dfrac{2\dfrac{1}{12} - 3\dfrac{5}{8}}{3\dfrac{1}{4} - 1\dfrac{1}{16} - 1\dfrac{3}{4}}$

Looking Back

35. Reduce the fraction $\dfrac{6{,}825}{25{,}935}$ by first finding the prime factorizations of both the numerator and denominator.

36. Do all of the complex fractions in exercises 1-34 have the same basic operation? If yes, what is it?

37. How does the least common multiple of two numbers differ from just any ordinary multiple of those same two numbers?

38. How does the greatest common factor of two numbers differ from just any ordinary common factor of those same two numbers?

39. If it is known that two numbers have the number 1 as their greatest common factor what are the prime numbers that *must* appear in the prime factorizations of both numbers?

40. What fundamental property is used to explain the rule for adding fractions that have the same denominator? (*Hint:* You may wish to use the following equation to help discover the answer.)

$$\frac{4}{11} + \frac{3}{11} = 4 \cdot \frac{1}{11} + 3 \cdot \frac{1}{11}$$

PRACTICE-FOR-SUCCESS ANSWERS

1. The multiplier is 15.

2. The multiplier is 18.

3. The multiplier is 20.

4. $\dfrac{135}{4} = 33\dfrac{3}{4}$

5. $\dfrac{131}{110} = 1\dfrac{21}{110}$

6. $\dfrac{-7}{12}$

SUMMARY

This chapter has laid the foundation for working with fractions, or rational numbers. A rational number is any number that can be written in the form $\dfrac{a}{b}$, where a and b are integers and $b \neq 0$. There are eight standard operations that are performed on fractions: reducing and expanding fractions; converting improper fractions to and from mixed number form; and adding, subtracting, multiplying, and dividing fractions.

To reduce a fraction we can prime factor both its numerator and denominator—for example, $\dfrac{30}{105} = \dfrac{2 \cdot 3 \cdot 5}{3 \cdot 5 \cdot 7} = \dfrac{2}{7}$ after we cancel out the common factors. To expand a fraction, we can multiply both the numerator and denominator by the same nonzero number. For example, to expand the fraction $\dfrac{2}{3}$ to one with a denominator of 57 we can multiply the numerator and denominator by 19. Thus, $\dfrac{2}{3} = \dfrac{2}{3} \cdot 1 = \dfrac{2}{3} \cdot \dfrac{19}{19} = \dfrac{2 \cdot 19}{3 \cdot 19} = \dfrac{38}{57}$. The processes of reducing and expanding fractions are based on two fundamental properties of the number 1. Any number times 1 equals itself and any nonzero number divided by itself equals 1. Symbolically, $x \cdot 1 = x$ and $\dfrac{x}{x} = 1$.

An improper fraction can be converted to a mixed number using a process closely related to the division check—for example, $\dfrac{29}{6} = \dfrac{6 \cdot 4 + 5}{6} = \dfrac{\cancel{6} \cdot 4}{\cancel{6}} + \dfrac{5}{6} = 4 + \dfrac{5}{6} = 4\dfrac{5}{6}$. When 29 is divided by 6, the quotient is 4 and the remainder is 5. Recall that *divisor* $\times$ *quotient* + *remainder* = *dividend*. Therefore, $6 \cdot 4 + 5 = 29$. A form of the division check is also used when we convert a mixed number to an improper fraction—for example, $3\dfrac{2}{7} = \dfrac{7 \cdot 3 + 2}{7} = \dfrac{23}{7}$.

Adding or subtracting fractions requires a common denominator. If fractions have unlike denominators, we use the technique of expanding the fractions to their lowest common denominator (LCD) before adding or subtracting. The LCD is the LCM of the denominators—for example,

$$\frac{7}{12} - \frac{19}{30} = \frac{7 \cdot 5}{12 \cdot 5} - \frac{19 \cdot 2}{30 \cdot 2} = \frac{35}{60} - \frac{38}{60} = \frac{35 - 38}{60} = \frac{-3}{60} = -\frac{1}{20}.$$

To multiply or divide two fractions does not require an LCD. Multiplication is straightforward; division uses the reciprocal concept. To multiply two fractions, multiply their numerators and denominators—for example, $\left(-\dfrac{3}{5}\right) \cdot \left(-\dfrac{45}{18}\right) = \dfrac{3 \cdot 45}{5 \cdot 18} = \dfrac{\cancel{3} \cdot \cancel{3} \cdot 3 \cdot \cancel{5}}{\cancel{5} \cdot 2 \cdot \cancel{3} \cdot \cancel{3}} = \dfrac{3}{2}$. To divide two fractions, multiply the first fraction by the reciprocal of the second. The reciprocal of the fraction $\dfrac{a}{b}$ is the fraction $\dfrac{b}{a}$—for example,

$$\left(-\frac{9}{105}\right) \div \left(-\frac{4}{35}\right) = \left(-\frac{9}{105}\right) \cdot \left(-\frac{35}{4}\right) = \frac{9 \cdot 35}{105 \cdot 4} = \frac{\cancel{3} \cdot 3 \cdot \cancel{5} \cdot \cancel{7}}{\cancel{3} \cdot \cancel{5} \cdot \cancel{7} \cdot 2 \cdot 2} = \frac{3}{4}.$$

A complex fraction is a fraction that contains another fraction in either its numerator, or denominator, or both. Complex fractions can be simplified by expanding the fraction and multiplying by the LCD of all the component fractions. When the numerator or denominator is a sum or a difference, the distributive law can also be applied, as in the following example:

$$\frac{\dfrac{2}{5} + \dfrac{7}{10}}{\dfrac{9}{20} - \dfrac{13}{25}} = \frac{\left(\dfrac{2}{5} + \dfrac{7}{10}\right) \cdot 100}{\left(\dfrac{9}{20} - \dfrac{13}{25}\right) \cdot 100} = \frac{\dfrac{2}{5} \cdot 100 + \dfrac{7}{10} \cdot 100}{\dfrac{9}{20} \cdot 100 - \dfrac{13}{25} \cdot 100} = \frac{40 + 70}{45 - 52} = -\frac{110}{7}$$

CHAPTER 3 REVIEW PROBLEMS

In problems 1–20, find the missing number.

1. $\dfrac{?}{11} = \dfrac{24}{44}$

2. $\dfrac{106}{?} = \dfrac{53}{44}$

3. $\dfrac{34}{29} = \dfrac{?}{116}$

4. $\dfrac{26}{29} = \dfrac{130}{?}$

5. $\dfrac{?}{166} = \dfrac{37}{83}$

6. $\dfrac{55}{?} = \dfrac{165}{21}$

7. $\dfrac{172}{16} = \dfrac{?}{4}$

8. $\dfrac{22}{67} = \dfrac{44}{?}$

9. $\dfrac{?}{170} = \dfrac{32}{85}$

10. $\dfrac{96}{?} = \dfrac{32}{29}$

11. $\dfrac{118}{164} = \dfrac{?}{82}$

12. $\dfrac{4}{13} = \dfrac{48}{?}$

13. $\dfrac{?}{154} = \dfrac{1}{22}$

14. $\dfrac{105}{?} = \dfrac{35}{11}$

15. $\dfrac{69}{111} = \dfrac{?}{37}$

16. $\dfrac{76}{68} = \dfrac{19}{?}$

17. $\dfrac{?}{42} = \dfrac{47}{21}$

18. $\dfrac{38}{?} = \dfrac{19}{84}$

19. $\dfrac{67}{48} = \dfrac{?}{96}$

20. $\dfrac{26}{25} = \dfrac{156}{?}$

In problems 21–40, perform addition or subtraction of the fractions as indicated.

21. $\dfrac{19}{56} + \dfrac{1}{4}$

22. $\dfrac{7}{10} - \dfrac{4}{25}$

23. $\dfrac{23}{36} - \dfrac{7}{24}$

24. $\dfrac{1}{2} + \dfrac{3}{26}$

25. $\dfrac{8}{33} + \dfrac{8}{9}$

26. $\dfrac{8}{45} - \dfrac{13}{30}$

27. $\dfrac{11}{15} - \dfrac{37}{40}$

28. $\dfrac{19}{14} + \dfrac{7}{4}$

29. $\dfrac{31}{26} - \left(\dfrac{-9}{8} \right)$

30. $\dfrac{29}{21} - \dfrac{11}{6}$

31. $2\dfrac{1}{4} - 5\dfrac{5}{38}$

32. $3\dfrac{7}{27} + 2\dfrac{1}{6}$

33. $5\dfrac{5}{13} - \dfrac{7}{5}$

34. $1\dfrac{7}{15} - \dfrac{31}{25}$

35. $\dfrac{17}{15} + \left(-7\dfrac{1}{8} \right)$

36. $3\dfrac{15}{22} + \left(\dfrac{-17}{6} \right)$

37. $\dfrac{1}{6} - 4\dfrac{1}{57}$

38. $\dfrac{16}{9} - \dfrac{18}{39}$

39. $2\dfrac{5}{6} - 1\dfrac{29}{63}$

40. $3\dfrac{7}{12} - 8\dfrac{10}{33}$

In problems 41–60, perform multiplication or division of the fractions as indicated.

41. $\dfrac{21}{10} \cdot \dfrac{1}{12}$

42. $\dfrac{6}{32} \div \dfrac{22}{28}$

43. $\dfrac{21}{86} \div \left(\dfrac{-6}{12}\right)$

44. $\dfrac{-1}{60} \div \dfrac{6}{5}$

45. $\dfrac{-16}{72} \div \left(\dfrac{-17}{15}\right)$

46. $\dfrac{-4}{10} \cdot \left(\dfrac{-4}{44}\right)$

47. $\dfrac{2}{21} \div \left(\dfrac{-7}{18}\right)$

48. $\dfrac{3}{14} \div \dfrac{18}{69}$

49. $\dfrac{5}{13} \cdot \left(\dfrac{12}{-30}\right)$

50. $\dfrac{-4}{26} \div \dfrac{7}{84}$

51. $\dfrac{-4}{63} \div \left(\dfrac{-8}{30}\right)$

52. $\dfrac{17}{60} \div \left(\dfrac{-18}{30}\right)$

53. $\left(18\dfrac{2}{3}\right) \div \dfrac{2}{9}$

54. $\dfrac{10}{32} \cdot \left(3\dfrac{4}{7}\right)$

55. $\left(2\dfrac{2}{11}\right) \div \left(3\dfrac{19}{44}\right)$

56. $\left(5\dfrac{1}{8}\right) \cdot \left(6\dfrac{7}{12}\right)$

57. $\dfrac{25}{6} \div \left(-7\dfrac{1}{9}\right)$

58. $\left(8\dfrac{1}{15}\right) \div \left(6\dfrac{2}{3}\right)$

59. $\left(-6\dfrac{1}{20}\right) \div \dfrac{11}{25}$

60. $\left(4\dfrac{5}{9}\right) \div \left(-8\dfrac{2}{27}\right)$

In problems 61–76, perform the indicated operations and simplify each expression to a single number. If your answer is a fraction it should be reduced.

61. $\left(\dfrac{4}{3}\right)^2 - \dfrac{16}{15}$

62. $\dfrac{\dfrac{30}{9} - \dfrac{9}{12}}{\dfrac{33}{9} + \dfrac{20}{2}}$

63. $\dfrac{27}{14} - \dfrac{21}{8} \div \dfrac{28}{16}$

64. $\dfrac{5}{8} + (-7) \cdot \left[\dfrac{9}{14} - \dfrac{5}{6}\right]^2$

65. $\dfrac{-2\dfrac{1}{24}}{\dfrac{11}{9} + \dfrac{1}{6}}$

66. $\dfrac{39}{60} \div \left(\dfrac{-23}{6} \div \dfrac{46}{13}\right)$

67. $\left(\dfrac{\dfrac{7}{8} - \dfrac{4}{9}}{\dfrac{7}{24} - \dfrac{1}{2}}\right)^2$

68. $4\dfrac{5}{9} - \left(\dfrac{1}{18}\right) \cdot \left[\dfrac{5}{2} + \dfrac{7}{14}\right]^2$

69. $\dfrac{\dfrac{21}{10} - \dfrac{38}{20}}{\dfrac{35}{10} + \dfrac{7}{2}}$

70. $\left\{ \left[\left(\dfrac{5}{8} \cdot \dfrac{2}{3} + \dfrac{1}{2} \right) \cdot \dfrac{2}{3} + \dfrac{5}{6} \right] \cdot \dfrac{2}{3} + \dfrac{1}{9} \right\} \cdot \dfrac{2}{3}$

71. $\left\{ \left[\left(\dfrac{7}{8} \cdot \dfrac{3}{4} + \dfrac{5}{32} \right) \cdot \dfrac{3}{4} + \dfrac{7}{64} \right] \cdot \dfrac{3}{4} + \dfrac{5}{128} \right\} \cdot \dfrac{3}{4}$

72. $5\dfrac{5}{6} - \dfrac{7}{20} \cdot \left[3\dfrac{1}{2} - \dfrac{71}{10} \right]^2$

73. $\left[6\dfrac{2}{3} - \left(3\dfrac{1}{8} \right) \cdot \left(2\dfrac{2}{5} \right) \right] \cdot \left(2\dfrac{1}{4} \right)^2$

74. $\dfrac{\dfrac{1}{2\dfrac{18}{35}}}{\left(\dfrac{5}{8} \right)^2 - \dfrac{15}{16}}$

75. $\dfrac{\left(3\dfrac{1}{6} \right)^2 - \dfrac{4}{9}}{\left(\dfrac{2}{3} \right)^2 + \left(\dfrac{5}{6} \right)^2}$

76. $\left\{ \left[\left(\dfrac{9}{10} - \dfrac{4}{5} \right) \cdot \dfrac{5}{4} + \dfrac{3}{8} \right] \cdot \dfrac{5}{4} + \dfrac{7}{16} \right\} \cdot \dfrac{5}{4}$

In problems 77–96, solve by first writing an expression that represents the problem. Then simplify your expression to a single number. If your answer is a fraction, it should be reduced.

77. Six and thirteen forty-fifths divided by the sum of four-ninths and two and seven-tenths.

78. Two and six thirty-fourths times the difference between seventeen-fourths and six and three-eighths.

79. Negative five subtract the product of negative three and one-half with the sum of fourteen-thirds and negative two.

80. One-half cubed divided by the quantity one-fourth to the fifth power.

81. The square of the difference between one-third and one-sixth all divided by the square of the sum of one-third and one-half.

82. The square of the difference between two-thirds and one-fourth all divided by the square of the difference between three-fourths and the quotient of one-half by four.

83. The difference between three-eighths and one-fourth all divided by the product of one-half with one-fourth.

84. How far can you travel on $10\frac{5}{6}$ gallons of gasoline if you are driving a car that averages $22\frac{1}{2}$ miles per gallon?

85. How long will it take you to drive 264 miles if you average $5\frac{1}{2}$ miles every 6 minutes?

86. If water weighs $62\frac{1}{2}$ pounds per cubic foot, how many cubic feet of water occupy a volume that weighs 1,525 pounds?

87. If Alison can run $5\frac{1}{4}$ miles in $32\frac{1}{2}$ minutes, how far would she run if she kept the same pace for an hour and a half?

88. A housing developer has a tract of land that occupies $10\frac{2}{3}$ acres. She plans on subdividing this land into $\frac{1}{3}$ acre lots. If she is also required to allow $\frac{3}{8}$ of the total land to be used for roads and a small park, how many lots will there be?

89. A model railroad builder is planning to build a small model bridge based on the size of a real bridge. If the scale the builder uses indicates that 25 feet will correspond to $1\frac{2}{3}$ inches, how tall will the model be if the actual bridge is 234 feet high?

90. On a map a distance of 75 miles is represented by $1\frac{3}{4}$ inches. How many miles are represented by $4\frac{5}{8}$ inches?

91. An estate worth $220,000 is to be divided among five heirs. The first heir is to receive $\frac{1}{8}$ of the total, the second heir is to receive $\frac{1}{5}$ of the total, the third heir should get $\frac{3}{16}$ of the total, and the fourth heir is to receive $\frac{1}{2}$ of the total of the first three heirs. The fifth heir is to receive whatever is left over after the first four heirs get their shares. The fifth heir is the second biggest winner in all of this but has to calculate his share as well as the shares of everyone else. How much money should the fifth heir expect to receive?

92. A water-bottling company fills empty bottles that weigh $1\frac{1}{4}$ ounces with $50\frac{7}{10}$ ounces of water each. A cap that weighs $\frac{1}{20}$ an ounce is screwed on top and seals each bottle. Twelve such bottles are packed in a cardboard case that weighs approximately $6\frac{1}{2}$ ounces. The cardboard cases are fastened shut with six large staples that weigh $\frac{1}{3}$ ounce each. Thirty such cases are placed on a shipping pallette. What is the total weight of the freight on ten such pallettes?

93. A gambler currently has $500. He loses half of the amount he currently has, then he gains back one third of the amount he currently has. Then he loses one third of what he currently has; then he gains back one eighth of what he currently has. On his final bet he risks everything he currently has and luckily wins, doubling his current amount. What fractional part of the original $500 does the gambler end up with?

94. If you want to frame a rectangular picture that measures $15\frac{1}{2}$ inches by $18\frac{3}{4}$ inches and you have $150\frac{5}{8}$ inches of framing material, how many inches of framing material do you have to spare?

95. A bouncing ball is such that it bounces back up half the height from which it has just fallen. If this ball is dropped from a height of 4 feet, how far has the ball traveled when it strikes the ground for the sixth time? (*Hint:* Draw a picture.)

96. If $1\frac{1}{2}$ teenagers can eat $1\frac{1}{2}$ pizzas in $1\frac{1}{2}$ minutes, how long will it take a dozen teenagers to eat a dozen pizzas? (*Hint:* First, determine how long it takes 3 teenagers to eat $1\frac{1}{2}$ pizzas. Then determine how long it takes 3 teenagers to eat 3 pizzas. Then determine how long it takes 12 teenagers to eat 3 pizzas, and finally determine how long it takes 12 teenagers to eat 12 pizzas.)

CHAPTER 3 PRACTICE TEST

In problems 1–6, reduce each fraction to lowest terms.

1. $\frac{36}{76}$ 2. $\frac{54}{57}$

3. $\frac{26}{78}$ 4. $\frac{136}{160}$

5. $\frac{68}{102}$ 6. $\frac{99}{108}$

In problems 7–12, expand or reduce each fraction to an equivalent fraction that has the given value for either the numerator or denominator.

7. $\frac{23}{17}$ numerator = 69   8. $\frac{159}{45}$ denominator = 15

9. $\dfrac{17}{6}$ denominator = 48   **10.** $\dfrac{3}{5}$ numerator = 60

11. $\dfrac{59}{48}$ numerator = 118   **12.** $\dfrac{5}{14}$ denominator = 42

In problems 13–18, find the value of the missing number.

13. $\dfrac{?}{39} = \dfrac{46}{13}$

14. $\dfrac{166}{?} = \dfrac{83}{51}$

15. $\dfrac{45}{21} = \dfrac{?}{7}$

16. $\dfrac{51}{90} = \dfrac{17}{?}$

17. $\dfrac{?}{121} = \dfrac{14}{11}$

18. $\dfrac{10}{23} = \dfrac{70}{?}$

19. Convert the mixed number $-3\dfrac{5}{18}$ to an improper fraction that is completely reduced.

20. Convert the improper fraction $\dfrac{-132}{24}$ to a mixed number with a reduced fractional part.

In problems 21–26, perform the indicated operations and simplify each expression to a single number. Reduce when possible.

21. $2\dfrac{1}{6} - \dfrac{18}{30}$

22. $\left(\dfrac{2}{3}\right)^3 - 2\dfrac{1}{6}$

23. $\dfrac{1}{2} \cdot \left[6\dfrac{1}{2} - 3\dfrac{2}{3}\right]$

24. $\left(2\dfrac{3}{4}\right) \div \left(-4\dfrac{1}{8}\right) \cdot \left(3\dfrac{1}{2}\right)$

25. $\dfrac{5}{8} \div \left(3\dfrac{3}{4}\right) - \left(\dfrac{5}{6}\right)^2$

26. $36 \cdot \left[-\dfrac{2}{5} - \left(\dfrac{-7}{6}\right) + 3\dfrac{8}{15}\right] \div \dfrac{3}{2}$

In problems 27 and 28, simplify the complex fractions.

27. $\dfrac{-2\dfrac{1}{15}}{\dfrac{7}{30} - 3\dfrac{3}{4}}$

28. $\dfrac{\dfrac{1}{18} - \dfrac{1}{10} + \dfrac{7}{9}}{\dfrac{7}{6} + 2\dfrac{11}{30}}$

In problems 29–32, write an expression corresponding to the given description. Then simplify your expression to a single number and reduce when possible. If a reduced fraction answer is improper, it should be converted to a mixed number.

29. It is $102\dfrac{3}{4}$ miles from a family's regular residence to their vacation cabin in the mountains. If they make 8 round trips per year to the cabin, what is the total accumulated mileage?

30. The formula that allows one to convert degrees Celsius to degrees Fahrenheit states: Multiply the number of degrees Celsius by $\frac{9}{5}$ and then add 32 to that result. How many degrees Fahrenheit are equivalent to 60 degrees Celsius?

31. To say 52 weeks equals 1 year is equivalent to saying a week is $\frac{1}{52}$ of 1 year. Also assume a month is equivalent to $4\frac{3}{10}$ weeks. How many fractional parts of 1 year are in 2 months and 3 weeks?

32. The area of a circle is known to be the number pi, written as π, times the square of the radius.

$$\text{Area} = \pi \cdot \text{radius}^2$$

If the number π is replaced by the fraction $\frac{22}{7}$ and if the radius is $5\frac{1}{4}$ feet, then the following formula will yield the area.

$$\text{Area} = \frac{22}{7} \cdot \left(5\frac{1}{4}\right)^2$$

Find the area as a reduced fraction.

CHAPTER FOUR

DECIMALS

This chapter focuses on numbers in decimal notation, the most frequently used way to write numbers. All calculators both display and calculate using numbers in decimal notation, and all branches of science and technology use numbers in decimal notation to collect data, perform calculations, and report results. Although foreign countries use different systems for currency, they all use a form of decimal notation to write amounts of money.

The mathematical topics covered include place values of decimals, the relationship between decimals and fractions, mixed operations with decimals and fractions, and square roots as decimals using a calculator. We also explore a technique for reducing square roots without using decimals; make conversions among decimals, fractions, and percents; and apply the concepts presented throughout the chapter to solve a variety of word problems.

4.1   DECIMAL NOTATION AND PLACE VALUES

OBJECTIVES

□ To write expanded forms of numbers in decimal notation

□ To convert numbers in decimal notation to words

□ To convert numbers in words to decimal notation

□ To convert numbers in decimal notation to fractions in lowest terms

Imagine that you go to the bank to deposit your paycheck of $12,500.42 for having a small but significant part in the movie *Indiana Jones Finds the Lost City of Atlantis,* and you withdraw $3,232.47 for a down payment on the sports car you have always wanted. Both dollar amounts are numbers given in decimal notation, as is the amount that would remain in your account, $9,267.95.

Place Value of Decimals

To demonstrate that decimal notation is an extension of the base ten place value system used for writing whole numbers, let's review the place values of whole numbers. Figure 4.1 delineates the place values of the number 5,063,198, which is read as "five million, sixty-three thousand, one hundred ninety-eight."

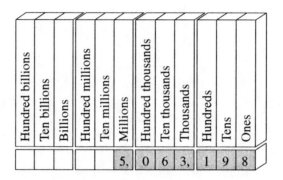

FIGURE 4.1   Place value chart showing the number 5,063,198

Each place value to the left is ten times the place value immediately to the right.

$$1,000 = 10 \cdot 100 \quad \text{Thousands are to the left of the hundreds.}$$

$$100 = 10 \cdot 10 \quad \text{Hundreds are to the left of the tens.}$$

$$10 = 10 \cdot 1 \quad \text{Tens are to the left of the ones.}$$

Therefore, one way to find the place value immediately to the right is to divide by 10. To the right of the thousands is the hundreds, because $1,000 \div 10 = 100$. To the right of the hundreds is the tens, because $100 \div 10 = 10$. To the right of the tens is the ones, because $10 \div 10 = 1$. The decimal point is located just to the right of the ones place, and directly after that is the tenths place, because, according to the pattern,

$$1 \div 10 = \frac{1}{10}$$

To the right of the tenths place is the *hundredths place*, because, according to the pattern,

$$\frac{1}{10} \div 10 = \frac{1}{10} \cdot \frac{1}{10} = \frac{1}{100}$$

To the right of the hundredths place is the *thousandths place*, because

$$\frac{1}{100} \div 10 = \frac{1}{100} \cdot \frac{1}{10} = \frac{1}{1,000}$$

Because dividing by 10 is identical to multiplying by $\frac{1}{10}$, each place value to the right is $\frac{1}{10}$ as large as the place value immediately to its left.

Figure 4.2 shows the place values of the first few places to the left and to the right of the decimal point.

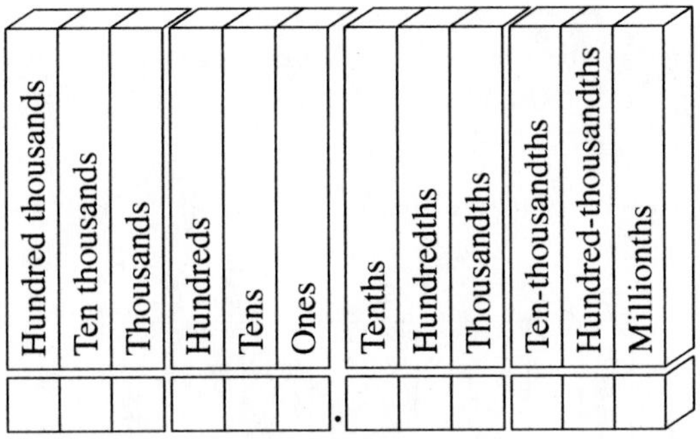

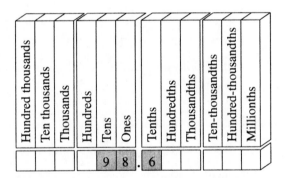

FIGURE 4.2   Place value chart showing hundred thousands to decimal point to millionths

Expanding Decimals

Whereas whole numbers only have digits on the left side of the decimal point, numbers in decimal notation may have digits on both sides of the decimal point. The decimal 98.6°, the normal body temperature of a person, is a number in decimal notation and is shown in the place value chart in Figure 4.3.

FIGURE 4.3   Place value chart showing the number 98.6

Recall that in Chapter 1 we wrote whole numbers in two expanded forms; we can write decimals in three expanded forms. The number 98.6, for example, can be written as:

$$98.6 = 9 \cdot 10 + 8 \cdot 1 + 6 \cdot \frac{1}{10}$$

$$98.6 = 90 + 8 + \frac{6}{10}$$

$$98.6 = 90 + 8 + 0.6$$

Note that in the third expanded form, 98.6 is written $90 + 8 + 0.6$ and not $90 + 8 + .6$. It is customary to write a zero to the left of the decimal point when a number in decimal notation has an absolute value between 0 and 1.

| | EXAMPLE 1 | Write 100.0197 in three expanded forms. Use a place value chart to determine the place value of each digit. |

SOLUTION   The place values are shown in Figure 4.4.

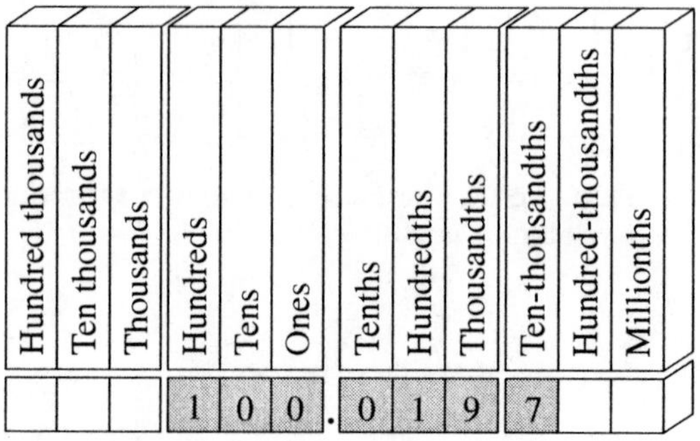

FIGURE 4.4   Place value chart showing the number 100.0197

$$100.0197 = 1 \cdot 100 + 1 \cdot \frac{1}{100} + 9 \cdot \frac{1}{1,000} + 7 \cdot \frac{1}{10,000}$$

$$100.0197 = 100 + \frac{1}{100} + \frac{9}{1,000} + \frac{7}{10,000}$$

$$100.0197 = 100 + 0.01 + 0.009 + 0.0007$$

Starting with the hundredths place, zeros are inserted as place holders.

■

Reading and Writing Decimals

Understanding decimals in expanded notation can assist us in writing decimals in words. The decimal 98.6 in one expanded form is $90 + 8 + \frac{6}{10}$ and in words it is *ninety-eight and six tenths*. The word *and* replaces the decimal point when we write the word name for a number in decimal notation. For another example, the decimal 84.07 in one expanded form is $80 + 4 + \frac{7}{100}$, and its word name is *eighty-four and seven hundredths*. In any word name for a decimal number, the place value of the rightmost decimal digit is the place value written after the word *and*. Thus, the word name for 22.871 is *twenty-two and eight hundred seventy-one thousandths*.

Commas are never used on the right side of the decimal point because the digits to the right of the decimal point are read entirely differently from the digits to the left. 4,242.4242 is read *"four thousand, two hundred forty-two and four thousand two hundred forty-two ten-thousandths."* On the left side the digits are grouped in periods, indicated by commas, whereas on the right side of the decimal point they are never grouped.

EXAMPLE 2	Write the word name for each of the following numbers in decimal notation.

a. 3.456   b. 62.0234   c. 18,000.00018   d. 0.003925

SOLUTION
a. 3.456   Three and four hundred fifty-six thousandths
b. 62.0234   Sixty-two and two hundred thirty-four ten-thousandths
c. 18,000.00018   Eighteen thousand and eighteen hundred-thousandths
d. 0.003925   Three thousand nine hundred twenty-five millionths

Ten-thousandths, hundred-thousandths, ten-millionths, hundred-millionths, and so on are hyphenated to avoid misinterpretation. For example, *six hundred ten thousandths* is the word name for 0.610 but *six hundred ten-thousandths* is the word name for 0.0600.   ■

EXAMPLE 3	Change the following word names to numbers written in decimal notation.

a. Sixty-four and seven tenths
b. Two hundred nine and sixteen ten-thousandths.
c. Zero and seven hundred seven hundred-thousandths
d. Forty-two

SOLUTION
a. Sixty-four and seven tenths is written 64.7.

b. Two hundred nine and sixteen ten-thousandths is written 209.0016. Four digits past the decimal point are required for ten-thousandths, so two place holder zeros are necessary.

c. Zero and seven hundred seven hundred-thousandths is written 0.00707. Five digits past the decimal point are required for hundred-thousandths, so two place holder zeros are necessary.

d. Forty-two is written 42. The whole number forty-two is easily written in decimal notation by simply placing a decimal point to the right of the digit in the ones place. Most calculators display the decimal point so forty-two would be displayed as 42. after you key in 4 and 2.   ■

Converting Decimals to Reduced Fractions

It has become common for people to read decimals using the word *point*. For example, many people say a normal temperature for a human, 98.6°, is "ninety-eight point six." Using the word *point* makes decimals easier to read, but more difficult to convert to fractions. 98.6 read properly is "ninety-eight and six tenths" or $98\frac{6}{10}$, which can be converted into a fraction in lowest terms.

$$98.6 = 98\frac{6}{10} = \frac{986}{10} = \frac{493}{5}$$

| **EXAMPLE 4** | Express each decimal as a fraction in lowest terms. |

    a. 0.4   **b.** 0.25   **c.** 0.0068   **d.** 0.375

SOLUTION   **a.** 0.4 is read as "zero and four tenths," or four tenths.

$$0.4 = \frac{4}{10} = \frac{2}{5} \qquad\qquad \text{Reduce by dividing by 2.}$$

b. 0.25 is read as "twenty-five hundredths."

$$0.25 = \frac{25}{100} = \frac{\cancel{25} \cdot 1}{\cancel{25} \cdot 4} = \frac{1}{4} \qquad \text{Reduce by factoring out the GCF.}$$

c. 0.0068 is read as "sixty-eight ten-thousandths."

$$0.0068 = \frac{68}{10,000} = \frac{\cancel{2} \cdot 34}{\cancel{2} \cdot 5,000} = \frac{\cancel{2} \cdot 17}{\cancel{2} \cdot 2,500} = \frac{17}{2,500}$$

                Reduce by dividing out the common factor 2
                two times.

d. 0.375 is read as "three hundred seventy-five thousandths."

$$0.375 = \frac{375}{1,000} = \frac{3 \cdot \cancel{5} \cdot \cancel{5} \cdot \cancel{5}}{2 \cdot 2 \cdot 2 \cdot \cancel{5} \cdot \cancel{5} \cdot \cancel{5}} = \frac{3}{8}$$

                Reduce using prime factorizations.

A helpful trick to find the prime factorization of multiples of 10 is to count the number of zeros after the 1. The number of zeros will tell how many 2s and 5s are needed in the prime factorization.

10 (1 zero) = 2 · 5   1,000 (3 zeros) = 2 · 2 · 2 · 5 · 5 · 5

100 (2 zeros) = 2 · 2 · 5 · 5   10,000 (4 zeros) = 2 · 2 · 2 · 2 · 5 · 5 · 5 · 5

                                                            ■

| **EXAMPLE 5** | Express each number in decimal notation as a reduced fraction. |

    a. 2.45   **b.** 17.   **c.** −9.056   **d.** −16.9

SOLUTION   **a.** 2.45 is read as "two and forty-five hundredths."

$$2.45 = 2\frac{45}{100} = \frac{245}{100} = \frac{\cancel{5} \cdot 7 \cdot 7}{2 \cdot 2 \cdot \cancel{5} \cdot 5} = \frac{49}{20}$$

                After converting the mixed number to an improper
                fraction, reduce using prime factorizations.

b. 17. is read as "seventeen."

$$17. = 17 = \frac{17}{1}$$

c. −9.056 is read as "negative nine and fifty-six thousandths."

$$-9.056 = -9\frac{56}{1,000} = -9\frac{\cancel{8} \cdot 7}{\cancel{8} \cdot 125} = -9\frac{7}{125} = -\frac{1,132}{125}$$

This example shows that the fractional part of the mixed number can be reduced first before converting the mixed number to an improper fraction.

d. -16.9 is read as "negative sixteen and nine tenths."

$$-16.9 = -16\frac{9}{10} = -\frac{169}{10}$$

Convert the mixed number to an improper fraction.

No reducing is necessary because 169 and 10 are relatively prime.   ■

P R A C T I C E   F O R   S U C C E S S

Practice 1.   Give the place value for the 6 in 451,290.867.

Practice 2.   Write 53.097 in three expanded forms.

Practice 3.   Write the word name for 861.0027.

Practice 4.   Write the decimal for two hundred and two hundred one hundred-thousandths.

Practice 5.   Convert 0.125 to a fraction in lowest terms.

Practice 6.   Convert -4.84 to a fraction in lowest terms.

EXERCISES 4.1

In exercises 1–10, write the decimal numbers in three expanded forms.

1. 9.3257	**2.** 3.7418	**3.** 864.39
4. 729.81	**5.** 7.006	**6.** 2.008
7. 12.05005	**8.** 21.08008	**9.** 196.789003
10. 425.123007		

In exercises 11–20, state the place value of the digit 7.

11. 74.329	**12.** 79,000.006	**13.** 32.478
14. 1.000007	**15.** 3.00007	**16.** 4.007
17. 7,000,000.8	**18.** 325,711.9	**19.** 3.71
20. 429,326.5817		

In exercises 21–30, write the word name for each decimal number.

21. 82.71	**22.** 44.69	**23.** 7.219
24. 6.417	**25.** 8,000.008	**26.** 4,000.047
27. 0.000059	**28.** 0.00089	**29.** 2,180,000.0099
30. 4,260,000.0198		

In exercises 31–40, change the following word names to numbers written in decimal notation.

31. Eighty-nine and ninety-seven hundredths

32. Sixty-nine and forty-three hundredths

33. Twenty and forty-six thousandths

34. Eighty and twenty-seven ten-thousandths

35. Zero and eleven hundred-thousandths

36. Zero and sixty-six millionths

37. One million and one tenth

38. Two hundred thousand and two hundredths

39. Nine million twenty-seven

40. Eight hundred sixty-seven thousand six

In exercises 41–60, express each decimal number as a fraction in lowest terms.

41. 0.6   **42.** 0.8   **43.** 0.75

44. 0.65   **45.** 0.0048 **46.** 0.0092

47. 0.125   **48.** 0.875   **49.** 0.4375

50. 0.28125 **51.** 4.95   **52.** −2.15

53. −17.5   **54.** −16.4   **55.** −3.021

56. 7.083   **57.** 123.   **58.** −8,849

59. −1.0625 **60.** 2.5625

Looking Back

61. Compare -27 and -30 using $>$ or $<$.

62. Add $84 + (-38) + (-27)$.

63. Subtract $-289 - (-300)$.

64. Simplify the expression $[-74 - (-80)] - [-42 + (-45)]$.

65. Benjamin earned \$875 last month and had expenditures of \$910. What was his gain or loss for the month?

In exercises 66–69, determine if the following statements are true or false. If they are false, give an example demonstrating why the statement is false.

66. The sum of two negative integers is always a positive integer.

67. The difference of two negative integers is always a negative integer.

68. Two different integers can have the same absolute value.

69. The difference of two positive integers is always a positive integer.

PRACTICE-FOR-SUCCESS ANSWERS

1. Hundredths

2. $5 \cdot 10 + 3 \cdot 1 + 9 \cdot \dfrac{1}{100} + 7 \cdot \dfrac{1}{1,000}$

$50 + 3 + \dfrac{9}{100} + \dfrac{7}{1,000}$

$50 + 3 + 0.09 + 0.007$

3. Eight hundred sixty-one and twenty-seven ten-thousandths

4. 200.00201

5. $\dfrac{1}{8}$

6. $-\dfrac{121}{25}$

4.2	ADDITION AND SUBTRACTION OF SIGNED DECIMALS

OBJECTIVES

☐ To compare signed decimals

☐ To add signed decimals

☐ To subtract signed decimals

☐ To use addition and subtraction to simplify expressions and solve word problems with signed decimals

In this section we will learn skills that are necessary for such common activities as making entries in a check book, updating the amount in a bank account, or balancing a checking account. We will learn to add and subtract signed decimals and how to solve word problems by adding and subtracting numbers in decimal notation.

Decimals that are either positive or negative are called **signed decimals**. Figure 4.5 shows a number line with divisions of 0.1. Recall that numbers get larger as we go to the right on a number line and get smaller as we go to the left, so, for example, $0.8 > 0.4$ and $-0.5 < 0.2$.

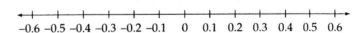

−0.6 −0.5 −0.4 −0.3 −0.2 −0.1   0   0.1   0.2   0.3   0.4   0.5   0.6

FIGURE 4.5   **Signed decimals in increments of 0.1**

Comparing Signed Decimals

Signed decimals can be easily compared when both decimals have the same number of places after the decimal point. Imagine that you have $4.62 to spend and your friend has $4.37. Who has more money to spend? Because $4.62 = \$4\dfrac{62}{100}$ and $4.37 = \$4\dfrac{37}{100}$, you have more money. You have $\dfrac{25}{100}$ of a dollar or $0.25 or a quarter more.

Not all signed decimals have the same number of decimal places past the decimal point. Imagine that you are asked to compare 0.9 and 0.867 and tell which is larger. Some might incorrectly argue that 0.867 is larger than 0.9 because 867 is larger than 9. If we insert zeros after 0.9 so it becomes the equivalent decimal 0.900, we can more easily compare the two decimals because then they will both have the same number of places past the decimal.

$$0.900 > 0.867 \text{ because } \frac{900}{1,000} > \frac{867}{1,000}$$

Therefore, $0.9 > 0.867$

What allows us to insert or delete any zeros that appear as the rightmost digits after the decimal point as we just did to help us compare decimals? 0.9, 0.90, 0.900, and 0.9000 are all equivalent because

$$0.9 = \frac{9}{10} \qquad 0.90 = \frac{90}{100} = \frac{\cancel{10} \cdot 9}{\cancel{10} \cdot 10} = \frac{9}{10}$$

$$0.900 = \frac{900}{1,000} = \frac{\cancel{100} \cdot 9}{\cancel{100} \cdot 10} = \frac{9}{10} \qquad 0.9000 = \frac{9,000}{10,000} = \frac{\cancel{1,000} \cdot 9}{\cancel{1,000} \cdot 10} = \frac{9}{10}$$

All four decimals are equal to $\frac{9}{10}$, so they are equivalent decimals. Rightmost zeros after the decimal point can be inserted or deleted as needed when we are operating with signed decimals.

EXAMPLE 1   Compare the following signed decimals using $>$, $<$, or $=$.

a. $0.2179 \,?\, 0.22$ **b.** $-1.7 \,?\, -1.734$

SOLUTION   **a.** $0.2179 \,?\, 0.22$

Insert zeros to 0.22 so that both numbers have an equal number of decimal places after the decimal point.

$$0.2179 < 0.2200 \text{ because } \frac{2,179}{10,000} < \frac{2,200}{10,000}$$

Therefore, $0.2179 < 0.2200$.

b. $-1.7 \,?\, -1.734$

Insert zeros to make $-1.7 = -1.700$.

$-1.700 = -1 + (-0.700)$ and $-1.734 = -1. + (-0.734)$

Because both signed decimals have the same integer part -1, we compare the portions after the decimal point. $-0.700 > -0.734$ because -0.700 is farther to the right on the number line. Therefore, $-1.7 > -1.734$.   ■

Adding Signed Decimals

Every time we go to the grocery store, the total bill is determined by adding numbers in decimal notation. Imagine that you are buying a few ingredients for salad, including a head of lettuce for $0.69, a package of carrots for $0.70, and a package of cherry tomatoes for $1.99. How much would these ingredients for the salad cost? One way to find the sum would be to change each of the decimals to fractions.

$$0.69 = \frac{69}{100}$$

$$0.70 = \frac{70}{100}$$

$$+ \ 1.99 = \frac{199}{100}$$

$$= \frac{338}{100} = 3\frac{38}{100} = 3.38$$

The ingredients for the salad would cost $3.38.

In the preceding problem instead of converting the decimals to fractions with the same denominator, we could have obtained the same result by lining up the decimal points in the numbers and adding the digits with the same place value. Carrying is done in the same manner in which it is done with whole numbers.

$$
\begin{array}{r}
{}^{2\ 1} \\
\$0.69 \\
0.70 \\
+\ 1.99 \\
\hline
\$3.38
\end{array}
$$

The decimal point in the sum is directly underneath the line of decimal points in the numbers we are adding. In a problem concerning money, we place the dollar sign in front of the first number to be added and in front of the sum as well.

The mathematical justification for aligning decimal points when adding decimals is the distributive law. For example, we can write the problem 2.00 + 0.05 in the form

$$2.00 + 0.05 = 200 \cdot \frac{1}{100} + 5 \cdot \frac{1}{100} = (200 + 5) \cdot \frac{1}{100} = \frac{205}{100} = 2.05$$

| **EXAMPLE 2** | Add each of the following decimals. |

a. 5.4 + 14.781   **b.** 86 + 29.36

SOLUTION   To add decimals, line up the decimal points and add the digits that have the same place value. Although it is not mandatory in addition, it is helpful to insert zeros so that each of the numbers has the same number of decimal places. Recall that the decimal point in the sum goes directly underneath the decimal points that are vertically aligned.

a. 5.4 + 14.781   **b.** 86 + 29.36

$$
\begin{array}{r}
{}^{11} \\
5.400 \\
+\ 14.781 \\
\hline
20.181
\end{array}
\qquad
\begin{array}{r}
{}^{1} \\
86.00 \\
+\ 29.36 \\
\hline
115.36
\end{array}
$$

■

We add signed decimals by using the same rules that we use to add integers. As we have seen in the previous examples, when the decimals are all positive, the sum is positive; and if both decimals are negative, the sum is negative. For example, imagine that you owe $72.50 on your credit card one month and do not pay it back, and then you make purchases of $66.94 the following month. How much do you owe on your credit card (not including finance charges)? To calculate your credit card debt, add your original debt and your new purchases.

$$\text{Original Debt} + \text{Purchases} = \text{New Balance}$$

$$-\$72.50 + (-\$66.94) = ?$$

$$
\begin{array}{r}
\overset{1}{}\ \$\ 72.50 \\
+\quad 66.94 \\
\hline
\$139.44
\end{array}
$$

The balance of your account is −$139.44 so your credit card debt is $139.44.

Imagine that on that same credit card you accidentally pay the company $193. To determine how much you overpaid and what your new balance is, calculate your credit card balance by adding your overpayment to the current debt.

$$\text{Current Debt} + \text{Payment} = \text{New Balance}$$

$$-\$139.44 + \$193. = ?$$

Adding signed decimals uses the same rules as adding integers. When we have one negative signed decimal and one positive signed decimal, we subtract the absolute value of the smaller signed decimal from the absolute value of the larger signed decimal and attach the sign of the number with the larger absolute value to the answer. We can write the problem in a vertical format with the decimal points lined up as we do in an addition problem.

$$
\begin{array}{r}
\$193. \\
-\quad 139.44 \\
\hline
\end{array}
$$

The subtraction cannot be accomplished as just written because we cannot subtract .44 from nothing. Zeros in the number with the larger absolute value are *mandatory* so that we have a quantity from which .44 can be subtracted. After inserting zeros so that both numbers have the same denominator, 100 in this instance, we can borrow and the problem can be done as follows:

$$
\begin{array}{r}
\overset{8\ 12\ 9}{\$1 9 3 . 0\ 0} \\
-\quad 139.44 \\
\hline
\$\ \ 53.56
\end{array}
$$

Your new balance is +$53.56, which represents the amount the credit card company owes you.

ADDING SIGNED DECIMALS

1. **To add decimals with like signs, write the numbers in a vertical format, lining up the decimal points. Add all digits with the same place value, carrying when necessary, and place the decimal point in the sum directly underneath the aligned decimal points. The sign of the sum is the sign of the original decimals.**

2. **To add decimals with opposite signs, take the absolute value of each decimal. Write the numbers in a vertical format subtracting the smaller absolute value from the larger absolute value. Line up the decimal points so that digits with the same place value are subtracted, borrowing when necessary, and place the decimal point in the difference directly underneath the aligned decimal points. The sign of the result is the sign of the decimal whose absolute value is larger.**

EXAMPLE 3	Add the following decimals.

a. $-0.82 + (-0.217)$ **b.** $12 + (-0.819)$

SOLUTION   **a.** $-0.82 + (-0.217)$

$$\begin{array}{r} {}^{1} \\ 0.820 \\ +\ 0.217 \\ \hline 1.037 \end{array}$$

Insert a zero (although it's not mandatory) so that both numbers have the same number of digits to the right of the decimal points.

$-0.82 + (-0.217) = -1.037$

b. $12 + (-0.819)$

$$\begin{array}{r} {}^{1}\ {}^{9}\ {}^{9} \\ 12.{}^{1}0\,{}^{1}0\,{}^{1}0 \\ -\ \ 0.819 \\ \hline 11.181 \end{array}$$

Insert mandatory zeros so that the smaller absolute value can be subtracted from the larger absolute value.

$12 + (-0.819) = 11.181$

The answer is positive because the decimal with the larger absolute value is positive.   ■

Subtracting Signed Decimals

We often subtract decimals to solve problems. In the 1936 Summer Olympic Games Jesse Owens won the gold medal by running the 100-meter dash in 10.3 seconds; in the 1988 Summer Olympic Games, Carl Lewis won the gold medal by running the 100-meter dash in 9.92 seconds. To determine how much faster Carl Lewis ran than Jesse Owens, we can write the problem in a horizontal format as $10.30 - 9.92 = 10.30 + (-9.92) = 0.38$. In a vertical format

$$\begin{array}{r} {}^{9}\ {}^{12} \\ 10.{}^{1}3\,{}^{1}0 \\ -\ \ 9.92 \\ \hline 0.38 \end{array}$$

Line up decimal points and insert mandatory zero.

Carl Lewis was 0.38 seconds faster than Jesse Owens.

> ## SUBTRACTING SIGNED DECIMALS
>
> 1. **Change subtraction to adding the opposite of the second decimal, using the rule**
>
> $$x - y = x + (-y)$$
>
> 2. **Apply the rules for adding signed decimals.**

EXAMPLE 4 Subtract the following decimals.

    a. $-2.97 - 328.615$ **b.** $-3.98 - (-2.499)$

SOLUTION **a.** $-2.97 - 328.615 = -2.97 + (-328.615)$ Change to adding the opposite.

$$
\begin{array}{r}
2.970 \\
+\ 328.615 \\
\hline
331.585
\end{array}
$$

Insert a zero so that each decimal has the same number of places after the decimal point and then add.

$-2.97 - 328.615 = -2.97 + (-328.615) = -331.585$

The answer is negative because the two signed decimals added are negative.

b. $-3.98 - (-2.499) = -3.98 + 2.499$

$$
\begin{array}{r}
\overset{8\ \ 17}{3.9\,\cancel{9}\,\cancel{8}\,{}^{1}0} \\
-\ 2.4\,9\,9 \\
\hline
1.4\,8\,1
\end{array}
$$

Insert a zero so that each decimal has the same number of places after the decimal point and then subtract.

$-3.98 - (-2.499) = -3.98 + 2.499 = -1.481$ ■

EXAMPLE 5 Simplify $(3.17 - 6.1) - (-7 + 3.971)$.

SOLUTION Following the horizontal format, we show the vertical alignment of the decimals that are added or subtracted.

$(3.17 - 6.1) - (-7 + 3.971) = [3.17 + (-6.1)] - (-7 + 3.971)$

                          Convert the subtraction in square brackets.

        $= [-2.93] - (-7 + 3.971)$

                Perform the addition in the brackets.

        $= -2.93 - (-3.029)$

                Add the decimals inside the parentheses.

        $= -2.93 + (+3.029)$

                Change the subtraction to adding the opposite.

        $= 0.099$

$$
\begin{array}{ccc}
\overset{5\ \ 10}{\cancel{6}.{}^{1}\cancel{1}0} & \overset{6\ \ 9\ \ 9}{\cancel{7}.\cancel{0}\cancel{0}0} & \overset{2\ \ 9}{\cancel{3}.\cancel{0}29} \\
-\ 3.1\,7 & -\ 3.9\,7\,1 & -\ 2.\,9\,30 \\
\hline
2.9\,3 & 3.0\,2\,9 & 0.0\,9\,9
\end{array}
$$

                                                ■

| EXAMPLE 6 | 100 grams of chocolate fudge contains 2.7 grams of protein, 12.2 grams of fat, and 75 grams of carbohydrate. How many more grams of carbohydrate than grams of fat are in 100 grams of chocolate fudge? |

SOLUTION   Subtract the grams of fat from the grams of carbohydrate.

$$\begin{array}{r} 7\overset{4}{\cancel{5}}.0 \\ -\ 12.2 \\ \hline 62.8 \end{array}$$

100 grams of chocolate fudge has 62.8 more grams of carbohydrate than grams of fat. (The amount of protein was extra information not needed to solve the problem.)   ■

P R A C T I C E   F O R   S U C C E S S

Practice 1.   Compare 0.274 and 0.2739 using $>$, $<$, or $=$.

Practice 2.   Add $7.2 + (-3.998)$.

Practice 3.   Subtract $8.1 - (-4.781)$.

Practice 4.   Simplify the expression $[3.2 + (-7.6)] - [4.29 - (-3.9)]$.

Practice 5.   The most miles ever cycled on an indoor track during a 24-hour period is approximately 516.0809 miles. The most miles ever cycled on an outdoor track during a 24-hour period is 502.3 miles. How many more miles were cycled on the indoor track than on the outdoor track?

EXERCISES 4.2

In exercises 1–10, compare the signed decimals using $>$, $<$, or $=$.

1. 0.34 ? 0.4   2. 3.7 ? 3.69
3. −4.32 ? −4.3   4. 6.67 ? 6.6
5. −10.5 ? 10.5   6. 21.118 ? −21.118
7. 12.05 ? 12.0501   8. −68.928 ? −68.92
9. −17.000 ? −17.7   10. 86.2 ? 86.2000

In exercises 11–30, add the decimals.

11. $8.4 + 8.791$ 12. $7.9 + 9.245$
13. $2.4 + 24.2468$ 14. $27.85 + 3.999$
15. $\$30.84 + \$29.87$ 16. $\$88.99 + \$121$
17. $-0.6 + 0.39$ 18. $0.8 + (-0.49)$
19. $18 + (-9.111)$ 20. $4.29 + (-17)$

21. $-82.71 + (-9)$

22. $-26 + 34.79$

23. $7.219 + (-12)$

24. $-6.417 + 1{,}001$

25. $8.008 + (-12.34)$

26. $400.2 + (-87.87)$

27. $0.87 + 0.452 + 0.9871$

28. $0.9876 + 0.871 + 0.9$

29. $2.98 + (-5.1) + 3.00076$

30. $4.53 + (-8.3) + (-12.00785)$

In exercises 31–50, subtract the decimals.

31. $89.7 - 2.8$

32. $245.8 - 3.9$

33. $0.47 - 0.3339$

34. $0.92 - 0.8744$

35. $3.4 - 4.97$

36. $4.2 - 3.198$

37. $-9.21 - (-4.6)$

38. $-7.84 - (-6.9)$

39. $-22 - (-6.21)$

40. $-55 - (-9.82)$

41. $\$88 - \$22.57$

42. $\$97 - \$34.61$

43. $84.319 - 29.5$

44. $95.219 - 37.8$

45. $-4.21 - 962.8$

46. $-9.88 - 889.732$

47. $47 - (-2.004)$

48. $82 - (-7.0008)$

49. $2.3 - 4.5 - 6.7$

50. $6.2 - 7.9 - 9.8$

In exercises 51–70, simplify the expressions.

51. $2.4 - 3.7 + 4.81$

52. $4.8 - 6.9 + 2.46$

53. $8.45 - 4.1111 + (-6.2)$

54. $16.4 - 2.8888 + (-9.7)$

55. $(5.81 - 8.2) - (-4 + 2.861)$

56. $(6.31 - 9.8) - (-8 + 3.429)$

57. $123 - (3.7 - 4.6)$

58. $84 - (2.9 - 6.2)$

59. $(3.64 + 2.9) - (2.11 + 825.7)$

60. $(2.56 + 4.7) - (6.33 + 274.9)$

61. $[15 - (15 - 0.16)] + (6.3 - 2.991)$

62. $[35 - (35 - 0.68)] + (8.2 - 6.871)$

63. $(74 - 265.31) + (22 - 19.952)$

64. $(48 - 784.82) + (66 - 25.337)$

65. $(2.5 - 3.704) - (4.98 - 3.6)$

66. $(3.2 - 4.903) - (6.84 - 2.7)$

67. $(\$32.67 + \$29.82) - (\$40.81 + \$10)$

68. $(\$52.81 + \$64) - (\$24 + \$57.92)$

69. $12.972 - [-4.02 + (2.7 - 9)]$

70. $87.345 - [-8.04 + (3.4 - 12)]$

In exercises 71–80, solve each problem.

71. Find the sum of $\$44.96$, $\$688$, and $\$22.04$.

72. Find the sum of $\$98$, $\$20.06$, and $\$1{,}273.96$.

73. Find the difference between 44 and -72.3.

74. Find the difference between -72.3 and 44.

75. Subtract $\$32.89$ from $\$100$.

76. Subtract $\$100$. from $\$32.89$.

77. Subtract 22.4 from the difference between 8.7 and 12.

78. Subtract 80.5 from the difference between 2.5 and 10.

79. Subtract 11.269 from the sum of 46 and 29.89.

80. Subtract 82.777 from the sum of 841 and 9.6.

Use the following information about our solar system to solve exercises 81–86.

Planet	Distance from Sun	Length of Year
Mercury	57.9 million km	88 Earth days
Venus	108.2 million km	225 Earth days
Earth	149.6 million km	365.3 Earth days
Mars	229.9 million km	387 Earth days
Jupiter	778.3 million km	11.86 Earth years

81. How much closer to the sun is Mercury than Earth?

82. How much closer to the sun is Venus than Earth?

83. What is the total of the distances from the sun to Mercury, Venus, and Mars?

84. What is the total of the distances from the sun to Earth, Mars, and Jupiter?

85. How much longer is a year on Mars than a year on Earth?

86. How much longer is a year on Earth than a year on Venus?

87. A videocassette recorder that regularly sells for $325 is marked down $25.05. What is the sale price for the VCR?

88. A suit that regularly sells for $225 is on sale for $168.75. How much has the suit been marked down?

89. Claudia's checking account shows a balance of $150. She writes checks to buy a jacket for $42.99 and a matching skirt for $23.99. She then visits an automatic teller machine to withdraw some cash from her account. How many $20 bills can Claudia withdraw and still have a balance above $0?

90. Manuel's checking account shows a balance of $225. If he deposits $32.50 and then writes checks for $22.35, $55.75, $33.87, $44.72, and $46, what will his new balance be?

91. The sum of three numbers is 4.5. If the smaller is 0.95 and the larger 2.308, what is the middle number?

92. The sum of three numbers is −10.2. If the smaller is −9.9 and the middle number is −0.3, what is the larger number?

Looking Back

93. Find the product of −369 and 271.

94. Find the product of −16 and −625.

95. Simplify the expression $-4[9 - 3(2 + 6)]$.

96. Simplify the expression $-3\{12 - 17[6 - (2 - 8)]\}$.

97. Find the product of $\dfrac{3}{1,000}$ and $\dfrac{7}{10}$.

98. Find the product of $\dfrac{99}{100}$ and $\dfrac{9}{10}$.

99. Describe in your own words how the word *factor* is used as a noun in mathematics.

PRACTICE-FOR-SUCCESS ANSWERS

1. >   **2.** 3.202   **3.** 12.881   **4.** −12.59   **5.** 13.7809 miles

---

4.3   MULTIPLICATION OF SIGNED DECIMALS

OBJECTIVES

□   To multiply signed decimals
□   To use multiplication of decimals to simplify expressions and solve word problems

We multiply decimals every time we make purchases at a store. Imagine that you are buying three cassette tapes by your favorite performer at $8.99 each. How much money have you spent, not including sales tax?

$$\begin{array}{r} \$\,8.99 \\ \times\quad 3 \\ \hline \$26.97 \end{array}$$

You have spent $26.97 and probably owe more, depending upon the sales tax in your state. In this example the decimal point in the product is critical; incorrectly placing the decimal point one place to the right would make the product $269.7 or $269.70 (a tremendous sum to pay for three cassette tapes).

Multiplying Signed Decimals

How is the correct location of the decimal point in the product determined? For instance, to solve (0.07) (0.2), we convert the decimals 0.07 and 0.2 to fractions and then multiply the fractions.

$$(0.07) \cdot (0.2) = \frac{7}{100} \cdot \frac{2}{10} \qquad \text{Convert the decimals to fractions.}$$

$$= \frac{14}{1{,}000} \qquad \text{Multiply but do not reduce to lowest terms.}$$

$$= 0.014 \qquad \text{Convert the fraction back to a decimal.}$$

By using fractions, we see that the product (0.07)(0.2) equals 0.014, a number that has three decimal places, which means that it has three digits to the right of the decimal point. The factor 0.07 has two decimal places and the factor 0.2 has 1 decimal place. The product 0.014 has three decimal places; therefore, we can determine the correct location of the decimal point in the product by counting the number of decimal places in each of the factors. The same problem can be done by arranging the decimals in a vertical format and performing multiplication as if they were whole numbers.

$$
\begin{array}{r r}
0.07 & \text{2 decimal places} \\
\times \quad 0.2 & +\ \text{1 decimal place} \\
\hline
0.014 & \leftarrow\text{3 decimal places}
\end{array}
$$

We have seen that the product of two decimals can be found in two different ways. The easier of the two ways is to multiply the two decimals as if they were whole numbers and then add the number of decimal places in the factors to find the total number of decimal places in the product. When we multiply decimals, unlike when we add or subtract them, the decimal points of the factors and the product are not aligned.

EXAMPLE 1	Multiply the following decimals.

a. (2.8) (4.3)   **b.** (417) (0.9)

SOLUTION

a. (2.8) (4.3)

$$
\begin{array}{r l}
2.8 & \text{1 decimal place} \\
\times \quad 4.3 & +\ \text{1 decimal place} \\
\hline
84 & \\
+\ 1120 & \\
\hline
12.04 & \leftarrow\text{2 decimal places}
\end{array}
$$

b. (417) (0.9)

$$
\begin{array}{r l}
417 & \text{0 decimal places} \\
\times \quad 0.9 & +\ \text{1 decimal place} \\
\hline
375.3 & \leftarrow\text{1 decimal place}
\end{array}
$$ ■

In the preceding examples, we saw that a positive decimal multiplied by a positive decimal equals a positive product. We use the same rules for multiplying signed decimals that we use for multiplying integers or signed fractions. If the two signed decimals have like signs, the product is positive, and if the two signed decimals have unlike signs, then the product is negative.

MULTIPLYING SIGNED DECIMALS

1. **Write the decimals in a vertical format without lining up the decimal points.**
2. **Multiply the decimals as if they were whole numbers.**
3. **Locate the decimal point in the product so that the number of decimal places in the product equals the sum of the number of decimal places in the factors. If more digits are needed in the product, insert zeros as place holders on the left.**
4. **If the two factors have like signs, the product is positive. If the two factors have unlike signs, the product is negative.**

EXAMPLE 2	Multiply the following signed decimals.

a. $(-0.031)(-0.039)$ **b.** $(7.8)(-3.997)$

SOLUTION   **a.** $(-0.031)(-0.039)$

$$
\begin{array}{r}
0.031 \\
\times \quad 0.039 \\
\hline
279 \\
+ \quad 930 \\
\hline
0.001209
\end{array}
$$

3 decimal places
+ 3 decimal places

←6 decimal places are needed, so two place holder zeros are inserted.

$(-0.031)(-0.039) = 0.001209$

b. $(7.8)(-3.997) = (-3.997)(7.8)$ Use the commutative law for multiplication so the multiplier has fewer digits.

$$
\begin{array}{r}
3.997 \\
\times \quad 7.8 \\
\hline
31976 \\
+ \quad 279790 \\
\hline
31.1766
\end{array}
$$

3 decimal places
+ 1 decimal place

←4 decimal places

$(7.8)(-3.997) = -31.1766$ ■

Multiplying by Powers of 10

Imagine that you buy bedroom furniture on credit and agree to pay the furniture company $185.70 a month for 10 months. What is the total amount you must pay back?

$$
\begin{array}{r}
\$185.70 \\
\times \quad 10 \\
\hline
\$1,857.00
\end{array}
$$

Over the 10-month period you must pay back a total of $1,857.00. Notice that when we multiplied by 10 in this problem, the decimal point in the product was *1 place to the right* of where it was in the first factor. Figure 4.6 demonstrates what happens when we multiply by powers of 10.

Decimal		Power of Ten		
(1.414)	×	(10)	=	14.14
(1.414)	×	(100)	=	141.4
(1.414)	×	(1,000)	=	1,414
(1.4140)	×	(10,000)	=	14,140
(1.41400)	×	(100,000)	=	141,400
(1.414000)	×	(1,000,000)	=	1,414,000

FIGURE 4.6   Multiplying 1.414 by powers of 10

In Figure 4.6 we see that when we multiply a decimal by 10, 100, 1,000, and so on, we can simply count the zeros in the power of 10 to determine the number of decimal places we move the decimal point to the right. Because 10,000,000 has seven zeros, the decimal point is moved over seven places to the right, so (1.414) (10,000,000) = 14,140,000, and four zeros are inserted to allow for the movement of seven decimal places.

EXAMPLE 3

Multiply.

a. (3.52) (100,000)   **b.** (−2.7169) (100)

SOLUTION

Move the decimal point in the first factor to the right the number of places that there are zeros in the power of 10.

a. (3.52) (100,000) = 352,000   **b.** (−2.7169) (100) = −271.69   ■

EXAMPLE 4

Simplify the following expressions.

a. $-\left|-4.61\right|^2$ **b.** 3.1[4.21 − 7.9]

SOLUTION

a. $-\left|-4.61\right|^2 = -\left[\left|-4.61\right| \cdot \left|-4.61\right|\right] = -[(4.61) \cdot (4.61)] = -21.2521$

$$
\begin{array}{r}
4.61 \\
\times \quad 4.61 \\
\hline
461 \\
27660 \\
+\ 184400 \\
\hline
21.2521
\end{array}
$$

b. 3.1[4.21 − 7.9] = 3.1[4.21 + (−7.9)]   Change to adding the opposite.
       = 3.1 [−3.69]   Add [4.21 + (−7.9)] = −3.69.
       = −11.439   Multiply.

$$
\begin{array}{r}
7.90 \\
-\ 4.21 \\
\hline
3.69
\end{array}
\qquad
\begin{array}{r}
3.69 \\
\times \quad 3.1 \\
\hline
369 \\
+\ 11070 \\
\hline
11.439
\end{array}
$$
     ■

EXAMPLE 5

Find the product of twenty-one thousand and four and seven tenths.

SOLUTION

The two numbers to be multiplied are twenty-one thousand (21,000) and four and seven tenths (4.7). The first "and" separates the two numbers and the second "and" connects the integer and decimal parts of the second number. The first "and" does not represent a decimal point because twenty-one thousand and four is not a correct word name for any decimal number.

$$
\begin{array}{r}
21,000 \\
\times \quad 4.7 \\
\hline
147000 \\
+\ 840000 \\
\hline
98,700.0 = 98,700
\end{array}
$$
     ■

| EXAMPLE 6 | Carlos has to copy 77 pages from different books for a sociology term paper. It costs 15 cents per page to use the copy machine in the school library. It costs 10 cents per page to use a copy machine at a local stationery store. How much money can he save by copying the pages at the stationery store instead of at the library? |

SOLUTION This problem, like others, can be solved using two different methods. One way to solve the problem is to calculate the cost of copying the 77 pages at the two locations and then find the difference between those costs. Because 100 cents is equivalent to 1 dollar, 15 cents $= 0.15$ or $\dfrac{15}{100}$ of a dollar and 10 cents $= 0.10$ or $\dfrac{10}{100}$ of a dollar.

Method 1

Cost of copying at school library $-$ cost of copying at local stationery store

$$(77) \cdot (0.15) - (77) \cdot (0.10)$$

$$11.55 - 7.70 = 3.85$$

Carlos can save $3.85 by copying the 77 pages at a local stationery store. Another way to solve the problem is to first find the savings of copying a single page at the stationery store and then multiply that amount by the number of pages to be copied.

Method 2

$$\text{Savings per page} \times \text{Number of pages}$$

$$(0.15 - 0.10) \cdot (77)$$

$$(0.05) \cdot (77) = 3.85$$

Again we conclude that Carlos saves $3.85 at the stationery store. Solving a problem in two different ways and arriving at the same answer usually verifies that the answer is correct. Of course the answer will not be correct if both ways chosen to solve the problem have errors and we arrive at the same answer twice simply by accident. ■

P R A C T I C E   F O R   S U C C E S S

Practice 1. Find the product of 7.1 and -62.8.

Practice 2. Find the product of eighty-two thousand forty-two and five and seven hundredths.

Practice 3. $-\left| -2.9 \right|^2$

Practice 4. $8.2[4.5 + (-3.9)]$

Practice 5. JoAnn makes a long distance call at night to Wyoming and talks 61 minutes at 12 cents per minute. She makes a call in the daytime to Oregon and talks 23 minutes at 23 cents per minute. She makes another call at night to North Carolina and talks 10 minutes at 12.5 cents per minute. What is her total expense for the three calls?

EXERCISES 4.3

In exercises 1–22, multiply the decimals.

1. $(-0.52)\,(0.25)$
2. $(0.87)\,(-0.34)$
3. $(-0.3)\,(-0.025)$
4. $(-0.075)\,(-0.8)$
5. $(2.5)\,(-0.095)$
6. $(7.2)\,(-0.015)$
7. $(-810)\,(-0.6)$
8. $(-400)\,(-0.8)$
9. $(0.452)\,(0.098)$
10. $(0.046)\,(0.926)$
11. $(2.98)\,(-0.009)$
12. $(4.53)\,(-0.006)$
13. $(-0.0005)\,(-0.08)$
14. $(-0.0004)\,(-0.04)$
15. $(0.6)\,(0.7)\,(0.9)$
16. $(0.5)\,(0.4)\,(0.8)$
17. $(-1.7)\,(-0.8)\,(-0.01)$
18. $(-2.6)\,(0.4)\,(-0.001)$
19. $(-40)\,(0.4)\,(0.04)$
20. $(-60)\,(0.6)\,(0.06)$
21. $(-2.3)\,(-3.1)\,(4.8)$
22. $(-6.6)\,(9.4)\,(-7.1)$

In exercises 23–32, find the product without using long multiplication or a calculator.

23. $(84.6)\,(10)$
24. $(97.234)\,(10)$
25. $(-2.97)\,(1{,}000)$
26. $(4.28)\,(-1{,}000)$
27. $(-8.2343)\,(1{,}000{,}000)$
28. $(-2.87676)\,(1{,}000{,}000)$
29. $(-100{,}000)\,(-8.2)$
30. $(-100{,}000)\,(-72.3)$
31. $(-0.863)\,(0.01)$
32. $(-0.3249)\,(-0.01)$

In exercises 33–52, simplify the expressions.

33. $(2.2)^2$
34. $(4.9)^2$
35. $(-4.21)^2$
36. $(-9.88)^2$
37. $-|0.5|^3$
38. $-|0.4|^4$
39. $-|-2.3|^2$
40. $-|-6.9|^2$
41. $[(-0.7)\,(0.5)]^2$
42. $[(0.8)\,(-0.9)]^2$
43. $8[3.4 + (-6.4)]$
44. $9[6.4 + (-3.5)]$
45. $(4.9 + 5.1)\,[9.6 + (-3.27)]$
46. $[8.2 + (-2.91)]\,(62.3 + 37.7)$
47. $(-8.93 - 1.07)^3$
48. $(-2.28 - 4.72)^2$
49. $-8[7.92 + (3.21 - 5.7)]$
50. $-5[3.25 + (2.76 - 9.9)]$
51. $2\{5.2 + 3[-4.99 - (0.5)^2]\}$
52. $-5\{8.32 + 2[-7.76 - (0.7)^2]\}$

In exercises 53–66, solve each problem.

53. Find the product of -0.6, 0.7, and 0.8.
54. Find the product of -0.4, 0.5, 0.7, and -0.9.
55. Find the product of twenty-four and seven and seven tenths.
56. Find the product of eighty-six and nine and two hundredths.
57. Find the product of negative ninety thousand and four and seventeen thousandths.

58. Find the product of negative twenty-two thousand and seven and nine hundredths.

59. If a television set costs $395 and the sales tax is paid at 0.0675 times the price, determine the sales tax and the total amount to be paid to purchase the television set. (*Hint:* Round the sales tax to the hundredths place.)

60. If an answer phone costs $145 and the sales tax is paid at 0.065 times the price, determine the sales tax and the total amount to be paid to purchase the answer phone.

61. To buy a car, Lydia can pay $5,250 in cash or make a downpayment of $350 and pay $224.99 a month for 24 months. How much money can be saved if the car is purchased by paying cash?

62. To buy a hot tub, Marty can pay $3,985 in cash or make a downpayment of $275 and pay $219.93 for 18 months. How much money can be saved if the hot tub is purchased by paying cash?

63. What is the cost of 21 gallons of unleaded gasoline at $1.02 per gallon?

64. What is the cost of copying 92 pages at 15 cents per page?

65. The formula for finding the circumference of a circle (the perimeter of a circle) is $C = 2 \cdot \pi \cdot r$. Using 3.14 as an approximation for π, find the circumference of a circle that has a radius of 24.5 cm.

66. The speed that a car can attain from a standing start is given by the formula $s = a \cdot t$ where s equals the speed, a equals acceleration, and t equals the time from the moment of starting. If a compact car is able to accelerate at the rate of 1.5 miles per hour each second, what speed will the car attain after 36.6 seconds?

Use the following nutritional information to solve exercises 67 to 72.

Selected Breads (1 slice)	Protein (in grams)	Carbohydrates (in grams)	Fiber (in grams)	Fat (in grams)
French bread	3.3	17.7	0.58	1.36
Oatmeal bread	2.1	12.0	0.86	1.1
Pumpernickel	2.9	15.4	1.33	1.1
Rye bread	2.1	12.0	1.65	0.9
White bread	2.1	12.1	0.68	1.0
Whole wheat	3.0	12.7	3.17	1.2

67. If you eat 4 slices of pumpernickel bread one day and 4 slices of whole wheat bread the next day, how many grams of fiber have you eaten? How many more grams of fiber are in 4 slices of whole wheat bread than in 4 slices of pumpernickel?

68. If you eat 3 slices of French bread one day and 3 slices of rye bread the next day, how many grams of carbohydrates have you eaten? How many more grams of carbohydrates are in 3 slices of French bread than in 3 slices of rye bread?

69. James eats a loaf (16 slices) of white bread one week while Matthew eats a loaf (16 slices) of whole wheat bread. How many more grams of fiber does Matthew consume than James?

70. Melanie eats half a loaf (8 slices) of oatmeal bread one week while Janet eats half a loaf (8 slices) of rye bread. How many more grams of protein does Melanie consume than Janet?

71. Determine the total number of grams of fat in 6 loaves of French bread.

72. Determine the total number of grams of carbohydrates in $2\frac{1}{2}$ loaves of pumpernickel.

Looking Back

73. Round 598,961,888 to nearest ten, thousand, ten million, and hundred million.

74. Round 2,759,461 to nearest hundred, ten thousand, hundred thousand, and million.

75. Divide −65,240 by 35.

76. Divide −84 into −7,056.

77. Divide 10 into −7,650.

78. Divide −16,300 by −100.

79. When a fraction is undefined, the denominator is _____.

80. When a fraction is equivalent to zero, the numerator is _____.

81. Division by zero is _____.

PRACTICE-FOR-SUCCESS ANSWERS

1. −445.88   **2.** 415,952.94   **3.** −8.41   **4.** 4.92   **5.** $13.86

4.4 DIVISION OF SIGNED DECIMALS

OBJECTIVES

☐   To round decimals

☐   To divide signed decimals by an integer

☐   To divide signed decimals

☐   To use division of signed decimals to simplify equations and solve word problems

The skills presented in this section have many applications. For example, imagine that you buy a car from your favorite aunt for $4,900.00. She asks you to pay her back for the car over a 4-year period on a month-to-month basis with no downpayment or interest. What are your monthly payments to your aunt going to be?

To determine how much you owe your aunt each month, you use division of decimals. You divide the amount you owe, $4,900.00, by 48 because over a 4-year period you will make 4 · 12 or 48 equal monthly payments. When you use a calculator to do the division, you compute a quotient of 102.08333. Remember that with money you need only two decimal places, so you approximate that you owe your aunt $102.08 per month for 48 months. You have rounded the quotient to the nearest hundredth, or nearest cent: your aunt rounds the quotient to the nearest dollar and decides to make your monthly payment $102.

Rounding Decimals

To find an approximate value for a number in decimal notation, we can use rounding, which was first introduced in Chapter 1. Rounding allows us to shorten numbers in decimal notation with several digits after the decimal point and to make them easier to use. Decimals can be rounded to tenths (one decimal place), hundredths (two decimal places), thousandths (three decimal places), and so on. The more digits that remain after the decimal point after rounding, the greater the precision. For example, 3.14159 is a more precise approximation of π than 3.14. However, 3.14, with fewer digits after the decimal point, is an approximation of π that is easier to use.

Rounding a number to the nearest tenth indicates that the number will be shortened to have just one decimal place after we have rounded. To round 0.68 to the nearest tenth, for example, we can use a number line to show where 0.68 lies between 0.60 (or 0.6) and 0.70 (0.7), as in Figure 4.7. Because 0.68 is closer to 0.70 (0.7) than to 0.60 (0.6), we round up: 0.68 to the nearest tenth is 0.7. We write $0.68 \approx 0.7$ to mean that 0.68 is approximately equal to 0.7.

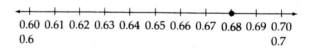

FIGURE 4.7   Decimal position of 0.68 on a number line

We can use another number line to help us round 1.25 to the nearest tenth. Figure 4.8 shows where 1.25 lies between 1.2 and 1.3. 1.25 is exactly halfway between 1.2 and 1.3. When the number we are rounding is equidistant between the two possible approximations, we will round up; therefore, $1.25 \approx 1.3$.

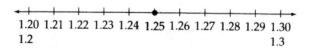

FIGURE 4.8   Decimal position of 1.25 on a number line

Again, we will use a number line to help us round 2.03 to the nearest tenth. Figure 4.9 shows where 2.03 lies between 2.0 and 2.1. Because 2.03 is closer to 2.0 than to 2.1, we round down; thus, $2.03 \approx 2.0$ rounded to the nearest tenth. In this case the zero in the tenths place stays as a placeholder to show the correct digit in the tenths place. The zero would be dropped if the number were to be rounded to the ones place.

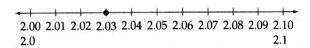

FIGURE 4.9   Decimal position of 2.03 on a number line

ROUNDING DECIMALS

1. **Identify the digit immediately to the right of the place value to which you are rounding.**
2. **If that digit is 0, 1, 2, 3, or 4 (digits less than 5), round *down*. Keep the digit in the place value to which you are rounding the same and delete any digits to the right of that place.**
3. **If that digit is 5, 6, 7, 8, or 9 (digits of 5 or greater), round *up*. Add 1 to the digit in the place value to which you are rounding and delete any digits to the right of that place.**
4. **Write zeros as needed after the rounded digit so that the rounded digit maintains the same place value as the original digit before it was rounded. (This rule applies only when rounding to a place value greater than the ones place.)**

| **EXAMPLE 1** | Round the following decimals. |

    a. Round 21.78943 to the nearest tenth.

    b. Round 467.98421 to the nearest hundredth.

    c. Round 2.48997 to four decimal places.

    d. Round 9.999 to one decimal place.

SOLUTION   **a.** $21.78943 \approx 21.8$ to the nearest tenth.
The digit immediately to the right of the digit in the tenths place is an 8, indicating that we *round up*.

    b. $467.98421 \approx 467.98$ to the nearest hundredth.
The digit immediately to the right of the digit in the hundredths place is a 4, indicating that we *round down*.

    c. $2.48997 \approx 2.4900$ to the nearest ten-thousandth.
The digit immediately to the right of the digit in the ten-thousandths place is a 7. To round up we add 1 ten-thousandth to 4899 and get 4900 ten thousandths.

    d. $9.999 \approx 10.0$ to one decimal place.
The digit immediately to the right of the digit in the first place is a 9, so we *round up*. When we add one tenth to nine tenths, we get ten tenths or 1 and zero tenths. We carry the 1 and add it to the 9 in the units place to get 10 and zero tenths. The 0 in the tenths place is essential because we are rounding to one decimal place. ■

Dividing Signed Decimals by Integers

Imagine that you are going to have a pizza party at your home to celebrate the good grade you received on your last prealgebra exam. You call in an order for three large pizzas for you and a few classmates, and you are told over the phone the price is $29.85 for the pizzas, not including tax. To determine your cost per pizza, you would divide the price of the pizzas by the number of pizzas. The problem $29.85 ÷ 3 can be written in the long division format as follows.

$$
\begin{array}{r}
9.95 \\
3\overline{)29.85} \\
\underline{27} \\
2\,8 \\
\underline{2\,7} \\
15 \\
\underline{15} \\
0
\end{array}
$$

Your cost per pizza would be $9.95. This solution was found by first placing the decimal point in the quotient directly above the decimal point in the dividend and then performing long division.

DIVIDING A SIGNED DECIMAL BY AN INTEGER

1. **Rewrite the problem using the long division format.**
2. **Place the decimal point in the quotient directly above the decimal point in the dividend.**
3. **Perform long division.**
4. **If no rounding is requested, continue dividing until the remainder is zero. If rounding is requested, round to the appropriate place.**
5. **Use the rules for dividing integers to determine the sign of the quotient.**

EXAMPLE 2

Divide the following signed decimals by integers.

a. $-1,201.62 ÷ 42$ **b.** $-0.2006 ÷ (-20)$

SOLUTION

After rewriting the problem in long division form, write the decimal point in the quotient directly above the decimal point in the dividend and then divide.

a. $-1,201.62 ÷ 42$

$$
\begin{array}{r}
28.61 \\
42\overline{)1,201.62} \\
\underline{84} \\
361 \\
\underline{336} \\
25\,6 \\
\underline{25\,2} \\
42 \\
\underline{42} \\
0
\end{array}
$$

Check

$$
\begin{array}{r}
28.61 \\
+\quad 42 \\
\hline
5722 \\
114440 \\
\hline
1,201.62 \ \checkmark
\end{array}
$$

$-1,201.62 ÷ 42 = -28.61$

b. $-0.2006 \div (-20)$

$$
\begin{array}{r}
0.01003 \\
20\overline{)0.20060} \\
\underline{20} \\
00 \\
\underline{0} \\
06 \\
\underline{0} \\
60 \\
\underline{60} \\
0
\end{array}
$$

Check
$$
\begin{array}{r}
0.01003 \\
\times \quad\;\; 20 \\
\hline
0.20060 \;\; \surd
\end{array}
$$

20 divided into the first 0 is 0 and is customarily written in the ones place to help us locate the decimal point. 20 into the first two digits (02) is also 0, and this 0 is placed in the tenths place. This 0 is mandatory because it is a place holder to the right of the decimal point. Without the zeros as place holders after the decimal point, the quotient would then be 0.13 and would be incorrect.

Also, a zero is inserted after the 6 in the dividend so that the long division can be completed. Inserting additional zeros after a digit to the right of the decimal point does not change the value of the number; $20.006 = 20.0060$ because both are equivalent to $20\frac{3}{500}$.

$-0.2006 \div (-20) = 0.01003$ ■

In the preceding examples each division resulted in a remainder of 0. When a division problem does not result in a remainder of 0, we continue dividing until the quotient has one more place to the right of the decimal point than the requested place for rounding. We then round the quotient to the requested place.

| **EXAMPLE 3** | Divide 35.781 by 7 and round the quotient to the nearest thousandth. |

SOLUTION   Continue dividing until the quotient has a digit in the ten-thousandths place (four decimal places) and then round to the nearest thousandth (three decimal places). Here we show only the divisor, dividend, and quotient.

$$
\begin{array}{r}
5.1115 \approx 5.112 \\
7\overline{)35.7810}
\end{array}
$$
■

Dividing by Powers of 10

In the last section we studied a pattern and found a quick way to multiply by powers of 10. We can study another pattern to find a quick way to divide decimals by powers of 10. From Figure 4.10 we see that when we divide a decimal by 10, 100, 1,000, and so on, we can count the zeros in the power of 10 to determine the number of decimal places to the left we move the decimal point in the dividend.

Decimal		Power of Ten		
1.414	÷	10	=	0.1414
01.414	÷	100	=	0.01414
001.414	÷	1,000	=	0.001414
0001.414	÷	10,000	=	0.0001414

FIGURE 4.10   Dividing 1.414 by powers of 10

EXAMPLE 4

Divide.

a. $4.872 \div 1,000$ **b.** $22.671 \div 10$

c. $-194,322.6 \div 1,000,000$ **d.** $0.1239 \div 10,000$

SOLUTION   Move the decimal point in the dividend as many places to the left as there are zeros in the power of 10.

a. $4.872 \div 1,000 = 0.004872$

b. $22.671 \div 10 = 2.2671$

c. $-194,322.6 \div 1,000,000 = -0.1943226$

d. $0.1239 \div 10,000 = 0.00001239$ ■

Dividing Signed Decimals by Signed Decimals

Imagine that you decide to train to become the fastest marathon runner in the world. (A marathon is approximately 26.2 miles.) A friend tells you that if you want to be the fastest ever, you will have to train to be able to run the marathon at an average rate of 13.1 miles per hour. What would be your time if you could run that fast and complete such an event?

To calculate the amount of time it would take you to run a marathon at 13.1 miles per hour, you could use the following formula.

$$t(\text{time in hours}) = \frac{d(\text{distance traveled in miles})}{r(\text{rate in miles per hour})}$$

Your time could be found according to the formula by dividing 26.2, the distance of the marathon, by 13.1, your rate of speed. The division problem is written

$$\frac{26.2}{13.1}$$

Because the divisor is a decimal, we change the problem so that the divisor is an integer. We multiply the divisor by 10 so that the decimal point in 13.1 moves 1 place to the right and the product is 131. But if we multiply the divisor by 10, we must also multiply the dividend by 10 to keep the fraction equivalent.

$$\frac{26.2 \cdot 10}{13.1 \cdot 10} = \frac{262}{131} = 2$$

or in long division format $13.1\overline{)26.2}$ becomes $131.\overline{)262.}^{\,2.}$

By multiplying by $\dfrac{10}{10}$ (or 1) the decimal point is shifted to the right an equal number of places in the divisor and dividend to give us an integer divisor. We divide and determine that it would take you exactly 2 hours to run the fastest marathon ever.

Any division problem with a decimal divisor can be changed so that the divisor is an integer. In the case of $0.324 \div 0.08$, for instance, the divisor and dividend are each multiplied by 100 so that the divisor is an integer. The decimal point is shifted 2 places to the right in both numbers.

$$\frac{0.324 \cdot 100}{0.08 \cdot 100} = \frac{32.4}{8} = 4.05$$

or in long division format

$$0.08\overline{)0.324} \quad \text{becomes} \quad 8.\overline{)32.40} \quad \leftarrow \text{Insert a zero.}$$

DIVIDING A SIGNED DECIMAL BY A SIGNED DECIMAL

1. **Rewrite the problem using the long division format without negative signs.**
2. **Multiply the divisor and dividend by the smallest power of 10 that changes the divisor into an integer. Move the decimal point in both the divisor and dividend the corresponding number of places to the right.**
3. **Place the decimal point in the quotient directly above the new location of the decimal point in the dividend.**
4. **Perform long division.**
5. **If no rounding is requested, continue dividing until the remainder is zero. If rounding is requested, round to the appropriate place.**
6. **Use the rules for dividing integers to determine the sign of the quotient.**

EXAMPLE 5	Divide the following signed decimals.

  a. $-1.4059 \div (-1.7)$ **b.** $1{,}162 \div (-0.28)$

SOLUTION   **a.** $-1.4059 \div (-1.7)$

Multiply the divisor and dividend by 10 to move the decimal point one place to the right in each number and make the divisor an integer.

$$
\begin{array}{r}
0.827 \\
1.7\overline{)1.4.059} \\
\underline{1\,3\,6} \\
45 \\
\underline{34} \\
119 \\
\underline{119} \\
0
\end{array}
\qquad
\textbf{Check}
\qquad
\begin{array}{r}
0.827 \\
\times \quad 1.7 \\
\hline
5789 \\
+ \quad 8270 \\
\hline
1.4059 \;\; \surd
\end{array}
$$

$-1.4059 \div (-1.7) = 0.827$ The signs are used to determine the quotient's sign.

b. $1,162 \div (-0.28)$

It is necessary to write a decimal point and two zeros to the right of the number in the dividend so that both numbers can be multiplied by 100 and the decimal point can be moved to the right two places in both the divisor and the dividend.

$$
\begin{array}{r}
4{,}150. \\
0.28\overline{)1{,}162.00.} \\
1\,12 \\
\hline
42 \\
28 \\
\hline
14\ 0 \\
14\ 0 \\
\hline
00 \\
0 \\
\hline
0
\end{array}
\qquad
\textbf{Check}
\qquad
\begin{array}{r}
4{,}150 \\
\times\quad 0.28 \\
\hline
33200 \\
+\quad 83000 \\
\hline
1{,}162.00 \ \sqrt{}
\end{array}
$$

$1,162 \div (-0.28) = -4,150$ The signs are used to determine the quotient's sign.   ■

EXAMPLE 6   Find the quotient of 0.0324 and (-0.097) rounded to the nearest thousandth.

SOLUTION

$$
\begin{array}{r}
0.3340 \approx 0.334 \\
0.097\overline{)0.032{,}4000} \\
29\ 1 \\
\hline
3\ 30 \\
2\ 91 \\
\hline
390 \\
388 \\
\hline
20 \\
0 \\
\hline
20
\end{array}
$$

←Three zeros are inserted so that the division can continue to the ten-thousandths place. The quotient is then rounded to the nearest thousandth.

Because this problem still has a remainder we could continue the division and insert more zeros, but it is not necessary to do so. The quotient has four decimal places and, thus, can be rounded to thousandths or to three places. $0.0324 \div (-0.097) = -0.334$ ■

Converting Fractions to Decimals

In Section 4.1 we converted numbers in decimal notation to fractions in lowest terms. Using division of decimals, we now can convert fractions to decimal numbers. Recall that a fraction denotes division so $\frac{3}{4}$ means $3 \div 4$.

Therefore, to change $\frac{3}{4}$ to a decimal, we divide 3 by 4 using decimals. In the process of dividing we insert zeros after the decimal point in the dividend so the division process can be continued.

$$\frac{3}{4} = 3 \div 4 = 0.75 \qquad 4\overline{)3.00}^{\,0.75} \quad \leftarrow\text{Insert zeros after the decimal point.}$$

The number 0.75 is an example of a **terminating decimal** because when 3 is divided by 4, the division ends or terminates when the remainder is 0. The fraction $\frac{3}{4}$ is thus equivalent to the terminating decimal 0.75. Table 4.1 includes some fractions with a numerator of 1 that are equivalent to terminating decimals.

$\frac{1}{2}$	$\frac{1}{4}$	$\frac{1}{5}$	$\frac{1}{8}$	$\frac{1}{10}$	$\frac{1}{20}$	$\frac{1}{25}$
0.5	0.25	0.2	0.125	0.1	0.05	0.04

TABLE 4.1   Fraction and terminating decimal equivalents

We can predict when a fraction will convert into a terminating decimal. If the denominator of a fraction has a prime factorization containing only 2s and 5s, then we know that it will be a terminating decimal. The fraction $\frac{1}{40}$ is a terminating decimal because the prime factorization of 40 is $2 \cdot 2 \cdot 2 \cdot 5$; $\frac{1}{40}$ is equivalent to 0.025.

Many fractions do not convert into terminating decimals with a final remainder of 0. If we convert $\frac{3}{11}$ to a decimal, for example, the division process will not terminate with a final remainder of 0.

To convert $\frac{3}{11}$, divide 3 by 11.

$$
\begin{array}{r}
0.2727... \\
11\overline{)3.0000} \\
\underline{2\,2} \\
80 \\
\underline{77} \\
30 \\
\underline{22} \\
80 \\
\underline{77} \\
3
\end{array}
$$

←Insert zeros after the decimal point.

←Dividing 11 into 30 again is exactly the same division that was done to start the problem, so the digits in the quotient will start to repeat.

When we divide 3 by 11 we will never get a remainder of 0; the fraction $\frac{3}{11}$ converts into the **repeating decimal** 0.2727.... To avoid writing the repeating block of digits 27 over and over again, we write a bar (or *vinculum*) over the 27 to indicate that the digits will repeat forever: $0.\overline{27}$. Table 4.2 lists some fractions with a numerator of 1 that convert to repeating decimals.

$\dfrac{1}{3}$	$\dfrac{1}{6}$	$\dfrac{1}{7}$	$\dfrac{1}{9}$	$\dfrac{1}{11}$	$\dfrac{1}{12}$	$\dfrac{1}{15}$
$0.\overline{3}$	$0.1\overline{6}$	$0.\overline{142857}$	$0.\overline{1}$	$0.\overline{09}$	$0.08\overline{3}$	$0.0\overline{6}$

TABLE 4.2   Fraction and repeating decimal equivalents

We can predict when a fraction will convert into a repeating decimal as opposed to a terminating decimal. If the denominator of a fraction has a prime factorization containing primes other than 2 and 5, then we know that it will be a repeating decimal. The fraction $\dfrac{1}{30}$ is a repeating decimal because the prime factorization of 30 is $2 \cdot 3 \cdot 5$; $\dfrac{1}{30}$ is equivalent to $0.0\overline{3}$.

CONVERTING A SIGNED FRACTION TO A SIGNED DECIMAL

1. **Divide the denominator into the numerator, adding zeros to the numerator as needed.**
2. **When the remainder is zero, terminate the division.**
3. **When the remainder is not zero, continue dividing until the digit(s) in the quotient start to repeat.**
4. **The sign of the decimal is the same as the sign of the fraction.**

EXAMPLE 7

Convert the following fractions to either a terminating or a repeating decimal. Show the vinculum symbol over those digits that repeat.

a. $\dfrac{88}{27}$ b. $\dfrac{13}{8}$

SOLUTION

To convert a signed fraction to a signed decimal, divide the denominator into the numerator.

a.
$$
\begin{array}{r}
3.259 \\
27\overline{)88.0000} \\
\underline{81} \\
7\,0 \\
\underline{5\,4} \\
1\,60 \\
\underline{1\,35} \\
250 \\
\underline{243} \\
70 \\
\end{array}
$$

←The partial dividend is 70.

←Dividing 27 into 70 here is the same as the second division, so the digits in the quotient will start to repeat.

$\dfrac{88}{27} = 3.2\overline{59}$

b.

$$\begin{array}{r} 1.625 \\ 8\overline{)13.000} \\ \underline{8} \\ 5\,0 \\ \underline{4\,8} \\ 20 \\ \underline{16} \\ 40 \\ \underline{40} \\ 0 \end{array}$$ ←Discontinue dividing when the remainder is 0.

$$\frac{13}{8} = 1.625$$ ■

An application of converting a fraction to a decimal is figuring out a person's batting average in either baseball or softball. Batting averages are calculated by dividing the number of hits by the number of times at bat and the averages are always rounded to the thousandths place.

EXAMPLE 8 | Dawn gets 25 hits in 74 times at bat playing for her college's softball team. What is her batting average?

SOLUTION | To calculate her batting average, divide the number of hits by the number of times at bat and round the answer to the nearest thousandth.

$$\text{Batting average} = \frac{\text{number of hits}}{\text{number of times at bat}}$$

$$\text{Dawn's batting average} = \frac{25}{74}$$

$$\begin{array}{r} 0.3378 \approx 0.338 \\ 74\overline{)25.0000} \end{array}$$

Dawn's batting average is 0.338. This indicates that if she were to bat 1,000 times during a season, she would get 338 hits: an excellent average.   ■

P R A C T I C E   F O R   S U C C E S S

Practice 1. Round 24.987234 to the nearest tenth, hundredth, thousandth, and ten-thousandth.

Practice 2. Divide −767.18 by 89.

Practice 3. Divide −334.8 by −0.07 and round to nearest thousandth.

Practice 4. Divide −23.2 by 10,000.

Practice 5. Convert $\frac{11}{13}$ to a decimal and round to the nearest hundredth.

Practice 6. Joe DiMaggio had 2,214 hits in 6,821 times at bat during his career in the major leagues. Determine Joe's lifetime batting average.

EXERCISES 4.4

In exercises 1–8, round to the nearest tenth.

1. 4.69
2. 21.96
3. 1,458.72
4. 2,949.44
5. 32.85999
6. 96.75778
7. 7.99
8. 29.97

In exercises 9–16, round to the nearest hundredth.

9. 12.115
10. 997.335
11. 220.996
12. 449.9871
13. 8.66432
14. 12.72349
15. 49.99642
16. 79.95783

In exercises 17–24, round to the nearest thousandth.

17. 18.3333
18. 69.2222
19. 861.0045
20. 279.0085
21. 3.000065
22. 14.000089
23. 999.999648
24. 777.999985

In exercises 25–30, round as indicated.

25. Round 0.61943 to four decimal places.
26. Round 0.80074 to three decimal places.
27. Round 2.9985 to one decimal place.
28. Round 45.9511 to two decimal places.
29. Round $27.895 to the nearest dollar.
30. Round $94.5221 to the nearest penny.

In exercises 31–50, divide the signed decimals. Round to the nearest thousandth as needed.

31. $48.15 \div (-15)$
32. $-97.234 \div (-2)$
33. $665.456 \div 8.8$
34. $438.207 \div (-7.7)$
35. $8,947.4 \div 28$
36. $1,607.04 \div 93$
37. $10 \div 0.7$
38. $22 \div 0.9$
39. $397.41 \div (-50)$
40. $-358.04 \div (-40)$
41. $0.6512 \div (-0.8)$
42. $-0.2984 \div (-0.4)$
43. $42.6 \div (-17)$
44. $-52.8 \div (-19)$
45. $(-1,100) \div (-0.25)$
46. $-7,700 \div 0.0035$
47. $-9.321 \div (-2.4)$
48. $8.764 \div (-3.7)$
49. $3,976.84 \div 9.8$
50. $793.82 \div 3.8$

In exercises 51–58, solve each division. Round to the nearest thousandth as needed.

51. Divide 28,712 by -0.008.   **52.** Divide $-5,760.324$ by 0.006.

53. Divide -0.65 into 82.   **54.** Divide 0.95 into -92.

55. Divide negative six thousand five hundred sixty-one ten-thousandths by negative twenty-seven thousandths.

56. Divide ninety-six thousandths into four and six thousand nine hundred forty-four ten-thousandths.

57. Divide negative twelve and five tenths into one.

58. Divide negative one by six and twenty-five hundredths.

In exercises 59–64, find the quotients without using a calculator or long division.

59. $2.839 \div (-100)$ **60.** $-6.394 \div 10$

61. $0.126 \div 10,000$ **62.** $-8.2 \div 1,000$

63. $-3,246 \div (-1,000,000)$ **64.** $7,871 \div (-100,000)$

In exercises 65–78, convert the fractions to either a terminating or repeating decimal.

65. $-\dfrac{3}{5}$ **66.** $-\dfrac{17}{20}$

67. $-\dfrac{5}{7}$ **68.** $-\dfrac{7}{11}$

69. $\dfrac{8}{9}$ **70.** $\dfrac{2}{3}$

71. $\dfrac{21}{25}$ **72.** $\dfrac{47}{50}$

73. $\dfrac{5}{6}$ **74.** $\dfrac{11}{12}$

75. $\dfrac{15}{8}$ **76.** $\dfrac{17}{16}$

77. $-\dfrac{11}{7}$ **78.** $-\dfrac{14}{13}$

In exercises 79–86, solve each problem.

79. The shortstop on a community college softball team gets 39 hits in 102 times at bat one season. What was her batting average?

80. The right fielder on a community college baseball team gets 51 hits in 129 times at bat one season. What was his batting average?

81. Girl Scout Troop 902 sold cookies to raise money for their troop. At the end of the sale, the troop had collected $3,497.50. If each box of cookies cost $2.50, how many boxes of cookies did the troop sell?

82. If a case (24 cans) of diet soda costs $4.32 on sale, what is the cost of one can?

83. The balance due after Kathy's downpayment on her car loan is $9,324. The interest on the loan is $870.28 per year for 4 years. If Kathy pays back the loan including the interest in 48 monthly payments, what will be the amount of each payment? (*Hint:* Round quotient to the nearest penny.)

84. Mario bought 6 textbooks at the college bookstore at a cost of $114.68 one semester. Find his average cost per book. (*Hint:* Round the quotient to the nearest penny.)

85. On a recent trip Dorothy drove her van 706 miles and used 48.6 gallons of gasoline. Determine the van's mileage per gallon to the nearest tenth of a mile.

86. On that same trip, during one stretch, Dorothy traveled 250 miles non-stop in 4.8 hours. Determine her average speed. Round your answer to the nearest mile per hour.

In exercises 87–92, use the following approximate information for working off the calories from eating the foods listed.

Food Consumed	Walking	Jogging	Waiting
Chocolate chip cookie (50 cal)	0.16 hour	0.04 hour	0.64 hour
Ice cream, $\frac{2}{3}$ cup (200 cal)	0.64 hour	0.17 hour	2.56 hours
Pizza, 1 slice (300 cal)	0.96 hour	0.25 hour	3.85 hours
Potato chips, 10 chips (115 cal)	0.37 hour	0.10 hour	1.47 hours

87. How many hours would you have to walk to work off 7 chocolate chip cookies?

88. How many hours would you have to wait without eating to work off 4 slices of pizza?

89. You eat 10 chocolate chip cookies. After waiting for 3 hours, approximately how many cookies have you worked off?

90. You eat 70 potato chips. After jogging for 0.50 hour, how many potato chips have you worked off?

91. If you eat 2 slices of pizza, $\frac{2}{3}$ cup of ice cream, and 3 chocolate chip cookies, how long would you have to walk to work off the food?

92. If you eat 2 cups of ice cream and 5 chocolate chip cookies, how long do you have to jog to work off the dessert?

Looking Back

93. Simplify -4^0.

94. Simplify $(-4)^0$.

95. Simplify $(-4)^2$.

96. Simplify -4^2.

97. In the exponential expression 7^3, the number _____ is called the base, the number _____ is called the exponent, and the value of the expression is _____.

98. What is right and what is wrong with writing $2^4 = 4^2$ and $3^2 = 2^3$?

99. Simplify 1^{35}.

PRACTICE-FOR-SUCCESS ANSWERS

1. 25.0 24.99 24.987 24.9872		**2.** −8.62		**3.** 4,782.857
4. −0.00232		**5.** 0.85		**6.** 0.325

4.5 SQUARE ROOTS AS DECIMALS

OBJECTIVES

- ☐ To find the square root of a perfect square
- ☐ To estimate and find the square root of a nonperfect square
- ☐ To determine if a square root is rational or irrational
- ☐ To simplify expressions that include square roots
- ☐ To use square roots to solve word problems

In Chapter 1 we learned that when a whole number is raised to the second power we say that we are "squaring" the number; 10^2 or "10 squared" = $10 \cdot 10 = 100$. In this section we will study the inverse operation to squaring, finding the square root of a number; the square root of 100 is 10.

Pythagorean Theorem

Understanding the concept of square root is necessary in order to be able to use one of the gems of geometry, the Pythagorean theorem. (Historians believe that this theorem was first developed about 2,500 years ago by the Greek mathematician and philosopher Pythagoras or by someone in his group, the Pythagoreans.) The Pythagorean theorem states that the square of the length of the hypotenuse (the longer side) of a right triangle equals the sum of the squares of the lengths of the legs (the two shorter sides). Figure 4.11 shows a right triangle (a triangle with a 90° angle) and the relationship of the sides according to Pythagoras.

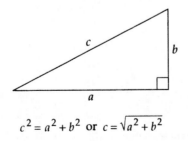

$$c^2 = a^2 + b^2 \text{ or } c = \sqrt{a^2 + b^2}$$

FIGURE 4.11   **Relationship between the sides of a right triangle**

We can see in the second form of the Pythagorean theorem, $c = \sqrt{a^2 + b^2}$, that the hypotenuse equals the square root of the sum of the squares of the lengths of the legs. (The symbol $\sqrt{}$ is called the *square root symbol* or *radical sign*, and is reserved for the positive square root of a number.) Using the Pythagorean theorem, if we know the lengths of the two legs and we know how to find square roots, we can find the length of the hypotenuse c. Suppose we know that two legs of a right triangle are 3 meters and 4 meters in length as in Figure 4.12, and we want to determine the length of the longer side, the hypotenuse.

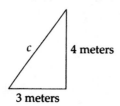

3 meters

FIGURE 4.12   Right triangle with legs of 3 meters and 4 meters

Using the second form of the Pythagorean theorem with leg $a = 3$ and leg $b = 4$,

$$c = \sqrt{a^2 + b^2}$$
$$c = \sqrt{3^2 + 4^2}$$
$$c = \sqrt{9 + 16}$$
$$c = \sqrt{25}$$

To find c we now have to find the **square root** of 25, the positive number whose square equals 25. The square root of 25 is 5 because $5^2 = 25$, so the hypotenuse of the right triangle is 5 meters.

Square Roots

While we were finding the hypotenuse of a right triangle, we learned that the square root of any number can be obtained by finding the positive number we need to square to get that number. Using the square root symbol $\sqrt{}$, we can write a few more examples.

$$\sqrt{144} = 12 \text{ because } 12^2 = 144$$
$$\sqrt{900} = 30 \text{ because } 30^2 = 900$$
$$\sqrt{\frac{81}{64}} = \frac{9}{8} \text{ because } \left(\frac{9}{8}\right)^2 = \frac{81}{64}$$

DEFINITION   SQUARE ROOT

If a is nonnegative and $a^2 = b$, then $\sqrt{b} = a$.

According to the definition of square root, if we know that $11^2 = 121$ then we know that $\sqrt{121} = 11$. We conclude that the more numbers that we identify as the squares of other numbers, the more square roots we will know.

Perfect Squares

Numbers that are the squares of other numbers, such as 1, 4, 9, 16, 25, and 36, are called *perfect square numbers*. In general a whole number is called a *perfect square* if another whole number exists whose square equals the first number.

DEFINITION	WHOLE NUMBER PERFECT SQUARE

A whole number n is called a perfect square if a whole number m exists such that $n = m^2$.

Most whole numbers, for example 7, and 22, are not perfect squares. The number 9 is a perfect square since $9 = 3^2$. Using the definition of a perfect square, we would say that $n = 9$ and $m = 3$. Table 4.3 lists the whole numbers from 1 to 16 and their squares.

1	2	3	4	5	6	7	8	9	10	11	12	13	14	15	16
1	4	9	16	25	36	49	64	81	100	121	144	169	196	225	256

TABLE 4.3 **Perfect square whole numbers from 1 to 256**

Because the square root of any number can be obtained by finding the positive number we need to square to get that number, the number directly above any perfect square number in the table is its square root.

EXAMPLE 1	Find the square roots of the following numbers using Table 4.3, the Appendix, or a calculator.

a. $\sqrt{169}$ **b.** $\sqrt{6{,}084}$

SOLUTION   **a.** Using Table 4.3:

$\sqrt{169} = 13$ because $13^2 = 169$

b. Using the Appendix, find 6,084 in the column n^2. Look two columns to the left to find $\sqrt{6,084}$.

n	primes	n^2	$\sqrt{n}$
78	$2 \cdot 3 \cdot 13$	6,084	8.8317608663

$\sqrt{6,084} = 78$ because $78^2 = 6,084$ ■

Square Roots of Nonperfect Squares

What are the square roots of numbers that are not perfect squares, for example, $\sqrt{40}$? The whole number 40, which is not a perfect square, lies on the number line between 36 and 49, so $\sqrt{40}$ lies between $\sqrt{36}$ and $\sqrt{49}$ on the number line or between 6 and 7. Because 40 is closer to 36 than to 49, we can estimate that $\sqrt{40}$, being greater than 6, is approximately 6.3. We can check our estimate by squaring 6.3.

$$
\begin{array}{r}
6.3 \\
\times\ \ 6.3 \\
\hline
189 \\
3780 \\
\hline
39.69
\end{array}
$$

Because $(6.3)^2 = 39.69$, which is close to 40, 6.3 is a good estimate for $\sqrt{40}$ but it is not the *exact* square root of 40. Numbers such as 40 that are not whole number perfect squares do not have an exact square root. We can only approximate their square roots because the square roots of nonperfect square numbers are nonrepeating, nonterminating decimals. The square roots of nonperfect squares are called **irrational numbers** because they cannot be written in the rational form $\frac{a}{b}$. The irrational numbers together with the rational numbers form the set of **real numbers.** Every point on the number line corresponds to a real number and every real number determines a point on the number line.

Although algorithms exist to approximate the square roots of nonperfect square numbers, it is more convenient to find their square roots using a square root table (the Appendix) or a calculator that has a square root key. $\sqrt{40} = 6.3245553 \ldots$ or, to the nearest thousandth, $\sqrt{40} \approx 6.325$.

EXAMPLE 2

Determine between what two consecutive whole numbers the following numbers lie. Then find their approximate square roots using either the Appendix or a calculator and round to the nearest thousandth.

a. $\sqrt{8}$　　**b.** $\sqrt{91}$

SOLUTION   **a.** The number $\sqrt{8}$ lies between $\sqrt{4}$ and $\sqrt{9}$ or between 2 and 3. Using the Appendix, find 8 in the column titled n and then look for the column titled $\sqrt{n}$ (three columns to the right) to find the $\sqrt{8}$.

n	primes	n^2	$\sqrt{n}$
8	2^3	64	2.8284271247

$$\sqrt{8} \approx 2.8284271247$$

$$\approx 2.828 \quad \text{(to the nearest thousandth)}$$

b. The number $\sqrt{91}$ lies between $\sqrt{81}$ and $\sqrt{100}$ or between 9 and 10. Using the Appendix, $\sqrt{91} \approx 9.5393920142 \approx 9.539$ (to the nearest thousandth).   ■

For a whole number that is not a perfect square, we can estimate to the tenths place what its square root will be. For instance, $\sqrt{48}$ is between $\sqrt{36}$ and $\sqrt{49}$ or between 6 and 7. Because $\sqrt{48}$ is much closer to $\sqrt{49}$ than to $\sqrt{36}$, we might estimate it to be 6.9. Looking at the Appendix we find $\sqrt{48} \approx 6.9282032303$, so our estimate was accurate to the tenths place. When we estimate we get a better feel for what the square root of the number is without having to consult a table or calculator. With practice we should be able to estimate with some accuracy the square roots of whole numbers to the tenths place.

EXAMPLE 3   Estimate the value of $\sqrt{150}$ to the nearest tenth. Then check your estimate using the table in the Appendix or a calculator.

SOLUTION   Using Table 4.3, $\sqrt{150}$ is between $\sqrt{144}$ and $\sqrt{169}$ or between 12 and 13. Because $\sqrt{150}$ is closer to $\sqrt{144}$ than to $\sqrt{169}$ and less than halfway between the two, a potential estimate (but certainly not the only reasonable estimate) is 12.2. According to the Appendix $\sqrt{150} \approx 12.247448714$, so our estimate was accurate to the tenths place.   ■

EXAMPLE 4   Use a calculator to find $\sqrt{2,718.2818}$ to the nearest thousandth.

SOLUTION $\sqrt{2,718.2818} \approx 52.137144 \approx 52.137$ ■

EXAMPLE 5   Determine whether the following numbers are rational or irrational and explain why.

a. $\sqrt{9}$ **b.** $\sqrt{30}$ **c.** $\sqrt{2.25}$ **d.** $\sqrt{\dfrac{25}{9}}$

SOLUTION   **a.** $\sqrt{9} = 3$ since $3^2 = 9$.

The number 3 can be written as $\dfrac{3}{1}$, so $\sqrt{9}$ is rational.

b. $\sqrt{30} = 5.4772255751 \ldots$

$\sqrt{30}$ cannot be written in the form $\dfrac{a}{b}$ because the decimal portion is nonterminating and nonrepeating.

c. Using a calculator, $\sqrt{2.25} = 1.5$ since $(1.5)^2 = 2.25$.

The number 1.5 can be written as $1\dfrac{5}{10} = \dfrac{15}{10} = \dfrac{3}{2}$, so $\sqrt{2.25}$ is rational.

d. $\sqrt{\dfrac{25}{9}} = \dfrac{5}{3} = 1.\overline{6}$. Even though this decimal is infinite, it is repeating.

The number $\dfrac{5}{3}$ is a rational number, so $\sqrt{\dfrac{25}{9}}$ is rational.   ■

So far we have only taken the square roots of positive numbers. What is the square root of a negative number? Some people might suggest that, for example, $\sqrt{-100} = -10$. However, $(-10) \cdot (-10) = 100$, which is not -100, so -10 is not the square root. Nor is 10 the square root of $\sqrt{-100}$ because $10 \cdot 10 = 100$, which is also not -100. No rational or irrational number square can possibly equal -100 so $\sqrt{-100}$ is undefined. If you try to calculate $\sqrt{-100}$ on a calculator, you will generate an error similar to that generated by dividing by 0. (However, you can calculate $\sqrt{0} = 0$.) For our purposes in this book, we will say that the square root of a negative number is undefined.

Mathematical expressions can also include square roots: for example, $\sqrt{144} - \sqrt{100}$. The square root symbol acts as a grouping symbol, so in the order of operations, we perform the operation inside the symbol first, then multiplications and divisions from left to right, followed by additions and subtractions from left to right.

EXAMPLE 6	Simplify the following expressions.

a. $\sqrt{121} - \sqrt{100} + \sqrt{81}$ **b.** $4\sqrt{36} + 7\sqrt{25}$

c. $\dfrac{\sqrt{196}}{\sqrt{169}} - \dfrac{\sqrt{49}}{\sqrt{169}}$ **d.** $(\sqrt{64})^2$

SOLUTION   Because the square root symbol acts as a grouping symbol, we find the square roots before performing any of the four fundamental operations.

a. $\sqrt{121} - \sqrt{100} + \sqrt{81} = 11 - 10 + 9 = 1 + 9 = 10$.

b. When a number is written next to the square root symbol, multiplication is implied.

$$4\sqrt{36} + 7\sqrt{25} = 4 \cdot \sqrt{36} + 7 \cdot \sqrt{25}$$
$$= 4 \cdot 6 + 7 \cdot 5$$
$$= 24 + 35$$
$$= 59$$

c. $\dfrac{\sqrt{196}}{\sqrt{169}} - \dfrac{\sqrt{49}}{\sqrt{169}} = \dfrac{14}{13} - \dfrac{7}{13} = \dfrac{7}{13}$

d. $(\sqrt{64})^2 = \sqrt{64} \cdot \sqrt{64} = 8 \cdot 8 = 64$

When a square root is squared, we get the number inside the square root symbol as the answer. ■

At the beginning of the section we saw that square roots are taken in geometry when we want to find the hypotenuse of a right triangle using the Pythagorean theorem. Square roots are used in applications in other fields as well; the next example is taken from physics.

EXAMPLE 7

A basketball is dropped from the top of a hotel which is 729 feet tall. The time it takes to reach the ground is given by the formula $t = \sqrt{\dfrac{d}{16}}$ (where t is the time in seconds and d is the distance in feet). How long will it take for the basketball to reach the ground?

SOLUTION

Because the basketball is dropped from a hotel 729 feet high, the ball will travel a distance d of 729 feet before reaching the ground.

$t = \sqrt{\dfrac{729}{16}} = \dfrac{27}{4} = 6.75$ The basketball will reach the ground in 6.75 seconds. ■

P R A C T I C E   F O R   S U C C E S S

Practice 1. Determine $\sqrt{676}$ by using the Appendix or a calculator.

Practice 2. Determine $\sqrt{70}$ by using the Appendix or a calculator and then round to the nearest thousandth.

Practice 3. Determine between which two whole numbers $\sqrt{110}$ lies. Then estimate the square root to the tenths place.

Practice 4. Determine if $\sqrt{1.4641}$ is rational or irrational.

Practice 5. Simplify $\sqrt{49} - \sqrt{64} - \sqrt{121}$.

Practice 6. Using the second form of the Pythagorean theorem, $c = \sqrt{a^2 + b^2}$, determine the length of the hypotenuse of a right triangle whose legs are 5 meters and 12 meters long, respectively.

EXERCISES 4.5

In exercises 1–10, find the square roots without using a table or a calculator.

1. $\sqrt{9}$

2. $\sqrt{0}$

3. $\sqrt{\dfrac{25}{4}}$ **4.** $\sqrt{\dfrac{81}{100}}$

5. $\sqrt{64}$ **6.** $\sqrt{36}$

7. $\sqrt{49}$ **8.** $\sqrt{144}$

9. $\sqrt{0.25}$ **10.** $\sqrt{0.0049}$

In exercises 11–18, find the square roots using the table in the Appendix or a calculator.

11. $\sqrt{625}$ **12.** $\sqrt{729}$

13. $\sqrt{8,836}$ **14.** $\sqrt{2,025}$

15. $\sqrt{5.76}$ **16.** $\sqrt{98.01}$

17. $\sqrt{841}$ **18.** $\sqrt{324}$

In exercises 19–26, determine between which two consecutive whole numbers the square roots lie. Then use either the table in the Appendix or a calculator to find the approximate value and round to the nearest thousandth.

19. $\sqrt{10}$ **20.** $\sqrt{37}$

21. $\sqrt{99}$ **22.** $\sqrt{24}$

23. $\sqrt{130}$ **24.** $\sqrt{240}$

25. $\sqrt{390}$ **26.** $\sqrt{890}$

In exercises 27–34, estimate the value of the square roots to the tenths place. Then check your estimate using either the Appendix or a calculator.

27. $\sqrt{7}$ **28.** $\sqrt{12}$

29. $\sqrt{120}$ **30.** $\sqrt{80}$

31. $\sqrt{30}$ **32.** $\sqrt{57}$

33. $\sqrt{200}$ **34.** $\sqrt{260}$

In exercises 35–42, find the square root using a calculator. Round to the nearest thousandth as needed.

35. $\sqrt{121,104}$ **36.** $\sqrt{155,236}$

37. $\sqrt{499}$ **38.** $\sqrt{599}$

39. $\sqrt{649.97}$ **40.** $\sqrt{721.981}$

41. $\sqrt{1,000}$ **42.** $\sqrt{2,000}$

In exercises 43–50, determine whether the following numbers are rational or irrational and explain why.

43. $\sqrt{2.56}$ **44.** $\sqrt{0.0121}$

45. $\sqrt{62}$ **46.** $\sqrt{85}$

47. $\sqrt{\dfrac{49}{144}}$ **48.** $\sqrt{\dfrac{4}{81}}$

49. $\sqrt{961}$ **50.** $\sqrt{3{,}025}$

In exercises 51–64, simplify the expressions.

51. $7(\sqrt{144} - 18)$ **52.** $95(\sqrt{169} - 15)$

53. $11\sqrt{100} + 7\sqrt{4}$ **54.** $27\sqrt{9} - 18\sqrt{81}$

55. $\sqrt{196} - \sqrt{64} - \sqrt{121}$ **56.** $\sqrt{16} - \sqrt{256} + \sqrt{144}$

57. $(\sqrt{100})^2$ **58.** $(\sqrt{36})^2$

59. $\dfrac{\sqrt{49}}{\sqrt{64}} - \dfrac{\sqrt{25}}{\sqrt{64}}$ **60.** $\dfrac{\sqrt{81}}{\sqrt{100}} - \dfrac{\sqrt{9}}{\sqrt{100}}$

61. $0.35\sqrt{1.44} - 40.6$ **62.** $0.62\sqrt{51.84} - 100.8$

63. $2.2(12 - 8\sqrt{56.25})$ **64.** $4.9(27 - 12\sqrt{90.25})$

In exercises 65–70, solve each problem using the Pythagorean theorem formula $c = \sqrt{a^2 + b^2}$.

65. Determine the hypotenuse of a right triangle whose legs are 6 meters and 8 meters.

66. Determine the hypotenuse of a right triangle whose legs are 9 centimeters and 40 centimeters.

67. Determine the hypotenuse of a right triangle whose legs are 7 inches and 24 inches.

68. Determine the hypotenuse of a right triangle whose legs are 8 meters and 15 meters.

69. Determine the hypotenuse of a right triangle whose legs are 11 feet and 60 feet.

70. Determine the hypotenuse of a right triangle whose legs are 36 kilometers and 77 kilometers.

In exercises 71–74, solve each problem using the formula $t = \sqrt{\dfrac{d}{16}}$ (where t is the time in seconds and d is the distance in feet).

71. A ball is dropped from the top of a building that is 144 feet high. How long will it take for the ball to reach the ground?

72. A ball is dropped from an airplane that is flying at an altitude of 7,921 feet. How long will it take for the ball to reach the ground?

73. A ball is dropped from the roof of a building and reaches the ground in 1 second. How tall is the building?

74. A ball is dropped from the roof of a building and reaches the ground in 2 seconds. How tall is the building?

Looking Back

75. What is the only even prime number?
76. Why is 1 not a prime number?
77. List the prime numbers less than 30.
78. List the prime numbers used in the denominators of fractions that can be converted to terminating decimals.
79. Prime factor 1,000.
80. Prime factor 1,600.
81. Prime factor 1,547.
82. Prime factor 561.
83. Add $\dfrac{1}{4} + \dfrac{3}{10} + \dfrac{7}{12}$.

PRACTICE-FOR-SUCCESS ANSWERS

1. 26
2. 8.367
3. Between 10 and 11, ≈ 10.5
4. Rational
5. -12
6. 13 meters

4.6   REDUCING SQUARE ROOTS

OBJECTIVES

☐ To use perfect square factors to reduce square roots
☐ To recognize completely reduced square roots
☐ To reduce square roots using prime factorizations

In the previous section we worked with decimal approximations of square roots of numbers. In this section we will introduce another technique for working with square roots that corresponds to how square roots of symbolic expressions are simplified in algebra.

Another way to discover which whole numbers are perfect squares without using a calculator or a table is to inspect the exponents in the prime factorization of the numbers. For example, consider the ten numbers shown in two columns of five numbers each. The five numbers in the left column are perfect squares, whereas the five numbers in the right column are not perfect squares. All these numbers are shown with their prime factorizations.

Perfect Squares	Not Perfect Squares
$100 = 2^2 \cdot 5^2$	$24 = 2^3 \cdot 3^1$
$144 = 2^4 \cdot 3^2$	$30 = 2^1 \cdot 3^1 \cdot 5^1$
$400 = 2^4 \cdot 5^2$	$108 = 2^2 \cdot 3^3$
$5{,}184 = 2^6 \cdot 3^4$	$800 = 2^5 \cdot 5^2$
$10{,}000 = 2^4 \cdot 5^4$	$2{,}000 = 2^4 \cdot 5^3$

After studying the exponents in the two lists you may discover that perfect square whole numbers have prime factorizations in which the exponents on all the primes are always even numbers; nonperfect square whole numbers always have at least one prime factor with an odd exponent.

EXAMPLE 1

Determine which of the following whole numbers are perfect squares.
 a. 366   **b.** 324   **c.** 200   **d.** 5,625

SOLUTION   **a.** Using the prime factorization technique we find $366 = 2^1 \cdot 3^1 \cdot 61^1$, and since at least one exponent is odd we know 366 is not a perfect square.

b. Using the prime factorization method we find $324 = 2^2 \cdot 3^4$, and since both exponents are even numbers we know 324 is a perfect square.

c. Using the prime factorization technique we find $200 = 2^3 \cdot 5^2$, and since at least one exponent is odd we know 200 is not a perfect square.

d. Without a calculator the best method to use to determine whether 5,625 is a perfect square or not is the prime factorization method. Using the prime factorization method we find $5{,}625 = 3^2 \cdot 5^4$, and since both exponents are even numbers we know 5,625 is a perfect square. ■

Reducing Square Roots

Reducing a square root is analogous to reducing a fraction in that the main idea is to make an equivalent value using smaller numbers. As an example with a fraction:

$$\frac{375}{500} = \frac{3}{4}$$

The numbers 3 and 4 are smaller and thus easier to work with compared to the numbers 375 and 500. An example using square roots is $\sqrt{50} = 5 \cdot \sqrt{2}$. The numbers 5 and 2 are smaller and easier to work with than the number 50. We can justify restructuring the equation as follows.

Square roots have a property that can be called **the product property of square roots,** and it is this property that provides the key to reducing a square root without using decimals. This property can also be stated by saying the square root of the product is the product of the square roots of the two factors. In fact, this property works with any number of factors, not just with two. For example if a, b, and c are three nonnegative numbers, then

$$\sqrt{a \cdot b \cdot c} = \sqrt{a} \cdot \sqrt{b} \cdot \sqrt{c}.$$

PRODUCT PROPERTY OF SQUARE ROOTS

If a and b are any two nonnegative numbers, then

$$\sqrt{a \cdot b} = \sqrt{a} \cdot \sqrt{b} \qquad \text{provided } a \geq 0, b \geq 0.$$

Here is how this property helps us reduce $\sqrt{50}$. We factor 50 using the number 25 as a perfect square factor.

$$\sqrt{50} = \sqrt{25 \cdot 2} \qquad \text{Factor } 50 = 25 \cdot 2.$$

$$= \sqrt{25} \cdot \sqrt{2} \qquad \text{Apply the product property of square roots to make a product of two square roots.}$$

$$= 5 \cdot \sqrt{2} \qquad \text{Simplify } \sqrt{25} = 5.$$

The real simplification occurs in the step in which the square root of the perfect square factor 25 is simplified to the value 5.

If you have a calculator you can use it to find a decimal approximation for $\sqrt{50}$. Using a calculator shows

$$\sqrt{50} \approx 7.07106781$$

If we also calculate $\sqrt{2}$ and then multiply it by 5 we get

$$5 \cdot \sqrt{2} \approx 5 \cdot (1.41421356) = 7.07106781$$

which shows that the decimal values for $\sqrt{50}$ and $5 \cdot \sqrt{2}$ are the same.

In general the technique of reducing any square root number involves factoring the number using only a perfect square factor and writing that perfect square number as the first factor.

EXAMPLE 2

Use the product property of square roots to reduce the following square roots by first finding a perfect square factor of each number and writing the perfect square factor first.

a. $\sqrt{75}$ **b.** $\sqrt{98}$ **c.** $\sqrt{405}$

SOLUTION

a. The first few entries in Table 4.3 are 4, 9, 16, and 25. Of these, only 25 is a factor of 75, so 25 is the first factor of 75.

$$\sqrt{75} = \sqrt{25 \cdot 3} = \sqrt{25} \cdot \sqrt{3} = 5 \cdot \sqrt{3}$$

b. The numbers 4, 9, 16, 25, and 36 are not factors of 98, but 49 is.

$$\sqrt{98} = \sqrt{49 \cdot 2} = \sqrt{49} \cdot \sqrt{2} = 7 \cdot \sqrt{2}$$

c. Search the list of perfect square factors until you find one that divides 405 evenly.

$$\sqrt{405} = \sqrt{81 \cdot 5} = \sqrt{81} \cdot \sqrt{5} = 9 \cdot \sqrt{5} \qquad ■$$

Another analogy holds between reducing fractions and reducing square roots. Sometimes a fraction cannot be reduced because it is already in lowest terms. At other times a fraction may only be partially reduced, and two or more reduction steps may be required to completely reduce it.

To discuss these possibilities with square roots, consider the problem of reducing $\sqrt{450}$. If you immediately recognize that 25 is a perfect square factor of 450, you can begin reducing the radical by writing

$$\sqrt{450} = \sqrt{25 \cdot 18} = \sqrt{25} \cdot \sqrt{18} = 5 \cdot \sqrt{18}$$

So $5 \cdot \sqrt{18}$ is a reduced form of $\sqrt{450}$ but it is not a complete reduction because 9 is a perfect square factor of 18. So to completely reduce $\sqrt{450}$, we should continue by writing

$$
\begin{aligned}
\sqrt{450} &= 5 \cdot \sqrt{18} \\
&= 5 \cdot \sqrt{9 \cdot 2} && \text{Factor } 18 = 9 \cdot 2. \\
&= 5 \cdot \sqrt{9} \cdot \sqrt{2} && \text{Apply the product property of square roots a second time.} \\
&= 5 \cdot 3 \cdot \sqrt{2} && \text{Simplify } \sqrt{9} = 3. \\
&= 15 \cdot \sqrt{2} && \text{Multiply } 5 \cdot 3 = 15.
\end{aligned}
$$

Because the number 2 under the square root symbol has no perfect square factor greater than 1, $\sqrt{450}$ has been completely reduced.

If we had recognized that $15^2 = 225$ and that 225 was the largest perfect square factor of 450, we could have completely reduced $\sqrt{450}$ with one application of the product property of square roots.

$$
\begin{aligned}
\sqrt{450} &= \sqrt{225 \cdot 2} && \text{Factor } 450 = 225 \cdot 2. \\
&= \sqrt{225} \cdot \sqrt{2} && \text{Apply the product property of square roots.} \\
&= 15 \cdot \sqrt{2} && \text{Simplify } \sqrt{225} = 15.
\end{aligned}
$$

DEFINITION	**COMPLETELY REDUCED SQUARE ROOT**

$\sqrt{x}$ is called completely reduced if the whole number x has no perfect square factor other than 1.

To determine whether $\sqrt{210}$ can be reduced or if it is already completely reduced, we analyze the prime factorization of 210.

$$210 = 2^1 \cdot 3^1 \cdot 5^1 \cdot 7^1$$

Since no exponent is larger than 1, we know 210 has no perfect square factor other than 1; $\sqrt{210}$ is completely reduced. Similarly, to determine if $\sqrt{224}$ is completely reduced, we again analyze the prime factorization of the given number.

$$224 = 2^5 \cdot 7^1$$

Since the exponent on the prime number base 2 is 5, we can rearrange the factors of 224 by separating the 2^5 factor into a product with an even and an odd exponent.

$$224 = 2^4 \cdot 2^1 \cdot 7^1$$

Since we can factor 224 using a perfect square number, $\sqrt{224}$ is not completely reduced.

$$\sqrt{224} = \sqrt{16 \cdot 14} = \sqrt{16} \cdot \sqrt{14} = 4 \cdot \sqrt{14}$$

This last example indicates that if a whole number has any prime factor with an exponent greater than 1, then the square root of that whole number can be reduced.

EXAMPLE 3

Determine whether the following square roots can be reduced by analyzing the exponents in the prime factorization of the given number. Perform the reduction process for those square roots that are not completely reduced.

a. $\sqrt{490}$ **b.** $\sqrt{1,001}$ **c.** $\sqrt{1,375}$

SOLUTION

a. First prime factor 490: $490 = 2^1 \cdot 5^1 \cdot 7^2$. Since the exponent on 7 is greater than 1, the square root is not completely reduced. $49 = 7^2$ is a perfect square factor so we write that number first.

$$\sqrt{490} = \sqrt{49 \cdot 10} = \sqrt{49} \cdot \sqrt{10} = 7 \cdot \sqrt{10}$$

b. First prime factor 1,001: $1,001 = 7^1 \cdot 11^1 \cdot 13^1$. Since no exponent is greater than 1, we conclude that $\sqrt{1,001}$ cannot be reduced.

c. First prime factor 1,375: $1,375 = 5^3 \cdot 11^1$. Since the exponent on 5 is greater than 1, we know $\sqrt{1,375}$ can be reduced. We begin by separating 5^3 into the product of $5^2 \cdot 5^1$, which makes even and odd powers on 5. Any odd number can be written as an even number plus 1, so in this case we break the odd number 3 into the sum $3 = 2 + 1$ and rewrite 5^3 as $5^2 \cdot 5^1$. Now we have $1,375 = 5^2 \cdot 5^1 \cdot 11^1$, and in this form we can more clearly identify the desired perfect square factoring $1,375 = 25 \cdot 55$.

$$\sqrt{1,375} = \sqrt{25 \cdot 55} = \sqrt{25} \cdot \sqrt{55} = 5 \cdot \sqrt{55}$$ ■

As when reducing fractions, you sometimes can intuitively guess appropriate factors when reducing square roots. But when the numbers are large it becomes more difficult to find the perfect square factors. The final technique we show also exploits the even exponents in the prime factorization process, stated in the key principle for eliminating a square root.

ELIMINATING A SQUARE ROOT

If b is any nonnegative number and n is an *even* whole number exponent, then

$$\sqrt{b^n} = b^{\frac{1}{2} \cdot n} \qquad \text{provided } b \geq 0.$$

In this book the principle for eliminating a square root will only be applied when the exponent n is an even number. If we apply this principle when n is odd, we will get a fractional exponent which, although mathematically correct, will not make any sense until proper fractional exponents are explained later in an algebra course. In this book we avoid exponents that are proper fractions.

As a simple example of this principle, consider the equation

$$\sqrt{25} = 5$$

rewritten in the form $\sqrt{5^2} = 5^{1/2 \cdot 2}$ Prime factor $25 = 5^2$ and eliminate the square root.

$$= 5^1 \qquad \text{Simplify } \frac{1}{2} \cdot 2 = 1.$$

$$= 5 \qquad \text{Drop the 1 exponent.}$$

To demonstrate how this principle works when the number b^n is a large perfect square, consider the prime factorization of the large number $291{,}600 = 2^4 \cdot 3^6 \cdot 5^2$. To calculate $\sqrt{291{,}600}$, use the preceding factorization with the product property of square roots and the principle of eliminating a square root.

$$\sqrt{291{,}600} = \sqrt{2^4 \cdot 3^6 \cdot 5^2} \qquad \text{Prime factor } 291{,}600.$$

$$= \sqrt{2^4} \cdot \sqrt{3^6} \cdot \sqrt{5^2} \qquad \begin{array}{l}\text{Apply the product property of} \\ \text{square roots for 3 factors.}\end{array}$$

$$= 2^{1/2 \cdot 4} \cdot 3^{1/2 \cdot 6} \cdot 5^{1/2 \cdot 2} \qquad \begin{array}{l}\text{Apply the square root elimination} \\ \text{principle.}\end{array}$$

$$= 2^2 \cdot 3^3 \cdot 5^1 \qquad \text{Calculate the new exponents.}$$

$$= 4 \cdot 27 \cdot 5 \qquad \text{Simplify the powers.}$$

$$= 540 \qquad \text{Multiply.}$$

The product property and the elimination principle of square roots can be used in conjunction with prime factorizations to simplify large nonperfect square roots. The only additional trick is to place only even powers in the first square root, as shown in the following example.

$$\sqrt{54{,}000} = \sqrt{2^4 \cdot 3^3 \cdot 5^3} \qquad \text{Prime factor } 54{,}000.$$

$$= \sqrt{2^4 \cdot 3^2 \cdot 3^1 \cdot 5^2 \cdot 5^1} \qquad \begin{array}{l}\text{Break down odd exponents by writ-} \\ \text{ing an even exponent followed by an} \\ \text{exponent of 1.}\end{array}$$

$$= \sqrt{2^4 \cdot 3^2 \cdot 5^2 \cdot 3^1 \cdot 5^1} \qquad \begin{array}{l}\text{Regroup, writing the even powers} \\ \text{first.}\end{array}$$

$$= \sqrt{2^4} \cdot \sqrt{3^2} \cdot \sqrt{5^2} \cdot \sqrt{3^1 \cdot 5^1} \qquad \begin{array}{l}\text{Apply the product property of} \\ \text{square roots.}\end{array}$$

$$= 2^{1/2 \cdot 4} \cdot 3^{1/2 \cdot 2} \cdot 5^{1/2 \cdot 2} \cdot \sqrt{3^1 \cdot 5^1} \qquad \begin{array}{l}\text{Eliminate the perfect square, square} \\ \text{roots.}\end{array}$$

$$= 2^2 \cdot 3^1 \cdot 5^1 \cdot \sqrt{3 \cdot 5} \qquad \text{Simplify the exponents.}$$

$$= 60 \cdot \sqrt{15} \qquad \text{Simplify the products.}$$

The final result is that $\sqrt{54{,}000}$ reduces to $60 \cdot \sqrt{15}$.

| EXAMPLE 4 | Reduce the following square roots by performing the given steps in order. |

1. Separate the even and odd powers and write the even powers first.
2. Use the product property of square roots.
3. Use the elimination property of square roots on each even power.
4. Simplify the final answer.

a. $\sqrt{2^4 \cdot 3^1 \cdot 5^2}$ **b.** $\sqrt{3^1 \cdot 5^6 \cdot 11^1 \cdot 13^4}$

SOLUTION **a.** $\sqrt{2^4 \cdot 3^1 \cdot 5^2} = \sqrt{2^4 \cdot 5^2 \cdot 3^1}$ Write the even powers first.

$\phantom{\sqrt{2^4 \cdot 3^1 \cdot 5^2}} = \sqrt{2^4} \cdot \sqrt{5^2} \cdot \sqrt{3^1}$ Apply the product property.

$\phantom{\sqrt{2^4 \cdot 3^1 \cdot 5^2}} = 2^{1/2 \cdot 4} \cdot 5^{1/2 \cdot 2} \cdot \sqrt{3^1}$ Eliminate even square roots.

$\phantom{\sqrt{2^4 \cdot 3^1 \cdot 5^2}} = 2^2 \cdot 5^1 \cdot \sqrt{3}$ Simplify exponents.

$\phantom{\sqrt{2^4 \cdot 3^1 \cdot 5^2}} = 20 \cdot \sqrt{3}$ Multiply out $2^2 \cdot 5^1$.

b. $\sqrt{3^1 \cdot 5^6 \cdot 11^1 \cdot 13^4} = \sqrt{5^6 \cdot 13^4 \cdot 3^1 \cdot 11^1}$ Write the even powers first.

$\phantom{\sqrt{3^1 \cdot 5^6 \cdot 11^1 \cdot 13^4}} = \sqrt{5^6} \cdot \sqrt{13^4} \cdot \sqrt{3^1 \cdot 11^1}$ Apply the product property.

$\phantom{\sqrt{3^1 \cdot 5^6 \cdot 11^1 \cdot 13^4}} = 5^{1/2 \cdot 6} \cdot 13^{1/2 \cdot 4} \cdot \sqrt{3 \cdot 11}$ Eliminate even square roots.

$\phantom{\sqrt{3^1 \cdot 5^6 \cdot 11^1 \cdot 13^4}} = 5^3 \cdot 13^2 \cdot \sqrt{33}$ Simplify exponents.

$\phantom{\sqrt{3^1 \cdot 5^6 \cdot 11^1 \cdot 13^4}} = 125 \cdot 169 \cdot \sqrt{33}$ Multiply out $5^3 \cdot 13^2$.

$\phantom{\sqrt{3^1 \cdot 5^6 \cdot 11^1 \cdot 13^4}} = 21{,}125 \cdot \sqrt{33}$ Multiply $125 \cdot 169$.   ■

| EXAMPLE 5 | Reduce the following square roots by performing the given steps in order. |

1. Break odd powers into products using an even exponent and an exponent of 1.
2. Separate the even and odd powers and write the even powers first.
3. Use the product property of square roots.
4. Use the elimination property of square roots on each even power.
5. Simplify the final answer.

a. $\sqrt{2^6 \cdot 3^5 \cdot 5^3}$ **b.** $\sqrt{2^3 \cdot 5^3 \cdot 11^3}$

SOLUTION **a.** $\sqrt{2^6 \cdot 3^5 \cdot 5^3} = \sqrt{2^6 \cdot 3^4 \cdot 3^1 \cdot 5^2 \cdot 5^1}$ Break down the odd powers.

$\phantom{\sqrt{2^6 \cdot 3^5 \cdot 5^3}} = \sqrt{2^6 \cdot 3^4 \cdot 5^2} \cdot \sqrt{3^1 \cdot 5^1}$ Write the even powers first.

$\phantom{\sqrt{2^6 \cdot 3^5 \cdot 5^3}} = 2^{1/2 \cdot 6} \cdot 3^{1/2 \cdot 4} \cdot 5^{1/2 \cdot 2} \cdot \sqrt{3 \cdot 5}$ Eliminate the even square roots.

$\phantom{\sqrt{2^6 \cdot 3^5 \cdot 5^3}} = 2^3 \cdot 3^2 \cdot 5^1 \cdot \sqrt{15}$ Simplify the exponents.

$\phantom{\sqrt{2^6 \cdot 3^5 \cdot 5^3}} = 360 \cdot \sqrt{15}$ Multiply out $2^3 \cdot 3^2 \cdot 5^1$.

b. $\sqrt{2^3 \cdot 5^3 \cdot 11^3} = \sqrt{2^2 \cdot 2^1 \cdot 5^2 \cdot 5^1 \cdot 11^2 \cdot 11^1}$ Break down the odd powers.

$= \sqrt{2^2 \cdot 5^2 \cdot 11^2} \cdot \sqrt{2^1 \cdot 5^1 \cdot 11^1}$ Write the even powers first.

$= 2^{1/2 \cdot 2} \cdot 5^{1/2 \cdot 2} \cdot 11^{1/2 \cdot 2} \cdot \sqrt{2 \cdot 5 \cdot 11}$ Apply the reduction principle.

$= 2^1 \cdot 5^1 \cdot 11^1 \cdot \sqrt{10 \cdot 11}$ Simplify the exponents.

$= 110 \cdot \sqrt{110}$ Multiply $2 \cdot 5 \cdot 11$.   ■

EXAMPLE 6   Reduce the square roots of large numbers by performing the given steps in order.

1. Prime factor the given number.
2. Break odd powers into products using an even exponent and an exponent of 1.
3. Separate the even and odd powers and write the even powers first.
4. Use the product property of square roots.
5. Use the elimination property of square roots on each even power.
6. Simplify the final answer.

a. $\sqrt{43{,}200}$ **b.** $\sqrt{296{,}352}$

SOLUTION   **a.** $\sqrt{43{,}200} = \sqrt{2^6 \cdot 3^3 \cdot 5^2}$ Prime factor 43,200.

$= \sqrt{2^6 \cdot 3^2 \cdot 3^1 \cdot 5^2}$ Break down the odd power 3^3.

$= \sqrt{2^6 \cdot 3^2 \cdot 5^2} \cdot \sqrt{3^1}$ Write the even powers first.

$= \sqrt{2^6} \cdot \sqrt{3^2} \cdot \sqrt{5^2} \cdot \sqrt{3}$

$= 2^{1/2 \cdot 6} \cdot 3^{1/2 \cdot 2} \cdot 5^{1/2 \cdot 2} \cdot \sqrt{3}$ Simplify even square roots.

$= 2^3 \cdot 3^1 \cdot 5^1 \cdot \sqrt{3}$ Simplify the exponents.

$= 120 \cdot \sqrt{3}$ Multiply out the powers.

b. $\sqrt{296{,}352} = \sqrt{2^5 \cdot 3^3 \cdot 7^3}$ Prime factor 296,352.

$= \sqrt{2^4 \cdot 2^1 \cdot 3^2 \cdot 3^1 \cdot 7^2 \cdot 7^1}$ Break down the odd exponents.

$= \sqrt{2^4 \cdot 3^2 \cdot 7^2} \cdot \sqrt{2^1 \cdot 3^1 \cdot 7^1}$ Write all the even exponents first.

$= \sqrt{2^4} \cdot \sqrt{3^2} \cdot \sqrt{7^2} \cdot \sqrt{2 \cdot 3 \cdot 7}$ Apply the product property.

$= 2^{1/2 \cdot 4} \cdot 3^{1/2 \cdot 2} \cdot 7^{1/2 \cdot 2} \cdot \sqrt{2 \cdot 3 \cdot 7}$ Apply the reduction principle.

$= 2^2 \cdot 3^1 \cdot 7^1 \cdot \sqrt{6 \cdot 7}$ Simplify the exponents.

$= 84 \cdot \sqrt{42}$ Multiply the leading factors.

■

P R A C T I C E   F O R   S U C C E S S

Practice 1.   Is the number 169 a perfect square? Is 196?

Practice 2.   Reduce $\sqrt{125}$.

Practice 3.   Can $\sqrt{78}$ be reduced? If yes, reduce it.

Practice 4.   Reduce $\sqrt{2^6 \cdot 3^2 \cdot 5^3}$.

Practice 5.   Reduce $\sqrt{1,568}$.

EXERCISES 4.6

In exercises 1–20, determine whether the given whole number is a perfect square. For those that are perfect squares, find the number whose square makes the given number.

1. 110	2. 294	3. 361
4. 729	5. 323	6. 529
7. 625	8. 525	9. 5,070
10. 1,575	11. 4,851	12. 325
13. 396	14. 792	15. 441
16. 961	17. 1,600	18. 900
19. 700	20. 468	

In exercises 21–40, completely reduce the given square root by using perfect square factors.

21. $\sqrt{45}$	22. $\sqrt{48}$	23. $\sqrt{20}$
24. $\sqrt{54}$	25. $\sqrt{32}$	26. $\sqrt{96}$
27. $\sqrt{112}$	28. $\sqrt{150}$	29. $\sqrt{108}$
30. $\sqrt{180}$	31. $\sqrt{162}$	32. $\sqrt{192}$
33. $\sqrt{432}$	34. $\sqrt{245}$	35. $\sqrt{320}$
36. $\sqrt{252}$	37. $\sqrt{343}$	38. $\sqrt{338}$
39. $\sqrt{392}$	40. $\sqrt{675}$	

In exercises 41–50, determine whether the given square root can be reduced. Completely reduce those that can be reduced.

41. $\sqrt{2,002}$	42. $\sqrt{605}$	43. $\sqrt{1,235}$
44. $\sqrt{1,771}$	45. $\sqrt{4,235}$	46. $\sqrt{1,445}$
47. $\sqrt{551}$	48. $\sqrt{1,023}$	49. $\sqrt{2,527}$
50. $\sqrt{5,819}$		

In exercises 51–60, reduce the given square root by rearranging the even and odd powers and applying the product and simplification properties.

51. $\sqrt{2^1 \cdot 5^2 \cdot 7^1}$ **52.** $\sqrt{3^1 \cdot 5^4 \cdot 11^1}$ **53.** $\sqrt{2^2 \cdot 3^1 \cdot 7^2}$

54. $\sqrt{2^1 \cdot 3^6 \cdot 7^2}$ **55.** $\sqrt{5^1 \cdot 3^4 \cdot 7^4}$ **56.** $\sqrt{2^6 \cdot 5^1 \cdot 11^2}$

57. $\sqrt{2^1 \cdot 5^1 \cdot 13^2}$ **58.** $\sqrt{2^1 \cdot 5^1 \cdot 11^1 \cdot 13^6}$ **59.** $\sqrt{7^1 \cdot 11^4 \cdot 13^4}$

60. $\sqrt{5^1 \cdot 7^1 \cdot 13^1 \cdot 17^2}$

Completely reduce the square roots in exercises 61–74.

61. $\sqrt{369}$ **62.** $\sqrt{1{,}116}$ **63.** $\sqrt{725}$

64. $\sqrt{448}$ **65.** $\sqrt{1{,}500}$ **66.** $\sqrt{1{,}728}$

67. $\sqrt{756}$ **68.** $\sqrt{944}$ **69.** $\sqrt{637}$

70. $\sqrt{1{,}539}$ **71.** $\sqrt{1{,}029}$ **72.** $\sqrt{960}$

73. $\sqrt{1{,}260}$ **74.** $\sqrt{3{,}024}$

By first prime factoring the given number, completely reduce the square roots of the large whole numbers in exercises 75–82.

75. $\sqrt{216{,}000}$ **76.** $\sqrt{6{,}223{,}392}$ **77.** $\sqrt{1{,}333{,}584}$

78. $\sqrt{107{,}604}$ **79.** $\sqrt{10{,}418{,}625}$ **80.** $\sqrt{1{,}920{,}800}$

81. $\sqrt{100{,}800}$ **82.** $\sqrt{1{,}372{,}000}$

Looking Back

83. Give an example of the associative law for addition.

84. Give an example of the commutative law for multiplication.

85. Give an example of the associative law for multiplication.

86. Give an example of the distributive law.

87. What is the reciprocal of the fraction $\dfrac{a}{b}$?

88. Simplify the complex fraction

$$\frac{3\frac{5}{6}}{\frac{8}{15} - \left(2\frac{1}{2}\right)}$$

89. How does the rule for adding two fractions differ from the rule for multiplying two fractions?

90. What is the rule for the placement of decimal points in a division problem with two decimal numbers?

PRACTICE-FOR-SUCCESS ANSWERS

1. Both numbers are perfect squares: $169 = 13^2$ and $196 = 14^2$.

2. $\sqrt{125} = 5 \cdot \sqrt{5}$

3. $\sqrt{78}$ cannot be reduced.

4. $\sqrt{2^6 \cdot 3^2 \cdot 5^3} = 120 \cdot \sqrt{5}$

5. $\sqrt{1{,}568} = 28 \cdot \sqrt{2}$

4.7   PERCENT

OBJECTIVES

- □ To convert a percent to a fraction or decimal
- □ To convert a fraction or decimal to a percent
- □ To convert between fractions, decimals, and percents
- □ To use percent to represent comparisons in word problems

Up to this point, we have studied whole numbers, integers, fractions, and decimals. Another type of number that is used extensively in our daily lives is **percent**. If you pick up a newspaper, the concept of *percent* can be found in many places: the front page section, the business section, the sports section, and in advertisements. If you watch television or listen to the radio, percent is mentioned in the news, business reports, and banking commercials. When you go to a restaurant, you use percent to determine the tip and when you pay income tax or property tax, percent is used to calculate how much you owe. Percent is used daily to calculate sales tax.

Percent is not a new kind of number but another way of writing fractions and decimals. Because the word *percent* means per hundred or divided by one hundred, a percent is a fraction whose denominator is 100. To write percent we use the % symbol: 1% is read as "one percent" and means $\frac{1}{100}$ as a fraction, or one hundredth.

Converting Percents to Fractions

Because 1% equals $\frac{1}{100}$, any percent can be converted to a fraction by dividing by 100. For instance, to convert 11% to a fraction, we omit the % symbol and divide by 100.

$$11\% = \frac{11}{100}$$

A percent containing a fraction can also be converted to a fraction by omitting the % symbol and dividing by 100. For example, $33\frac{1}{3}\%$ (a commonly used percent) can be converted using complex fractions as follows.

$$33\frac{1}{3}\% = \frac{33\frac{1}{3}}{100} = \frac{\left(33 + \frac{1}{3}\right) \cdot 3}{100 \cdot 3} = \frac{99 + 1}{300} = \frac{100}{300} = \frac{1}{3}$$

CONVERTING PERCENTS TO FRACTIONS

Omit the % symbol and divide by 100. If necessary, reduce the resulting fraction.

| **EXAMPLE 1** | Convert the following percents to reduced fractions. |

a. 44%   **b.** $87\frac{1}{2}\%$ **c.** 105%   **d.** 200%   **e.** 6.5%

SOLUTION   To express percent as a fraction, omit the percent sign and divide by 100.

a. $44\% = \frac{44}{100} = \frac{2 \cdot 2 \cdot 11}{2 \cdot 2 \cdot 5 \cdot 5} = \frac{11}{25}$

b. $87\frac{1}{2}\% = \frac{87\frac{1}{2}}{100} = \frac{\left(87 + \frac{1}{2}\right) \cdot 2}{100 \cdot 2} = \frac{174 + 1}{200} = \frac{175}{200} = \frac{25 \cdot 7}{25 \cdot 8} = \frac{7}{8}$

c. $105\% = \frac{105}{100} = \frac{3 \cdot 5 \cdot 7}{2 \cdot 2 \cdot 5 \cdot 5} = \frac{21}{20}$

d. $200\% = \frac{200}{100} = \frac{100 \cdot 2}{100 \cdot 1} = \frac{2}{1} = 2$

e. $6.5\% = \frac{6.5}{100} = \frac{6\frac{1}{2}}{100} = \frac{\left(6 + \frac{1}{2}\right) \cdot 2}{100 \cdot 2} = \frac{12 + 1}{200} = \frac{13}{200}$ ■

Converting Percents to Decimals

To convert a percent to a fraction, we omit the % symbol and divide by 100 and so to convert a percent to a decimal, we again omit the % symbol and divide by 100. The resulting fraction is then converted to a decimal. For example, 95% can be converted to a decimal as follows.

$$95\% = \frac{95}{100} = \frac{95.}{100} = 0.95$$

When we divide by 100, the decimal point in the dividend moves two places to the left. We can thus convert any percent to a decimal by dividing by 100, which is equivalent to moving the decimal point in the percent number two places to the left.

CONVERTING PERCENTS TO DECIMALS

Omit the % symbol and divide by 100.
To divide by 100, shift the decimal point two places to the left.

EXAMPLE 2   Convert the following percents to decimals.

a. 3%   b. 6.75%   c. $5\frac{1}{2}\%$ d. 0.15%

SOLUTION   a. $3\% = \dfrac{3}{100} = \dfrac{3.}{100} = 0.03$

b. $6.75\% = \dfrac{6.75}{100} = 0.0675$

c. First convert the fractional part to its decimal equivalent.

$5\frac{1}{2}\% = 5.5\% = \dfrac{5.5}{100} = 0.055$

d. $0.15\% = \dfrac{0.15}{100} = 0.0015$ ■

Converting Decimals to Percents

To convert a percent to a decimal, we drop the % symbol and divide by 100, so it follows logically that to convert a decimal to a percent we multiply by 100 and then attach a percent sign.

CONVERTING DECIMALS TO PERCENTS

Multiply by 100 and attach a % symbol.
To multiply by 100, shift the decimal point two places to the right.

EXAMPLE 3   Convert the following decimals to percents.

a. 0.9   b. 1.25   c. 0.025   d. 3

SOLUTION   a. $0.9 = (0.90 \cdot 100)\% = (90.)\% = 90\%$

b. $1.25 = (1.25 \cdot 100)\% = (125.)\% = 125\%$

c. $0.025 = (0.025 \cdot 100)\% = (2.5)\% = 2.5\%$

d. $3 = (3 \cdot 100)\% = (300)\% = 300\%$ ■

Converting Fractions to Percents

A method that works for any denominator is to first convert the fraction to a decimal using division and then convert the decimal to a percent by multiplying by 100 and attaching a % symbol. Using this method, the fraction $\frac{41}{50}$ is converted as follows.

$$\frac{41}{50} = 0.82 \qquad\qquad \text{Divide 50 into 41 to convert the fraction to a decimal.}$$
$$= (0.82 \cdot 100)\% \qquad \text{Apply the rule for converting a decimal to a percent.}$$
$$= (82.)\%$$
$$= 82\%$$

EXAMPLE 4

Convert the following fractions to percent by first converting the fractions to decimals.

a. $\frac{7}{20}$ b. $\frac{3}{2}$ c. $\frac{5}{7}$ d. $\frac{1}{6}$

SOLUTION   a. $\frac{7}{20} = 0.35 = (0.35 \cdot 100)\% = (35.)\% = 35\%$

b. $\frac{3}{2} = 1.5 = (1.5 \cdot 100)\% = (150.)\% = 150\%$

c. When the denominator of the fraction is not a factor or multiple of 100, rounding may be necessary. Insert 4 zeros so the quotient can be rounded to the nearest thousandth, then convert the decimal to percent.

$\frac{5}{7} \approx 0.714$ $\begin{array}{r} 0.7142 \approx 0.714 \\ 7\overline{)5.0000} \end{array}$

$\frac{5}{7} \approx 0.7142 = (0.714 \cdot 100)\% = (71.4)\% = 71.4\%$

d. $\frac{1}{6} \approx 0.167$ $\begin{array}{r} 0.1666 \approx 0.167 \\ 6\overline{)1.0000} \end{array}$

$\frac{1}{6} \approx 0.167 = (0.167 \cdot 100)\% = (16.7)\% = 16.7\%$ ■

Another method to convert a fraction to a percent is to expand or reduce the fraction to an equivalent fraction whose denominator is 100 and then convert that fraction to a percent. The fraction $\frac{7}{25}$ is expanded and converted to a percent as follows.

$$\frac{7}{25} = \frac{7 \cdot 4}{25 \cdot 4} = \frac{28}{100} = 28\%$$

The fraction $\frac{28}{100} = 28\%$ because, by definition, percent is a fraction whose denominator is 100.

This method of converting first to an equivalent fraction whose denominator is 100 and then to a percent is applied when the denominator of the original fraction is a factor of 100, such as 2, 4, 5, 10, 20, 25, or 50. It can also be applied when the denominator is a multiple of 100, such as 200, 300, or 400.

| **EXAMPLE 5** | Convert the following fractions to percents by first converting each fraction to have a denominator of 100. |

$$\textbf{a.} \ \frac{9}{10} \qquad \textbf{b.} \ \frac{17}{20} \qquad \textbf{c.} \ \frac{11}{50} \qquad \textbf{d.} \ \frac{53}{200}$$

SOLUTION **a.** $\dfrac{9}{10} = \dfrac{9 \cdot 10}{10 \cdot 10} = \dfrac{90}{100} = 90\%$

b. $\dfrac{17}{20} = \dfrac{17 \cdot 5}{20 \cdot 5} = \dfrac{85}{100} = 85\%$

c. $\dfrac{11}{50} = \dfrac{11 \cdot 2}{50 \cdot 2} = \dfrac{22}{100} = 22\%$

d. $\dfrac{53}{200} = \dfrac{53 \div 2}{200 \div 2} = \dfrac{26.5}{100} = 26.5\%$ ■

As we have just seen, fractions and decimals can be written as percent and percents can be written as fractions or decimals. Given either the fractional, decimal, or percent form of a number, we can write the equivalent form of the other two. For example, $\dfrac{1}{4}$ is equivalent to 0.25 as a decimal and 25% as a percent.

| **EXAMPLE 6** | Complete the following table of equivalent forms of fractions, decimals, and percents. |

	Fraction	Decimal	Percent
a.	$\dfrac{3}{8}$		
b.		0.96	
c.			$83\dfrac{1}{3}\%$
d.		0.075	

SOLUTION **a.** First convert $\dfrac{3}{8}$ to a terminating decimal and then convert the decimal to a percent.

$$\frac{3}{8} = 0.375 \qquad \begin{array}{r} 0.375 \\ 8\overline{)3.000} \end{array}$$

$$0.375 = (0.375 \cdot 100)\% = (37.5)\% = 37.5\% \text{ or } 37\frac{1}{2}\%$$

b. First convert 0.96 to a percent and then convert the percent to a fraction.

$$0.96 = (0.96 \cdot 100)\% = (96.)\% = 96\%$$

$$96\% = \frac{96}{100} = \frac{24}{25}$$

c. First convert $83\frac{1}{3}\%$ to a fraction and then convert $83\frac{1}{3}\%$ to a decimal.

$$83\frac{1}{3}\% = \frac{83\frac{1}{3}}{100} = \frac{\left(83 + \frac{1}{3}\right) \cdot 3}{100 \cdot 3} = \frac{249 + 1}{300} = \frac{250}{300} = \frac{5}{6}$$

$$83\frac{1}{3}\% \approx 83.33\% = \frac{83.33}{100} = 0.8333$$

d. First convert 0.075 to a percent and then convert 0.075 to a fraction.

$$0.075 = (0.075 \cdot 100)\% = (7.5)\% = 7.5\%$$

$$0.075 = \frac{75}{1,000} = \frac{25 \cdot 3}{25 \cdot 40} = \frac{3}{40}$$

The table of fraction, decimal, and percent equivalents is completed as shown.

	Fraction	Decimal	Percent
a.	$\frac{3}{8}$	0.375	37.5% or $37\frac{1}{2}\%$
b.	$\frac{24}{25}$	0.96	96%
c.	$\frac{5}{6}$	≈ 0.8333	$83\frac{1}{3}\%$
d.	$\frac{3}{40}$	0.075	7.5%

The Appendix includes a table of commonly used fraction, decimal, and percent equivalents similar to the above table. ■

Percent sometimes occurs in word problems to show comparisons. For example, if at a community college 53 out of every 100 students are women, what percent of the students are women? What percent are men? To determine the percent of women, write 53 out of 100 as a fraction and then convert to a percent.

$$\frac{53}{100} = 53\%$$

53% of the students at the college are women. Because 100% represents the entire student body at the college, to determine the percent that are men, we subtract the 53% that are women from 100%.

$$100\% - 53\% = 47\%$$

47% of the students at the college are men.

| EXAMPLE 7 | In an elementary algebra class 30 out of 45 students passed the class successfully with a grade of C or better. What percent passed the class? What percent did not? Write answers as exact percents. |

SOLUTION   Write 30 out of 45 as a fraction, reduce the fraction, and then convert the fraction to an exact percent.

$$\frac{30}{45} = \frac{\cancel{15} \cdot 2}{\cancel{15} \cdot 3} = \frac{2}{3}$$

$$\frac{2}{3} = 0.66\frac{2}{3} \qquad 3\overline{)2.00}\ \ 0.66\frac{2}{3}$$

Insert two zeros so the quotient has a digit in the hundredths place. Write the remainder over the divisor.

$$= 66\frac{2}{3}\% \qquad \text{Convert to an exact percent.}$$

$66\frac{2}{3}\%$ passed the elementary algebra class.

To determine the percent that did not pass, subtract $66\frac{2}{3}\%$ from 100%, the percent equivalent to the entire class.

$$\left(100 - 66\frac{2}{3}\right)\% = 33\frac{1}{3}\%$$

$33\frac{1}{3}\%$ did not pass the elementary algebra class.   ■

P R A C T I C E   F O R   S U C C E S S

Practice 1.   Convert $22\frac{1}{2}\%$ to a reduced fraction.

Practice 2.   Convert 6.75% to a decimal.

Practice 3.   Convert 0.6 to a percent.

Practice 4.   Convert $\frac{16}{25}$ to a percent.

Practice 5.   Convert $\frac{9}{11}$ to the nearest tenth of a percent.

Practice 6.   Convert $87\frac{1}{2}\%$ to both a decimal and a fraction.

Practice 7.   If 89 out of 100 smokers plan to quit smoking some time soon, what percent plan to quit soon? What percent plan to continue?

EXERCISES 4.7

In exercises 1–20, convert the percents to reduced fractions.

1. 17%   2. 99%   3. 115%   4. 175%

5. 80%   6. 20%   7. $12\frac{1}{2}\%$ 8. $83\frac{1}{3}\%$

9. 72%   10. 96%   11. 100%   12. 300%

13. $66\frac{2}{3}\%$ 14. $37\frac{1}{2}\%$ 15. 7.5%   16. 11.5%

17. $\frac{1}{4}\%$ 18. $\frac{1}{2}\%$ 19. 212%   20. 336%

In exercises 21–40, convert the percents to decimals.

21. 19%   22. 37%   23. 6%   24. 8%

25. 82%   26. 64%   27. 400%   28. 200%

29. 125%   30. 250%   31. 6.5%   32. 5.5%

33. 6.75%   34. 11.25%   35. 0.25%   36. 0.75%

37. $7\frac{1}{2}\%$ 38. $5\frac{1}{4}\%$ 39. $\frac{1}{4}\%$ 40. $\frac{2}{5}\%$

In exercises 41–60, convert the decimals to percent.

41. 0.87   42. 0.33   43. 0.08   44. 0.06

45. 0.7   46. 0.5   47. 9.11   48. 2.52

49. 1.125   50. 1.875   51. 2   52. 5

53. $0.33\frac{1}{3}$ 54. $0.16\frac{2}{3}$ 55. $0.05\frac{1}{2}$ 56. $0.07\frac{1}{4}$

57. 0.1625   58. 0.96875   59. 0.005   60. 0.00375

In exercises 61–77, convert fractions to percent. if the denominator is not a factor or multiple of 100, round to the nearest tenth of a percent.

61. $\frac{7}{10}$ 62. $\frac{11}{20}$ 63. $\frac{3}{7}$ 64. $\frac{9}{11}$

65. $\frac{49}{50}$ 66. $\frac{3}{25}$ 67. $\frac{5}{2}$ 68. $\frac{11}{4}$

69. $\frac{5}{13}$ 70. $\frac{8}{15}$ 71. $\frac{135}{200}$ 72. $\frac{195}{300}$

73. $\frac{21}{25}$ 74. $\frac{19}{50}$ 75. $\frac{5}{6}$ 76. $\frac{3}{8}$

77. $\frac{11}{12}$

In exercises 78–82, complete the table of equivalent forms of fractions, decimals, and percents.

	Fraction	Decimal	Percent
78.	$\dfrac{1}{8}$		
79.		0.24	
80.			$33\dfrac{1}{3}\%$
81.		0.425	
82.			50%

In exercises 83–92, solve each problem by converting to percent.

83. In the 1988 presidential election, George Bush received 53.37% of the vote and Michael Dukakis received 45.65% of the vote. What percent voted for other candidates?

84. In 1830, 70.5% of the labor force had farm occupations; in 1980, 2.2% of the labor force had farm occupations. What percent of the labor force had nonfarm occupations in 1830? In 1980?

85. In one basketball game Michael Jordan made 20 of 35 field goal attempts. What percent did he make?

86. In one basketball game James Worthy made 10 of 18 field goal attempts. What percent did he make?

87. In a prealgebra class 12 out of 39 students earned a B grade. What percent earned a B grade?

88. In an elementary algebra class 10 out of 32 students earned a B grade. What percent earned a B grade?

89. Apple pie is 47.6% water. Express as a decimal the part of the apple pie that is not water.

90. Popcorn is 3.1% water. Express as a decimal that part of popcorn that is not water.

91. One credit card company has an annual percentage interest rate of 16.5%. Express 16.5% as a decimal and as a fraction.

92. One department store has an annual percentage interest rate of 19.8%. Express 19.8% as a decimal and as a fraction.

Looking Back

93. State whether the following is true or false: In an expression containing the operations of addition and multiplication, the operation of addition is always performed before multiplication.

94. State whether the following is true or false: In an expression containing the operations of multiplication and division, the operation of multiplication is always performed before division.

95. Simplify $12\left[\dfrac{1}{4} + \dfrac{2}{3}\right]$.

96. Simplify $15\left[\dfrac{3}{5} + \dfrac{1}{3}\right]$.

97. Simplify $\left(\dfrac{7}{8}\right)^2 - \left(\dfrac{1}{2}\right)^3$.

98. Simplify $\left(\dfrac{3}{4}\right)^3 - \left(\dfrac{1}{8}\right)^2$.

99. State whether the following expression is true or false: $5^2 = 2^5$.

PRACTICE-FOR-SUCCESS ANSWERS

1. $\dfrac{9}{40}$ **2.** 0.0675 **3.** 60% **4.** 64%

5. 81.8% **6.** 0.875, $\dfrac{7}{8}$ **7.** 89%, 11%

SUMMARY

This chapter presents all of the fundamental topics related to decimal numbers. In studying the place value of decimals, for example, we noted that the digit 7 in the number 0.435708 is in the ten-thousandths place and the digit 8 is in the millionths place. When rounded to the nearest thousandth, $0.435708 \approx 0.436$. Written in words, the original number is zero and four hundred thirty-five thousand, seven hundred eight millionths; written in expanded form, $0.435708 = 0.4 + 0.03 + 0.005 + 0.0007 + 0.000008$, and written as a reduced fraction, $0.435708 = \dfrac{435{,}708}{1{,}000{,}000} = \dfrac{108{,}927}{250{,}000}$.

We reviewed the four fundamental operations with decimals. Addition and subtraction require the alignment of the decimal points. In the multiplication of decimals, the number of decimal places in the answer equals the sum of the number of decimal places in the factors. When multiplying by powers of 10, we shift the decimal point.

The rule for placing the decimal point in a division problem is based on the concept of equivalent fractions and multiplying by powers of 10. For example, to divide the decimal 151.2 by 0.063, we begin by writing $0.063\overline{)151.2}$. The divisor is converted to a whole number by shifting the decimal point in 0.063 three places to the right. The decimal in 151.2 is also shifted three places to the right. The justification for these shifts can be understood by viewing the same division problem in a fraction form. In this case the two shifts are justified by the principle of multiplying the fraction by 1 where $1 = \dfrac{1,000}{1,000}$.

$$\frac{151.2}{0.063} = \frac{151.2}{0.063} \times 1 = \frac{151.2}{0.063} \times \frac{1,000}{1,000} = \frac{151.2 \times 1,000}{0.063 \times 1,000} = \frac{151,200}{63.}$$

$$\begin{array}{r} 2,400. \\ 63.\overline{)151,200.} \end{array}$$

The chapter also covers the distinction between rational and irrational numbers. Rational numbers are always finite or repeating decimals, but irrational numbers are always nonrepeating decimals. Perfect squares have rational square roots, whereas nonperfect squares have irrational square roots. To reduce a square root, we apply the prime factorization technique together with the product property of square roots. For example, to reduce $\sqrt{3,750}$, we begin by prime factoring and writing the even powers first:

$$\sqrt{3,750} = \sqrt{2 \cdot 3 \cdot 5^4} = \sqrt{5^4} \cdot \sqrt{2 \cdot 3} = 5^{1/2 \cdot 4} \cdot \sqrt{6} = 5^2 \cdot \sqrt{6} = 25\sqrt{6}$$

Another topic covered in this chapter is the conversion of a percent to a reduced fraction or a decimal by dropping the percent symbol (%) and dividing by 100—for example, $15\% = \dfrac{15}{100} = \dfrac{3}{20}$, or $8.25\% = \dfrac{8.25}{100} = 0.0825$. The opposite operations are converting decimals or fractions into percents. To convert a decimal to a percent, multiply by 100 and attach the percent symbol. For example, $0.0523 = (0.0523 \times 100)\% = 5.23\%$. To convert a fraction to a percent, first divide to convert the fraction to a decimal and then convert the decimal to a percent—for example, $\dfrac{18}{5} = 3.6$ and $3.6 = (3.6 \times 100)\% = 360.\%$. Percents, decimals, and fractions are the three most commonly used forms of numbers.

CHAPTER 4 REVIEW PROBLEMS

1. Determine the place value of the 7 in 0.23417.
2. Determine the place value of 8 in 32.819.
3. Write 2.094 in three expanded forms.
4. Write 22.7 in three expanded forms.
5. Write the word name for 20.2.
6. Write the word name for 6.0089.
7. Change five hundred four and seventy-four ten-thousandths to a number in decimal notation.
8. Change six thousand and ninety-three hundred-thousandths to a number in decimal notation.
9. Convert 0.3125 to a fraction in lowest terms.
10. Convert −7.15 to a fraction in lowest terms.

11. Compare -0.519 and -0.52 using $<, >$, or $=$.

12. Compare -2.96 and 2.9 using $<, >$, or $=$.

13. Round 9.993 to the nearest tenth.

14. Round 74,861.33715 to the nearest ten-thousandth.

15. Convert $\dfrac{1}{6}$ to a decimal.   16. Convert $\dfrac{17}{40}$ to a decimal.

17. Determine $\sqrt{1,225}$.   18. Determine $\sqrt{7,921}$.

19. Determine $\sqrt{97}$ and round to the nearest thousandth.

20. Determine $\sqrt{79}$ and round to the nearest thousandth.

21. Determine between which two whole numbers $\sqrt{130}$ lies and estimate the square root to the nearest tenth.

22. Determine between which two whole numbers $\sqrt{75}$ lies and estimate the square root to the nearest tenth.

23. Reduce $\sqrt{98}$.   24. Reduce $\sqrt{68}$.

25. Reduce $\sqrt{2^4 \cdot 5^1 \cdot 7^2}$.   26. Reduce $\sqrt{2^6 \cdot 5^3 \cdot 11^1}$.

27. Reduce $\sqrt{2,000}$.   28. Reduce $\sqrt{42,875}$.

29. Convert 72% to a reduced fraction.

30. Convert $91\dfrac{2}{3}\%$ to a reduced fraction.

31. Convert $5\dfrac{1}{4}\%$ to a decimal.   32. Convert $\dfrac{1}{5}\%$ to a decimal.

33. Convert $\dfrac{7}{6}$ to a percent.   34. Convert $\dfrac{3}{2}$ to a percent.

35. Convert 0.0675 to a percent.   36. Convert 0.085 to a percent.

Perform the indicated operations in problems 37–50.

37. $3.9 + (-7.415)$ 38. $3.17 - (-10.439)$

39. $(-2.1)(-0.007)$ 40. $(1.75)(-1.75)$

41. $-451.39 \div (-27)$ 42. $-441.2 \div 91$

43. $0.821 - 10$ 44. $-6.2 + (-12.898)$

45. $-8.6 \div 1,000$ 46. $12.3 \div 0.001$

47. $(2.26)(-2.26)$ 48. $(-4.7)(0.3)$

49. $88 \div (-0.8)$ 50. $-3,000 \div 0.006$

Simplify the expressions in problems 51–60.

51. $[5.1 - (-0.39)](4.2 - 8.65)$ 52. $0.7[-3.58 - 4(2.7 - 9.1)]$

53. $\left(\dfrac{-9.4}{4.7}\right) \div \left(\dfrac{-0.008}{-0.2}\right)$ 54. $17.7 + (-3.21) - 94 - 7.851$

55. $(-12 \div 0.06)[4.1 + 3.6(-2.1)]$ 56. $|-4.37|[3.9 + 2.68 \div (-0.04)]$

57. $\dfrac{1}{2}(3.2 - 4) + 0.4\left(\dfrac{9}{10} - \dfrac{7}{5}\right)$ 58. $\dfrac{-0.007 + (6.9 + 3.1)^2}{-0.03}$

59. $4.2\left\{\sqrt{64} - \sqrt{100}\left[\dfrac{2}{5} - (3 - 0.8)\right]\right\}$

60. $-3.1(8.7 - 10) + 8.9(-7.2 \div 0.1) + \dfrac{\sqrt{121} + (7.09 + 1.91)}{-\dfrac{10}{3}}$

Solve the word problems in 61–69.

61. On Monday Alicia walked 2.3 miles and on Tuesday she walked 1.5 times as far as she walked on Monday. How far did she walk on Tuesday?

62. A baseball player has 21 hits in her first 52 times at bat. What is her batting average?

63. At least 1 out of every 5 homes in the United States has some type of video game machine. What percent of the homes in the United States have a video game machine?

64. What is the product of $\dfrac{4}{5}$ and the difference of 2.2 and 8?

65. Warren buys an aerobics workout videocassette for $24.99 plus $1.69 in sales tax. If he hands the cashier 2 twenty-dollar bills, how much change does he receive?

66. In a quarter-mile race, a quarter horse can achieve a maximum speed of 47.5 miles per hour, whereas man can achieve a maximum speed of 27.89 miles per hour. How much faster than a man can a quarter horse run for a distance of a quarter mile?

67. At $1.54 per gallon, what is the cost of $10\dfrac{4}{5}$ gallons of gasoline?

68. John makes long distance calls to his friend Jesse in another state and talks 43 minutes at a cost of $5.29. What is the average cost per minute to the nearest cent?

69. What is the square root of 121 multiplied times the quotient of 9.4 and −0.047?

CHAPTER 4 PRACTICE TEST

1. Write 27.0831 in three expanded forms.
2. Change seventeen million and fifty-five thousandths to a number in decimal notation.
3. Write 0.6875 as a fraction in lowest terms.
4. Convert $\dfrac{2}{7}$ to a decimal.
5. Round 17.98096 to the nearest hundredth.
6. Determine $\sqrt{\dfrac{324}{49}}$.   7. Reduce $\sqrt{2^8 \cdot 5^3 \cdot 7^3}$.

8. Reduce $\sqrt{3{,}250}$.

9. Convert $66\frac{2}{3}\%$ to a reduced fraction.

10. Convert $7\frac{3}{4}\%$ to a decimal. **11.** Convert $\frac{15}{16}$ to a percent.

12. Convert 0.9 to a percent.

Perform the indicated operations in problems 13–18.

13. $12.91 + (-0.78) + (-28)$ **14.** $(-4.69)\,(0.8)$

15. $-96 \div (-0.016)$ **16.** $-2.398 - (-4.2)$

17. $329.36 \div (-92)$ **18.** $(-0.3)\,(-0.4)\,(-0.09)$

Simplify the following expressions.

19. $[12.5 - (-0.73)]\,(2.9 + 97.1)$ **20.** $|-9.2|\,[6.4 + 97.5 \div (-15)]$

21. $\dfrac{4}{5}(2.29 - \sqrt{100}) + 0.26\left(\dfrac{7}{10} - \dfrac{19}{25}\right)$

22. $\dfrac{-3.2(7 - 2.9)^2}{6 - (2.7 - 4.7)}$

23. Subtract 22.89 from the product of -0.9 and -0.07.

24. If a gallon of gasoline costs $1.56, how many gallons of gasoline can you buy for $20? Give your answer to the nearest tenth of a gallon.

25. A bookkeeper earns $15.50 per hour and is paid time-and-a-half (1.5 times the rate per hour) for every hour worked over 40 hours. If a bookkeeper works $45\frac{1}{2}$ hours one week, how much money does she earn?

EXPONENTS

In Chapter 1 we defined and used positive whole number exponents. In this chapter we expand the range of numbers that can be used to represent exponents. We begin by defining **zero** and **negative exponents** and develop a more complete set of rules — the same basic rules that are used in algebra — that will allow us to manipulate and simplify expressions with integer exponents. We also examine the relationship between standard notation and scientific notation and review the basic terminology used in the metric system.

5.1   ZERO AND NEGATIVE EXPONENTS

OBJECTIVES

- To understand zero and negative integer exponents
- To convert bases with negative exponents to fractions with positive exponents and vice versa
- To simplify expressions that use signed exponents and fractional bases
- To solve word problems that contain zero and negative exponents

Signed exponents are used not only in algebra but also in scientific and engineering work. Scientists make daily use of numbers written in a notation that uses exponents and that corresponds to the way scientific calculators perform calculations and display results. One of the features that distinguishes a scientific calculator from an ordinary calculator is the ability to display exponents.

Zero as an Exponent

The exponential expressions we discussed in Chapter 1 could use any number for a base but the exponent had to be a positive whole number. Recall that exponents are used to indicate how many times to repeat the base as a factor in a product. Thus,

$$7^5 = 7 \cdot 7 \cdot 7 \cdot 7 \cdot 7 \quad \text{five sevens multiplied} \quad \text{base} = 7, \text{exponent} = 5$$

To understand how to extend the exponent definition so it can be applied to any integer, study the following list of powers of the base 2. The exponents decrease by one as we read down the list of exponents on the left. Each number on the right of the = sign is the same as the number above it divided by 2.

$$2^4 = 16$$
$$2^3 = 8 \qquad 8 = 16 \div 2$$
$$2^2 = 4 \qquad 4 = 8 \div 2$$
$$2^1 = 2 \qquad 2 = 4 \div 2$$
$$2^0 = ? \qquad ? = 2 \div 2$$

If we continue the pattern of dividing the previous number by 2, then the last number to the right of the = sign should be $2 \div 2 = 1$. So it should seem reasonable to conclude that

$$2^0 = 1$$

Now we will make a list of decreasing powers using -3 as a base. In this list we discover a pattern in which each number to the right of each = sign is the same as the number above it divided by -3.

$$(-3)^4 = 81$$
$$(-3)^3 = -27 \qquad -27 = 81 \div (-3)$$
$$(-3)^2 = 9 \qquad 9 = (-27) \div (-3)$$
$$(-3)^1 = -3 \qquad -3 = 9 \div (-3)$$
$$(-3)^0 = ? \qquad ? = (-3) \div (-3)$$

If we continue the pattern of dividing the previous number by -3 then the last number to the right of the = sign should be $(-3) \div (-3) = 1$. So it should seem reasonable to conclude that

$$(-3)^0 = 1$$

We could make powers for any base other than 0 that would show a pattern similar to that already shown with the bases 2 and -3. Successively smaller powers are determined by dividing by the base. Since division by 0 is undefined, we exclude 0 as a base in making the definition of a zero exponent.

Thus, any number to the power of 0 equals 1 except that 0^0 *is not defined.* Of course it does not make any sense to say a base is repeated 0 times. Some may think $5^0 = 0$ because they associate the 0 exponent with multiplication and they know $5 \cdot 0 = 0$. Others may think $5^0 = 5$ because a 0 exponent is the same as "doing nothing" to 5, so the answer should be 5. But according to the definition, $5^0 = 1$.

DEFINITION	**ZERO EXPONENT**

$$b^0 = 1 \qquad \textbf{provided } b \neq 0$$

| **EXAMPLE 1** | Calculate the following exponential expressions using the definition for a zero exponent when the definition applies. |

a. 7^0 **b.** -5^0 **c.** $(-5)^0$ **d.** 0^4 **e.** 0^0

SOLUTION
a. $7^0 = 1$, since the base is 7, which is nonzero, and the exponent is zero.

b. $-5^0 = -(5^0) = -(1) = -1$. The base is $+5$.

The base is not -5 because the $-$ sign is outside the parentheses. This problem can be read as "the opposite of the zero power of five."

c. $(-5)^0 = 1$, since the base is -5, which is nonzero, and the exponent is zero. The only restriction in making the definition of b^0 is that $b \neq 0$. In this problem the base is negative but even a negative base to a zero power equals the number positive 1.

d. $0^4 = 0$. The definition of a zero exponent cannot be applied to this problem. The definition does not say the base cannot ever be equal to zero, only that we cannot have a zero base and a zero exponent at the same time. We can have zero base as long as the exponent is strictly positive, so this problem can be worked by the exponent definition given in Chapter 1: $0^4 = 0 \cdot 0 \cdot 0 \cdot 0 = 0$.

e. 0^0 is undefined since the base $= 0$ and the exponent $= 0$. Just as division by 0 is undefined, so is 0^0.   ■

Negative Exponents

By continuing the pattern of dividing by 2 each time the exponent is decreased by 1, we obtain the following extended lists of powers. Remember, dividing by 2 is the same as multiplying by $\frac{1}{2}$.

$$2^3 = 8$$

$$2^2 = 4 \qquad\qquad 4 = 8 \cdot \frac{1}{2}$$

$$2^1 = 2 \qquad\qquad 2 = 4 \cdot \frac{1}{2}$$

$$2^0 = 1 \qquad\qquad 1 = 2 \cdot \frac{1}{2}$$

$$2^{-1} = \frac{1}{2} = \frac{1}{2^1} \qquad\qquad \frac{1}{2} = 1 \cdot \frac{1}{2}$$

$$2^{-2} = \frac{1}{4} = \frac{1}{2^2} \qquad\qquad \frac{1}{4} = \frac{1}{2} \cdot \frac{1}{2}$$

$$2^{-3} = \frac{1}{8} = \frac{1}{2^3} \qquad\qquad \frac{1}{8} = \frac{1}{4} \cdot \frac{1}{2}$$

According to the pattern, 2^{-6} would be $\frac{1}{2^6}$. A base raised to a negative exponent can be written as a fraction with a numerator of 1 and a denominator equal to the same base raised to a positive power, as given in the definition of a negative exponent.

DEFINITION	NEGATIVE EXPONENT

If n is a positive integer and b is any nonzero number, then we define

$$b^{-n} = \frac{1}{b^n} \qquad n > 0, b \neq 0$$

Just as negative numbers probably seem unintuitive when first defined, negative exponents when first encountered may also appear to be contrary to common sense. The definitions given for zero and negative exponents are consistent with previously learned ideas about exponents. The more experience we gain with negative exponents, the more comfortable we will feel about them.

EXAMPLE 2   Calculate the following exponential expressions using the definition for negative exponents when the definition applies.

a. 7^{-2} b. $(-3)^{-2}$ c. $(-2)^{-5}$ d. 0^{-2}

SOLUTION   a. $7^{-2} = \dfrac{1}{7^2} = \dfrac{1}{7 \cdot 7} = \dfrac{1}{49}$

This example shows that even though the exponent is negative, the result is positive. In general, whenever the base is positive the result will always be positive, regardless of the sign of the exponent.

b. $(-3)^{-2} = \dfrac{1}{(-3)^2} = \dfrac{1}{(-3) \cdot (-3)} = \dfrac{1}{9}$

This example shows it is possible for a negative base to be raised to a negative power to yield a positive answer. When both the base and exponent are negative integers, the result will be positive or negative depending on whether the absolute value of the exponent is even or odd.

c. $(-2)^{-5} = \dfrac{1}{(-2)^5} = \dfrac{1}{(-2) \cdot (-2) \cdot (-2) \cdot (-2) \cdot (-2)} = \dfrac{1}{-32} = -\dfrac{1}{32}$

When this example is compared with that in part c, it shows that a negative base raised to a negative power does not always result in a positive answer. Here it is the odd exponent that makes the final answer a negative number.

d. 0^{-2} is undefined since the base $= 0$ and the exponent is negative. Just as division by 0 is undefined, so is zero raised to a negative power. In general, the base 0 can only have a positive exponent.   ▪

The concept of the reciprocal of a number may help with understanding how to simplify exponential expressions with negative exponents. The definition for a negative exponent says

$$b^{-n} \quad \text{equals the reciprocal of } b^n$$

The reciprocal of b^n is $\dfrac{1}{b^n}$. The following example illustrates how reciprocals are used to simplify negative and zero powers applied to bases that are fractions or mixed numbers. We also use reciprocals in connection with fractions; for example, the reciprocal of the fraction $\dfrac{2}{3}$ can be written and simplified as

$$\frac{1}{\dfrac{2}{3}} = \frac{3}{2}$$

EXAMPLE 3   Calculate the following exponential expressions using the definition for negative exponents.

a. $\left(\dfrac{1}{2}\right)^{-2}$ **b.** $\left(\dfrac{3}{4}\right)^{-3}$ **c.** $\left(-\dfrac{1}{3}\right)^{-4}$ **d.** $\left(7\dfrac{1}{2}\right)^{-2}$

SOLUTION   **a.** $\left(\dfrac{1}{2}\right)^{-2} = \dfrac{1}{\left(\dfrac{1}{2}\right)^2} = \dfrac{1}{\dfrac{1}{2}\cdot\dfrac{1}{2}} = \dfrac{1}{\dfrac{1}{4}} = \dfrac{4}{1} = 4$

b. $\left(\dfrac{3}{4}\right)^{-3} = \dfrac{1}{\left(\dfrac{3}{4}\right)^3} = \dfrac{1}{\dfrac{3}{4}\cdot\dfrac{3}{4}\cdot\dfrac{3}{4}} = \dfrac{1}{\dfrac{27}{64}} = \dfrac{64}{27}$

c. $\left(-\dfrac{1}{3}\right)^{-4} = \dfrac{1}{\left(-\dfrac{1}{3}\right)^4} = \dfrac{1}{\left(-\dfrac{1}{3}\right)\cdot\left(-\dfrac{1}{3}\right)\cdot\left(-\dfrac{1}{3}\right)\cdot\left(-\dfrac{1}{3}\right)}$

$$= \dfrac{1}{\dfrac{1}{81}} = \dfrac{81}{1} = 81$$

d. $\left(7\dfrac{1}{2}\right)^{-2} = \left(\dfrac{15}{2}\right)^{-2} = \dfrac{1}{\left(\dfrac{15}{2}\right)^2} = \dfrac{1}{\dfrac{225}{4}} = \dfrac{4}{225}$ ■

When a fractional base is raised to a negative power and the definition of a negative exponent is applied directly, then the expression will soon involve a complex fraction. Although complex fractions can be simplified, the following rule can be used as a shortcut to eliminate complex fractions. For example,

$$\left(\frac{3}{4}\right)^{-2} = \frac{1}{\left(\dfrac{3}{4}\right)^{-2}} = \frac{1}{\dfrac{9}{16}} = \frac{16}{9} = \left(\frac{4}{3}\right)^2$$

can be done in one step as $\left(\dfrac{3}{4}\right)^{-2} = \left(\dfrac{4}{3}\right)^2$

SIMPLIFYING A FRACTION RAISED TO A NEGATIVE POWER

If n is a positive integer and a and b are nonzero numbers, then

$$\left(\frac{a}{b}\right)^{-n} = \left(\frac{b}{a}\right)^{n} \qquad a \neq 0,\, b \neq 0,\, n > 0$$

Another rule that is sometimes used to expand fractions raised to any power functions somewhat like a distributive law for exponents. This rule can be understood by studying the following example.

$$\left(\frac{4}{5}\right)^{3} = \frac{4}{5} \cdot \frac{4}{5} \cdot \frac{4}{5} = \frac{4 \cdot 4 \cdot 4}{5 \cdot 5 \cdot 5} = \frac{4^{3}}{5^{3}} = \frac{64}{125}$$

The shortcut involves distributing the exponent 3 across both the numerator and denominator and thereby skipping two of the middle steps shown in the previous example.

$$\left(\frac{4}{5}\right)^{3} = \frac{4^{3}}{5^{3}}$$

This shortcut can be applied when the exponent is either zero or negative, as in the rule for expanding a power of a fraction.

EXPANDING A POWER OF A FRACTION

If n is any integer and a and b are any nonzero numbers, then

$$\left(\frac{a}{b}\right)^{n} = \frac{a^{n}}{b^{n}} \qquad a \neq 0,\, b \neq 0$$

EXAMPLE 4　Use the rule for expanding fractional bases raised to various powers to help simplify the following exponential expressions.

　　a. $\left(\dfrac{3}{2}\right)^{-3}$　**b.** $\left(2\dfrac{1}{2}\right)^{-4}$　**c.** $\left(-\dfrac{2}{5}\right)^{-5}$　**d.** $\left(-\dfrac{1}{2}\right)^{-6}$

SOLUTION　**a.** $\left(\dfrac{3}{2}\right)^{-3} = \left(\dfrac{2}{3}\right)^{3} = \dfrac{2^{3}}{3^{3}} = \dfrac{8}{27}$

In this problem we simplify the negative exponent before we simplify the power of the fraction.

　　b. $\left(2\dfrac{1}{2}\right)^{-4} = \left(\dfrac{5}{2}\right)^{-4} = \left(\dfrac{2}{5}\right)^{4} = \dfrac{2^{4}}{5^{4}} = \dfrac{16}{625}$

First we convert the mixed number to an improper fraction, then we simplify the negative exponent, and finally we simplify the power of the fraction.

c. $\left(-\dfrac{2}{5}\right)^{-5} = \left(\dfrac{-2}{5}\right)^{-5} = \left(\dfrac{5}{-2}\right)^{5} = \dfrac{5^5}{(-2)^5} = \dfrac{3,125}{-32} = -\dfrac{3,125}{32}$

This is another problem that shows that a negative base raised to an odd power yields a negative number.

d. $\left(-\dfrac{1}{2}\right)^{-6} = \left(\dfrac{-1}{2}\right)^{-6} = \left(\dfrac{2}{-1}\right)^{6} = \dfrac{2^6}{(-1)^6} = \dfrac{64}{1} = 64$

This is another example of how an even exponent yields a positive answer even though the base is negative. This example also shows how a combination of a fractional base and a negative exponent yields a number that is larger than the original base fraction. ■

A useful skill is the ability to translate word descriptions of exponential expressions into forms of mathematical expressions that can then be simplified, as shown in the following example.

EXAMPLE 5

Translate the following word descriptions into mathematical expressions and then simplify each expression to a single number.

a. The sum of the negative five power of the fraction negative one-half and the zero power of five.

b. The difference between the negative two power of eight and the negative three power of negative two.

SOLUTION

a. $\left(-\dfrac{1}{2}\right)^{-5} + 5^0 = \left(-\dfrac{2}{1}\right)^{5} + 5^0$ Simplify the negative power of the fraction.

$\qquad\qquad\qquad = -32 + 1$ $(-2)^5 = -32$ and $5^0 = 1$

$\qquad\qquad\qquad = -31$

b. $8^{-2} - (-2)^{-3} = \dfrac{1}{8^2} - \dfrac{1}{(-2)^3}$ Use the rule $b^{-n} = \dfrac{1}{b^n}$.

$\qquad\qquad\qquad = \dfrac{1}{64} - \dfrac{1}{-8}$ Simplify the exponents.

$\qquad\qquad\qquad = \dfrac{1}{64} + \dfrac{-1}{-8}$ Simplify the subtraction.

$\qquad\qquad\qquad = \dfrac{1}{64} + \dfrac{1}{8}$ Simplify the second fraction's signs.

$\qquad\qquad\qquad = \dfrac{1}{64} + \dfrac{8}{64}$ Make a common denominator.

$\qquad\qquad\qquad = \dfrac{9}{64}$ ■

PRACTICE FOR SUCCESS

Practice 1. Simplify the expression $(-8)^0$.

Practice 2. Simplify the expression $(-2)^{-5}$.

Practice 3. Simplify the expression 0^{-6}.

Practice 4. Simplify the expression $\left(-\dfrac{1}{8}\right)^{-3}$.

Practice 5. Simplify the expression $\left(-5\dfrac{2}{3}\right)^{-2}$.

Practice 6. Write the following description as a mathematical expression and then simplify it to a single number: The sum of the negative three power of negative two and the negative two power of negative three.

EXERCISES 5.1

In exercises 1–28, simplify the expressions, which include terms with 0 and negative powers. Any answers that are fractions should be completely reduced.

1. 5^{-2}	2. 6^{-2}
3. 7^{-2}	4. 8^{-1}
5. 9^{-1}	6. 4^{-3}
7. 5^{-3}	8. 6^{-3}
9. 6^0	10. 7^0
11. 0^0	12. $(-8)^0$
13. $(-8)^{-2}$	14. $(-3)^{-3}$
15. 10^0	16. 1^0
17. 0^1	18. 0^{-3}
19. 0^{-5}	20. $(-11)^{-2}$
21. $(-10)^{-2}$	22. 12^{-2}
23. $(-2)^{-6}$	24. $(-1)^{-7}$
25. $(-1)^{20}$	26. $(-4)^{-3}$
27. $(-1)^{35}$	28. $(-12)^{-2}$

In exercises 29–60, simplify the expressions with 0 and negative powers. Any answers that are fractions should be completely reduced.

29. 0^{-8}	30. $\left(\dfrac{1}{2}\right)^{-4}$
31. $\left(-\dfrac{1}{2}\right)^{-5}$	32. $(-30)^0$

33. $\left(-\dfrac{2}{3}\right)^{-3}$ 34. $\left(-\dfrac{3}{2}\right)^{-2}$

35. $\left(3\dfrac{1}{3}\right)^{-2}$ 36. $\left(\dfrac{3}{4}\right)^{-2}$

37. $\left(-\dfrac{3}{4}\right)^{-3}$ 38. $\left(-\dfrac{1}{6}\right)^{-2}$

39. $\left(\dfrac{1}{7}\right)^{-2}$ 40. $\left(2\dfrac{1}{2}\right)^{-5}$

41. $(-8)^{-3}$ 42. $\left(\dfrac{6}{5}\right)^{-2}$

43. $\left(\dfrac{1}{8}\right)^{-2}$ 44. $\left(-\dfrac{5}{4}\right)^{-2}$

45. $(-6)^{-3}$ 46. $\left(\dfrac{3}{4}\right)^{-1}$

47. $\left(3\dfrac{3}{4}\right)^{-2}$ 48. $\left(-\dfrac{1}{2}\right)^{-7}$

49. $\left(\dfrac{5}{4}\right)^{-2}$ 50. $\left(\dfrac{4}{3}\right)^{-1}$

51. $\left(-3\dfrac{1}{4}\right)^{-1}$ 52. $(-2)^{-3} + (-3)^{-2}$

53. $\left(\dfrac{1}{2}\right)^{-2} + \left(\dfrac{1}{3}\right)^{-3}$ 54. $(-4)^{-2} + 2^{-4}$

55. $\left(\dfrac{1}{4}\right)^{-2} - \left(-\dfrac{1}{3}\right)^{-3}$ 56. $(-3)^2 + (-4)^3$

57. $\left(-\dfrac{1}{2}\right)^{-3} - \left(-\dfrac{1}{3}\right)^{-2}$ 58. $(3)^{-2} + (4)^{-3}$

59. $\left(2\dfrac{1}{2}\right)^{-3} + \left(-3\dfrac{1}{5}\right)^{2}$ 60. $\left(-\dfrac{1}{4}\right)^{-3} + \left(-\dfrac{1}{5}\right)^{-2}$

In exercises 61–70, translate each word description into a mathematical expression and then simplify the expression to a single number.

61. The sum of the negative two power of the fraction two-thirds and the zero power of the fraction negative five-sixths.

62. The sum of the negative three power of the square root of thirty-six and the negative two power of the fraction four-thirds.

63. The difference between the negative five power of negative one-half and the negative three power of negative one-third.

64. The difference between the negative four power of one-fourth and the negative two power of negative one.

65. The sum of negative five raised to the negative two power and negative ten raised to the negative two power.

66. The sum of the zero power of the fraction negative three-fourths and the zero power of the fraction negative five-sevenths.

67. The difference of the zero power of the fraction negative five-eighths and the zero power of the fraction three-eighths.

68. The sum of the mixed number two and one-fifth raised to the negative two power and the negative one power of the opposite of eleven.

69. The complex fraction whose numerator is the negative three power of the fraction one-half and whose denominator is the negative two power of the fraction negative one-fourth.

70. The difference between the negative three power of negative one and the negative one power of the number negative three.

Looking Back

71. Is the number 784 a perfect square?

72. Reduce the fraction $\dfrac{1,001}{3,553}$.

73. Reduce $\sqrt{480}$.

74. What is the GCF of 2,093 and 4,823?

75. Compare the meaning of $\dfrac{5}{0}$ versus the meaning of $\dfrac{0}{5}$.

76. What is the basic operation for the expression
$[(-2)^3 + 60 \div 15 - 32 \cdot 4]^{-2}$?

77. Write the fraction $\dfrac{3}{8}$ as a sum of the reciprocals of two whole numbers.

78. Round the value of $\sqrt{39}$ to the nearest ten thousandth.

PRACTICE-FOR-SUCCESS ANSWERS

1. 1   **2.** $-\dfrac{1}{32}$ **3.** 0^{-6} is undefined

4. -512 **5.** $\dfrac{9}{289}$ **6.** $(-2)^{-3} + (-3)^{-2} = -\dfrac{1}{72}$

5.2

MULTIPLICATION AND DIVISION WITH SIGNED EXPONENTS

OBJECTIVES

- To recognize products and quotients of exponential expressions that use the same base
- To simplify products of exponential expressions that have the same base
- To simplify quotients of exponential expressions that have the same base
- To solve word problems involving products and quotients with signed exponents

In the first section of this chapter we introduced the basic definitions for zero and negative exponents. In this section we will develop two rules that help simplify combinations of signed exponential expressions; one rule governs products and the other rule governs quotients.

Multiplying Exponential Expressions

Consider the following examples in which we multiply various exponential expressions with a common base. We show different powers of the same base and we write the final answers as a single power of that base.

$$2^2 \cdot 2^3 = 4 \cdot 8 = 32 = 2^5$$

$$2^4 \cdot 2^{-1} = 16 \cdot \frac{1}{2} = 8 = 2^3$$

$$5^3 \cdot 5^{-3} = 125 \cdot \frac{1}{5^3} = 125 \cdot \frac{1}{125} = 1 = 5^0$$

If we compare the first two exponents on the left at the beginning of each problem with the final exponent on the right at the end of each problem, we can make a connection between the three exponents. The exponent in the answer is equal to the sum of the two exponents at the beginning of the problem. This fact is easily justified when the exponents are both positive whole numbers, for in this case each exponent tells the number of times the base occurs in the product. For example,

$$3^2 \cdot 3^4 = (3 \cdot 3) \cdot (3 \cdot 3 \cdot 3 \cdot 3) = 3^6 = 3^{2+4}$$

The same relationship holds when the exponents are zero or negative.

$$5^0 \cdot 5^3 = (1) \cdot (5 \cdot 5 \cdot 5) = 5^3 = 5^{0+3}$$

$$2^{-2} \cdot 2^{-3} = \frac{1}{2^2} \cdot \frac{1}{2^3} = \frac{1}{4} \cdot \frac{1}{8} = \frac{1}{32} = \frac{1}{2^5} = 2^{-5} = 2^{-2+(-3)}$$

The **addition rule for a product of powers,** sometimes called the **addition rule for exponents,** says that when multiplying two powers of the same base we can simply write the base once and add the exponents.

ADDITION RULE FOR A PRODUCT OF POWERS

If m and n denote any integers and if b is any nonzero number, then

$$b^m \cdot b^n = b^{m+n} \qquad \text{provided } b \neq 0$$

This rule is also valid when the base $b = 0$, but then we must restrict m and n to positive integers. Since 0 bases are less common and are easily handled anyway, we don't make this special case as part of the general rule.

The same base must appear in both exponential expressions when this rule is applied, so the rule cannot be applied to the problem

$$2^3 \cdot 5^4 = ?$$

because the base 2 differs from the base 5. However, this problem can be worked directly using the order of operations: $2^3 \cdot 5^4 = 8 \cdot 625 = 5,000$.

| **EXAMPLE 1** | Use the addition rule for exponents to help simplify the following exponential expressions which are multiplied. The final answers should be simplified to single numbers or fractions. Any fractions should be completely reduced. |

a. $3^8 \cdot 3^{-7}$ **b.** $18^4 \cdot 18^{-4}$ **c.** $72^{-3} \cdot 72^2$

d. $\left(\dfrac{3}{4}\right)^{-5} \cdot \left(\dfrac{3}{4}\right)^4$ **e.** $26^{-21} \cdot 26^{23}$ **f.** $2^6 \cdot 3^4$

SOLUTION   **a.** $3^8 \cdot 3^{-7} = 3^{8+(-7)} = 3^1 = 3$

b. $18^4 \cdot 18^{-4} = 18^{4+(-4)} = 18^0 = 1$

c. $72^{-3} \cdot 72^2 = 72^{-3+2} = 72^{-1} = \dfrac{1}{72}$

d. $\left(\dfrac{3}{4}\right)^{-5} \cdot \left(\dfrac{3}{4}\right)^4 = \left(\dfrac{3}{4}\right)^{-5+4} = \left(\dfrac{3}{4}\right)^{-1} = \left(\dfrac{4}{3}\right)^1 = \dfrac{4}{3}$

e. $26^{-21} \cdot 26^{23} = 26^{-21+23} = 26^2 = 676.$

f. $2^6 \cdot 3^4$ The addition rule for exponents cannot be applied to this problem because there is no common base: $2 \neq 3$. However, we can still calculate this directly by writing $2^6 \cdot 3^4 = 64 \cdot 81 = 5{,}184$.   ■

Dividing Exponential Expressions

The rule for adding exponents when we multiply has a counterpart in the operation of division. In the following examples consider the two exponents at the start of each division problem and try to discover the relationship with the final exponent in the answer.

$$\frac{2^5}{2^2} = \frac{32}{4} = 8 = 2^3$$

$$3^4 \div 3^2 = 81 \div 9 = 3^2$$

$$\frac{4^4}{4^1} = \frac{256}{4} = 64 = 4^3$$

The rule for division is to subtract exponents. Since subtraction is not commutative, the order of subtraction is important; we subtract the bottom or second exponent from the top or first exponent. Written in symbolic form, we have the **subtraction rule for exponents.** As in multiplication the same base must be used when the exponents are subtracted. This rule is valid when either exponent is positive, zero, or negative. The following examples further illustrate the subtraction of exponents when the operation is division.

SUBTRACTION RULE FOR A QUOTIENT OF POWERS

If m and n denote any integers and if b is any nonzero number, then

$$\frac{b^m}{b^n} = b^{m-n} \qquad \text{provided } b \neq 0$$

| **EXAMPLE 2** | Simplify the following division operations by applying the subtraction rule for exponents. |

$$\textbf{a.}\ \frac{3^5}{3^7} \qquad \textbf{b.}\ \frac{2^5}{2^{-3}} \qquad \textbf{c.}\ \left(\frac{2}{3}\right)^0 \div \left(\frac{2}{3}\right)^2 \qquad \textbf{d.}\ \frac{(-2)^5}{(-2)^{-5}}$$

SOLUTION **a.** $\dfrac{3^5}{3^7} = 3^{5-7} = 3^{-2} = \dfrac{1}{3^2} = \dfrac{1}{9}$

b. $\dfrac{2^5}{2^{-3}} = 2^{5-(-3)} = 2^{5+(+3)} = 2^8 = 256$

Even though the basic operation is division, the answer yields a power larger than the power in the numerator or denominator. This surprising result is a consequence of dividing by a negative power; the double minus signs in the subtraction operation yield a positive exponent.

This problem can also be worked without using the subtraction rule for exponents if we first expand the negative exponent part. However, this requires more steps.

$$\frac{2^5}{2^{-3}} = \frac{2^5}{\dfrac{1}{2^3}} \qquad \text{Apply the definition for a negative exponent to the } 2^{-3} \text{ term.}$$

$$= 2^5 \cdot \frac{2^3}{1} \qquad \text{To divide by a fraction, multiply by the divisor's reciprocal.}$$

$$= 2^5 \cdot 2^3 \qquad \frac{x}{1} = x \text{ where } x = 2^3.$$

$$= 2^{5+3} \qquad \text{Apply the addition rule for exponents.}$$

$$= 2^8 = 256$$

c. $\left(\dfrac{2}{3}\right)^0 \div \left(\dfrac{2}{3}\right)^2 = \left(\dfrac{2}{3}\right)^{0-2} = \left(\dfrac{2}{3}\right)^{-2} = \left(\dfrac{3}{2}\right)^2 = \dfrac{9}{4}$

d. $\dfrac{(-2)^5}{(-2)^{-5}} = (-2)^{5-(-5)} = (-2)^{5+(+5)} = (-2)^{10} = 1{,}024$

This is another example of subtraction yielding double minus signs, which eventually results in an unexpected +10 exponent. This also shows that a negative base will yield a positive answer when the final exponent is an even number.   ■

In some problems with exponential expressions the answers may be extremely large. In these cases it is simpler to leave an answer in exponential form rather than to attempt to multiply the base a large number of times. For example, using the addition rule for exponents we can simplify

$$20^{-33} \cdot 20^{-14} = 20^{-47} = \frac{1}{20^{47}}$$

Since it would be too time-consuming to attempt to multiply out 20^{47} because the resulting number would be extremely large, we leave the answer using a positive exponent. A scientific calculator can be used to make a decimal approximation for extremely large quantities, such as 20^{47}, or for extremely small quantities, such as $\dfrac{1}{20^{47}}$. When the absolute value of the exponent is 5 or less we usually work out the answer, but we leave larger powers in exponential form. We also usually convert final answers so they have nonnegative exponents.

EXAMPLE 3

Simplify the following expressions using the multiplication and division rules for exponents. If an answer is too large or too small to compute, leave the answer in exponential form with a positive exponent.

a. $\dfrac{9^9}{9^{27}}$ **b.** $10^{-15} \div 10^{-28}$ **c.** $\dfrac{17^{-12}}{17^{-14}}$ **d.** $\left(\dfrac{4}{5}\right)^{13} \div \left(\dfrac{4}{5}\right)^{-10}$

SOLUTION   **a.** $\dfrac{9^9}{9^{27}} = 9^{9-27} = 9^{-18} = \dfrac{1}{9^{18}}$

We convert the negative exponent to a positive one but because 9^{18} is a sufficiently large number, we leave the answer in exponential form without multiplying out the power.

b. $10^{-15} \div 10^{-28} = 10^{-15-(-28)} = 10^{-15+(+28)} = 10^{13}$

Because 10^{13} is so large, we leave the answer in exponential form.

c. $\dfrac{17^{-12}}{17^{-14}} = 17^{-12-(-14)} = 17^{-12+(+14)} = 17^2 = 289$

Because the exponent is less than 5, we multiply out the result.

d. $\left(\dfrac{4}{5}\right)^{13} \div \left(\dfrac{4}{5}\right)^{-10} = \left(\dfrac{4}{5}\right)^{13-(-10)} = \left(\dfrac{4}{5}\right)^{13+(+10)} = \left(\dfrac{4}{5}\right)^{23}$

Because the exponent is so large, we leave the answer in exponential form. ▪

The next example contains expressions with a mixture of more than one product or quotient at a time. To work a problem of this type, we must perform the operations according to the order of operations agreement. Each time either the addition or subtraction of exponents is performed, the exponential parts must contain the same base.

EXAMPLE 4

Simplify the following expressions using the multiplication and division rules for exponents. If an answer is too large or too small to compute then leave the answer in exponential form with a positive exponent.

a. $\dfrac{(-3)^{-4} \cdot (-3)^6}{(-3)^{-9} \cdot (-3)^7}$ **b.** $\dfrac{(-2)^{-25} \div (-2)^{-28}}{(-2)^{42} \div (-2)^{-38}}$

SOLUTION   **a.** $\dfrac{(-3)^{-4} \cdot (-3)^6}{(-3)^{-9} \cdot (-3)^7} = \dfrac{(-3)^{-4+6}}{(-3)^{-9+7}}$ The division bar acts as a grouping symbol.

$= \dfrac{(-3)^2}{(-3)^{-2}}$ Simplify the numerator and denominator separately.

$= (-3)^{2-(-2)}$ Apply the rule $\dfrac{b^m}{b^n} = b^{m-n}$.

$= (-3)^{2+(+2)}$ Convert subtraction to adding the opposite.

$= (-3)^4 = 81$

b. $\dfrac{(-2)^{-25} \div (-2)^{-28}}{(-2)^{42} \div (-2)^{-38}}$ The fraction bar acts as a grouping symbol.

$= \dfrac{(-2)^{-25-(-28)}}{(-2)^{42-(-38)}}$ Simplify the numerator and denominator separately.

$= \dfrac{(-2)^{-25+(+28)}}{(-2)^{42+(+38)}}$ Convert subtractions to adding the opposite.

$= \dfrac{(-2)^{3}}{(-2)^{80}}$

$= (-2)^{3-80}$ Apply the subtraction rule for exponents $\dfrac{b^m}{b^n} = b^{m-n}$.

$= (-2)^{-77}$

$= \dfrac{1}{(-2)^{77}}$ Rewrite as a fraction with a positive exponent.

$= -\dfrac{1}{2^{77}}$ Since the base is negative and the exponent is odd, the final answer is negative. ∎

The last example in this section illustrates how to write mathematical expressions from verbal descriptions that contain products and quotients of signed powers.

EXAMPLE 5 Translate the following word descriptions into mathematical expressions and then simplify each expression to a single number.
a. The product of the eighth power of negative three with the negative ten power of negative three.
b. The negative six power of negative two divided by the negative eight power of negative two.

SOLUTION   **a.** $(-3)^8 \cdot (-3)^{-10} = (-3)^{8+(-10)} = (-3)^{-2} = \dfrac{1}{9}$

b. $\dfrac{(-2)^{-6}}{(-2)^{-8}} = (-2)^{-6-(-8)} = (-2)^{-6+(+8)} = (-2)^2 = 4$ ∎

PRACTICE FOR SUCCESS

Practice 1. Simplify $(-5)^6 \cdot (-5)^{-7}$.

Practice 2. Simplify $\dfrac{(-2)^5}{(-2)^{-4}}$.

Practice 3. Simplify $\left(-\dfrac{8}{3}\right)^{-6} \cdot \left(-\dfrac{8}{3}\right)^{6}$.

Practice 4. Simplify $(-6)^6 \div (-6)^{-6}$.

Practice 5.   Simplify $\dfrac{3^{-5} \cdot 3^8}{3^{-6} \cdot 3^{10}}$.

Practice 6.   Write the following description as a mathematical expression and then simplify it to a single number: The quotient of the seventh power of negative four with the negative three power of negative four.

EXERCISES 5.2

In exercises 1–24, use the addition and subtraction rules for exponents to simplify each expression.

1. $3^6 \cdot 3^{-7}$

2. $3^5 \div 3^2$

3. $2^{-8} \cdot 2^5$

4. $5^{-8} \cdot 5^9$

5. $\dfrac{5^8}{5^9}$

6. $\dfrac{5^9}{5^8}$

7. $10^{-5} \cdot 10^5$

8. $\dfrac{10^2}{10^{-2}}$

9. $\dfrac{10^{-2}}{10^2}$

10. $\dfrac{10^{-3}}{10^{-3}}$

11. $10^{-3} \cdot 10^{-3}$

12. $2^{-2} \cdot 2^{-3}$

13. $\dfrac{2^{-3}}{2^{-2}}$

14. $(-5)^{-2} \cdot (-5)^3$

15. $3^4 \cdot 2^{-3}$

16. $\dfrac{0^{-5}}{0^5}$

17. $8^{-7} \cdot 8^7$

18. $\dfrac{2^{-3}}{2^{-3}}$

19. $12^{-12} \cdot 12^{14}$

20. $\dfrac{15^{-3}}{15^{-2}}$

21. $309^{-25} \cdot 309^{26}$

22. $\dfrac{47^5}{47^4}$

23. $\dfrac{50^{-6}}{50^{-7}}$

24. $93^6 \cdot 93^{-7}$

In exercises 25–44, use the addition and subtraction rules for exponents to simplify each expression. If the final answer contains an exponent whose absolute value is larger than 5, leave the answer as an exponential expression with a positive exponent.

25. $(-3)^{-3} \cdot (-3)^5$

26. $\dfrac{7^{-8}}{7^{-10}}$

27. $(-2)^{-4} \cdot (-2)^{-3}$

28. $\dfrac{(-5)^8}{(-5)^{-3}}$

29. $(-6)^{-2} \cdot (-6)^5$

30. $(-4)^{-12} \cdot (-4)^{-6}$

31. $\dfrac{2^8}{2^{-8}}$

32. $\dfrac{3^{-9}}{3^9}$

33. $\dfrac{(-7)^{-4}}{(-7)^5}$

34. $\dfrac{(-13)^{-6}}{(-13)^6}$

35. $\dfrac{(27)^{13}}{(27)^{-13}}$

36. $\dfrac{\left(\dfrac{2}{3}\right)^{12}}{\left(\dfrac{2}{3}\right)^{-10}}$

37. $\left(-\dfrac{1}{5}\right)^6 \div \left(-\dfrac{1}{5}\right)^{-8}$

38. $\left(3\dfrac{5}{6}\right)^8 \cdot \left(3\dfrac{5}{6}\right)^{10}$

39. $\dfrac{2^7 \cdot 2^{-10}}{2^{-8} \cdot 2^{12}}$

40. $\dfrac{(-3)^5 \div (-3)^{-7}}{(-3)^8 \cdot (-3)^9}$

41. $\dfrac{4^{-5} \div 4^{-8}}{4^{-6} \div 4^{-9}}$

42. $\dfrac{\left(\dfrac{1}{2}\right)^{-3} \div \left(\dfrac{1}{2}\right)^{-5}}{\left(\dfrac{1}{2}\right)^{-4} \cdot \left(\dfrac{1}{2}\right)^{-2}}$

43. $\dfrac{(-2)^{-10} \div (-2)^{-5}}{(-2)^{10} \div (-2)^{-8}}$

44. $\dfrac{\left(-\dfrac{2}{3}\right)^{-3} \cdot \left(-\dfrac{2}{3}\right)^{-2}}{\left(-\dfrac{2}{3}\right)^6 \div \left(-\dfrac{2}{3}\right)^{-4}}$

In exercises 45–54, translate each word description into a mathematical expression and then simplify the expression to either a single power or a single number.

45. The negative three power of negative three times the positive six power of negative three.

46. The negative two power of six divided by the negative four power of six.

47. The negative ten power of negative five times the positive ten power of negative five.

48. The positive four power of negative five times the negative six power of negative five.

49. The quotient of the product of the negative six power of two and the positive eight power of two with the negative one power of two.

50. The product of the six power of negative eight and the negative ten power of negative eight all divided by the negative five power of negative eight.

51. The product of the three power of negative twelve and the positive six power of negative twelve and the negative eleven power of negative twelve.

52. The quotient of negative three raised to the second power with positive three raised to the negative two power.

53. The quotient of two products: the first product consists of the negative three power of five and the eighth power of five; the second product consists of the negative four power of five and the seventh power of five.

54. The product which consists of four factors; the negative nine power of negative two, the negative six power of negative two, the twelfth power of negative two, and the negative one power of negative two.

Looking Back

55. Simplify $[(-3)^3 + 2^5]^{(-3)}$.

56. List four whole numbers less than 10 that are perfect squares.

57. Simplify $\dfrac{\dfrac{5}{6} - \dfrac{3}{4}}{\dfrac{7}{8} - 2\dfrac{1}{2}}$.

58. What is the basic operation for the expression in exercise 57?

59. Name two whole numbers that are neither prime nor composite.

60. Explain why the expression $\sqrt{-25}$ is undefined.

61. Rewrite the expression $7 \cdot (-25) + 3 \cdot (-25)$ using the distributive law.

62. What is the difference between an integer and a whole number?

PRACTICE-FOR-SUCCESS ANSWERS

1. $-\dfrac{1}{5}$ **2.** -512 **3.** 1 **4.** $(-6)^{12} = 6^{12}$ **5.** $\dfrac{1}{3}$ **6.** $(-4)^{10} = 4^{10}$

5.3   POWERS OF POWERS

OBJECTIVES

☐ To recognize an expression containing a power of a power

☐ To simplify powers of powers

☐ To know the implied order of operations for multiple powers without parentheses

☐ To simplify a power of a product

☐ To solve word problems that contain powers of powers with signed bases and exponents

In the previous sections in this chapter we have discussed six of the standard rules for working with exponents. In this section we will develop the final two rules for working with exponents and then we will summarize the eight standard rules for working with exponents that we have presented in this book.

Product Rule for Powers of Powers

The next rule given in this section tells how to simplify one power followed by another. Consider the following problem.

$$(2^2)^3 = (4)^3 = 4 \cdot 4 \cdot 4 = 64 = 2^6$$

This problem is an example of an expression with a double power, or what may be called a power of a power. The power inside the parentheses is a square, whereas the power outside the parentheses is a cube. We expand the expression by starting with the expression inside the parentheses, $2^2 = 4$. Then we apply the cube power to the number 4 and arrive at the answer 64, which we then write as a power of the original base 2.

Look at the first and last parts of the problem $(2^2)^3 = 2^6$, and try to find a relationship between the two exponents at the beginning of the problem and the single exponent at the end.

Next, consider another problem, $(4^3)^5$. To work this problem we will first expand the outer exponent 5.

$(4^3)^5 = (4^3) \cdot (4^3) \cdot (4^3) \cdot (4^3) \cdot (4^3)$ $b^5 = b \cdot b \cdot b \cdot b \cdot b$, where $b = (4^3)$.

    $= 4^{3+3+3+3+3}$ Apply the addition rule for exponents four times.

    $= 4^{3 \cdot 5}$ Repeated addition is equivalent to multiplication.

    $= 4^{15}$

Again, compare the beginning two exponents with the final exponent in the answer to see a rule for simplifying a power raised to a power.

$$(4^3)^5 = 4^{15}$$

The rule for simplifying problems with powers raised to powers is called the **product rule for powers of powers,** or the **product rule for exponents.** The first remark to make about this rule is to compare it to the addition rule for exponents given in Section 5.2.

PRODUCT RULE FOR POWERS OF POWERS

If m and n denote any integers and if b is any nonzero number, then

$$(b^m)^n = b^{m \cdot n} \quad \text{provided } b \neq 0$$

$$b^m \cdot b^n = b^{m+n} \qquad \text{Addition rule for exponents}$$

Sometimes these two rules are confused because both involve multiplication and both involve two different powers. One of the differences, however, is that the base b occurs twice on the left side of the equation in the addition rule, whereas the base b occurs only once on the left side in the product rule.

$$(b^m)^n = b^{m \cdot n} \qquad \text{Product rule for exponents}$$

Another difference is the presence of parentheses in the product rule and the fact that the exponents are multiplied in the product rule whereas the exponents are added in the addition rule.

The product rule for exponents is valid when either or both exponents are zero or negative. For example,

$$(2^{-3})^4 = (2^{-3}) \cdot (2^{-3}) \cdot (2^{-3}) \cdot (2^{-3}) = 2^{(-3)+(-3)+(-3)+(-3)} = 2^{-12}$$

$$(5^3)^{-2} = \frac{1}{(5^3)^2} = \frac{1}{(5^3) \cdot (5^3)} = \frac{1}{5^{3+3}} = \frac{1}{5^6} = 5^{-6}$$

$$(4^{-2})^{-3} = \frac{1}{(4^{-2})^3} = \frac{1}{(4^{-2}) \cdot (4^{-2}) \cdot (4^{-2})} = \frac{1}{4^{(-2)+(-2)+(-2)}} = \frac{1}{4^{-6}} = 4^6$$

$$(2^0)^3 = (2^0) \cdot (2^0) \cdot (2^0) = 2^{0+0+0} = 2^0$$

In each of the preceding examples we can verify that the final exponent in the answer can be obtained by multiplying the two initial exponents.

EXAMPLE 1

Use the product rule for exponents to help simplify the following exponential expressions containing powers of powers. If the result is too large or too small to calculate efficiently, leave your final answer as a power of the base. Final answers should contain only positive exponents.

a. $(3^3)^2$ **b.** $(7^{-2})^5$ **c.** $(6^3)^{-6}$ **d.** $(9^4)^0$ **e.** $[(-5)^{-4}]^{-8}$ **f.** $(0^{-2})^3$

SOLUTION   **a.** $(3^3)^2 = 3^{3 \cdot 2} = 3^6 = 729$

The final power and base are sufficiently small that we multiply out the result.

b. $(7^{-2})^5 = 7^{-2 \cdot 5} = 7^{-10} = \dfrac{1}{7^{10}}$

This time the final power is sufficiently large that we do not multiply out the result, but we do leave the answer with a positive exponent.

c. $(6^3)^{-6} = 6^{3 \cdot (-6)} = 6^{-18} = \dfrac{1}{6^{18}}$

Again the final power is sufficiently large that we do not multiply out the result; leave the answer with a positive exponent.

d. $(9^4)^0 = 9^{4 \cdot 0} = 9^0 = 1$

e. $[(-5)^{-4}]^{-8} = (-5)^{(-4) \cdot (-8)} = (-5)^{32} = 5^{32}$

Because the exponent is so large we do not multiply out the result. However, we can simplify the negative base to a positive base because the exponent is an even number.

f. $(0^{-2})^3$

We cannot use the product rule on this problem because 0 bases are not allowed in the rule. 0^{-2} is undefined because it combines a zero base and a negative exponent; therefore, the answer is undefined.   ■

Grouping Symbols and Powers of Powers

When we first introduced the order of operations in Chapter 1, we gave the problem $2 + 3 \cdot 7$ and asked whether it made any difference which of the two operations we performed first. The same question can be asked about double powers. The answer is clear when parentheses are present, but a question arises when two operations are to be performed and there are no parentheses dictating which operation should be performed first.

Consider $16 \div 8 \div 2$. In Chapter 1 we saw that there is a great difference between $(16 \div 8) \div 2$ and $16 \div (8 \div 2)$ and we learned that the associative law does not hold for division. The question we will now address is whether there is an associative law for powers of powers. For example, consider the meaning of the problem

$$2^{3^4}$$

Here we have deliberately omitted parentheses, but if we were to insert parentheses into the problem, we could insert them in two different ways. Let's consider the difference, if any, between

$$(2^3)^4 \text{ and } 2^{(3^4)}$$

If we perform the operations in parentheses first, we find

$$(2^3)^4 = (8)^4 = 8 \cdot 8 \cdot 8 \cdot 8 = 4{,}096 = 2^{12}$$

whereas $\qquad 2^{(3^4)} = 2^{(81)}$

These examples show that, as with division and subtraction, using parentheses makes a real difference with powers of powers and, therefore, *the associative law does not hold for powers of powers.* Recognizing the invalidity of the associative law for double powers then raises the question of which of the two possible interpretations for

$$2^{3^4}$$

is really correct.

The answer is an agreement on the order of operations for powers of powers. Mathematicians have agreed that the implied order of operations should be from right to left, so the intended meaning is

$$2^{3^4} = 2^{(3^4)}$$

Note the order reversal from the agreement for the division problem $16 \div 8 \div 2$, which without parentheses would be worked from left to right.

Expressions such as 2^{3^4} arise very infrequently in algebra, but while learning about the order of operations, we should be aware of the real difference between

$$(2^3)^4 \text{ and } 2^{(3^4)}$$

and we should know that the associative law does not hold for powers of powers. Most of the problems in algebra will take on the form $(b^m)^n = b^{m \cdot n}$, which can be handled with the multiplication rule for powers of powers.

Power of a Product

The last rule we will present for working with exponents is analogous to the rule we gave in Section 5.1 for taking a power of a fraction:

$$\left(\frac{a}{b}\right)^n = \frac{a^n}{b^n}$$

If we consider the fraction $\frac{a}{b}$ as a quotient, the preceding rule is one that simplifies a power of a quotient. An analogous rule simplifies a power of a product, for example,

$$(4 \cdot 5)^3 = (4 \cdot 5) \cdot (4 \cdot 5) \cdot (4 \cdot 5) = (4 \cdot 4 \cdot 4) \cdot (5 \cdot 5 \cdot 5) = (4^3) \cdot (5^3)$$

The general rule for simplifying the power of a product holds when the exponent is zero or negative and holds for products of three, four, or any number of factors. For example,

$$(a \cdot b \cdot c)^n = a^n \cdot b^n \cdot c^n \text{ and } (a \cdot b \cdot c \cdot d)^n = a^n \cdot b^n \cdot c^n \cdot d^n$$

SIMPLIFYING A POWER OF A PRODUCT

If a and b are nonzero numbers and n is any integer, then

$$(a \cdot b)^n = a^n \cdot b^n \qquad a \neq 0, b \neq 0$$

In part e of Example 1 in this section we wrote the equation $(-5)^{32} = 5^{32}$ and we justified this step because a negative number raised to an even power gives the same result as a positive number raised to the same even power. For example $(-3)^2 = 9$ and $3^2 = 9$.

Another way to justify $(-5)^{32} = 5^{32}$ is to apply the rule for simplifying the power of a product.

$$(-5)^{32} = [(-1) \cdot 5]^{32} = (-1)^{32} \cdot 5^{32} = 1 \cdot 5^{32} = 5^{32}$$

EXAMPLE 2   Simplify the following exponential expressions using the power of a product rule. If parts of the answer are too large or too small to calculate efficiently, leave those parts in exponential form. Final answers should contain only positive exponents.

a. $(5 \cdot 7)^8$ **b.** $\left(\frac{1}{2} \cdot 3\right)^4$ **c.** $(6 \cdot 4)^{-2}$ **d.** $\left(-\frac{1}{3} \cdot 7 \cdot 11\right)^{-8}$

SOLUTION   **a.** $(5 \cdot 7)^8 = 5^8 \cdot 7^8$ Because both 5^8 and 7^8 are rather large, we leave the answer as a product of these two powers.

b. $\left(\frac{1}{2} \cdot 3\right)^4 = \left(\frac{1}{2}\right)^4 \cdot 3^4 = \frac{1}{16} \cdot 81 = \frac{81}{16}$

c. $(6 \cdot 4)^{-2} = 6^{-2} \cdot 4^{-2} = \frac{1}{6^2} \cdot \frac{1}{4^2} = \frac{1}{36} \cdot \frac{1}{16} = \frac{1}{576}$

d. $\left[-\dfrac{1}{3} \cdot 7 \cdot 11\right]^{-8} = \left[(-1) \cdot \dfrac{1}{3} \cdot 7 \cdot 11\right]^{-8}$ Factor inside the square brackets.

$= (-1)^{-8} \cdot \left(\dfrac{1}{3}\right)^{-8} \cdot 7^{-8} \cdot 11^{-8}$ Apply the rule to four factors.

$= \dfrac{1}{(-1)^8} \cdot \left(\dfrac{3}{1}\right)^{8} \cdot \dfrac{1}{7^8} \cdot \dfrac{1}{11^8}$ Simplify the negative powers.

$= \dfrac{1}{1} \cdot 3^8 \cdot \dfrac{1}{7^8} \cdot \dfrac{1}{11^8}$

$= \dfrac{3^8}{7^8 \cdot 11^8}$ Leave the answer in fractional form.   ■

SUMMARY OF RULES FOR SIGNED EXPONENTS

In the following rules assume m and n are integers and assume $b \neq 0$.

$$b^0 = 1 \qquad\qquad b^{-n} = \frac{1}{b^n}$$

$$b^m \cdot b^n = b^{m+n} \qquad\qquad \frac{b^m}{b^n} = b^{m-n}$$

$$(a \cdot b)^n = a^n \cdot b^n \qquad\qquad \left(\frac{a}{b}\right)^n = \frac{a^n}{b^n}$$

$$(b^m)^n = b^{m \cdot n} \qquad\qquad \left(\frac{a}{b}\right)^{-n} = \left(\frac{b}{a}\right)^n \qquad a \neq 0$$

We conclude this section with an example of how to translate and simplify written descriptions of mathematical expressions.

EXAMPLE 3   Write a mathematical expression that corresponds to each written description and then simplify your expression to a single number or fraction.

a. Negative two raised to the power that consists of the second power of two.

b. The negative third power of the expression that is the second power of negative three.

c. Negative three raised to the power that is the sum of the third power of negative three and the second power of five.

SOLUTION   **a.** $(-2)^{(2^2)} = (-2)^4 = 16$

b. $[(-3)^2]^{-3} = (-3)^{-6} = \dfrac{1}{(-3)^6} = \dfrac{1}{729}$

c. $(-3)^{[(-3)^3 + 5^2]} = (-3)^{(-27+25)} = (-3)^{-2} = \dfrac{1}{9}$ ■

PRACTICE FOR SUCCESS

Practice 1. Simplify the expression $(7^3)^4$.

Practice 2. Simplify the expression $(8^{-5})^{-3}$.

Practice 3. Simplify the expression $[(-2)^3]^{-6}$ and leave your answer with both a positive base and a positive exponent.

Practice 4. Write the expression $(7 \cdot 11 \cdot 19)^7$ as a product of three powers.

Practice 5. Write the following as a mathematical expression and simplify to a single number: The negative three power of the expression negative two raised to the power of negative two.

EXERCISES 5.3

In exercises 1–20, use the product rule for exponents to simplify the given expressions. If an answer is sufficiently large, if may be left in exponential form but only with a positive exponent.

1. $[(-2)^3]^5$
2. $(3^{-2})^{-4}$
3. $[(-3)^{-3}]^{(-3)}$
4. $(2^{-5})^4$
5. $(4^{-6})^{-5}$
6. $(8^{-3})^5$
7. $(8^5)^{-3}$
8. $(0^{-3})^4$
9. $(0^{-5})^{-7}$
10. $(6^7)^8$
11. $\left[\left(\frac{1}{2}\right)^3\right]^{-5}$
12. $\left[\left(\frac{2}{3}\right)^8\right]^{-3}$
13. $\left[\left(-\frac{3}{4}\right)^2\right]^{-6}$
14. $\left[\left(2\frac{1}{2}\right)^4\right]^7$
15. $\left[\left(-\frac{1}{3}\right)^{-3}\right]^3$
16. $\left[\left(\frac{3}{5}\right)^{-5}\right]^{-3}$
17. $[(-5)^{-6}]^{(-7)}$
18. $[(-8)^2]^{-4}$
19. $(0^{-5})^{-4}$
20. $(5^{-5})^{-5}$

In exercises 21–32, use either the product rule for exponents or the rule for expanding a power of a product to change the given expression. Answers with large numbers may be left in exponential form but only with positive exponents.

21. $(6 \cdot 9)^3$
22. $(8 \cdot 13)^5$
23. $(2 \cdot 17)^{-3}$
24. $(5 \cdot 19)^{-6}$
25. $[(-4)^2]^{-4}$
26. $\left[\frac{1}{3} \cdot 8\right]^5$
27. $\left[\frac{1}{2} \cdot 7\right]^{-8}$
28. $\left[\left(-\frac{7}{8}\right)^{-9}\right]^{-10}$
29. $\left[\left(-\frac{5}{6}\right)^{-5}\right]^{-6}$
30. $\left[\frac{3}{5} \cdot \frac{4}{7}\right]^6$
31. $[(-2) \cdot (-3)]^{-4}$
32. $[(-9) \cdot (-8)]^{-7}$

In exercises 33–42, translate each word description into a mathematical expression and then simplify the expression to a single number.

33. The negative two power of the expression that consists of negative one raised to the negative five power.

34. The negative three power of the expression that consists of two raised to the negative two power.

35. The number positive three raised to the power that is the sum of the zero power of five and the fifth power of zero.

36. The negative three power of the expression that consists of the number negative three raised to the negative two power.

37. The negative three power of the product of negative twelve and two-thirds.

38. The negative two power of the product of thirty-six and negative four-ninths.

39. Negative two raised to the power that is the sum of the third power of negative two and the second power of positive three.

40. Negative four raised to the power that is the sum of the third power of negative four and the second power of negative eight.

41. Negative five raised to the power that is the sum of the third power of negative five and the third power of positive five.

42. The base is the second power of negative four and the exponent is the sum of the third power of negative two and the positive third power of positive two.

Looking Back

43. What is the basic operation for the expression

$$[(-2)^3 + 20 \div 5] \cdot (3^2 - 8) \div [60 - 2 \cdot (-6)^3]$$

44. Find the GCF of 789 and 357.

45. What power of 3 makes 729?

46. Name three mathematical operations that are not commutative.

47. Rewrite $(-5) \cdot [8 + 6 + (-4)]$ using the distributive law.

48. Simplify

$$\frac{\dfrac{3}{5} - \dfrac{7}{12}}{1\dfrac{3}{4} - 2\dfrac{8}{15}}$$

49. Simplify

$$\frac{\left(\dfrac{1}{2}\right)^{-6}}{\left(\dfrac{1}{2}\right)^{-4}}$$

50. Simplify $\left(-\dfrac{2}{3}\right)^{-8} \cdot \left(-\dfrac{2}{3}\right)^{5}$.

PRACTICE-FOR-SUCCESS ANSWERS

---

1. 7^{12} **2.** 8^{15} **3.** $\dfrac{1}{2^{18}}$ **4.** $7^7 \cdot 11^7 \cdot 19^7$ **5.** $[(-2)^{-2}]^{-3} = 64$

5.4	**DECIMALS AND SIGNED POWERS OF 10**

OBJECTIVES

☐ To convert signed powers of 10 to standard notation

☐ To convert decimal numbers multiplied by signed powers of 10 to numbers in standard notation

---

☐ To simplify expressions with a mixture of notation

☐ To solve word problems with decimals and powers of 10

In this section we will examine the relationships between numbers written in decimal form and powers of 10. Numbers written in decimal form are said to be in **standard notation,** sometimes called **ordinary notation.** In standard notation a number is written as a sequence of digits from 0 to 9 and may be followed by a decimal point and another sequence of digits from 0 to 9. For example, numbers like 256.617 and 3.12 and 4.0 and even the number 78 are said to be written in standard notation. Sometimes numbers are written in forms that can be converted to numbers in standard notation; powers of 10 are just such expressions. Various powers of 10 converted to standard notation are shown as follows.

$$10^0 = 1 \qquad 10^3 = 1{,}000$$
$$10^1 = 10 \qquad 10^4 = 10{,}000$$
$$10^2 = 100 \qquad 10^5 = 100{,}000$$

By inspecting the preceding list we can see a direct relationship between the exponents on 10 and the number of zeros written after the digit 1 when the powers of 10 are converted to standard notation: *The number of zeros following the digit 1 is equal to the exponent.*

Next we consider the following list of negative powers of 10 converted to standard decimal notation.

$$10^{-1} = \frac{1}{10^1} = \frac{1}{10} = 0.1$$

$$10^{-2} = \frac{1}{10^2} = \frac{1}{100} = 0.01$$

$$10^{-3} = \frac{1}{10^3} = \frac{1}{1,000} = 0.001$$

$$10^{-4} = \frac{1}{10^4} = \frac{1}{10,000} = 0.0001$$

$$10^{-5} = \frac{1}{10^5} = \frac{1}{100,000} = 0.00001$$

This list indicates that when negative powers of 10 are involved, the number of zeros between the decimal point and the digit 1 is one less than the absolute value of the exponent.

Another way to consider the relationship between powers of 10 and standard decimal notation is to think of each power of 10 as controlling the shifting of the decimal point. In this case it is convenient to always start with the number **1.** and shift the decimal point to the right or to the left of the digit 1, depending on whether the exponent is positive or negative.

If the exponent is positive, we shift right and if the exponent is negative, we shift left. These directions are easy to remember because they correspond to the way signed numbers are located to the left and right of 0 on a number line. The number of decimal places that are shifted is always equal to the absolute value of the exponent.

CONVERTING POWERS OF 10 TO STANDARD NOTATION

Let n denote any integer; n may be positive, negative, or zero. To convert 10^n to standard notation, perform the following steps.

1. Begin by writing the number 1.
2. If n is positive, shift the decimal point to the right.
3. If n is negative, shift the decimal point to the left.
4. The number of places to shift is $|n|$.
5. Fill in a 0 for each new decimal place value position.
6. For decimals less than 1, write a leading 0 to indicate the whole number part is zero.

EXAMPLE 1   Use the given rules to convert the following powers of 10 to standard notation.

a. 10^5 **b.** 10^{-4} **c.** 10^0

SOLUTION   **a.** 10^5

Begin by writing 1. The exponent 5 is positive so we shift the decimal point 5 places to the right, filling in 0s for each new decimal place that appears.

1.

$\rightarrow$ Shift 1st place to the right and fill in a 0.

10.

$\rightarrow$ Shift 2nd place to the right and fill in a 0.

100.

$\rightarrow$ Shift 3rd place to the right and fill in a 0 and add a comma in the whole number part.

1,000.

$\rightarrow$ Shift 4th place to the right and fill in a 0.

10,000.

$\rightarrow$ Shift 5th place to the right, fill in 0, and stop.

100,000.

$10^5 = 100,000$

b. 10^{-4}

Begin by writing 1. The exponent 4 is negative so we shift the decimal point 4 places to the left, filling in 0s for each new decimal place that appears.

1.

$\leftarrow$ Shift 1st place to the left, but don't fill in a 0.

.1

$\leftarrow$ Shift 2nd place to the left and fill in a 0.

.01

$\leftarrow$ Shift 3rd place to the left and fill in a 0.

.001

$\leftarrow$ Shift 4th place to the left and fill in a 0.

.0001

    Write a leading 0 for the whole number part.

0.0001

$10^{-4} = 0.0001$

c. 10^0

Begin by writing 1. Since the exponent is 0 we shift the decimal point 0 places, which means we don't shift it at all. Since the resulting number is not less than 1 it already shows its whole number part as being equal to 1.

$10^0 = 1.$ ■

  The idea of thinking of the power of 10 as controlling the shifting of the decimal point proves useful when any decimal number is multiplied by a power of 10. A positive exponent indicates a shift to the right and a negative exponent indicates a shift to the left. If the exponent is zero then no shifting takes place, since $10^0 = 1$ and multiplying a number by 1 does not change the number.

  In many areas of science and engineering it is common to write decimal numbers multiplied by powers of 10. There is a special notation for this purpose, called *scientific notation*, that will be introduced in the next section. Extremely large or extremely small numbers are sometimes more conveniently written using this notation.

For example, the average distance from the earth to the sun is 93 million miles, which can be written as

$$9.3 \times 10^7 \text{ miles}$$

Here we use the symbol $\times$ to denote multiplication. As another example, a proton is a tiny atomic particle which if weighed (at rest) would tip the scales at

$$3.687 \times 10^{-27} \text{ pounds}$$

In general the letter x is used in algebra to denote an unknown variable and should not be confused with the symbol $\times$ for multiplication. Earlier we introduced the raised dot symbol for multiplication, but when working with decimal numbers the raised dot might be confused with a decimal point. So for this section and the next we make an exception and use the symbol $\times$ rather than a raised dot to indicate a decimal number times a power of 10.

The remaining problems in this section are concerned with converting decimal numbers multiplied by powers of 10 to standard notation. To prepare for this work, we present the rules for converting a decimal number times a power of 10 to standard notation.

CONVERTING A DECIMAL NUMBER TIMES A POWER OF 10 TO STANDARD NOTATION

Let n denote any integer; n may be positive, negative, or zero. Let d denote any decimal number that may be positive or negative but not zero. To convert $d \times 10^n$ to standard notation, perform the following steps.

1. Begin by writing down the number d, which should already contain a decimal point.
2. If n is positive, shift the decimal point to the right.
3. If n is negative, shift the decimal point to the left.
4. The number of places to shift is $|n|$.
5. Fill in a 0 for each new decimal place value position.
6. Insert or drop leading 0s to indicate the proper whole number part of the decimal.

| **EXAMPLE 2** | Use the conversion rules to convert the following decimal numbers multiplied by powers of 10. |

    a. 2.361×10^2 **b.** 476.25×10^{-3}

    c. -0.0096485×10^4 **d.** 0.0261×10^{-3}

SOLUTION   **a.** 2.361×10^2

Begin by writing down the decimal number 2.361. The exponent 2 on 10 is positive, so we shift the decimal point 2 places to the right.

2.361

$\rightarrow$ Shift 1st place to the right.

23.61

$\rightarrow$ Shift 2nd place to the right.

236.1   Since the whole number part is 236 we simply stop.

$2.361 \times 10^2 = 236.1$

b. 476.25×10^{-3}

Begin by writing down the decimal number 476.25. The exponent 3 is negative, so we shift the decimal point 3 places to the left.

476.25

$\leftarrow$ Shift 1st place to the left.

47.625

$\leftarrow$ Shift 2nd place to the left.

4.7625

$\leftarrow$ Shift 3rd place to the left.

.47625

0.47625   Add a leading 0 for the whole number part.

$476.25 \times 10^{-3} = 0.47625$

c. -0.0096485×10^4

Begin by writing down the decimal number -0.0096485. The exponent 4 is positive, so we shift the decimal point 4 places to the right.

-0.0096485

-00964.85

-964.85 Drop the leading 0s since the whole number part is -964.

d. 0.0261×10^{-3}

Begin by writing down the decimal number 0.0261. The exponent 3 is negative, so we shift the decimal point 3 places to the left.

0.0261

.0000261

0.0000261   Add a leading 0 for the whole number part.   ■

Many mathematical expressions use a mixture of notations to write numbers. In this section we will convert all numbers to standard notation before we perform the operations to simplify the expressions.

EXAMPLE 3   Simplify each of the following expressions to a single number. Those parts that contain a mixture of notations can be converted to standard notation before the operations are performed. Leave your answers in standard notation.

a. $1.29 \times 10^2 + 346.31 \times 10^{-1}$

b. $8.7 \times 10^3 - (-127.4 \times 10^1) - 1{,}476 \times 10^{-3}$

SOLUTION   **a.** $1.29 \times 10^2 + 346.31 \times 10^{-1}$

$\qquad = 129. + 34.631$ Convert to standard notation.

$\qquad = 163.631$ Add the decimal numbers.

   b. $8.7 \times 10^3 - (-127.4 \times 10^1) - 1{,}476 \times 10^{-3}$

$\qquad = 8{,}700. - (-1{,}274.) - 1{,}476. \times 10^{-3}$ Convert 1st two numbers to standard notation and place a decimal point in the 3rd.

$\qquad = 8{,}700. + (+1{,}274) - 1.476$ Convert the 3rd number to standard notation and change the subtraction to addition.

$\qquad = 9{,}974. - 1.476$ Add the 1st two decimals then subtract the 3rd.

$\qquad = 9{,}972.524$ ■

P R A C T I C E   F O R   S U C C E S S

Practice 1. Convert 10^7 to standard notation.

Practice 2. Convert 10^{-6} to standard notation.

Practice 3. Convert 457.921×10^5 to standard notation.

Practice 4. Convert 72.91×10^{-8} to standard notation.

Practice 5. Simplify the following expression by first converting the terms to standard notation and then performing the operations. Leave your answer in standard notation.

$$31.92 \times 10^{-4} - 0.0023 \times 10^{-2} - (-1{,}768.3 \times 10^{-7})$$

EXERCISES 5.4

In exercises 1–16, convert each signed power of 10 into a number in standard notation.

1. 10^6 2. 10^4

3. 10^{-1} 4. 10^{-2}

5. 10^{-5} 6. 10^8

7. 10^{-3} 8. 10^{-7}

9. 10^5 10. 10^{-4}

11. 10^{-8} 12. 10^7

13. 10^9 14. 10^{-9}

15. 10^2 16. 10^{-6}

In exercises 17–32, convert each expression into a number in standard notation.

17. 3.0684×10^5 18. 0.10475×10^{-6}

19. 3.411×10^8 20. 93.25×10^9

21. 172.59×10^{-1} 22. 63.1×10^{-5}

23. 8.8881×10^{-9} 24. 26.57×10^1

25. 68.790×10^{-8} 26. 4.848×10^3

27. 6.309×10^4 28. 95.36×10^6

29. 37.92×10^{-6} 30. 9.906×10^2

31. 967.01×10^{-2} 32. 2.3013×10^{-3}

In exercises 33–50, simplify each expression by first converting each term into a number in standard notation and then performing the operations. Leave your answers in standard notation.

33. $1.56 \times 10^2 + 4.246 \times 10^3$ 34. $108 \times 10^{-3} + 8.88 \times 10^{-2}$

35. $62.73 \times 10^4 - 1.534 \times 10^2$ 36. $6.253 \times 10^{-3} + 47.7 \times 10^{-5}$

37. $49.72 \times 10^0 + 7.804 \times 10^{-1}$ 38. $87.68 \times 10^3 + 9.170 \times 10^2$

39. $15.38 \times 10^1 - 70.49 \times 10^{-1}$ 40. $6.097 \times 10^{-2} + 9.242 \times 10^{-3}$

41. $59.39 \times 10^3 - 2.434 \times 10^4$ 42. $5.200 \times 10^3 - 253.3 \times 10^0$

43. $4.228 \times 10^{-5} + 37.40 \times 10^{-2} + 8.554 \times 10^{-3}$

44. $27.01 \times 10^0 - 75.69 \times 10^1 - 49.10 \times 10^2$

45. $7.227 \times 10^3 + 7.50 \times 10^2 - 5.348 \times 10^1$

46. $961.9 \times 10^{-2} - 243.9 \times 10^{-3} - 20.90 \times 10^{-2}$

47. $4.133 \times 10^{-1} + 29.77 \times 10^{-2} - 494 \times 10^{-3}$

48. $440.3 \times 10^3 + 33.83 \times 10^2 - 8.675 \times 10^1$

49. $957 \times 10^{-4} + 8,725 \times 10^{-4} + 7,610 \times 10^{-4}$

50. $6.483 \times 10^2 - 20.67 \times 10^5 - 753.1 \times 10^3$

In exercises 51–60, translate each word description into a mathematical expression and then simplify the expression to a single number. Write your answers in standard notation.

51. The product of ten raised to the negative fifth power with ten raised to the negative two power.

52. The quotient of ten raised to the second power with ten raised to the negative four power.

53. The quotient of ten raised to the negative sixth power with ten raised to the negative ten power.

54. The decimal number thirty-six and five tenths times ten raised to the negative six power.

55. Negative two and four hundred seventeen thousandths multiplied by ten raised to the fifth power.

56. The sum of two and sixty-eight hundredths times ten raised to the negative two power with negative three and forty-six hundredths times ten raised to the negative one power.

57. Negative five and three tenths times ten to the third power added to six thousand seven hundred eighty-three and two tenths times ten raised to the negative two power.

58. The sum of the two products consisting of negative six and four hundred seventy-nine thousandths times ten to the negative one power and the number nine hundred thirty-seven hundred-thousandths times ten to the third power.

59. The sum of three products consisting of forty-five and ninety-one hundredths times ten to the negative one power and negative eight hundred seventy-one and eight tenths times ten to the negative two power and two thousand one hundred eighteen ten-thousandths times ten raised to the third power.

60. The sum of three products which consist of the numbers six thousand five hundred eighty-three times ten to the zero power and thirty-four thousand eight hundred fifty-one times ten to the negative second power and twenty-three ten-thousandths times ten to the eighth power.

Looking Back

61. Name three mathematical operations for which the associative law fails to hold.

62. State the divisibility test for the number 3.

63. Name all the numbers that are simultaneously not positive and not negative.

64. What is the difference between a reduced fraction and a mixed number?

65. Define $|x|$.

66. What is the definition of equivalent fractions?

67. State the fundamental theorem of arithmetic.

68. What does it mean for two whole numbers to be called relatively prime?

PRACTICE-FOR-SUCCESS ANSWERS

1. 10,000,000.   2. 0.000001   3. 45,792,100.   4. 0.0000007291

5. 0.00334583

5.5   SCIENTIFIC NOTATION

OBJECTIVES

□ To know the definition of a number written in scientific notation

□ To recognize numbers written in scientific notation

□ To convert numbers written in standard notation to scientific notation and vice versa

□ To perform operations on numbers written in scientific notation

□ To solve word problems using numbers in scientific notation

Every scientific field uses a special notation for writing numbers, which is particularly useful for writing very large or very small numbers. Chemistry, physics, and astronomy are three fields that commonly use numbers written in scientific notation, and all scientific calculators and computers have provisions for displaying or printing numbers in scientific notation.

An example of the need for this kind of notation is the problem of writing the number that is the distance that light travels in one year. Astronomers call this distance *one light year.* In terms of miles this number is approximately 5.88×10^{12} miles. As an ordinary decimal number this value would be written as 5,880,000,000,000 miles, but this number is 13 digits long and cannot be keyed into a standard calculator (which will normally accept numbers with at most 10 digits).

A number can also be too small to fit in the display of an ordinary calculator, such as the number of inches that constitute the radius of an electron, a tiny atomic particle. The radius of an electron is approximately 1.1094×10^{-13} inch, which would be written in standard decimal notation as 0.00000000000011094 inch. If we include the leading 0, this decimal number is 18 digits long and, thus, cannot be keyed into a standard calculator.

DEFINITION   A NUMBER WRITTEN IN SCIENTIFIC NOTATION

A number of the form $d \times 10^n$ is said to be in scientific notation if
1. **d is a number written in decimal form with an explicit decimal point.**
2. **d is such that $1 \leq |d|$.**
3. **d is such that $|d| < 10$.**
4. **n is any integer.**

The following are numbers written in standard notation with the same values written in scientific notation to the right of each = sign.

$$43 = 4.3 \times 10^1$$

$$-279 = -2.79 \times 10^2$$

$$0.00248 = 2.48 \times 10^{-3}$$

Another way of describing scientific notation is to say that we require exactly one nonzero digit to the left of the decimal point in the decimal number that is multiplied by an integer power of 10. This is the same as saying that the decimal number's absolute value is larger than or equal to one but is strictly less than ten. To make this point, we show examples of four numbers that are not in scientific notation and then write the same numbers in three different notations (Tables 5.1 and 5.2).

Not in Scientific Notation	Explanation
26.34×10^2	$\lvert 26.34 \rvert$ is not less than 10.
-0.125×10^{-3}	$\lvert -0.125 \rvert$ is not greater than or equal to 1.
4.0×5^2	5^2 is not written as a power of 10.
$\dfrac{5}{8} \times 10^5$	$\dfrac{5}{8}$ is not written in decimal form.

TABLE 5.1 Numbers not written in scientific notation

Neither Standard nor Scientific Notation	Standard Notation	Scientific Notation
26.34×10^2	$2,634.$	2.634×10^3
-0.125×10^{-3}	-0.000125	-1.25×10^{-4}
4.0×5^2	$4.0 \times 25 = 100.$	$1. \times 10^2$
$\dfrac{5}{8} \times 10^5$	$0.625 \times 10^5 = 62,500.$	6.25×10^4

TABLE 5.2 Numbers in three different notations

Every number except 0 can be written in scientific notation. This is not to say that every number *must* be written in scientific notation, only that it is always possible. Were it not for the technicality that a number in scientific notation must have exactly one nonzero digit to the left of the decimal point, we could even write 0 in a scientific format as $0 = 0. \times 10^0$.

EXAMPLE 1

Indicate which of the following numbers are in scientific notation. Tell which part of the definition fails for those that are not in scientific notation.

a. $6.792 \times 10^{\pi}$ b. $\dfrac{9}{4} \times 10^{-5}$ c. 0.75×10^5

d. -54.729×10^{-6} e. -0.00632×10^2 f. -7.918×10^{21}

SOLUTION

a. $6.792 \times 10^{\pi}$ This is not in scientific notation because the exponent on 10 is not an integer, the number π is an irrational number.

b. $\dfrac{9}{4} \times 10^{-5}$ This is not in scientific notation because the fraction $\dfrac{9}{4}$ is not written as a decimal number with an explicit decimal point.

c. 0.75×10^5 This is not in scientific notation because the decimal number 0.75 is not greater than or equal to 1 (in absolute value).

d. -54.729×10^{-6} This is not in scientific notation because the absolute value of the decimal number part -54.729 is not less than 10. This number is in "pseudoscientific notation."

e. -0.00632×10^{2} This is not in scientific notation because the decimal number part -0.00632 has an absolute value that is less than 1.

f. -7.918×10^{-21} This number is in scientific notation because it agrees with all four parts of the definition.   ■

WRITING A NUMBER IN SCIENTIFIC NOTATION

1. **If the number is a fraction or is in pseudoscientific notation, first convert the number to a decimal in standard notation.**
2. **If the number is negative, start by writing its sign. If the number is positive, you may omit the sign.**
3. **Read the number from the left until you reach the first nonzero digit.**
4. **Write the first nonzero digit followed by a decimal point, followed by the remaining digits through the rightmost nonzero digit.**
5. **Write $\times$ 10 but leave the exponent off the base 10.**
6. **Starting with the position of the decimal point where it is written, count the number of places required to move the decimal point to its position in the number when written in standard notation.**
7. **Write the signed power of 10. If the decimal shifted to the left, the sign should be negative, and if it shifted to the right, the sign should be positive.**

EXAMPLE 2   Convert the following numbers to scientific notation by first converting to standard notation and then using the stated rules to convert to scientific notation.

   a. 5,792,300   **b.** -0.000732 **c.** $\dfrac{1}{2}$ **d.** -0.00514×10^{-5}

SOLUTION   **a.** 5,792,300

We first write this number with an explicit decimal point, as a positive number whose first nonzero digit is the 5.

5,792,300.

Write 5 followed by a decimal point and then copy the remaining digits to the right of the 5. The two zeros need not be copied.

5.7923

Next, write $\times$ 10.

5.7923 $\times$ 10

Finally, shift the decimal point from its current position 6 places to the right until it matches its position in the standard decimal. The exponent on 10 is positive six.

$5{,}792{,}300 = 5.7923 \times 10^{6}$

b. -0.000732

This number is written as a standard decimal. We begin writing down a minus sign because the number is negative. Then reading from the left we find that 7 is first nonzero digit, so we write 7 followed by a decimal point and then we copy the remaining digits.

-7.32

Next, we write $\times$ 10, leaving space to write an exponent on the 10.

-7.32×10

Finally, we shift the decimal point 4 places left to make it appear in the same position it had in the original number. Thus, the power of 10 will be -4.

$-0.000732 = -7.32 \times 10^{-4}$

c. $\dfrac{1}{2}$

First, we convert the fraction to the decimal.

0.5

Then, we read from left to right until we reach the first nonzero digit, 5. We write the 5 followed by a decimal point.

$5.$

There are no digits to the right of 5, so we write $\times$ 10.

$5. \times 10$

Finally, we shift the decimal point back to its position in the original number, in this case one place to the left. The exponent on 10 is -1.

$\dfrac{1}{2} = 0.5 = 5. \times 10^{-1}$

d. -0.00514×10^{-5}

This number is in pseudoscientific notation so we first convert to standard notation.

$-0.00514 \times 10^{-5} = -0.0000000514$

We begin writing down a minus sign because the number is negative. Reading from the left we find the first nonzero digit, followed by a decimal point, and then the remaining digits.

-5.14

Next, we write $\times$ 10, leaving space to write an exponent on the 10.

-5.14×10

Finally we shift the decimal point 8 places left to make it appear in the same position it had in the original number. Thus, the power of 10 will be -8.

$-0.00514 \times 10^{-5} = -5.14 \times 10^{-8}$ ■

Multiplication and Division in Scientific Notation

Now that we can convert numbers to scientific notation, we can explain how to simplify expressions that contain numbers in this form. The two operations that are particularly suited to this format are multiplication and division. The idea is to multiply or divide the decimal parts and then apply the rules for exponents to effectively multiply or divide the powers of 10 separately. As an example of multiplication, here we show how the decimal parts and the powers of 10 are handled separately.

$$(4.1 \times 10^5) \times (3.1 \times 10^3) = (4.1 \times 3.1) \times (10^5 \times 10^3)$$

Multiply the decimal parts and the power of 10 parts separately.

$$= (12.71) \times (10^{5+3})$$

Apply the addition rule for exponents.

$$= 12.71 \times 10^8$$

This result is not in scientific notation.

$$= 1.271 \times 10^9$$

Leave the final answer in scientific notation.

Division problems are handled in a similar manner. Here we use fractions to illustrate how the decimal and power of 10 parts get separated. Standard division of decimals applies to the decimal parts, whereas the division rule for exponents is applied to the powers of 10.

$$(2.496 \times 10^6) \div (3.2 \times 10^5) = \frac{2.496 \times 10^6}{3.2 \times 10^5}$$

Show the division in fractional form.

$$= \frac{2.496}{3.2} \times \frac{10^6}{10^5}$$

Separate the decimal and power of 10 parts.

$$= 0.78 \times 10^{6-5}$$

Divide the decimal parts and subtract exponents.

$$= 0.78 \times 10^1$$

This result is not in scientific notation.

$$= 7.8 \times 10^0$$

The final answer should be converted to scientific notation.

EXAMPLE 3   Perform the following multiplication and division by operating on the decimal parts and exponential parts separately. Convert your final answers to scientific notation.

a. $(6.57 \times 10^{-9}) \times (-3.74 \times 10^{16})$ **b.** $\dfrac{2.03852 \times 10^{-12}}{4.51 \times 10^{-17}}$

SOLUTION   **a.** $(6.57 \times 10^{-9}) \times (-3.74 \times 10^{16}) = (6.57 \times -3.74) \times (10^{-9} \times 10^{16})$

Rearrange the decimal and power of 10 parts.

$$= (-24.5718) \times (10^{-9+16})$$

Multiply the decimals and powers of 10 separately.

$$= -24.5718 \times 10^7$$

This is not in scientific notation.

$$= -2.45718 \times 10^8$$

Convert to scientific notation.

b. $\dfrac{2.03852 \times 10^{-12}}{4.51 \times 10^{-17}} = \dfrac{2.03852}{4.51} \times \dfrac{10^{-12}}{10^{-17}}$

Separate the decimal and power of 10 parts.

$= 0.452 \times 10^{-12-(-17)}$

Divide the decimal parts and subtract the exponents.

$= 0.452 \times 10^{-12+(+17)}$

Convert subtraction to adding the opposite.

$= 0.452 \times 10^{5}$

This is not in scientific notation.

$= 4.52 \times 10^{4}$

Convert to scientific notation. ■

In general, scientific notation is convenient only for multiplication and division problems. If a problem has addition or subtraction operations, we first convert the numbers into standard notation before performing the addition or subtraction. The final example in this section is a word problem that uses numbers in scientific notation.

EXAMPLE 4

A nanosecond is one billionth of a second, which can be written as $1. \times 10^{-9}$ second. A millisecond is one thousandth of a second, which can be written as $1. \times 10^{-3}$ second. In a microcomputer it takes 3 milliseconds to perform an addition of two numbers, and it takes 150 nanoseconds for the same computer to read its own memory. How many memory reads can this computer perform in the same time it takes to perform one addition? Write the answer in both standard and scientific notations.

SOLUTION

To determine how many times faster the memory read operation is compared to the addition operation, divide the time for one addition by the time for one memory read operation. The time required to perform one addition is $3. \times 10^{-3}$ second and the time required to perform one memory read operation is $150. \times 10^{-9}$ second.

$$\frac{3. \times 10^{-3}}{150. \times 10^{-9}} = \frac{3.}{150.} \times \frac{10^{-3}}{10^{-9}} = 0.02 \times 10^{-3-(-9)}$$

$$= 0.02 \times 10^{6} = 20{,}000 = 2. \times 10^{4}$$

The microcomputer can perform twenty thousand memory reads in the same time it takes it to perform one addition. ■

P R A C T I C E   F O R   S U C C E S S

Practice 1. Is -72.36×10^{5} in scientific notation? Why or why not?

Practice 2. Is 0.0715×10^{-3} in scientific notation? Why or why not?

Practice 3. Convert -89.13×10^{-5} to scientific notation.

Practice 4. Convert $-\dfrac{7}{8} \times 10^{0}$ to scientific notation.

Practice 5.   Simplify $(-5.34 \times 10^{-5}) \times (-6.5 \times 10^4)$ and leave your answer in scientific notation.

Practice 6.   Simplify $\dfrac{-7.9645 \times 10^{-2}}{9.37 \times 10^{-5}}$ and leave your answer in scientific notation.

Practice 7.   In the metric system a meter is a unit of measurement that is a little longer than one yard. If the radius of the sun is 6.9×10^8 meters and if the radius of the earth is 6.4×10^6 meters, how many times larger is the radius of the sun compared to that of the earth?

EXERCISES 5.5

In exercises 1–14, tell whether or not the given number is in scientific notation. For those numbers that are not in scientific notation, tell which part of the definition fails to be satisfied.

1. $\dfrac{1}{2} \times 10^5$ 2. 0.01285×10^{-6}

3. 92.76×10^{-2} 4. $6.78 \times 10^{2.6}$

5. $9.231 \times 10^{3.1}$ 6. 46.93×10^{-3}

7. -0.732×10^4 8. 0.0036×10^4

9. $\dfrac{3}{5} \times 10^{-6}$ 10. 5.361×10^8

11. $\sqrt{2} \times 10^6$ 12. $8.31 \times 10^{-1/2}$

13. 7.822×10^{-99} 14. 5.672×10^{-28}

In exercises 15–34, convert each number to scientific notation.

15. 12.36×10^{-1} 16. 158.42×10^2

17. 0.0219×10^{-2} 18. $9{,}875$

19. -1 20. -0.0001

21. 0.000001 22. 10^7

23. 10^{-3} 24. $100{,}000$

25. $\dfrac{5}{8}$ 26. $\sqrt{25}$

27. $\sqrt{16}$ 28. $\dfrac{7}{16} \times 10^{-3}$

29. 0.01 30. $\dfrac{7}{50} \times 10^2$

31. 4×5^2 32. -6×8^2

33. -9×12^{-2} 34. 27×6^{-2}

Simplify the expressions in exercises 35–55 and leave your answers in scientific notation.

35. $9 \times 10^3 + 9 \times 10^2 + 9 \times 10^1$

36. $7.2 \times 10^3 - 4.1 \times 10^0 - 1.61 \times 10^{-2}$

37. $8.7 \times 10^3 - (-127.4 \times 10^1) - 1,476 \times 10^{-3}$

38. $(2.36 \times 10^2) \cdot (4.1 \times 10^{-3})$

39. $\dfrac{1.4518 \times 10^2}{4.27 \times 10^{-1}}$

40. $(-4.9 \times 10^3) - (-3.21 \times 10^2)$

41. $(-2.1 \times 10^{-1}) - (-4.6 \times 10^{-2})$

42. $(-2.4 \times 10^{-12}) \cdot (-3.9 \times 10^{-13})$

43. $(5.429 \times 10^{21}) \cdot (2.0 \times 10^{-41})$

44. $(6.84 \times 10^5) \div (4.0 \times 10^{-4})$

45. $(-6.8 \times 10^{-2}) \cdot (-2.1 \times 10^3)$

46. $\dfrac{9.2 \times 10^{-1}}{4.6 \times 10^{-4}}$

47. $(-2.9 \times 10^8) \cdot (3.07 \times 10^{-12})$

48. $\dfrac{-8.48 \times 10^{-3}}{-8.0 \times 10^{-5}}$

49. $(-7.23 \times 10^{-10}) \cdot (-5.6 \times 10^{-15})$

50. $\dfrac{(-4.9 \times 10^{-2}) \cdot (2.2 \times 10^5)}{-7.7 \times 10^{-6}}$

51. $\dfrac{(3.6 \times 10^2) \cdot (-6.8 \times 10^3)}{-5.1 \times 10^{-6}}$

52. $\dfrac{(4.2 \times 10^{-2}) \cdot (-2.5 \times 10^{-7})}{-3.5 \times 10^{-5}}$

53. $\dfrac{(3.6 \times 10^2) + (1.2 \times 10^2)}{2.4 \times 10^2}$

54. $\dfrac{(7.2 \times 10^{-3}) \cdot (5.1 \times 10^{-6})}{(4.0 \times 10^5) \cdot (3.0 \times 10^{-8})}$

55. $\dfrac{(5.6 \times 10^2) \div (-2.8 \times 10^3)}{(3.0 \times 10^1) \div (2.4 \times 10^0)}$

Solve each word problem in exercises 56–65. Write your answers in both standard and scientific notation.

56. If the height of the average person is 70 inches and if the size of a certain poliomyelitis virus is 5.6×10^{-7} inch, how many times bigger is a human compared to this virus?

57. The age of the earth in seconds is approximately 1.2×10^{17} seconds, whereas the age of the pyramid of Cheops is approximately 1.5×10^{11} seconds. How many times older is the earth compared to the pyramid of Cheops?

58. If you retire from work when you are approximately $2. \times 10^9$ seconds old, and if the average number of seconds required for the earth to orbit around the sun is 3.2×10^7 seconds, approximately how many times will the earth orbit the sun before you retire?

59. If the distance from the earth to the moon is approximately 1.25×10^9 feet, and the distance from the earth to the sun is approximately 5.0×10^{11} feet, approximately how many times farther away from the earth is the sun compared to the moon?

60. If there are 365 days in a year, 24 hours in a day, 60 minutes in an hour, and 60 seconds in a minute, how many seconds are in a year? Write your answer in scientific notation.

61. In microscopic physics the unit of time used in many measurements is called the *shake*, which is $1. \times 10^{-8}$ second. Which number is bigger, the number of shakes in one second or the number of seconds in one year?

62. Use the formula $time = \dfrac{distance}{rate}$ to find how long it takes light to travel from the moon to the earth. Assume light travels at a speed of 1.8×10^5 miles per second and that the distance from the moon to the earth is approximately 2.4×10^5 miles.

63. If sound travels at a speed of 1.0×10^3 feet per second, how long does it take sound to travel the length of a football field 1.0×10^2 yards long? (*Hint:* Convert yards to feet using 1 yard = 3 feet and then use the formula *time = distance ÷ rate.*)

64. Sound travels faster in water than it does in air because water is more dense than air. If the speed of sound in air is 1.3×10^4 inches per second while the speed of sound in water is 5.72×10^4 inches per second, how many times faster is the speed of sound in water compared to that in air?

65. Assuming light travels at a speed of 1.8×10^5 miles per second and that sound travels at a speed of 2×10^{-1} miles per second, how many times faster is light compared to sound?

Looking Back

66. Place the correct symbol < or > between the two mixed numbers $-3\frac{8}{15}$? $-3\frac{47}{90}$.

67. Reduce the fraction $\frac{901}{1,007}$.

68. What is the basic operation for the expression $56 \div 7 + 9 \cdot 6 - \sqrt{36}$?

69. Simplify the complex fraction

$$\frac{\dfrac{7}{15} - \dfrac{37}{90}}{\dfrac{23}{45} + \dfrac{11}{18}}$$

70. How many even numbers are prime numbers?

71. How many odd numbers are composite numbers?

72. Determine whether or not the number 953 is prime.

PRACTICE-FOR-SUCCESS ANSWERS

1. No. The absolute value of the decimal part is greater than 10.

2. No. The absolute value of the decimal part is less than 1.

3. -8.913×10^{-4}

4. -8.75×10^{-1}

5. 3.471×10^{0}

6. -8.5×10^{2}

7. The radius of the sun is 107.8125 times larger than the radius of the earth.

| **5.6** | **THE METRIC SYSTEM** |

OBJECTIVES

☐	To learn how the metric system is based
☐	To learn the basic prefix names used in the metric system
☐	To learn the fundamental metric system unit names for length, area, volume, and weight
☐	To learn the most common metric system unit abbreviations
☐	To be able to convert between different metric units

The metric system is a universal system for measuring in the scientific world. In most countries of the world other than the United States, the metric system also serves as the fundamental system of measurement associated with commercial enterprises. However, the metric system has always been used by the scientific community in the United States, and for this reason students need to learn the fundamentals of the system.

The system of measurement commonly used in the United States is based on the old English system but will be referred to as the U.S. customary system. In terms of length, 12 inches equal one foot, 3 feet equal one yard, and 5,280 feet equal one mile. To convert between inches and feet or between yards and miles requires knowing the proper conversion factors, and, therefore, requires knowing two different numbers for each unit of measurement to convert to either the next smaller or the next larger unit.

Because the relationship between various metric quantities is based on powers of 10, we do not have to memorize any special numbers to convert between smaller and larger units. To convert to the next smaller unit we multiply by 10, and to convert to the next larger unit we divide by 10. This simplicity of converting to smaller or larger units is the main advantage of the metric system. In fact, all that is required to learn the metric system is to know the names of the units and the names of the conversion factors.

In this book we will not translate between the metric system and the U.S. customary system. Just as when we speak French or German or Spanish we normally do all our thinking and writing in that language, when learning the metric system we will stay within the system and not perform conversions between that system and our customary system.

Metric System Prefixes

In Sections 5.4 and 5.5 we studied the relationships between powers of 10 and decimal numbers and scientific notation. Table 5.3 lists the prefix names that are associated with various integer powers of 10. These prefix names are used with each kind of measurement unit, such as length, area, volume, and weight; some are used less frequently than others.

Length

The first measurement we will study is length. The fundamental unit of length in the metric system is called the **meter**. Although a meter can be

Prefix Name	Multiplier Value
tera	$10^{12} = 1,000,000,000,000$
giga	$10^{9} = 1,000,000,000$
mega	$10^{6} = 1,000,000$
kilo	$10^{3} = 1,000$
hecto	$10^{2} = 100$
deka	$10^{1} = 10$
deci	$10^{-1} = 0.1$
centi	$10^{-2} = 0.01$
milli	$10^{-3} = 0.001$
micro	$10^{-6} = 0.000001$
nano	$10^{-9} = 0.000000001$
pico	$10^{-12} = 0.000000000001$

TABLE 5.3   Prefix names used in the metric system

defined scientifically, all we need to know is that a meter is a little longer than one yard. To place a meter in a more familiar context, we can say that a meter is 39.37 inches, but we need not memorize this fact. Perhaps a better way of expressing it would be to say that a meter is about the length of a large baseball bat.

If you travel by car in a foreign country, you will find that road signs give the distances between cities or towns using the **kilometer** as the unit of measurement. Looking at Table 5.3, we see that the prefix **kilo** is associated with the third power of 10. Since $10^3 = 1,000$ we can easily discern that one kilometer is equivalent to 1,000 meters.

To find the length of a pencil we would need a unit of measurement somewhat smaller than the length of a baseball bat. Because the meter is the fundamental unit of measurement in the metric system, when we need units much smaller than a meter we begin by dividing a meter by 10. Dividing by 10 is the same as multiplying by the decimal 0.1, and from Table 5.3 we can see the prefix name associated with the multiplier 0.1 is **deci.** Thus, a **decimeter** is $\frac{1}{10}$ of a meter.

Decimeters are not used as much as the next smaller unit, which is the **centimeter,** abbreviated **cm.** In Table 5.3 the prefix **centi** is associated with the value $10^{-2} = 0.01 = \frac{1}{100}$; thus, a centimeter is $\frac{1}{100}$ of a meter. (Chances are that you will be able to find a scale on a ruler that uses centimeters.) A centimeter is approximately the distance between the two prongs of a plug or the two holes in a standard electrical outlet; a pencil would be about 15 cm long.

When units of measurement even smaller than centimeters are required, we keep dividing by powers of 10. A **millimeter,** abbreviated **mm,** is $\frac{1}{1,000}$ of a meter, which is the same as $\frac{1}{10}$ of a centimeter. From Table 5.3 we see the prefix **milli** is associated with 10^{-3}. When things are really small we can measure them in **micrometers.** The prefix **micro** is associated with the numerical value of 10^{-6}, which is one one-millionth.

Table 5.4 lists a few of the metric length names and shows their corresponding abbreviations. Although hectometers and dekameters are defined,

Length Name	Abbreviation
kilometer	km
meter	m
centimeter	cm
millimeter	mm

TABLE 5.4   Abbreviations of length measurements

these names are not in common use within the metric system. The abbreviations in Table 5.4 will be used in the exercises in this book.

EXAMPLE 1   Using a ruler with a centimeter scale, measure the dimensions of a standard $8\frac{1}{2} \times 11$ inch piece of paper and give your answers with one decimal place of accuracy.

SOLUTION   A standard-size piece of paper measures 21.6 cm $\times$ 27.9 cm.   ■

We will often want to convert between units within the metric system. Such conversions are easy since the metric system units are based on powers of 10.   ■

EXAMPLE 2   Convert the answer in example 1 to millimeters.

SOLUTION   To convert from centimeters to millimeters, multiply by 10, which is equivalent to shifting the decimal point one place to the right: 21.6 cm = 216. mm and 27.9 cm = 279. mm. A standard-size piece of paper is 216 mm $\times$ 279 mm.   ■

EXAMPLE 3   Convert your answers in example 1 to kilometers but write your answers in scientific notation.

SOLUTION   To convert from centimeters to kilometers, we first convert to meters. Since a centimeter is $\frac{1}{100}$ of a meter, we divide centimeters by 100 to convert to meters. To convert from a smaller unit to a larger unit we always divide, so to convert from meters to kilometers we continue to divide but in this case the factor is 1,000. So overall to convert from centimeters to kilometers we divide by $100 \times 1,000 = 100,000$, which is equivalent to multiplying by 10^{-5}.

$21.6 \times 10^{-5} = 0.000216 = 2.16 \times 10^{-4}$

$27.9 \times 10^{-5} = 0.000279 = 2.79 \times 10^{-4}$

A standard-size piece of paper measures 2.16×10^{-4} km by 2.79×10^{-4} km.

■

Volume

The second measurement we discuss is volume. In the metric system the fundamental unit of volume is the **liter**, which is familiar to many as the size of some soft drink and bottled water containers. A liter can be defined to be that volume enclosed in a cube that measures 10 centimeters on each edge. Since the volume of a cube is calculated by "cubing" the length of a side, we see that

$$1 \text{ liter} = (10 \text{ cm})^3 = 10^3 \text{ cm}^3 = 1{,}000 \text{ cm}^3$$

One cubic centimeter is about the size of a sugar cube, so 1 liter is the volume occupied by approximately 1,000 sugar cubes.

All of the prefixes in Table 5.4 applied to meters can be applied to liters. Thus, a kiloliter is a volume of 1,000 liters and a milliliter is a volume that is $\frac{1}{1{,}000}$ of a liter. Learning some of the prefixes in Table 5.4 makes learning the meaning of most of the rest of the names in the metric system easy.

In the field of medicine, where small amounts of drugs are used, the preferred unit of volume is the cubic centimeter, abbreviated **cc.** Thus, $1 \text{ cm}^3 = 1 \text{ cc} = 1 \text{ m}\ell$. Abbreviations of a few of the more commonly used volume names appear in Table 5.5.

Volume Name	Abbreviation
kiloliter	$k\ell$
liter	ℓ
milliliter	$m\ell$
cubic centimeter	cc

TABLE 5.5 ■ Abbreviations of volume names

EXAMPLE 4 Convert 2.45×10^5 liters into kiloliters.

SOLUTION To convert from liters to kiloliters, we divide by $1{,}000 = 10^3$.

$$\frac{2.45 \times 10^5}{10^3} = 2.45 \times 10^{5-3} = 2.45 \times 10^2 = 245$$

245 $k\ell$ ■

EXAMPLE 5 Convert 679.33 milliliters to liters and write the numerical part of your answer in scientific notation.

SOLUTION To convert from milliliters to liters, we divide by 1,000 or multiply by 10^{-3}.

$$679.33 \div 1{,}000 = 679.33 \times 10^{-3} = 0.67933 = 6.7933 \times 10^{-1}$$

$6.7933 \times 10^{-1} \ell$ ■

| **EXAMPLE 6** | A box measures 102.5 m × 200 m × 80 m. What is the volume of the box in liters? Write the numerical part of your answer in scientific notation. |

SOLUTION   Because the question asks for the answer in liters and because a liter is 1,000 cm^3, we first convert each dimension to cm before multiplying to calculate the volume. We always multiply when we convert from a larger unit to a smaller unit, so to convert m to cm we multiply by 100. The volume of a box is length × width × height, or the product of the three dimensions of the box:

(102.5 × 100 cm) (200 × 100 cm) (80 × 100 cm)

$$= (102,500)(20,000)(8,000) \text{ cm}^3 = 1.64 \times 10^{13} \text{ cm}^3$$

Finally, we divide this last number by 10^3 to convert the answer to liters.

$$\frac{1.64 \times 10^{13}}{10^3} = 1.64 \times 10^{13-3} = 1.64 \times 10^{10}$$

$1.64 \times 10^{10} \, \ell$ ■

Area

Area is measured in terms of square units regardless of the system being used. In the United States large land areas are measured in units called acres and in the metric system they are measured in units called **ares** (pronounced "airs") or sometimes hectares. From Table 5.3 we find the prefix *hecto* means 100 so 1 hectare is equivalent to 100 ares. One are is the area of a square that measures 10 m on a side, so one are is equivalent to 100 m^2. Since the meter and centimeter are the common metric system units for linear measurement, we find that m^2 or cm^2 are also commonly used units for areas in the metric system.

| **EXAMPLE 7** | Convert 35.4 m^2 into ares. |

SOLUTION   Because one are is equivalent to 100 m^2, we divide by 100 to get ares from m^2.

$$\frac{35.4}{100} = 0.354$$

So 35.4 m^2 = 0.354 are.   ■

| **EXAMPLE 8** | Convert 3.59 × 10^5 cm^2 into m^2. |

SOLUTION   Divide by 10^4 to convert cm^2 to m^2, (because 1 m = 100 cm).
$(1 \text{ m})^2 = (100 \text{ cm})^2 = 10,000 \text{ cm}^2 = 10^4 \text{ cm}^2$

$$\frac{3.59 \times 10^5}{10^4} = 3.59 \times 10^{5-4} = 3.59 \times 10^1 = 35.9$$

The answer is 35.9 m^2.   ■

Weight or Mass

In the metric system what we might otherwise call weight is called **mass.** In physics it is important to distinguish between weight and mass. It was the English physicist Isaac Newton who studied the motion of the planets and gave the world his famous second law of motion that is expressed by the equation

$$\text{force} = \text{mass} \times \text{acceleration}$$

Now if acceleration is constant, which it is if you are on the surface of the earth where acceleration is due to gravity, then you could equate force with mass. In the English system, forces are measured in terms of pounds, but in the metric system the fundamental unit is one of mass so it's important to know the distinction between weight and mass.

The difference between weight and mass is best illustrated by saying that on the moon the force of gravity is only $\frac{1}{6}$ that of what it is on earth; if you weigh 150 pounds on earth you would weigh only 25 pounds on the moon. Thus weight is dependent on where the measurement takes place. However, you would have the same mass whether you were standing on the moon or on the earth, so mass is independent of where it is measured.

The fundamental unit of mass in the metric system is the **gram.** A typical paper clip has a mass that is about equivalent to one gram. Since a single paper clip does not weigh very much, another unit called the **kilogram** is also commonly used. From Table 5.3 we conclude that a kilogram is equivalent to 1,000 grams because the prefix *kilo* implies a factor of 1,000. In the U.S. customary system, one kilogram is equivalent to about 2.2 pounds. Table 5.6 lists the commonly used abbreviations of mass names.

Mass Name	Abbreviation
metric ton	t
kilogram	kg
gram	g
centigram	cg
milligram	mg

TABLE 5.6   **Abbreviations of mass names**

For really large masses the unit called a **metric ton** is used. By definition a metric ton is 1,000 kilograms, and since a kilogram is 1,000 grams we can also describe a metric ton as 10^6 grams. This could also be called a *megagram* but the term *metric ton* is preferred.

EXAMPLE 9   Convert 500 mg to grams.

SOLUTION   1 mg is $\frac{1}{1,000}$ of a gram, which can also be expressed as 1 g = 1,000 mg. To convert mg to grams we divide by 1,000.

$$\frac{500}{1,000} = \frac{1}{2} = 0.5$$

500 mg = 0.5 g   ■

| **EXAMPLE 10** | Convert 0.0054 kg to grams. |

SOLUTION   1 kg is the same as 1,000 grams, so to convert from kg to grams we multiply by 1,000.

$(0.0054) \cdot (1,000) = 5.4$

$0.0054 \text{ kg} = 5.4 \text{ g}$ ■

Prefixes in Computer Terms

Some of the metric system prefixes are also used in computer science, but unfortunately they then have slightly different meanings. Memory capacities of computer disks are measured in what are called *megabytes,* and sizes of computer files are commonly measured in what are called *kilobytes.* But in computer terms kilo does not mean 10^3 and mega does not mean 10^6. In the context of computers kilo means 1,024, which is close to 1,000 but is not exactly the same as 1,000. In terms of computer disk capacities a megabyte means 1,048,576 bytes, which is close to 10^6 bytes but is not exactly the same.

The meanings of the computer prefixes are based on the exact powers of 2, which are closest to the powers of 10 corresponding to the metric system prefixes. Thus, since $2^9 = 512$ and $2^{11} = 2,048$, the power of 2 nearest 1,000 is $2^{10} = 1,024$. Similarly the power of 2 nearest 10^6 is $2^{20} = 1,048,576$.

Even the very name *microcomputer* uses the prefix *micro* because the heart of such a machine is called a *microprocessor.* The timing and speeds at which computers perform operations are sometimes measured in terms called *microseconds* and *milliseconds;* the high-speed clocks that reside inside computers are driven by crystals that vibrate in time units that are powers of 2. In any event, depending on the context in which they are used, the metric system prefixes may be given slightly different meanings. As used in this book, however, the prefixes will always have the meanings given in Table 5.3.

PRACTICE FOR SUCCESS

Convert the given units to the units indicated.

Practice 1. $1,500 \text{ m} = ? \text{ km}$

Practice 2. $28 \ \ell = ? \text{ cm}^3$

Practice 3. $38 \text{ cm}^2 = ? \text{ mm}^2$

Practice 4. $2.3 \times 10^4 \text{ mg} = ? \text{ g}$

Practice 5. $38 \text{ a} = ? \text{ m}^2$

Practice 6. $750 \text{ cm}^3 = ? \ \ell$

Practice 7.   Using a ruler with a centimeter scale, measure the size of a dollar bill in terms of centimeters. Give your answers for the dimensions within one decimal place of accuracy.

EXERCISES 5.6

In exercises 1–38, convert from the given units to the units indicated.

1. $6.5 \, t = ? \, kg$
2. $1.4 \, km = ? \, m$
3. $450 \, mg = ? \, kg$
4. $365 \, cm = ? \, m$
5. $2{,}560 \, m = ? \, km$
6. $0.04 \, kg = ? \, g$
7. $0.02 \, t = ? \, kg$
8. $560 \, mm = ? \, cm$
9. $0.28 \, l = ? \, m\ell$
10. $2.5 \, k\ell = ? \, \ell$
11. $580 \, g = ? \, kg$
12. $250 \, m\ell = ? \, \ell$
13. $0.4 \, g = ? \, cg$
14. $0.008 \, cg = ? \, mg$
15. $18 \, m^2 = ? \, cm^2$
16. $0.06 \, cm = ? \, mm$
17. $2 \times 10^4 \, kg = ? \, t$
18. $3.7 \times 10^5 \, m = ? \, km$
19. $4.6 \times 10^{-6} \, kg = ? \, mg$
20. $0.0004 \, m = ? \, cm$
21. $2.7 \times 10^{-2} \, km^2 = ? \, m^2$
22. $8.5 \times 10^5 \, g = ? \, kg$
23. $9.35 \times 10^6 \, kg = ? \, t$
24. $3.6 \times 10^{-4} \, cm = ? \, mm$
25. $8.44 \times 10^8 \, m\ell = ? \, \ell$
26. $4.55 \times 10^9 \, k\ell = ? \, \ell$
27. $2.38 \times 10^{-5} \, kg = ? \, g$
28. $6.7 \times 10^{12} \, \ell = ? \, k\ell$
29. $4.07 \times 10^7 \, cg = ? \, g$
30. $9.11 \times 10^2 \, mg = ? \, cg$
31. $9.45 \times 10^6 \, cm^2 = ? \, m^2$
32. $6.208 \times 10^4 \, mm = ? \, cm$
33. $7.25 \times 10^{-3} \, t = ? \, kg$
34. $8.04 \times 10^{-1} \, km = ? \, m$
35. $8.62 \times 10^8 \, mg = ? \, kg$
36. $1.114 \times 10^7 \, cm = ? \, m$
− 37. $3.2 \times 10^{-6} \, \ell = ? \, m\ell$
38. $4.1 \times 10^{-10} \, kg = ? \, cg$

− 39. Measure the diameter of a quarter using a ruler with a centimeter scale and write the answer with one decimal place of accuracy.

40. Measure the diameter of a dime using a ruler with a centimeter scale and write the answer with one decimal place of accuracy.

41. Using a ruler with a centimeter scale, measure the dimensions of a standard 3×5 card and write the answer with one decimal place of accuracy.

42. Using any ruler, mark a length that is exactly 10 inches long. Then, using a ruler with a centimeter scale, measure the length and write the answer accurate to one decimal place.

43. Measure the size of a standard audiocassette using a ruler with a centimeter scale and write the answer with one decimal place of accuracy.

◉ Looking Back

44. Find $\sqrt{58}$ and round the answer to the nearest ten-thousandth.

45. Reduce $\sqrt{688}$.

46. Convert $\dfrac{155}{310}$ to a percent.

47. Simplify $\left(\dfrac{2}{3}\right)^{-3}$.

48. What is the basic operation for the expression
$$\sqrt{30^2 + 50 - 9} - \frac{5\left|-30\right| + 7^2}{60^3 + \sqrt{0}}?$$

49. Simplify
$$\frac{\dfrac{2}{3} + \dfrac{7}{8}}{\dfrac{5}{6} - \dfrac{3}{4}}$$

and write the answer as a mixed number.

50. Describe what it means for a whole number to be a perfect square in terms of the exponents in the prime factorization of the number.

PRACTICE-FOR-SUCCESS ANSWERS

1. 1.5 km	**2.** 28,000 cm^3	**3.** 3,800 mm^2
4. 23 g	**5.** 3,800 m^2	**6.** 0.75 ℓ

7. A dollar bill measures 15.7 cm long × 6.7 cm wide.

SUMMARY

This chapter expanded the range of numbers that can be used as exponents by including zero and negative integers as exponents. The basic definition for a negative exponent is $b^{-n} = \dfrac{1}{b^n}$, whereas the basic definition for a zero exponent is $b^0 = 1$. In both cases the base b is not allowed to be equal to 0. The other fundamental rules for working with exponents are

1. The addition rule for a product of powers

$$b^m \cdot b^n = b^{m+n} \qquad 2^{-4} \cdot 2^3 = 2^{-1} = \frac{1}{2}$$

2. The subtraction rule for a quotient of powers

$$\frac{b^m}{b^n} = b^{m-n} \qquad \frac{3^4}{3^{-5}} = 3^{4-(-5)} = 3^9$$

3. The product rule for powers of powers

$$(b^m)^n = b^{m \cdot n} \qquad (2^{-4})^{-3} = 2^{12}$$

4. The rule for a power of a product
$$(a \cdot b)^n = a^n \cdot b^n \qquad (2 \cdot 3)^4 = 2^4 \cdot 3^4$$

5. The rule for a power of a fraction
$$\left(\frac{a}{b}\right)^n = \frac{a^n}{b^n} \qquad \left(\frac{-1}{2}\right)^3 = \frac{(-1)^3}{2^3} = \frac{-1}{8} = -\frac{1}{8}$$

6. The rule for a fraction to a negative power
$$\left(\frac{a}{b}\right)^{-n} = \frac{b^n}{a^n} \qquad \left(\frac{2}{5}\right)^{-2} = \frac{5^2}{2^2} = \frac{25}{4}$$

Scientific notation is usually used to represent numbers that are either very small or very large — for example, the decimal 0.000000000823 is more compactly represented by writing 8.23×10^{-10}. Scientific notation results in a number greater than or equal to 1 but less than 10 times a signed power of 10. As another example, $759,000,000,000 = 7.59 \times 10^{11}$.

The metric system is based on powers of 10. The four most commonly used metric prefixes are

$$\text{mega} = 10^6 \quad \text{and} \quad \text{kilo} = 10^3 \qquad \text{(positive powers of 10)}$$
$$\text{centi} = 10^{-2} \quad \text{and} \quad \text{milli} = 10^{-3} \qquad \text{(negative powers of 10)}$$

The metric names associated with physical measurements are meters for length, grams for weight, and liters for volume.

CHAPTER 5 REVIEW PROBLEMS

In problems 1–19, simplify the expressions, which contain zero and signed powers. Any answers that are fractions should be completely reduced.

1. 5^{-2}

2. 2^{-5}

3. $(-3)^{-2}$

4. $(-4)^{-2}$

5. $\left(\frac{1}{2}\right)^{-3}$

6. $\left(\frac{2}{3}\right)^{-2}$

7. 0^{-5}

8. $(-1)^{-3}$

9. $(-0)^5$

10. $\left(-\frac{3}{4}\right)^{-2}$

11. $\left(-\frac{5}{3}\right)^{-1}$

12. $(-18)^0$

13. $(-20)^0$

14. $(-6)^{-2}$

15. $\left(-\frac{1}{2}\right)^{-4}$

16. $(-5)^{-3}$

17. $\left(-\dfrac{8}{9}\right)^0$

18. 0^0

19. $\left(-\dfrac{2}{3}\right)^{-3}$

In problems 20–38, use the addition and subtraction rules for exponents to simplify each expression. If the final answer is too large to calculate as a single number, leave your answer as an exponential expression with a positive exponent.

20. $2^{-6} \cdot 2^8$

21. $3^{-8} \cdot 3^5$

22. $(-4)^{-5} \cdot (-4)^{-6}$

23. $(-5)^7 \cdot (-5)^8$

24. $(-3)^{-10} \div (-3)^{-13}$

25. $(-4)^{-10} \div (-4)^{-8}$

26. $\dfrac{(-5)^6}{(-5)^{-6}}$

27. $\dfrac{2^{-12}}{2^{-15}}$

28. $(7^{-30}) \cdot (7^{28})$

29. $(5)^7 \div (-5)^{-7}$

30. $(-10)^{-5} \div (-10)^{-6}$

31. $(-8)^{-8} \div (8)^{-8}$

32. $(-6)^{-6} \div 6^6$

33. $0^5 \div 5^0$

34. $9^{-9} \cdot (-9)^9$

35. $2^{-9} \div 2^{-7} \cdot 2^8$

36. $0^8 \div (-8)^0$

37. $\left(\dfrac{1}{3}\right)^{-3} \div (3)^{-3}$

38. $\left(\dfrac{1}{4}\right)^4 \div (-4)^{-4}$

In problems 39–52, use the product rule for exponents to simplify the given expression. If an answer is sufficiently large it may be left in exponential form, but any such answer should be written with a positive exponent and a positive base.

39. $\left[\left(\dfrac{1}{2}\right)^{-3}\right]^{-5}$

40. $[(3)^{-3}]^{-6}$

41. $[(-4)^3]^{-6}$

42. $[(-1)^{-1}]^3$

43. $[(-1)^{-1}]^{-1}$

44. $[2^2]^0$

45. $[0^5]^4$

46. $[-8^0]^{-8}$

47. $(-6^0)^{-5}$

48. $[(-5)^0]^{-3}$

49. $[-2^3]^{-4}$

50. $[-0^5]^3$

51. $\left[\left(-\dfrac{1}{2}\right)^{-5}\right]^8$

52. $\left[\left(-\dfrac{1}{3}\right)^{-3}\right]^3$

In problems 53–62, tell whether or not the given number is in scientific notation. For those numbers that are not in scientific notation, tell which part of the definition fails to be satisfied.

53. 3.62×10^{-5}

54. 4.59×10^{12}

55. -18.1×10^6

56. 0.0019×10^{-8}

57. $\sqrt{3} \times 10^8$

58. $9.17 \times 10^{\sqrt{2}}$

59. $6.72 \times 10^{-1/2}$

60. 64.59×10^{-3}

61. 1.0×10^{10}

62. 10^9

In problems 63–76, simplify the expressions and leave your answers in scientific notation.

63. $\dfrac{13.57 \times 10^{-6}}{5.9 \times 10^{-2}}$

64. $\dfrac{45.44 \times 10^8}{-7.1 \times 10^{-5}}$

65. $(-1.3 \times 10^5)(7.0 \times 10^{-6})$

66. $(-5.2 \times 10^4)(3.5 \times 10^{-7})$

67. $\dfrac{24.03 \times 10^6}{8.9 \times 10^{-6}}$

68. $(-1.42 \times 10^{-3})(0.5 \times 10^5)$

69. $(4.4 \times 10^{-8})(5.0 \times 10^{12})$

70. $\dfrac{40.88 \times 10^5}{7.3 \times 10^{-3}}$

71. $\dfrac{(5.1 \times 10^2)(3.4 \times 10^{-3})}{(1.7 \times 10^{-5})}$

72. $\dfrac{(-8.5 \times 10^5) \div (1.7 \times 10^{-3})}{(-5.0 \times 10^6)}$

73. $\dfrac{(9.5 \times 10^{-6}) \div (1.9 \times 10^3)}{(5.0 \times 10^{-8})}$

74. $\dfrac{(4.2 \times 10^{-2})(3.5 \times 10^{-3})}{(4.9 \times 10^{-6})}$

75. $\dfrac{(7.5 \times 10^{-3}) \div (2.5 \times 10^{-4})}{(6.0 \times 10^{-2})}$

76. $\dfrac{(4.5 \times 10^5) \cdot (5.4 \times 10^{-3})}{(6.9 \times 10^7) \div (2.3 \times 10^{-5})}$

In problems 77–82, translate each word description into a mathematical expression and then simplify the expression to a single number.

77. The sum of the negative three power of the fraction negative one-fourth and the negative two power of the fraction negative one-fifth.

78. The negative eight power of the fraction negative three-fourths divided by the negative ten power of the fraction negative three-fourths.

79. The sum of the three numbers that are nine times the fourth power of ten plus nine times the third power of ten plus nine times the negative one power of ten.

80. The negative three power of the quotient of the number negative two raised to the zero power with the number negative two raised to the power of negative two.

81. The negative six power of the product of negative three raised to the negative four power with the positive four power of the number negative three.

82. The quotient of the negative four power of negative three with the negative five power of negative three all divided by the positive two power of negative three.

In problems 83–86, convert from the given units to the units indicated.

83. $260 \text{ mg} = ? \text{ kg}$

84. $0.25 \, \ell = ? \text{ m}\ell$

85. $624 \text{ cm} = ? \text{ m}$

86. $2.5 \text{ cm}^2 = ? \text{ m}^2$

CHAPTER 5 PRACTICE TEST

Use the rules for exponents to simplify problems 1–14. Any answers that are fractions should be reduced and other answers should be written without negative exponents. Base and exponent combinations that are too large may be left in exponential form, but all bases should be positive.

1. 5^{-2} **2.** 3^{-3}

3. $\left(\dfrac{1}{2}\right)^{-4}$ **4.** $\left(\dfrac{1}{3}\right)^{-2}$

5. $(-0)^5$ **6.** 0^{-3}

7. 0^0 **8.** $(-5)^0$

9. $\left(-\dfrac{1}{2}\right)^{-3}$ **10.** $\left(-\dfrac{1}{5}\right)^{-2} + (-1)^{-5}$

11. $(-3)^{-6} \div (-3)^6$ **12.** $\dfrac{2^8}{2^{-12}}$

13. $(12^{-28})(12^{12})$ **14.** $[(-2)^{-3}]^8$

In problems 15–18, state whether or not the given number is in scientific notation. For those numbers that are not in scientific notation, tell why.

15. $5.6 \times 10^{-3/5}$ **16.** -0.003×10^{-8}

17. 25.6×10^{12} **18.** -3.291×5^{-4}

Perform the computations in problems 19–23 and leave your answers in scientific notation.

19. $8.1 \times 10^4 + 9.2 \times 10^3 + 7.5 \times 10^2$ **20.** $5.4 \times 10^{-4} - 0.062 \times 10^{-2}$

21. $(8.4 \times 10^{-5}) \cdot (2.5 \times 10^8)$ **22.** $\dfrac{92.0 \times 10^6}{4.6 \times 10^{-3}}$

23. $\dfrac{(4.0 \times 10^{-5}) \cdot (6.2 \times 10^6)}{8.0 \times 10^{-3}}$

Write expressions that correspond to the word descriptions given in problems 24–27 and then simplify the expressions according to the directions given for Practice Test problems 1–14.

24. Negative three raised to the power of negative five, times the positive ten power of negative three.

25. The negative three power of negative two plus the negative two power of negative three.

26. The negative two power of the sum of five and negative two.

27. Divide the sixth power of negative two by the eighth power of negative two.

In problems 28–29, convert from the given units to the indicated units.

28. 2.6×10^3 km = ? m   **29.** 3.6×10^{-4} m^2 = ? cm^2

CHAPTER SIX

ALGEBRAIC EXPRESSIONS
AND FORMULAS

Chapter 6 begins the formal study of algebra, introduces some fundamental ideas of algebra that are not part of arithmetic, and lays the foundation for understanding the nature of algebraic expressions. Arithmetic and algebra can be distinguished by the fact that arithmetic is primarily concerned with numerical computations, whereas algebra is concerned more with manipulations of symbolic expressions and is used to formulate complex relationships.

The chapter expands on the variable concept and discusses the fundamental operations on polynomials. We examine the adding, subtracting, and multiplying of polynomials and the dividing of polynomials by monomials. We also focus on the applications of formulas and the substitution of numerical values for variables in literal formulas. The work with variables and formulas in this chapter provides the background for the work with equations in Chapter 7.

6.1   VARIABLES, POLYNOMIALS, AND LIKE TERMS

OBJECTIVES

- To distinguish between variables and constants
- To recognize appropriate variable names
- To be familiar with the terms monomial, binomial, trinomial, polynomial, coefficient
- To recognize like and unlike terms
- To determine the degree of a polynomial
- To apply the distributive law when operating on polynomials

In this section we will introduce some of the terminology that is used in algebra. Every discipline has its own special jargon and algebra is no exception. An exposure to some terminology will help us effectively communicate with other people about mathematics.

Variables and Constants

The first step toward understanding symbolic expressions begins with the definition of a **variable.**

DEFINITION	VARIABLE
	A variable is a symbol that is used to represent any number selected from a specified set of numbers.

For the most part, single letters of the alphabet are used as variables in algebra. For example, the equation used to convert degrees Celsius to degrees Fahrenheit is

$$F = \frac{9}{5} \cdot C + 32$$

In this equation we are using two letters of the alphabet, F and C, as variables. Both F and C can take on different values at different times. For example, water freezes at $0°$ Celsius and water boils at $100°$ Celsius; when these values are inserted (one at a time) into the formula we find the Fahrenheit temperatures for freezing water and boiling water.

When $C = 0$, $F = \frac{9}{5} \cdot 0 + 32 = 0 + 32 = 32$

When $C = 100$, $F = \frac{9}{5} \cdot 100 + 32 = 9 \cdot 20 + 32 = 180 + 32 = 212$

In terms of degrees Fahrenheit, water freezes at $32°$ Fahrenheit and boils at $212°$ Fahrenheit. Thus, variables like F and C can take on different values at different times; F and C are symbols that represent numbers, but the values of those numbers can vary.

Not all symbols used to represent numbers are variables, however. For example, the following formula gives the area A of a circle of radius r.

$$A = \pi \cdot r^2$$

In this formula A and r are symbols that represent numbers and thus are variables, but the symbol π also represents a number and π is not a variable. π is an example of a symbol in mathematics that always represents the same number; because π does not vary, it is therefore not a variable. π represents the constant value whose first few decimal places are given by $\pi \approx$ 3.14159265359. **Constants** are symbols that always represent the same number. We can say that a constant is a quantity that cannot vary because it can take on only one value.

Range of Values

Many times the set of numbers associated with a variable is not explicitly specified. Unless otherwise stated or implied, we assume the set of numbers is the set of real numbers. However, in the case of the equation for the area of a circle, the radius r would normally not be allowed to be negative. (What would a circle with a negative radius look like?) However, r could be zero, in which case the circle would degenerate to a point with zero area. Similarly, since A is the product of the positive number π times the square of another number, A can never take on a negative value; therefore, most variables that appear in equations must be restricted.

In the case of the temperature conversion formula, it is possible for either or both F and C to be negative, but there may also be practical limits to the range of values. For example, unless you work in a cryogenic science lab or work with superconductors, temperatures less than $-100°C$ are rare. The temperature of the sun has been estimated to be about $10,000°F$ and except for thermonuclear reactions, no temperatures on earth approach that value. When variables represent physical quantities, there are physical considerations that may limit the range of values.

When a variable represents a real number, even of limited range over an interval, the variable may take on any one of an infinite number of different values. If x represents a number between 2 and 3, then x may take on an infinite number of values. But cases also exist in which variables take on only a finite number of values. If the letter s were used to represent the sum of the two numbers on the dice at a Las Vegas craps table, then s could only take on one of eleven discrete values, namely the whole numbers 2, 3, 4, 5, 6, 7, 8, 9, 10, 11, and 12.

It is also worthwhile to point out that the same letter can represent different quantities in different situations. The formula to convert inches to feet can be expressed by the equation

$$F = \frac{I}{12} \qquad \text{where } F = \text{feet and } I = \text{inches}$$

In this case F would represent feet, not degrees Fahrenheit. F can have a negative value when F represents degrees Fahrenheit, but it is difficult to imagine how F could be negative if F represents a distance measured in feet.

Terms with Variables

In Chapter 1 we defined a *term* to be a mathematical expression written using numbers connected only by the operations of multiplication and/or division. Since variables represent numbers, we will now extend this definition to allow a variable to take the place of any number. Examples of terms written using variables are the following:

$$5xy \qquad \frac{a}{b+c} \qquad 15x^3y^{-5} \qquad \frac{4a+8b}{3c+2d}$$

It is essential that we understand the meaning and the order of the operations of algebraic expressions written using variables. The term

$$15x^3y^{-5} \qquad \text{would be read as}$$

"15 times x cubed times y to the negative fifth power"

Whenever a number is written next to a variable in algebra, an implied multiplication operation connects the number and the variable. Whenever two or more variables are written next to each other, the implied operation between those variables is multiplication.

In Section 1.3 we introduced the use of the raised dot symbol · to denote multiplication. This symbol is essential to separate the two factors when the factors are numbers. For example, if we intend to write the product of five times three we must write $5 \cdot 3$. If we intend to write the number fifty-three we simply put 5 and 3 together and write 53. In either context the raised dot (or lack thereof) makes the intended meaning clear.

In algebra when a numeral is multiplied by a variable the dot symbol may be omitted. For example, $5 \cdot x$ may be written more simply as $5x$. There is no danger of confusing adjacent digits with the intended operation in this case because variables will be letters of the alphabet. It is simpler to write $5x$ than $5 \cdot x$ even if it requires a subtle explanation. This idea of multiplication is also an extension of the concept presented in Section 2.4: When parentheses surround factors the dot for the multiplication operation may be omitted.

Names as Variables

We mention a special case at this point even though it isn't fully discussed until later in the book. This case is significant for students who intend to study a programming language because in computer science it is desirable to use variable names that are made up of more than one letter.

$$FV = PV(1 + i)^n$$

is used to compute the compound interest earned when you make a one-time deposit in an account. This equation calculates compound interest: Money you have today will be worth more in the future because it can earn interest in the meantime. In the formula the letters FV stand for Future Value and the letters PV stand for Present Value. In this case FV does not represent the product of two variables called F and V, it is the complete name of a single variable. Similarly, PV is the name of a single variable. If you were given the formula

$$\text{distance} = \text{rate} \times \text{time}$$

you would not interpret the word *rate* as representing the product of four variables, $r \cdot a \cdot t \cdot e$. In this context *rate* represents one variable and there is no implicit multiplication operation between adjacent letters. So there are times when a variable name consists of more than one letter, but in algebra, 99% of the time, variable names only consist of one letter.

Also in algebra, we tend to prefer the use of lowercase letters rather than uppercase letters; the variable a is considered different from the variable A. In some computer languages variable names are considered case-sensitive if the language makes a distinction between upper- and lowercase letters and considered case-insensitive if case doesn't make any difference. In algebra variables are considered case-sensitive and the preference is to use single lowercase letters for variables, usually taken from the end of the alphabet. Thus, x and y are two of the most popular variable names used in algebra.

Monomials

One kind of expression occurs so frequently in algebra that it is given a special name: **monomial.** The following are examples of seven different monomials:

$$5x^2 \qquad -17x^3y^5 \qquad 8x^4y^3z^7 \qquad x^3 \qquad 36y \qquad -b^2 \qquad \frac{2}{3}x^5$$

DEFINITION	MONOMIAL

A monomial is the product of a number and one or more variables raised to nonnegative integer powers.

The **numerical coefficient** of a monomial is the number that precedes the variables. So the numerical coefficients of the first three monomials in the preceding list are the numbers 5, -17, and 8. In general, any factor in a monomial is the **coefficient** of the remaining factors in the monomial. So in the monomial $-17x^3y^5$ the coefficient of y^5 is $-17x^3$. In the monomial $8x^4y^3z^7$ we would say the coefficient of z^7 is $8x^4y^3$, the coefficient of y^3z^7 is $8x^4$, and the coefficient of $x^4y^3z^7$ is 8. In algebra when the word *coefficient* is used without any kind of qualification it means the numerical coefficient.

In the previous examples we see that every monomial is a term but some terms are not monomials. For example, the following four terms are not monomials.

$\dfrac{4a + 9b}{2c}$	Division by variables is not allowed.
$3x^{-2}$	Negative exponents are not allowed.
$\sqrt{15x^3}$ and $\lvert -6x^2 \rvert$	Square roots and absolute values should not be applied to the variable.

However, $\sqrt{15}\,x^3$ and $\lvert -6 \rvert x^2$ are monomials, because in these cases the square root and absolute value operations only apply to the numerical coefficients.

Since 1 times any number yields the same number, we know that $1 \cdot x^3 = x^3$, so in the list of examples we would say the implied numerical coefficient of the monomial x^3 is the number 1 (which is not required to be written). Similarly, the term $-b^2$ is considered to be a monomial whose numerical coefficient is implicitly understood to be the number -1, even though we don't explicitly write the number 1. The negative sign in the expression $-b^2$ stands in the place of the number -1.

The monomial $36y$ also deserves special mention since the power on the variable y is implied. Since $y^1 = y$ we do not have to write the power on y explictly. When no power is written, the power is assumed to be 1, just as the numerical coefficient that precedes x^3 is assumed to be 1. Numbers that appear to be missing should not be assumed to be zero; in these two cases the missing numbers are assumed to be 1s.

Polynomials, Binomials, and Trinomials

Monomials are the fundamental building blocks for expressions called **polynomials.** In general a polynomial is the expression that results when one or more monomials are connected by the operations of addition or subtraction. Polynomials are thus expressions, since in Section 1.5 we defined an expression to be a sum or difference of one or more terms. However, not all expressions are polynomials: For example, $6x^2 + \dfrac{x + w}{z}$ is not a polynomial because the second term is not a monomial. The following are four examples of polynomials.

$$-6x^5 + 15x^4 - 3x^3 + 8x^2 \qquad 5x^2 + 6x - 10$$
$$5x^2 + 36a^2 - b^2 + 8x^4y^3z^7 \qquad 9a^3b^2c^5 + 4x^2y^2$$

A polynomial that is a sum or difference of two monomials is called a **binomial** and a polynomial that is composed of three monomials is called a **trinomial.** This terminology is easy to master if you remember that the meaning of the prefix *mono* is one, the meaning of *bi* is two, the meaning of *tri* is three, and the meaning of *poly* is several, including the cases of one or two or three or more. Monomials, binomials, and trinomials are all polynomials.

The first two polynomials just shown contain only the variable x, so they are called polynomials in one variable. Only the last polynomial presented is a binomial, and it is a polynomial of the five variables $a, b, c, x,$ and y. When a polynomial contains only one variable it is traditional to write the polynomial with the largest power of that variable first, followed by the lower powers of the variable in order. Thus, the first polynomial of our example is said to be written in terms of decreasing powers of x. The highest power of x in the first polynomial is 5 and the powers decrease from 5 down to 2 as you read from left to right across the polynomial. This order is sometimes called *descending order.*

The polynomial to the right of the first is a trinomial with powers of x written in decreasing order. The single term consisting of the number 10 is considered to be a monomial even though it is not followed by an explicit power of a variable for the following reason: Any constant can be considered to be multiplied by any nonzero variable that is raised to a zero power. For example,

$$10 = 10 \cdot 1 = 10 \cdot x^0 \quad \text{since } x^0 = 1 \quad \text{whenever } x \neq 0$$
$$\text{Thus, } 5x^2 + 6x + 10 = 5x^2 + 6x^1 + 10x^0$$

In the right side of this last equation the decreasing powers of x are very evident; however, the left side is simpler to write. It is not necessary to write the 1 power on x in the second term, nor is it necessary to show the 0 power of x multiplying the constant 10 in the third term.

| EXAMPLE 1 | Classify the following expressions as polynomials or not. For those expressions that are polynomials, further classify them as monomials, binomials, or trinomials. |

a. $3x^2 + x^3 - 5x^4$ **b.** $3x^5y^2 - \frac{1}{2}y^4z^3 - 4abc$

c. $\sqrt{285}\,a^5b^3 - 25x^5$ **d.** $-5x^4a^3 + 15x^{-3} - x^2$

e. -3 **f.** $\dfrac{3x^3 + 8x^2}{13x}$

SOLUTION **a.** Polynomial that is a trinomial.

b. Polynomial that is a trinomial.

c. Polynomial that is a binomial. Note that $\sqrt{285}$ is a numerical coefficient.

d. Not a polynomial because of the -3 exponent in the middle term.

e. Polynomial that is a monomial. A single constant is always a monomial.

f. Not a polynomial because of the division by the variable x. The fraction in part b is allowed because the fraction is the numerical coefficient.   ■

Degree of a Polynomial

When a polynomial in one variable is written in terms of decreasing powers of that variable the highest power is considered significant and is given a special name. The **degree** of a polynomial in one variable is the largest power of the variable that occurs in the expression. For example, the degree of the polynomial

$$6x^5 - 8x^3 + 9x^2$$

is 5 since the largest power of x in any of the three monomials is 5.

Polynomials in two or more variables also have a degree but the definition in these cases is a little more involved. Each monomial has a degree that is the sum of the exponents on the variables that are multiplied in that monomial. The degree of the entire polynomial is the number that is the largest of the degrees of the component monomials. For example, the polynomial

$$-7x^2y^3z^2 + 4x^5y^4 - 12xy^2z^3 + 5xyz$$

is made up of four monomials whose individual degrees are 7, 9, 6, and 3 respectively. The degree 3 of the rightmost monomial is arrived at by adding $1 + 1 + 1$ because the exponents on each of the variables x, y, and z in that monomial are assumed to be 1. Since 9 is the largest sum, we say the degree of the polynomial is 9 and so the second monomial in this polynomial determines the degree of the entire polynomial.

| EXAMPLE 2 | State the degree of each of the polynomials shown below. |

a. $2x^3 - 7xy^2 + 5x^2y^2$

b. $2.5x^3y^3 + 4x^2y - x^2y^4$

c. $-8x^5 + 9x^7 + 2x^3y^3$

SOLUTION   **a.** The degree is 4, determined by the third monomial.

b. The degree is 6, determined by either the first or third monomials.

c. The degree is 7, determined by the second monomial.   ■

Like Terms

One of the first kinds of symbolic manipulation in algebra concerns the addition and subtraction of what are called **like terms.** In the beginning all such terms will be monomials, but later we will see examples of combining terms that are not monomials. The definition of like terms is presented here.

DEFINITION	LIKE TERMS

Two monomials are called like terms if they consist of exactly the same variables with the same powers on those variables.

For example, $-5x^2y^5$ and $8x^2y^5$ are like terms because both are monomials with the same variables and the same powers on those variables. Like terms are allowed to differ only in their numerical coefficients, if they differ at all; otherwise, like terms are almost identical.

However, the terms $3x^3y^4$ and $6x^3y^4z^2$ are not like terms even though the first term has all the same powers of x and y as the second term. Because the first term is missing the variable z, these two monomials are not like terms and so are called **unlike terms.**

In fact identical terms such as $5x^2y^3$ and $5x^2y^3$ are like terms since they have exactly the same variables with the same powers. Usually like terms have different numerical coefficients but they are not required to be different; only the variables and powers must be the same.

The significance of like terms is that they can be added and/or subtracted and replaced by a simpler equivalent expression. In their typical form polynomials are written as sums and differences of unlike terms. Although any two unlike terms can be connected by addition, their sum cannot be simplified.

Adding and Subtracting Like Terms

Before we show how addition and subtraction of like terms is performed we need to review the distributive law; this law is the basis for combining like terms. In Section 1.8 we wrote the distributive law in the two forms

$$x \cdot (y + z) = x \cdot y + x \cdot z \quad \text{and} \quad x \cdot z + y \cdot z = (x + y) \cdot z$$

and demonstrated how this law can be used to change a sum of products into a product of a sum and vice versa. The variables x, y, and z represent numbers. We are going to rewrite the distributive law using the second form and we are going to use special symbols to represent the variables.

(Our reason for doing so will become clear in a moment.) Here x is replaced by the $\triangle$ symbol, y is replaced by the $\bigcirc$ symbol, and z is replaced by the $\boxed{}$ symbol.

$$\triangle \cdot \boxed{} + \bigcirc \cdot \boxed{} = (\triangle + \bigcirc) \cdot \boxed{}$$

In this case the triangle, rectangle, and circle are symbols that represent numbers; they are variables.

Remember that variables represent numbers; we never want to lose sight of the fact that a monomial is just a fancy way of writing a number that is undetermined. The monomial x^3y^2, for example, represents a number even though we do not know the value of the number. If we were told that $x = 2$ and $y = -5$, then we could calculate that

$$x^3y^2 = (2)^3(-5)^2 = 8 \cdot 25 = 200$$

In this case writing x^3y^2 is just a conceptual way of writing the number 200. Since a polynomial is a sum or difference of several monomials, a polynomial is also a way of writing a number that is yet to be determined.

Now consider the problem of adding the two monomials

$$3x^3y^2 + 5x^3y^2$$

If we draw rectangles around the two parts that make these monomials like terms and draw a triangle and a circle around the other two parts that remain, we can apply the distributive law and write the steps that demonstrate how like terms can be added.

$$3x^3y^2 + 5x^3y^2 = \triangle\!\!\!\!\!\diagup 3 \cdot \boxed{x^3y^2} + \textcircled{5} \cdot \boxed{x^3y^2}$$

Apply the distributive law:
$$\triangle \cdot \boxed{} + \bigcirc \cdot \boxed{} = $$
$$(\triangle + \bigcirc) \cdot \boxed{}$$

$$= (\,\triangle\!\!\!\!\!\diagup 3 + \textcircled{5}\,) \cdot \boxed{x^3y^2}$$
$$= (3 + 5)x^3y^2 \qquad\qquad \text{Drop the geometric symbols.}$$
$$= (8)x^3y^2 \qquad\qquad\quad\; 3 + 5 = 8$$
$$= 8x^3y^2 \qquad\qquad\quad\;\; \text{Drop the parentheses.}$$

Written in one line, the end result is $3x^3y^2 + 5x^3y^2 = 8x^3y^2$. This equation demonstrates how two symbolic expressions can be combined into a single, simpler expression.

Some people say you can add apples and apples but you cannot add apples and oranges. This can be illustrated in a more concrete, mathematical way. Intuitively we know two apples plus three apples makes five apples. Using the distributive law we can show this as

$$\text{two apples} + \text{three apples} = 2 \cdot \boxed{\text{apples}} + 3 \cdot \boxed{\text{apples}}$$

$$= (2 + 3) \cdot \boxed{\text{apples}}$$

$$= (5) \cdot \text{apples} = \text{five apples}$$

But if we try to add apples and oranges, the distributive law cannot be applied because apples and oranges are not like terms.

$$2 \cdot \text{apples} + 3 \cdot \text{oranges} = ?$$

→These two terms do not constitute a common factor.

The distributive law always requires a common factor in the terms that are products, and since there is no common factor, the distributive law cannot be applied.

In the future when we combine like terms we will usually not use all of the foregoing symbolism and so we will use fewer steps. But when first starting out it is a good idea to write the steps that show the use of the distributive law. Although we have written the distributive law using the addition operation, the law is just as valid with the operation of subtraction. The following steps show how the distributive law is used to subtract two like terms.

$$\triangle \cdot \boxed{} - \bigcirc \cdot \boxed{} = (\triangle - \bigcirc) \cdot \boxed{}$$

$$8x^4y^5 - 12x^4y^5 = (8 - 12)x^4y^5 \qquad \text{Apply the distributive law.}$$
$$x^4y^5 \text{ is the common factor.}$$
$$= (-4)x^4y^5$$
$$= -4x^4y^5 \qquad \text{Drop the parentheses.}$$

EXAMPLE 3

Add or subtract the following pairs of like terms, where possible. First describe the common factor and then show the application of the distributive law. If the terms have no common factor and, thus, are not like terms, then state that is the case.

a. $7x^2y + 6x^2y$ **b.** $-9a^3b^2 - 6a^3b^2$

c. $8xy^2 + 9ab^2$ **d.** $-10x^5y^3z^4 + x^5y^3z^4$

SOLUTION

a. x^2y is the common factor.

$$7x^2y + 6x^2y = (7 + 6)x^2y \qquad\qquad \text{Apply the distributive law.}$$
$$= (13)x^2y \qquad\qquad\qquad \text{Add the terms in parentheses.}$$
$$= 13x^2y \qquad\qquad\qquad \text{Drop the parentheses.}$$

b. a^3b^2 is the common factor.

$$-9a^3b^2 - 6a^3b^2 = (-9-6)a^3b^2 \qquad \text{Apply the distributive law.}$$
$$= (-15)a^3b^2 \qquad\qquad \text{Subtract.}$$
$$= -15a^3b^2 \qquad\qquad \text{Drop the parentheses.}$$

c. The two monomials are not like terms so the distributive law cannot be applied.

d. The common factor is $x^5y^3z^4$.

$$-10x^5y^3z^4 + x^5y^3z^4 = -10x^5y^3z^4 + 1x^5y^3z^4 \qquad \text{The coefficient on the second term is 1.}$$
$$= (-10 + 1)x^5y^3z^4 \qquad \text{Apply the distributive law.}$$
$$= (-9)x^5y^3z^4 \qquad\qquad \text{Add the coefficients.}$$
$$= -9x^5y^3z^4 \qquad\qquad \text{Drop the parentheses.} \qquad ■$$

Adding Polynomials

Once we have mastered adding and subtracting like terms that are monomials the next step is to learn to add any two polynomials. In the next two sections we will take up the operations of subtraction and multiplication and in Section 6.4 we will take up the operation of division. Learning algebra is almost like learning arithmetic all over again; we are relearning the basic operations of addition, subtraction, multiplication, and division for symbolic expressions.

In Section 1.7 we introduced the associative and commutative laws for addition. An understanding of these laws, together with the distributive law, forms the basis for adding polynomials. Although the commutative law was given using only two terms, the law can be applied repeatedly to any number of terms, using two terms at a time. Also the associative law was shown using three terms, but in fact the law can be applied to more than just three terms. Let's add the two polynomials

$$(-8x^3 + 5x^2 - 10x) + (6x^3 - 9x^2 + 7x)$$

Since addition is associative we can drop all the grouping symbols and write the sum of all six monomials without any parentheses.

$$-8x^3 + 5x^2 - 10x + 6x^3 - 9x^2 + 7x$$

We would like to rearrange the terms but since subtraction is not commutative we first change the subtraction operations into additions and change the signs of the numerical coefficients of the two terms that are subtracted.

$$-8x^3 + 5x^2 + -10x + 6x^3 + -9x^2 + 7x$$

Since addition is commutative we can now rearrange the order of the terms, placing like terms together; that is, we put the cubes next to each other, then the squares next to each other, and so on, writing the terms in decreasing powers of x.

$$-8x^3 + 6x^3 + 5x^2 + -9x^2 + -10x + 7x$$

Then we again apply the associative law by inserting parentheses to emphasize the regrouping of like terms. We want to add like terms two at a time, which is not the usual left to right order, so we apply the associative law for addition.

$$(-8x^3 + 6x^3) + (5x^2 + -9x^2) + (-10x + 7x)$$

We add the like terms within each pair of parentheses and then simplify the numerical coefficients. (Note the use of the distributive law.)

$$(-8 + 6)x^3 + (5 + -9)x^2 + (-10 + 7)x$$
$$(-2)x^3 + (-4)x^2 + (-3)x$$

We continue to simplify by dropping the parentheses, which are now no longer necessary.

$$-2x^3 + -4x^2 + -3x$$

Finally, we convert addition of the opposites of numbers to subtraction operations.

$$-2x^3 - 4x^2 - 3x$$

When all this work is summarized in one line, we can see that in this case adding together two polynomials of degree three results in another polynomial of degree three.

$$(-8x^3 + 5x^2 - 10x) + (6x^3 + -9x^2 + 7x) = -2x^3 - 4x^2 - 3x$$

Although the preceding steps were explanatory, we write fewer steps in actual practice. The essential steps show the proper grouping of the like terms and the explicit use of the distributive law. A general rule of thumb is to write as many steps as you deem necessary and only skip a step when it is easy to mentally perform the next operation.

The steps we have just followed demonstrate how to convert subtraction operations into additions. We must convert to addition to be able to commute the terms so that like terms can be placed adjacent to one another. Then we apply the distributive law to combine like terms and simplify the final answer.

| **EXAMPLE 4** | Add the following pairs of polynomials by combining like terms. Simplify your answers. |

a. $(8xy - x + 3y) + (17xy + 7x - 6y)$
b. $(5a^2b + 3ab^2 - 12ab) + (4ab^2 - 7a^2b + 5ab)$

SOLUTION **a.** $(8xy - x + 3y) + (17xy + 7x - 6y)$ Drop grouping symbols and convert subtractions to additions of opposites.

$= 8xy + -1x + 3y + 17xy + 7x + -6y$

$= 8xy + 17xy + -1x + 7x + 3y + -6y$ Commute the terms.

$= (8 + 17)xy + (-1 + 7)x + (3 + -6)y$ Apply the distributive law 3 times.

$= 25xy + 6x + -3y$ Simplify the coefficients.

$= 25xy + 6x - 3y$ Change adding an opposite back into a subtraction operation.

b. $(5a^2b + 3ab^2 - 12ab) + (4ab^2 - 7a^2b + 5ab)$

$= 5a^2b + 3ab^2 + -12ab + 4ab^2 + -7a^2b + 5ab$

$= 5a^2b + -7a^2b + 3ab^2 + 4ab^2 + -12ab + 5ab$

$= (5 + -7)a^2b + (3 + 4)ab^2 + (-12 + 5)ab$

$= -2a^2b + 7ab^2 + -7ab$

$= -2a^2b + 7ab^2 - 7ab$ ■

PRACTICE   FOR   SUCCESS

Practice 1.   What kind of polynomial, if any, is $-6x^5 + 3x^3 - 15x^2$?

Practice 2.   What kind of polynomial, if any, is $3a^4b^2 + 7a^5b^{-3}$?

Practice 3.   What kind of polynomial, if any, is $\sqrt{6}$?

Practice 4.   What is the degree of the polynomial $-9x^4y^3 + 7x^2y^4 - 20x^4y^4$?

Practice 5.   Add the polynomials $(2x^3y + 5xy^2 - 6xy) + (-7xy^2 - 8xy + 4x^3y)$.

EXERCISES 6.1

In exercises 1–14, classify each expression as a polynomial or not. For those expressions that are polynomials, give their degree and further classify them as monomials, binomials, or trinomials.

1. 3
3. $5x^3 + 8x^2 - 4x$
5. $2x - 3x^{-1}$
7. $\sqrt{3x} + 2$
9. $3\sqrt{x} + |-2|$
11. $9x^4y^2 - 10x^5y^3 + 7$
13. $-5a^2b^3c + 6x^2y^3z + 4x$

2. $7x + 2$
4. $8x^5 - 6x^{-3}$
6. $|5x^3 + 8x|$
8. $|-6|x^3 + \sqrt{7}x$
10. $-3a^3b^2$
12. $-6a^3b^2 + 3a^2b^{-3}$
14. $-3x - 7y - 9$

In exercises 15–30, use the distributive law to add or subtract the like terms where possible. If the two given terms are not like terms, then state that they cannot be added or subtracted.

15. $15x + 6x$
17. $21x^2 + 5x^2$
19. $-3a^2 + 9a^2$
21. $3x^2y^3 + 5x^3y^2$
23. $x^2y - 8x^2y$
25. $-8a^2b^4 + a^2b^4$
27. $5xy^2 - 9y^2$
29. $x^3y^2 - 4x^3y^2$

16. $4a + 8a$
18. $7y - 4y$
20. $8x^2y - 4x^2y$
22. $9ab^3 - 12ab^3$
24. $5a^2b^3c^4 - a^2b^3c^4$
26. $16p^2q + 10p^2q$
28. $21ab^2 - 8ab$
30. $-5xy^3 + 6xy^3$

Use the distributive law to add the polynomials in exercises 31–46.

31. $12x + 3x + 18x$
32. $19a^2 - 31a^2 + 15a^2$
33. $(5x^2y + 3xy^2) + (-8x^2y + 2xy^2)$
34. $(-27x^3y^4 - 12x^4y^3) + (3x^3y^4 + 10x^4y^3)$
35. $(8a^6 - 13a^5) + (2a^5 - 7a^6)$
36. $(a^3b + -5b^3a) + (16b^3a - a^3b)$

37. $(9c^2 + 8c + 7) + (-10c^2 - 7c - 6)$

38. $(-8x^3 + 5x^2 - 6x) + (10x^3 - 4x^2 + 8x)$

39. $(6x^4 - 10x^4 + 5x^4) + (3x^4 + 5x^4 - 7x^4)$

40. $(3a^3b^2 + 5a^2b^3 + 7ab) + (-5a^3b^2 - 5a^2b^3 - 6ab)$

41. $(8 + 5x - 3x^2 + 4x^3) + (-6x^3 + 4x^2 - 3x + 10)$

42. $(5ab^2 - 10a^2b + 7a^2b^2) + (13a^2b - 4a^2b^2 + 5ab^2)$

43. $(8x^5 + 6x^4 - 7x^3 + 10x) + (-9x + 3x^3 - 2x^4 - x^5)$

44. $(5xy^2z^5 + 12x^2yz^3 + 8x^2y^2z^3) + (-6x^2yz^3 - 10x^2y^2z^3 - 4xy^2z^5)$

45. $(-8ab^2c^4 - 2a^2bc^4 + a^2b^2c^4) + (9a^2b^2c^4 - 3a^2bc^4 + 12ab^2c^4)$

46. $(6xy^3z^6 + 13x^3yz^4 + 9x^3y^3z^4) + (3x^3yz^4 + 2x^3y^3z^4 + 14xy^3z^6)$

Looking Back

47. Completely reduce $\sqrt{21,600}$.

48. Write 0.0028 as a reduced fraction.

49. Compare -0.688 and -0.6869 using $>$ or $<$.

50. Divide -5.55 by 10,000.

51. Using a calculator find the value of $\sqrt{1.8496}$.

52. Convert 6.75% to a reduced fraction.

53. Convert $\dfrac{9}{40}$ to a percent.

54. Add: $\dfrac{3}{15} + \left(\dfrac{-7}{12}\right)$ and write your answer as a reduced fraction.

PRACTICE-FOR-SUCCESS ANSWERS

1. trinomial	**2.** not a polynomial	**3.** monomial
4. 8	**5.** $6x^3y - 2xy^2 - 14xy$	

6.2 MULTIPLICATION BY MONOMIALS AND SUBTRACTION OF POLYNOMIALS

OBJECTIVES

- ☐ To multiply any two monomials
- ☐ To multiply any polynomial by any monomial
- ☐ To subtract any polynomial from another polynomial

In the first section of this chapter we examined how to add or subtract any two monomials and how to add any two polynomials. In this section we will learn how to multiply any two monomials, how to subtract any two polynomials, and how to multiply a polynomial by a monomial. Before reading this section, it might be helpful to review the exponent rules as summarized near the end of Section 5.3.

Multiplying Two Monomials

To multiply two monomials requires the associative and commutative laws for multiplication as well as the addition rule for exponents. Recall that a monomial can be thought of as a number that is determined when the variables are assigned particular values. Since numbers can be multiplied and since monomials are undisclosed forms of numbers, monomials can also be multiplied. Consider the problem of multiplying the monomial $5x^2y^3$ times the monomial $3xy^2$.

$$(5x^2y^3)\,(3xy^2) = 5 \cdot x^2 \cdot y^3 \cdot 3 \cdot x \cdot y^2$$ Drop the parentheses and show all the multiplication operations.

$$= 5 \cdot 3 \cdot x^2 \cdot x \cdot y^3 \cdot y^2$$ Apply the commutative law and reorder the factors.

$$= (5 \cdot 3) \cdot (x^2 \cdot x) \cdot (y^3 \cdot y^2)$$ Apply the associative law and regroup the factors.

$$= (15) \cdot (x^{2+1}) \cdot (y^{3+2})$$ Multiply the corresponding parts.

$$= 15x^3y^5$$ Simplify the exponents on the variables and drop the parentheses.

If we write the original problem and the final answer in one line we can see that the result of multiplying the two monomials is another monomial.

$$(5x^2y^3)\,(3xy^2) = 15x^3y^5$$

In actual practice we usually would not write all of the preceding steps but we would show the reordering of the parts. It is also a good idea to clearly show how the addition rule for exponents is applied. We tend to write final answers with the variables in alphabetical order, even though the commutative law for multiplication does not require the variables that are multiplied to appear in any particular order. Alphabetical order simply helps arrange our work in a more organized fashion.

EXAMPLE 1

Multiply the following pairs of monomials.
a. $(4x^3y^6)\,(7x^2y)$ **b.** $(-9a^2y^3x^2)\,(-4y^5x^2a^2)$

SOLUTION   **a.** $(4x^3y^6)\,(7x^2y) = (4 \cdot 7)\,(x^3x^2)\,(y^6y)$ Reorder and regroup the factors.

$$= (28)\,(x^{3+2})\,(y^{6+1})$$ Simplify the products.

$$= 28x^5y^7$$ Drop the parentheses and show the answer as a monomial.

b. $(-9a^2y^3x^2)\,(-4y^5x^2a^2)$

$$= (-9)\,(-4)\,(a^2a^2)\,(x^2x^2)\,(y^3y^5)$$ Reorder and regroup the terms.

$$= (36)\,(a^{2+2})\,(x^{2+2})\,(y^{3+5})$$ Simplify the products.

$$= 36a^4x^4y^8$$ ■

Multiplying a Polynomial by a Monomial

In Section 1.8 we stated that the distributive law was probably the most important law in all of algebra. This law forms the basis for adding like terms and also forms the basis for multiplying a monomial times a polynomial; remember, monomials and polynomials are symbolic forms of numbers. Next, we will show how to apply the distributive law to multiply a monomial by a polynomial. To do this we will write an example of the distributive law that uses three terms in the expression that is the sum. Symbolically we have

$$\bigcirc(\triangle + \square + \bigtriangleup) = \bigcirc\triangle + \bigcirc\square + \bigcirc\bigtriangleup$$

Use the preceding form to multiply the monomial $5x^2$ times the polynomial $3x^4 + 2x^3 + 7x^2$.

$(5x^2)(3x^4 + 2x^3 + 7x^2)$ Show $5x^2$ multiplying on the left side of the polynomial.

$= ((5x^2))(\triangle{3x^4} + \square{2x^3} + (7x^2))$

Show the geometric symbols.

$= (5x^2)\triangle{3x^4} + (5x^2)\square{2x^3} + (5x^2)(7x^2)$

Apply the distributive law.

$= (5x^2)(3x^4) + (5x^2)(2x^3) + (5x^2)(7x^2)$ Replace the symbols with parentheses.

$= (5 \cdot 3)(x^2x^4) + (5 \cdot 2)(x^2x^3) + (5 \cdot 7)(x^2x^2)$ Reorder the regroup the factors.

$= 15x^6 + 10x^5 + 35x^4$ Simplify the products.

In practice it is not necessary to introduce the geometric symbolism, nor is it necessary to write as many steps as we have just shown; these steps were explanatory. The next example shows how we would normally multiply monomials by polynomials. The key rule is the distributive law, which can be applied to several terms in a sum and which also applies when the operation connecting the terms is subtraction instead of addition.

EXAMPLE 2   Use the distributive law to simplify the products of the following monomials and polynomials.
a. $(2x^5y^4)(8x^3y^2 + 3xy^3 - 5x^4y^5)$
b. $(-5a^3b^2)(-4a^4b^3 - 7a^2b^4 - 3a^4b)$

SOLUTION   **a.** $(2x^5y^4)(8x^3y^2 + 3xy^3 - 5x^4y^5)$
$= (2x^5y^4)(8x^3y^2) + (2x^5y^4)(3xy^3) - (2x^5y^4)(5x^4y^5)$
Apply the distributive law.
$= (2 \cdot 8)(x^5x^3)(y^4y^2) + (2 \cdot 3)(x^5x)(y^4y^3) - (2 \cdot 5)(x^5x^4)(y^4y^5)$
Reorder and regroup the terms.
$= 16x^8y^6 + 6x^6y^7 - 10x^9y^9$
b. $(-5a^3b^2)(-4a^4b^3 - 7a^2b^4 - 3a^4b)$
$= (-5a^3b^2)(-4a^4b^3) - (-5a^3b^2)(7a^2b^4) - (-5a^3b^2)(3a^4b)$
Apply the distributive law.

$$= (-5)(-4)(a^3a^4)(b^2b^3) - (-5 \cdot 7)(a^3a^2)(b^2b^4) - (-5 \cdot 3)(a^3a^4)(b^2b)$$

Reorder and regroup the terms.

$$= 20a^7b^5 - (-35)a^5b^6 - (-15)a^7b^3$$

$$= 20a^7b^5 + 35a^5b^6 + 15a^7b^3 \qquad \text{Simplify the double minus signs to additions.}$$

■

Subtracting Two Polynomials

The last topic in this section is the subtraction of any two polynomials. Subtraction can be seen as a special case of multiplying a polynomial times a monomial. When b is a number, the expression $-b$ represents the number that is the opposite of b. But $-b$ can also be written as a product that uses the number -1.

$$-b = (-1) \cdot b$$

The opposite of b is the same as multiplying the number -1 times b. When b is a polynomial we can interpret $(-1) \cdot b$ as the product of the monomial (-1) times the polynomial b. If a and b represent two polynomials, their difference can be written as

$$a - b = a + (-1) \cdot b$$

The following steps show how to subtract two polynomials by converting subtraction to adding negative 1 times the polynomial to be subtracted and using the distributive law to simplify the result.

Subtract $9x^5 - 7x^4 + 3x^3$ from $-6x^5 - 10x^4 + 5x^3$.

Show both polynomials in parentheses so the subtraction order is clear.

$$(-6x^5 - 10x^4 + 5x^3) - (9x^5 - 7x^4 + 3x^3)$$

Convert the main subtraction operation to adding (-1) times the second polynomial.

$$= (-6x^5 - 10x^4 + 5x^3) + (-1)(9x^5 - 7x^4 + 3x^3)$$

Apply the distributive law to perform the multiplication by (-1).

$$= (-6x^5 - 10x^4 + 5x^3) + (-1)(9x^5) - (-1)(7x^4) + (-1)(3x^3)$$

Simplify the monomial products.

$$= -6x^5 - 10x^4 + 5x^3 + (-9)x^5 - (-7)x^4 + (-3)x^3$$

To prepare for commuting terms, change all subtraction operations to additions.

$$= -6x^5 + (-10)x^4 + 5x^3 + (-9)x^5 + (+7)x^4 + (-3)x^3$$

Apply the commutative law for addition to arrange like terms together in decreasing powers.

$$= -6x^5 + (-9)x^5 + (-10)x^4 + (+7)x^4 + 5x^3 + (-3)x^3$$

Regroup the like terms.

$$= [-6x^5 + (-9)x^5] + [-10x^4 + (+7)x^4] + [5x^3 + (-3)x^3]$$

Add the like terms using the distributive law.

$$= [-6 + (-9)]x^5 + [-10 + (+7)]x^4 + [5 + (-3)]x^3$$

Simplify the coefficients.

$$= -15x^5 + [-3]x^4 + 2x^3$$

Convert adding the opposite to a subtraction operation.

$$= -15x^5 - 3x^4 + 2x^3$$

Although the preceding explanation and series of steps show the essential details for performing the subtraction of two polynomials, we can usually take one shortcut. Adding -1 times the polynomial being subtracted is the best way to understand how the distributive law is applied when a sum of terms gets subtracted as a group. However, the shortcut involves a simple sign change of each numerical coefficient within the second set of parentheses. *We subtract by changing the subtraction operation to addition and changing the sign of each numerical coefficient in the polynomial being subtracted.*

$(-6x^5 - 10x^4 + 5x^3) - (9x^5 - 7x^4 + 3x^3)$

> Change the subtraction between the polynomials to addition and change the signs within the second set of parentheses.

$= -6x^5 - 10x^4 + 5x^3 + (-9)x^5 - (-7)x^4 + (-3)x^3$

> Then convert all subtractions to adding the opposites.

$= -6x^5 + (-10)x^4 + 5x^3 + (-9)x^5 + (+7)x^4 + (-3)x^3$

> Then commute the terms so that like terms are adjacent.

$= -6x^5 + (-9)x^5 + (-10)x^4 + 7x^4 + 5x^3 + (-3)x^3$

> Add the like terms.

$= -15x^5 + (-3)x^4 + 2x^3$

> Convert adding the opposite to a subtraction operation.

$= -15x^5 - 3x^4 + 2x^3$

In the last two lines of the demonstration we converted the operation of adding a negative number back into a subtraction operation. Most people would consider the last line the simplest form of the answer, but what appears simpler to one person may not be simpler to another. One secret for determining when one expression can be considered simpler than another concerns the amount of ink. Imagine that you are a typesetter or a printer: Whichever form would require the least amount of ink to print will usually be considered the simpler form. If we compare the last two expressions in the preceding example we find that the second one would require the least amount of ink to print; that is why it is considered simpler.

EXAMPLE 3

Subtract the following pairs of polynomials using the technique of changing the subtraction operation to addition and changing the signs of all the numerical coefficients of the polynomial that is subtracted. Simplify your final answers.

a. Subtract $-6x^4 + 13x^3 - 9x^2$ from $8x^4 + 7x^3 - 12x^2$

b. $(-7x^9y^7 - 14x^7y^5 - 5x^5y^3) - (-8x^9y^7 - 7x^7y^5 + 3x^5y^3)$

SOLUTION

a. Write parentheses around both polynomials and subtract the second polynomial from the first.

$(8x^4 + 7x^3 - 12x^2) - (-6x^4 + 13x^3 - 9x^2)$

> Convert the main subtraction to addition and change the signs of second polynomial's numerical coefficients.

$= (8x^4 + 7x^3 - 12x^2) + [+6x^4 + (-13)x^3 - (-9)x^2]$

> Change the remaining subtractions to adding the opposite.

$$= 8x^4 + 7x^3 + (-12)x^2 + (+6)x^4 + (-13)x^3 + (+9)x^2$$

Commute the terms so that like terms are adjacent to one another.

$$= 8x^4 + 6x^4 + 7x^3 + (-13)x^3 + (-12)x^2 + 9x^2$$

Associate like terms in groups.

$$= (8x^4 + 6x^4) + [7x^3 + (-13)x^3] + (-12x^2 + 9x^2)$$

Apply the distributive law to add like terms.

$$= (8 + 6)x^4 + [7 + (-13)]x^3 + (-12 + 9)x^2$$

Simplify the coefficients within the square brackets.

$$= 14x^4 + (-6)x^3 + (-3)x^2$$

Simplify the adding of opposites by changing back to subtraction operations.

$$= 14x^4 - 6x^3 - 3x^2$$

b. $(-7x^9y^7 - 14x^7y^5 - 5x^5y^3) - (-8x^9y^7 - 7x^7y^5 + 3x^5y^3)$

Convert the main subtraction to addition and change the signs of the second polynomial's numerical coefficients.

$$= (-7x^9y^7 - 14x^7y^5 - 5x^5y^3) + [+8x^9y^7 - (-7)x^7y^5 + (-3)x^5y^3]$$

Change the remaining subtractions to adding opposites.

$$= -7x^9y^7 + (-14)x^7y^5 + (-5)x^5y^3 + 8x^9y^7 + 7x^7y^5 + (-3)x^5y^3$$

Commute the terms so that like terms are adjacent to one another.

$$= -7x^9y^7 + 8x^9y^7 + (-14)x^7y^5 + 7x^7y^5 + (-5)x^5y^3 + (-3)x^5y^3$$

Apply the distributive law to add the like terms.

$$= (-7 + 8)x^9y^7 + (-14 + 7)x^7y^5 + [-5 + (-3)]x^5y^3$$

Simplify the numerical coefficients within the grouping symbols.

$$= x^9y^7 + (-7)x^7y^5 + (-8)x^5y^3$$

Simplify the adding of opposites by changing back to subtraction operations.

$$= x^9y^7 - 7x^7y^5 - 8x^5y^3 \qquad ■$$

P R A C T I C E   F O R   S U C C E S S

Practice 1. Multiply the two monomials $(-5x^5y^3)(8x^6y^4)$.

Practice 2. Multiply the two monomials $(-3a^7b^6c^4)(-9a^3b^2c^5)$.

Practice 3. Perform the following multiplication $(-4x^7y^4)(2x^2y^6 + 6x^9y^3)$.

Practice 4. Perform the following multiplication $(-2a^3b^6c^5)(8ab^4c^3 - 5a^4b^7c^4 - a^5c)$.

Practice 5. Subtract $2x^2 - 4x + 3$ from $x^2 - 6x + 5$.

Practice 6. Subtract $a^2 - ab^3 + b^2 - 3a^2b$ from $8ab^3 + 10a^2b - 9b^2 - 5a^2$.

EXERCISES 6.2

In exercises 1–20, multiply the monomials.

1. $(3x^2)(6x^3)$

2. $(-4a^3)(2a)$

3. $(-5x^4)(-4x^5)$

4. $(3ab^2)(-7a^3b)$

5. $(-9xy^3)(-2x^3y^3)$

6. $(-14xy^2z^3)(3x^3yz^2)$

7. $(6x^5y^2)(4xy^3)$

8. $(-8a^2b^3)(4ab)$

9. $(5a^3b^2c)(-2ab^2c^3)$

10. $(-5xy^3z)(5x^2y^2)$

11. $(-3a^3b^3c^3)(-4a^2b^2c^2)$

12. $(3p^3q^2)(-2pq)$

13. $(6xy^2z^4)(-3y^3z^2)$

14. $(x^4y^5z)(-2x^5y^2z^4)$

15. $\left(-\frac{2}{5}x\right)\left(\frac{3}{4}y\right)\left(\frac{15}{21}z^2\right)$

16. $(-6a^2b^3)(3ab^2)(a^3b)$

17. $(-6x^2y^3)(2x^3y^5z)(2y^2z^2)$

18. $(-xz^3)(2x^3z^2)(-3y^2z^4)$

19. $(abcd)(2ab^2c^3d^4)(3a^2c^2d)$

20. $(-5a^3b^3)(3b^2c^3)(a^4c^2)$

In exercises 21–38, use the distributive law to multiply the polynomials by the monomials.

21. $(8x)(3x^2 + 5x)$

22. $(4a^3)(a^3 + 2a^2)$

23. $(6x^2)(2x - 3x^2)$

24. $(-3x^4)(5x^2 - 8x^3)$

25. $(8a^2)(9a^3 - 5a^2)$

26. $(0.35a^2b^2)(0.8ab^3 + 2.65a^2b^3)$

27. $(x^2y^3)(-2x^2y + 3x^3y^2)$

28. $(-2x^2y)(-3xy^4 - 6x^2y^3)$

29. $(x^3y^2)(xy^4 + x^2y^3)$

30. $(-3p^2q^2)(-4pq^2 + 5p^2q)$

31. $(4w^3)(2w + 5w^2 + 7w^3)$

32. $(9a^2)(3a^3 - 2a + 4a^2)$

33. $\left(\frac{3}{5}p^2qr^3\right)\left(\frac{15}{6}p^3 + \frac{4}{3}q^2 + \frac{20}{21}r\right)$

34. $(5xy^3)(2x^4 + 3x^2y^4 - 9x^2y)$

35. $(-3x^2y)(8x^3y^5 - 4x^2y + 6x^3y^2)$

36. $(5ab)(6a^2b^3 + 4ab^2 + 6a^3b + 4a^3b^4)$

37. $(-4x^2y^3)(6x^8y^7 - 3x^5y^6 - 5x^4y^5 + 8)$

38. $(-2x^3y^4z^2)(-3xy^2z + 5x^2y^3z^3 - 10x^3y^4z^5)$

Perform the subtraction of the polynomials in exercises 39–50.

39. $(5x^2 + 3x) - (8x^2 + 2x)$

40. $(3a^5 - 6a^3) - (4a^5 + 8a^3)$

41. $(5x^3 + 7x^2 - 9x) - (3x^3 + 5x^2 - 3x)$

42. $(-8a^5 + 10a^4 - 2a^3) - (6a^5 - 3a^4 + 4a^3)$

43. $(3x + 4x^2 - 8x^3) - (9x^3 + 5x^2 + 8x)$

44. $(1 + a + a^2 + a^3) - (3a^3 + 2a^2 + a + 1)$

45. $(2.75x^4y^5 + 3.92xy^3 + 4.5x^4y^2) - (2.63xy^3 + 6.39x^4y^5 - 5.44x^4y^2)$

46. $(6a^3b^2 + 3a^2b^3 - a^2b^2) - (8a^2b^3 - 3a^3b^2 - 2a^2b^2)$

47. $(3z^7 - 8z^5 + z^3) - (8z^3 + 2z^5 - 3z^7)$

48. $(5xy^5z^3 - 2x^4y^2z^2 + 3x^3y^3z^4) - (5x^4y^2z^2 - 6x^3y^3z^4)$

49. $(16a^2bc^5 + 8a^3b^2c^3) - (a^3b^2c^3 + 12a^2bc^5)$

50. $(8x^3y^4z^5 + 3x^2y^2z^3) - (10x^2y^2z^3 + 12x^3y^4z^5)$

Perform the mixed operations as indicated in exercises 51–62 and simplify your final answers.

51. $(6w)(3w^5) + (2w^2)(4w^4)$

52. $(-5x^2)(4x^5) + (8x^3)(3x^4)$

53. $(-6a)(9a^6) + (4a^4)(3a^3) - (9a^2)(a^2)$

54. $(6a^4b)(3a^3b^2) - (8a^5b^4)(3a^2b) - (5ab^3)(3a^6b^2)$

55. $(6x^2y)(4x^3y^5) - (3x)(7x^4y^5) + (9xy^3)(4x^4y^2)$

56. $(3a^2b^3)(2a^3b) + (8ab)(2a^2b^5) - (4a^3b^2)(3a^2b^2)$

57. $(7y^3z^3)(3z^3y^2) - (4y^4z^2)(5yz^3) + (2y^3z^2)(6y^2z^4)$

58. $(9a^3b^5)(2a^4b) - (7a^4b^2 \cdot 3a - 4a^2b \cdot 5a^5b^5)$

59. $(6x^4y)(3x^3y^2) - (8x^5y^4 \cdot 3x^2y - 9x^2y^2 \cdot 2x^5y)$

60. $\dfrac{2}{3}ab\left(\dfrac{5}{6}a^2b^3 + \dfrac{9}{8}ab^2\right) + \left(\dfrac{1}{4}a^2b^3\right)\left(\dfrac{20}{7}ab + \dfrac{16}{5}\right)$

61. $6y^2z^3(3y^2z^2 + 8y^2z^3) + (3y^4z)(2z^5 + 3z^4)$

62. $3xy^4(5x^4y^3 - 2x^5y^4) + (2x^2y^3)(x^3y^4 - 8x^4y^5)$

👁 Looking Back

63. Simplify $\left(\dfrac{6}{5}\right)^{-2}$.

64. Simplify $\dfrac{2^{-5}}{2^{-2}}$.

65. Simplify $(0^2)^4$.

66. Convert -35.23×10^{-3} to scientific notation.

67. Simplify $\left[\dfrac{2}{3} + \left(-\dfrac{1}{2}\right)^3\right]^{-1}$.

68. Round the value of $\sqrt{57}$ to the nearest thousandth.

69. What power of 2 makes 2,048?

70. Write the expression and simplify: The square root of the third power of the sum of the three numbers negative twenty-five, forty-three, and eighteen.

PRACTICE-FOR-SUCCESS ANSWERS

1. $-40x^{11}y^7$ **2.** $27a^{10}b^8c^9$

3. $-8x^9y^{10} - 24x^{16}y^7$ **4.** $-16a^4b^{10}c^8 + 10a^7b^{13}c^9 + 2a^8b^6c^6$

5. $-x^2 - 2x + 2$ **6.** $9ab^3 + 13a^2b - 10b^2 - 6a^2$

6.3 MULTIPLICATION OF POLYNOMIALS

OBJECTIVES

☐ To use the distributive law to multiply a binomial times a binomial

☐ To multiply two binomials using the FOIL method

☐ To use the distributive law to multiply any two polynomials

In the previous section we learned how to use the distributive law to multiply a monomial times a polynomial. In this section we are going to apply the distributive law to problems in which the multiplier may be a binomial or a trinomial. We will learn how to mimic the process of long multiplication with whole numbers to multiply any two polynomials. Our first examples will discuss the case of a binomial times a binomial and then we will take up more general cases that involve trinomials.

A polynomial in the variable x is a symbolic expression that represents a single number when x is assigned a value. We want to emphasize the role of a polynomial as representing a single number because we usually write the distributive law using single letters to represent numbers.

$$x \cdot (y + z) = x \cdot y + x \cdot z$$

In this form the single letter x represents a number and the term in parentheses is a binomial. Now imagine that we replace the single letter x with another binomial $(v + w)$, which also represents a single number. Every place we have written the letter x we will now write the binomial $(v + w)$. Then the distributive law takes on the form of a product of two binomials.

$$x(y + z) = x \cdot y + x \cdot z$$

$$(v + w) \cdot (y + z) = (v + w) \cdot y + (v + w) \cdot z \qquad \text{Replace } x \text{ with } (v + w).$$

Next we apply the distributive law two more times to expand the expressions to the right of the equal sign in the last equation.

$$(v + w) \cdot (y + z) = v \cdot y + w \cdot y + v \cdot z + w \cdot z$$

By applying the distributive law three times we have shown that the product of the two binomials $(v + w)$ and $(y + z)$ is the sum of four products.

FOIL Method

The four products arrived at when multiplying two binomials can be remembered most easily by using the acronym for First Outer Inner Last: **FOIL.** This refers to the four products formed when multiplying two binomials as shown in Figure 6.1. The First terms make the product $v \cdot y$, the Outer terms make the product $v \cdot z$, the Inner terms make the product $w \cdot y$, and the Last terms make the product $w \cdot z$.

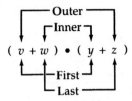

FIGURE 6.1 **Terms connected using the acronym FOIL**

EXAMPLE 1

Identify the four products of terms that are made using the acronym FOIL.

a. $(a + b) \cdot (x + y)$ **b.** $(3x + 2y) \cdot (2v + 5w)$

c. $(5x + 3) \cdot (7x + 8)$ **d.** $(2x + 8y) \cdot (3y + 4x)$

SOLUTION

a. First $= a \cdot x$ Outer $= a \cdot y$
Inner $= b \cdot x$ Last $= b \cdot y$

b. First $= 3x \cdot 2v = 6vx$ Outer $= 3x \cdot 5w = 15wx$
Inner $= 2y \cdot 2v = 4vy$ Last $= 2y \cdot 5w = 10wy$

c. First $= 5x \cdot 7x = 35x^2$ Outer $= 5x \cdot 8 = 40x$
Inner $= 3 \cdot 7x = 21x$ Last $= 3 \cdot 8 = 24$

d. First $= 2x \cdot 3y = 6xy$ Outer $= 2x \cdot 4x = 8x^2$
Inner $= 8y \cdot 3y = 24y^2$ Last $= 8y \cdot 4x = 32xy$ ■

Next we show a typical example of how the distributive law is used four times in arriving at the answer to the product of two binomials in which the inner and outer terms are like terms. Although a quick answer may be obtained using the FOIL method, using the distributive law repeatedly is the way to understand the reasoning behind the FOIL method.

EXAMPLE 2

Use the distributive law four times to arrive at the answer for the product

$$(x + 4) \cdot (x + 6)$$

SOLUTION

In the first application of the distributive law we distribute the term $(x + 4)$ across the binomial $(x + 6)$. Then we apply the distributive law two more times in expanding the expressions $(x + 4) \cdot x$ and $(x + 4) \cdot 6$. The fourth and last application of the distributive law occurs in adding the like terms $4x$ and $6x$.

$$
\begin{aligned}
(x + 4) \cdot (x + 6) &= (x + 4) \cdot x + (x + 4) \cdot 6 \\
&= x \cdot x + 4 \cdot x + 6 \cdot x + 4 \cdot 6 \\
&= x^2 + 4 \cdot x + 6 \cdot x + 24 \\
&= x^2 + (4 + 6) \cdot x + 24 \qquad \text{Add the like terms.} \\
&= x^2 + 10x + 24
\end{aligned}
$$

The answer is a trinomial because the inner and outer terms were like terms and, thus, could be combined into a single term, so the final answer is a sum of three products.   ■

In all of the preceding discussions the connecting operation between the terms of the binomials was addition. The FOIL method can also be applied when subtractions connect the terms. We work the first part of the following example by converting subtractions into adding opposites and then work the second part by assuming the minus signs can be carried along with the numerical coefficients.

EXAMPLE 3

Use the FOIL method to expand the following products.

a. $(3x - 2) \cdot (4x - 3)$ **b.** $(5 - 3y) \cdot (6y - 7)$

SOLUTION

a. $(3x - 2) \cdot (4x - 3)$ Convert subtractions to adding opposites.

$= (3x + -2) \cdot (4x + -3)$

$\qquad\qquad \textbf{F} \qquad\quad \textbf{O} \qquad\qquad \textbf{I} \qquad\qquad \textbf{L}$

$= (3x) \cdot (4x) + (3x) \cdot (-3) + (-2) \cdot (4x) + (-2) \cdot (-3)$

$= 12x^2 - 9x - 8x + 6$

$= 12x^2 - 17x + 6$

b. $(5 - 3y) \cdot (6y - 7)$

$\qquad\quad \textbf{F} \qquad \textbf{O} \qquad\quad \textbf{I} \qquad\quad \textbf{L}$

$= 5 \cdot 6y + 5 \cdot (-7) - 3y \cdot 6y + 3y \cdot 7$ $(-3y) \cdot (-7) = +3y \cdot 7$

$= 30y - 35 - 18y^2 + 21y$ Combine like terms and write the

$= -18y^2 + 51y - 35$ final answer in terms of decreasing-
                                      powers of y.   ■

Another way to view the FOIL method mimics the arrangement used to multiply two 2-digit numbers. Consider the vertical arrangement used to multiply 12×34.

$$
\begin{array}{r}
12 \\
\times \ \ 34 \\
\hline
48 \\
36 \\
\hline
408
\end{array}
$$

The number 48 is arrived at essentially by distributing the digit 4 in 34 across the digits 2 and 1 in the number 12. Similarly, the number 36 is obtained by distributing the digit 3 in 34 across the digits 2 and 1 in the number 12. Then we perform vertical addition of the numbers 48 and 36 to obtain the final answer.

When multiplying binomials we can also arrange the work in a vertical format and mimic the process used to multiply whole numbers. In Example 4 we use this format to show the complete solution to part c of Example 1.

EXAMPLE 4	Use the vertical format to multiply the two binomials $(5x + 3) \cdot (7x + 8)$.

SOLUTION

$$
\begin{array}{r}
5x + 3 \\
\times \quad 7x + 8 \\
\hline
40x + 24 \\
35x^2 + 21x \quad\quad \\
\hline
35x^2 + 61x + 24
\end{array}
$$

■

When performing multiplication of polynomials in this format, we line up like terms vertically.

General Form for Multiplying Two Polynomials

The FOIL method is probably the most popular method used to multiply two binomials. The vertical format is less common for multiplying binomials but more convenient when one of the factors is a trinomial or larger. The following example shows how the vertical format is used to multiply a trinomial times a binomial. Note that Example 5 is analogous to the multiplication of 213×32. The digit 2 in the multiplier 32 is distributed across each of the three digits of the first number 213, then the digit 3 in the multiplier 32 is distributed across each of the three digits of the first number, 213.

$$
\begin{array}{r}
213 \\
\times \quad 32 \\
\hline
426 \\
639 \quad\; \\
\hline
6,816
\end{array}
$$

EXAMPLE 5	Use the vertical format to multiply $(9x^2 + 5x + 3) \cdot (2x + 4)$.

SOLUTION

$$
\begin{array}{r}
9x^2 + 5x + 3 \\
\times \quad\quad\quad 2x + 4 \\
\hline
36x^2 + 20x + 12 \\
18x^3 + 10x^2 + \; 6x \quad\quad\quad \\
\hline
18x^3 + 46x^2 + 26x + 12
\end{array}
$$

When writing the terms of the product we have been careful to write the partial products in decreasing powers of x and to vertically align like terms, which makes the final additions easy to perform. ■

The distributive law is the mathematical principle that is used to justify the method we use to obtain our answers for products of two polynomials.

We will now show Example 5 worked in a horizontal format that makes use of the distributive law.

$(2x + 4) \cdot (9x^2 + 5x + 3)$

$\quad = (2x + 4) \cdot 9x^2 + (2x + 4) \cdot 5x + (2x + 4) \cdot 3$

$\qquad\qquad$ Distribute $(2x + 4)$ across the trinomial $(9x^2 + 5x + 3)$.

$\quad = 2x \cdot 9x^2 + 4 \cdot 9x^2 + 2x \cdot 5x + 4 \cdot 5x + 2x \cdot 3 + 4 \cdot 3$

$\qquad\qquad$ Distribute each monomial across the three binomials.

$\quad = 18x^3 + 36x^2 + 10x^2 + 20x + 6x + 12$

$\quad = 18x^3 + (36 + 10)x^2 + (20 + 6)x + 12$

$\qquad\qquad$ Simplify the monomial products.

$\quad = 18x^3 + 46x^2 + 26x + 12 \quad$ Add the like terms.

We applied the distributive law six times in working the problem in a horizontal format. Although the vertical format is faster, working the problem horizontally allows us to see more clearly the use of the distributive law. In future math courses most problems like these will be written in the horizontal format. The final example of this section shows how to multiply two trinomials that contain subtractions.

EXAMPLE 6   Multiply $(4x^2 - 7x + 3) \cdot (3x^3 - 6x^2 - 5x)$ using the vertical format.

SOLUTION

$$
\begin{array}{r}
3x^3 - 6x^2 - 5x \\
\times \quad 4x^2 - 7x + 3 \\
\hline
9x^3 - 18x^2 - 15x \\
- 21x^4 + 42x^3 + 35x^2 \\
12x^5 - 24x^4 - 20x^3 \\
\hline
12x^5 - 45x^4 + 31x^3 + 17x^2 - 15x
\end{array}
$$

■

P R A C T I C E   F O R   S U C C E S S

Practice 1.   Multiply the following two binomials using the FOIL method: $(5x + 2) \cdot (8 + 6a)$

Practice 2.   Multiply the following two binomials using the FOIL method and write your answer as a trinomial: $(7x - 3) \cdot (3x - 4)$

Practice 3.   Multiply the following two binomials using the FOIL method and write your answer as a trinomial: $(-10a + 3b) \cdot (4b - 9a)$

Practice 4.   Multiply the two binomials using the vertical format: $(8x - 3y) \cdot (-2x - 5y)$

Practice 5.   Use the vertical format to multiply $(6x^3 - 8x^2 + 9x) \cdot (7x - 2)$.

Practice 6.   Use the vertical format to multiply $(3x^5 + 4x^3 - 7x) \cdot (2x^3 - 4x^2 - 3x)$.

EXERCISES 6.3

Multiply the polynomials in exercises 1-30.

1. $(x + z) \cdot (w + s)$ 2. $(a + d) \cdot (c + b)$
3. $(8x + 2y) \cdot (3x + 4y)$ 4. $(5a + 3b) \cdot (11a + 6b)$
5. $(5w - 3x) \cdot (4x - 7w)$ 6. $(2a + 5b) \cdot (4b - 4a)$
7. $(-2x + 6y) \cdot (3x - 5y)$ 8. $(3x - 7) \cdot (5x - 6)$
9. $(8a - 5b) \cdot (4b - 9a)$ 10. $(6x + y) \cdot (x - 10y)$
11. $(-3x - 7) \cdot (4x - 9)$ 12. $(9a - 3b) \cdot (b - 10a)$
13. $(3x^2 + 5x) \cdot (4x^2 - 8x)$ 14. $(-11x^2 + 14x) \cdot (2x^2 - 3x)$
15. $(-4x^3 + 3x^2) \cdot (2x^2 - 6x)$ 16. $(6a^4 - a^3) \cdot (-2a^2 - a^3)$
17. $(2x^3 + 12x^2 - 3x) \cdot (-6x + 10)$ 18. $(6x^3 - 7x^2 + 5x) \cdot (3x - 2)$
19. $(4x^3 - 3x^2 - 8x) \cdot (4x - 5)$ 20. $(-8b^4 - 7b^3 + 4b^2) \cdot (3b^2 - 2b)$
21. $(9a^5 - 6a^3 + 7a) \cdot (3a^3 - 5a^2)$ 22. $(3x^5 + 5x^4 - 6x^3) \cdot (4x^2 - 2x)$
23. $(8y^4 - 6y^3 + 10y^2) \cdot (-3y^2 + 5y)$
24. $(9x^3 + 5x^2 + 8x) \cdot (-5x^2 - 6x^3)$
25. $(8z^3 + 2z^5 - 3z^7) \cdot (5z^4 - 2z^3)$
26. $(x^6 - 5x^4 + 3x^2) \cdot (-4x^3 - 5x^2)$
27. $(3x^2 - 8x + 5) \cdot (4x^2 + 6x + 2)$
28. $(4x^3 - 7x^2 + 6x) \cdot (3x^3 + 5x - 4)$
29. $(-5x^4 - 3x^3 + 6x^2) \cdot (x^3 - 8x^2 + 4x)$
30. $(6x^5 - x^4 - 4x^3) \cdot (3x^4 + 5x^3 - 9x^2)$

Looking Back

31. What is the meaning of the word *percent*?
32. Convert 0.35% to a reduced fraction.
33. Find the GCF of 1,800 and 6,720.
34. Reduce $\sqrt{272}$.
35. Convert $\dfrac{9}{40}$ to a percent.
36. Convert 2.3% to a number in scientific notation.
37. Simplify $\left[\left(\dfrac{2}{3}\right)^{-2} + 1\right]^{-2}$.
38. Name two different pairs of operations that are considered inverse operations.

PRACTICE-FOR-SUCCESS ANSWERS

1. $40x + 30ax + 16 + 12a$ **2.** $21x^2 - 37x + 12$
3. $-90a^2 - 67ab + 12b^2$ **4.** $-16x^2 - 34xy + 15y^2$
5. $42x^4 - 68x^3 + 79x^2 - 18x$
6. $6x^8 - 12x^7 - x^6 - 16x^5 - 26x^4 + 28x^3 + 21x^2$

6.4 DIVISION BY MONOMIALS

OBJECTIVES

☐ To divide any two monomials

☐ To convert between terms with negative exponents and fractions

☐ To divide a polynomial by a monomial

Before reading this section you might wish to review negative exponents and the exponent rules as summarized near the end of Section 5.3.

Dividing Two Monomials

To divide two monomials requires the subtraction rule for exponents. Since numbers can be divided (except you cannot divide by 0) and since monomials represent numbers, it should be possible to divide one monomial by another nonzero monomial.

Let's consider the problem of dividing the monomial $42x^5y^7$ by the monomial $3xy^2$. We will write the division problem in a fractional form.

$$\frac{42x^5y^7}{3xy^2} = \frac{42}{3} \cdot \frac{x^5}{x} \cdot \frac{y^7}{y^2}$$ Separate the fraction into a product of distinct fractions, making a fraction for the numerical coefficients and a fraction for each variable.

$$= 14 \cdot x^{5-1} \cdot y^{7-2}$$ Simplify each fraction separately.
$$= 14 \cdot x^4 \cdot y^5$$ Simplify the subtraction of the exponents.
$$= 14x^4y^5$$ Drop the dot notations for the products.

Now if we write the original problem and the final answer in one line using the standard symbol for division, we can see that the result of dividing the two monomials is another monomial.

$$(42x^5y^7) \div (3xy^2) = 14x^4y^5$$

Manipulating Negative Exponents

In some problems the answers will not be monomials because they may involve negative exponents. Strictly speaking, a monomial is not allowed to have negative exponents on any of its variables. Before introducing examples of division that involve negative exponents, we are first going to discuss how to convert expressions that contain negative powers of variables to and from fractional forms.

Convert the following expression to an equivalent expression without the negative power.

$$5x^2y^{-3}$$

Since $y^{-3} = \dfrac{1}{y^3}$ we can write

$$5x^2y^{-3} = 5x^2 \cdot \frac{1}{y^3} = \frac{5x^2}{1} \cdot \frac{1}{y^3} = \frac{5x^2}{y^3}$$

Convert the following expression to an equivalent expression that is not in fractional form but that is allowed to have negative exponents.

$$\frac{-6a^3}{b^2c^5}$$

Separate the fraction into a product of three fractions. There is one fraction for the entire numerator and one fraction for each of the two factors in the denominator. (Note the use of 1s in the fractions.) Then convert the reciprocals of the powers into negative powers.

$$\frac{-6a^3}{b^2c^5} = \frac{-6a^3}{1} \cdot \frac{1}{b^2} \cdot \frac{1}{c^5} = -6a^3 \cdot b^{-2} \cdot c^{-5} = -6a^3b^{-2}c^{-5}$$

EXAMPLE 1 Convert the following expressions to equivalent expressions without negative powers.

a. $4x^3y^{-5}$ **b.** $-2a^{-3}b^{-2}$ **c.** $6x^{-5}y^6z^{-4}$

SOLUTION **a.** $4x^3y^{-5} = 4x^3 \cdot \dfrac{1}{y^5} = \dfrac{4x^3}{1} \cdot \dfrac{1}{y^5} = \dfrac{4x^3}{y^5}$

b. $-2a^{-3}b^{-2} = -2 \cdot \dfrac{1}{a^3} \cdot \dfrac{1}{b^2} = \dfrac{-2}{1} \cdot \dfrac{1}{a^3} \cdot \dfrac{1}{b^2} = \dfrac{-2}{a^3b^2}$

c. $6x^{-5}y^6z^{-4} = \dfrac{6}{1} \cdot \dfrac{1}{x^5} \cdot \dfrac{y^6}{1} \cdot \dfrac{1}{z^4} = \dfrac{6y^2}{x^5z^4}$ ■

EXAMPLE 2 Convert the following fractions to equivalent expressions without the fraction notation but that may have negative powers.

a. $\dfrac{8}{x^2y^5}$ **b.** $\dfrac{-3}{a^2b^4}$ **c.** $\dfrac{-10}{x^6y^2z^3}$

SOLUTION **a.** $\dfrac{8}{x^2y^5} = \dfrac{8}{1} \cdot \dfrac{1}{x^2} \cdot \dfrac{1}{y^5} = 8x^{-2}y^{-5}$

b. $\dfrac{-3}{a^2b^4} = \dfrac{-3}{1} \cdot \dfrac{1}{a^2} \cdot \dfrac{1}{b^4} = -3a^{-2}b^{-4}$

c. $\dfrac{-10}{x^6y^2z^3} = \dfrac{-10}{1} \cdot \dfrac{1}{x^6} \cdot \dfrac{1}{y^2} \cdot \dfrac{1}{z^3} = -10x^{-6}y^{-2}z^{-3}$ ■

Dividing Two Terms with Negative Exponents

When negative exponents are involved it is possible to divide two terms that are not monomials and arrive at an answer that is also not a monomial. Problems that, strictly speaking, do not contain monomials are just as interesting if not more so because they do involve negative exponents. The following is an example that shows how to divide two terms that are similar to monomials but that contain negative exponents.

$$\text{Divide } (-39a^{-3}b^2) \text{ by } (-3a^{-2}b^{-4}).$$

$(-39a^{-3}b^2) \div (-3a^{-2}b^{-4})$	Begin with the correct order for division.
$= \dfrac{-39a^{-3}b^2}{-3a^{-2}b^{-4}}$	Change to fraction notation for division.
$= \dfrac{-39}{-3} \cdot \dfrac{a^{-3}}{a^{-2}} \cdot \dfrac{b^2}{b^{-4}}$	Separate into a product of several fractions.
$= 13 \cdot a^{-3-(-2)} \cdot b^{2-(-4)}$	Apply the subtraction rule for exponents.
$= 13 \cdot a^{-3+(+2)} \cdot b^{2+(+4)}$	Convert subtractions to adding opposites.
$= 13 \cdot a^{-1} \cdot b^6$	Simplify the exponents.
$= 13 \cdot \dfrac{1}{a^1} \cdot b^6$	Write the answer without using a negative exponent.
$= \dfrac{13b^6}{a}$	The final form of the answer requires the least amount of ink to print.

EXAMPLE 3

Divide the following pairs of terms by converting to fractional notation and applying the subtraction rule for exponents. Write the final answers without negative exponents.

a. $(14x^8y^{-6}) \div (-7x^{-2}y)$ **b.** $(-36a^{-7}b^6c^{-8}) \div (9a^{-3}bc^{-5})$

SOLUTION   **a.** $(14x^8y^{-6}) \div (-7x^{-2}y)$

$= \dfrac{14x^8y^{-6}}{-7x^{-2}y}$	Convert the division to fractional form.
$= \dfrac{14}{-7} \cdot \dfrac{x^8}{x^{-2}} \cdot \dfrac{y^{-6}}{y}$	Separate into several fractions.
$= -2x^{8-(-2)}y^{-6-1}$	Apply the subtraction rule for exponents.
$= -2x^{10}y^{-7}$	Simplify the exponents.
$= -2x^{10} \cdot \dfrac{1}{y^7}$	Convert the negative power to a fractional form.
$= \dfrac{-2x^{10}}{y^7}$	Write the final answer as a fraction without negative exponents.

b. $(-36a^{-7}b^6c^{-8}) \div (9a^{-3}bc^{-5})$

$= \dfrac{-36a^{-7}b^6c^{-8}}{9a^{-3}bc^{-5}}$	Show the division in a fractional form.

$$= \frac{-36}{9} \cdot \frac{a^{-7}}{a^{-3}} \cdot \frac{b^6}{b} \cdot \frac{c^{-8}}{c^{-5}}$$ Separate the fraction into several fractions.

$$= -4a^{-7-(-3)}b^{6-1}c^{-8-(-5)}$$ Apply the subtraction rule for exponents.

$$= -4a^{-4}b^5c^{-3}$$ Simplify the exponents.

$$= -4 \cdot \frac{1}{a^4} \cdot b^5 \cdot \frac{1}{c^3}$$ Convert negative powers to fractions.

$$= \frac{-4b^5}{a^4c^3}$$ Show the final answer without negative exponents.

■

Dividing a Polynomial by a Monomial

Next we will show how to apply the distributive law to divide a polynomial by a monomial. The reason the distributive law works for this type of problem is the same as that already demonstrated in Section 3.3, where we introduced addition of signed fractions. In fact, if we reexamine the rule for adding fractions with like denominators we can make the desired connection. All we need to do is read the rule backwards and recognize that dividing a sum by a term like b is the same as multiplying the sum by the reciprocal of b. This is also intimately connected to the earlier statement we made that a fraction bar acts as a grouping symbol.

$$\frac{a + c}{b} = (a + c) \div b$$ Rewrite using the symbol $\div$ for division. This shows how the fraction bar acts as a grouping symbol.

$$= (a + c) \cdot \frac{1}{b}$$ Dividing by b is the same as multiplying by $\frac{1}{b}$.

$$= a \cdot \frac{1}{b} + c \cdot \frac{1}{b}$$ Apply the distributive law.

$$= \frac{a}{b} + \frac{c}{b}$$ The result is the sum of two fractions with the same denominator.

We have always shown the distributive law in its usual form where we distribute a product across a sum. The following equation is an example of distributing a division across a sum.

$$\frac{a + b + c}{d} = \frac{a}{d} + \frac{b}{d} + \frac{c}{d}$$

The justification for this equation can be made by applying the distributive law to the expression

$$(a + b + c) \div d = (a + b + c) \cdot \frac{1}{d}$$

The preceding equations are directly applicable to the problem of dividing a polynomial by a monomial if we replace each of the single letters a, b, c, and d with monomials. We can do this because each single letter represents a number and monomials also represent numbers; the distributive law works for addition as well as subtraction.

Use the form just given to divide the polynomial $36x^6 + 45x^4 - 24x^3$ by the monomial $-3x^2$.

$(36x^6 + 45x^4 - 24x^3) \div (-3x^2)$

$= \dfrac{36x^6 + 45x^4 - 24x^3}{-3x^2}$ Convert the division to fractional form.

$= \dfrac{36x^6 + 45x^4 + (-24x^3)}{-3x^2}$ Convert the subtraction in the numerator.

$= \dfrac{36x^6}{-3x^2} + \dfrac{45x^4}{-3x^2} + \dfrac{-24x^3}{-3x^2}$ Show three distinct fractions that are added.

$= \dfrac{36}{-3} \cdot \dfrac{x^6}{x^2} + \dfrac{45}{-3} \cdot \dfrac{x^4}{x^2} + \dfrac{-24}{-3} \cdot \dfrac{x^3}{x^2}$ Separate the factors.

$= -12x^{6-2} + (-15)x^{4-2} + 8x^{3-2}$ Simplify the fractions.

$= -12x^4 + (-15)x^2 + 8x$ Simplify the exponents.

$= -12x^4 - 15x^2 + 8x$ Convert adding the opposite to subtraction.

In practice it is not necessary to write as many steps as are shown in the preceding explanation. The next example shows how we would normally divide polynomials by monomials. The key is understanding how a fraction bar acts as a grouping symbol and how the distributive law can be applied to distribute a single denominator across each of the several terms in a numerator.

EXAMPLE 4   Use the distributive law to perform the following divisions. Write your final answers without negative exponents.
a. $(12x^3y^7 - 18x^4y^8 - 24x^4y^5) \div (-6x^2y^5)$
b. $(-15x^3y^2z^{-3} + 30xy^3z^4 - 25x^4yz^5) \div (-5xy^{-3}z^{-2})$

SOLUTION   a. $(12x^3y^7 - 18x^4y^8 - 24x^4y^5) \div (-6x^2y^5)$

$= \dfrac{12x^3y^7 - 18x^4y^8 - 24x^4y^5}{-6x^2y^5}$ Convert the division to fractional form.

$= \dfrac{12x^3y^7 + (-18)x^4y^8 + (-24)x^4y^5}{-6x^2y^5}$ Convert the subtractions.

$= \dfrac{12x^3y^7}{-6x^2y^5} + \dfrac{-18x^4y^8}{-6x^2y^5} + \dfrac{-24x^4y^5}{-6x^2y^5}$ Make three distinct fractions.

$= -2x^{3-2}y^{7-5} + 3x^{4-2}y^{8-5} + 4x^{4-2}y^{5-5}$ Simplify the fractions.

$= -2xy^2 + 3x^2y^3 + 4x^2$

b. $(-15x^3y^2z^{-3} + 30xy^3z^4 - 25x^4yz^5) \div (-5xy^{-3}z^{-2})$

$= \dfrac{-15x^3y^2z^{-3} + 30xy^3z^4 - 25x^4yz^5}{-5xy^{-3}z^{-2}}$ Convert $\div$ to fractional form.

$= \dfrac{-15x^3y^2z^{-3} + 30xy^3z^4 + (-25)x^4yz^5}{-5xy^{-3}z^{-2}}$ Convert the subtraction to addition.

$$= \frac{-15x^3y^2z^{-3}}{-5xy^{-3}z^{-2}} + \frac{30xy^3z^4}{-5xy^{-3}z^{-2}} + \frac{-25x^4yz^5}{-5xy^{-3}z^{-2}}$$

$$= 3x^{3-1}y^{2-(-3)}z^{-3-(-2)} + (-6)x^{1-1}y^{3-(-3)}z^{4-(-2)} + 5x^{4-1}y^{1-(-3)}z^{5-(-2)}$$

$$= 3x^2y^5z^{-1} + (-6)x^0y^6z^6 + 5x^3y^4z^7$$

$$= \frac{3x^2y^5}{z} - 6y^6z^6 + 5x^3y^4z^7$$

Convert the negative power to a fractional form.   ■

P R A C T I C E   F O R   S U C C E S S

Practice 1.   Convert $-5x^{-5}y^3z^{-2}$ to an equivalent expression in fractional form without any negative exponents.

Practice 2.   Convert $\dfrac{3a^7}{b^2c^5}$ to an equivalent expression not in fractional form but that may have negative powers of some of the variables.

Practice 3.   Perform the following division and write your answer without negative exponents: $(-32x^7y^4) \div (-8x^8y^6)$

Practice 4.   Perform the following division and write your answer without negative exponents: $(45a^3b^{-6}c^5) \div (9ab^{-2}c^{-3})$

Practice 5.   Divide the polynomial $28a^4b^2 + 35ab^6 - 21a^3b^4$ by the term $-7a^{-2}b^3$.

Practice 6.   Divide the term $-11x^3y^{-4}z^{-3}$ into the expression
$-55x^3y^2z^{-3} + 33xy^3z^4 - 77x^{-2}yz^{-2}$

EXERCISES 6.4

In exercises 1–10, convert each expression into an equivalent expression, which may be a fractional form, that is without negative exponents.

— 1. $5x^2y^{-3}$ 2. $5x^{-2}y^5$

3. $-4a^{-2}b^2$ 4. $a^{-3}b^{-5}$

5. $-6x^3y^{-3}$ 6. $-10a^3b^{-3}c^{-2}$

7. $4a^{-4}b^{-5}c^3$ 8. $4x^{-2}y^{-3}z^{-5}$

9. $6x^{-4}y^5z^{-8}$ 10. $a^{-4}b^{-7}c^5$

In exercises 11–20, convert each fractional expression into an equivalent expression that uses negative exponents.

11. $\dfrac{3a^7}{b^2c^5}$ 12. $\dfrac{4y^2}{x^3z^4}$

13. $\dfrac{6x^2z^3}{y^5}$ 14. $\dfrac{-10}{a^2b^3}$

15. $\dfrac{14}{x^5yz^3}$ 16. $\dfrac{-13y^2}{x^2z^2}$

17. $\dfrac{1}{x^5}$

18. $\dfrac{1}{a^2b^3c^4}$

19. $\dfrac{y^3}{x^3}$

20. $\dfrac{a^2b^3}{c^4}$

In exercises 21–32, perform the indicated divisions and leave your answers without negative exponents.

21. $\dfrac{15x^5}{3x^2}$

22. $\dfrac{-45a^7}{-9a^3}$

23. $\dfrac{6x^3}{2x}$

24. $\dfrac{15a^6}{3a^{-2}}$

25. $\dfrac{20a^3b^2c}{4a^2bc^3}$

26. $\dfrac{26x^5y^7z^4}{-2x^3y^2z^{-1}}$

27. $\dfrac{16x^6y^2}{2x^2y^{-1}}$

28. $\dfrac{12a^5b^6}{4ab^3}$

29. $\dfrac{-33a^{-2}b^{-3}}{11a^{-3}b^{-4}}$

30. $\dfrac{x^{-3}y^5}{x^{-4}y^{-2}}$

31. $\dfrac{-42a^3b^4c^5}{7a^2bc^3}$

32. $\dfrac{38ab^6c^{-3}}{19ab^8c^5}$

In exercises 33–50, use the distributive law for division to simplify each expression and leave your answers without negative exponents.

33. $\dfrac{46x^5 + 36x^3}{2x^2}$

34. $\dfrac{40a^6b^4 + 24a^7b^2}{8a^3b^{-1}}$

35. $\dfrac{20x^5y^8 - 8x^6y^6}{-4x^{-2}y^3}$

36. $\dfrac{-39p^3q^4 + 26p^5q^5}{-13p^{-2}q^2}$

37. $\dfrac{35a^3b^4c^6 + 49a^5bc^6}{7a^3bc^{-2}}$

38. $\dfrac{12x^2y^3z^5 + 36x^3y^5z^3}{6x^2y^3z}$

39. $\dfrac{21x^3y^4z^5 - 14x^4yz^3}{7x^4y^2z^4}$

40. $\dfrac{54a^{-3}b^2 + 36a^3b^{-2}}{18a^{-2}b^{-3}}$

41. $\dfrac{32x^{-5}y^3 - 48x^2y^{-3}}{-8x^{-2}y^{-3}}$

42. $\dfrac{105a^4b^{-5} + 75a^{-2}b}{15a^{-3}b^{-2}}$

43. $\dfrac{-48x^{-1}y^{-1}z^{-1} + 60xyz}{12x^{-1}y^2z^{-3}}$

44. $\dfrac{64a^3b^{-2}c + 80a^{-3}b^2c^{-1}}{16a^{-1}b^2c^{-2}}$

45. $\dfrac{32p^3r - 48p^7r - 56pr^5}{-8p^5r^3}$

46. $\dfrac{28x^3y^5 + 36x^{-1}y^3 + 44x^2y^{-3}}{4x^{-2}y^4}$

47. $\dfrac{39a^3b^{-4} - 30ab^{-1} + 48a^{-2}b^3}{-3a^{-2}b^4}$

48. $\dfrac{40x^{-3}y^2 + 25x^{-1}y^{-1} + 30x^{-2}y^3 - 20xy^{-3}}{5x^{-2}y^{-2}}$

49. $\dfrac{24x^5y^{-1} - 30x^{-3}y^2 + 60x^{-1}y^3 - 48}{6x^{-3}y^5}$

50. $\dfrac{22x^{-3}y^2z^4 - 20x^2y^5z + 34x^{-1}yz^{-1} + 50xyz}{2x^{-2}y^{-3}z^4}$

Looking Back

51. Explain the difference between a term and an expression.

52. What is the value of 0^0?

53. Is 484 a perfect square?

54. Find $\sqrt{\dfrac{1}{4}}$ as an exact fraction.

55. Explain why $\sqrt{-16}$ is impossible.

56. Convert 0.24% to a reduced fraction.

57. According to the order of operations agreement, which comes first, addition or subtraction?

58. Name three different kinds of grouping symbols commonly used in mathematics.

PRACTICE-FOR-SUCCESS ANSWERS

1. $\dfrac{-5y^3}{x^5z^2}$ 2. $3a^7b^{-2}c^{-5}$ 3. $\dfrac{4}{xy^2}$

4. $\dfrac{5a^2c^8}{b^4}$ 5. $\dfrac{-4a^6}{b} - 5a^3b^3 + 3a^5b$ 6. $5y^6 - \dfrac{3y^7z^7}{x^2} + \dfrac{7y^5z}{x^5}$

6.5   LITERAL FORMULAS

OBJECTIVES

☐ To comprehend how symbolic expressions are used to represent relationships between numeric quantities

☐ To understand formulas for mathematical and geometric relationships

☐ To learn some natural laws within various applied sciences and the math of finance

☐ To learn to substitute numeric values for variables in various types of formulas

☐ To simplify expressions according to the order of operations and the use of grouping symbols

In this section we are going to introduce a number of formulas that can be used to describe relationships between numeric quantities represented by both variables and constants. The main objective is to gain experience with substituting specific values for variables and simplifying expressions. Except for substituting values for variables, the expressions we will work with will be similar to those already given in the first five chapters.

When we introduce a formula, our objective is not to memorize the formula or to understand its derivation. Learning the significance, meaning, and derivation of a formula and learning how and when to apply formulas are topics we will not be concerned with in this section. There will be more reading than usual in this section, but reading the examples helps place the formulas and variables in the context of the problems.

We will completely describe the units that must be used with the formulas we give. Some problems associated with analyzing units will be left for a later course in algebra. However, for some of the problems we do not explicitly give all the numbers needed in the problem. It may be necessary to adjust some of the values given or to look up a physical or mathematical constant in one of the tables at the end of this book.

In some of the following examples we will present two different versions of the same formula. For example, in Section 6.1 we gave the formula

$$F = \frac{9}{5}C + 32$$

which can be used to convert degrees Celsius to degrees Fahrenheit. To convert from Fahrenheit to Celsius we use the formula

$$C = \frac{5}{9}(F - 32)$$

(We will not explain here how this second formula can be derived from the first; the symbolic manipulation of literal formulas will be covered in Chapter 7. In this section our concern with a formula is primarily the application of the formula and not its derivation.)

Pythagorean Theorem

In Chapter 4 we discussed the Pythagorean theorem: If a, b, and c, represent the lengths of the three sides of a triangle in which the angle opposite the side measuring c is a right angle (90°), then the relationship between the sides is given by the formula

$$a^2 + b^2 = c^2 \tag{6.1}$$

When this formula is solved for the variable c we have

$$c = \sqrt{a^2 + b^2} \tag{6.2}$$

EXAMPLE 1   Use this last formula to find c when $a = 10$ and $b = 24$.

SOLUTION $c = \sqrt{10^2 + 24^2} = \sqrt{100 + 576} = \sqrt{676} = 26.$ ■

Capacity of a Room

You have probably seen the little signs in public meeting rooms that read something like

> The capacity of this room is 320 persons.

Have you ever wondered what formula is used to calculate the capacity of a room? Just based on physical area, the following formula can be used to determine the number of people that can safely occupy a room. This formula assumes that some of the people will be standing and some of the people will be sitting.

$$N = \frac{A - 6.7S}{6.25} \tag{6.3}$$

where N = the number of people, A = the floor area of the room, and S = the number of seats in the room. The constant 6.25 appears in the formula because we assume a person who stands in the room will occupy 6.25 square feet of area. The constant 6.7 is indirectly related to the area occupied by a seated person.

EXAMPLE 2

Use the formula for occupancy of a room to calculate how many people would be allowed to occupy a room 2,200 square feet in size that contains 150 seats.

SOLUTION

The value 2,200 replaces the variable A and the value 150 replaces S.

$$N = \frac{2,200 - 6.7(150)}{6.25} = \frac{2,200 - 1,005}{6.25} = \frac{1,195}{6.25} = 191.2$$

The final result is not an exact whole number so we would round this result to a whole number. As a practical matter, in an actual room full of people you probably could not tell the difference between 191 people or 192 people, but to be on the side of comfort we will round the number down and give the answer as 191 people.   ■

Radar Detector

A radar detector works on the principle of bouncing an electromagnetic wave off an object. A wave is reflected back and the time delay between outgoing and incoming signals is measured. The following formula gives the distance between an object and a radar source signal,

$$d = \frac{tc}{2} \tag{6.4}$$

where t = the delay time in seconds, c = the velocity of light in terms of miles per second, and d = the distance to the object in terms of miles.

EXAMPLE 3

How far away, to the nearest half of a mile, is an object if the time delay is observed to be 25.3 millionths of a second?

SOLUTION

In this problem we are not given the value for the speed of light but this value can be found in the Appendix in the Table of Common Measurements under Miscellaneous Physical Constants. The desired value for c is

186,282.397 miles per second. The time delay is written in the fraction form $\frac{25.3}{10^6}$ seconds. Thus,

$$d = \frac{\left(\frac{25.3}{10^6}\right)(186{,}282.397)}{2} = \frac{(0.0000253)(186{,}282.397)}{2} = \frac{4.7129446441}{2}$$

$$= 2.35647232205 \approx 2.5$$

(to the nearest $\frac{1}{2}$, 2.35 is closer to 2.5 than it is to 2.0)

The object is not quite two and one-half miles away. ■

Volume of a Sphere

From geometry we have the formula for the volume of a sphere of radius r

$$V = \frac{4}{3}\pi r^3 \tag{6.5}$$

As long as r and V are measured with corresponding units (the units for V will be the units for r cubed), the answer for V will be in terms of cubic units.

EXAMPLE 4 What is the volume in cubic feet of a weather balloon that is 12 feet in diameter?

SOLUTION In this example we are not given the radius of the balloon but we are given its diameter, and we are expected to be able to determine the radius when given the diameter. The radius is simply half the diameter so we replace the variable r in the above formula with the number 6. The decimal value for π is obtained from the Table of Common Measurements under Mathematical Constants: $\pi \approx 3.14159$. We will carry out our decimal calculations to five decimal places.

$$V = \frac{4}{3}\pi r^3 \approx \frac{4}{3}(3.14159) \cdot 6^3 = \frac{4}{3}(3.14159) \cdot 216$$

$$= (1.33333)(3.14159) \cdot 216 = (4.18878) \cdot 216 = 904.77648 \quad ■$$

Law of the Lever

If a person uses a bar to lift an object at one end by pushing down at the other end, working with a pivot or support point called a *fulcrum* (see Figure 6.2), then the following formula holds

$$w_1 \cdot d_1 = w_2 \cdot d_2 \tag{6.6}$$

where w_1 is the weight in pounds that the person needs to push down on that end of the bar, d_1 is the distance measured in feet between the pivot point and the person-end of the bar, w_2 is the weight of the object, and d_2 is the distance between the object-end of the bar and the pivot point.

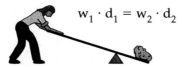

FIGURE 6.2   Law of the lever

Four variables appear in this formula, which are written using **subscripts**. A subscripted variable is a letter of the alphabet that is written with a whole number for a subscript. Even though the letters may be the same, different numerical subscripts represent different variables. We read w_1 as "w sub one" and we read w_2 as "w sub two": w_1 and w_2 are distinct variables.

Although the law of the lever could be written as

$$a \cdot b = c \cdot d$$

we would have four different variables to remember and we would not be able to tell at a glance which two represented weights and which two represented distances. Using subscripts on variables like w and d has the advantage of making clear which variables represent weight and distance. The two w variables represent weight measured in pounds and the two d variables represent distances measured in feet.

When the formula is solved for w_2, we have

$$w_2 = \frac{w_1 \cdot d_1}{d_2} \tag{6.7}$$

EXAMPLE 5   How heavy an object can a 140-pound person lift with a bar that is 10 feet long if she uses a fulcrum that is positioned 2 feet along the bar from the object at one end and if she decides to stand with all her weight at the other end of the bar?

SOLUTION   We let w_1 be the weight of the person. We are given $d_2 = 2$ and we reason that the remaining 8 feet of the 10-foot bar represents d_1.

$$w_2 = \frac{140 \cdot 8}{2} = \frac{1,120}{2} = 560$$

The person can lift an object that weighs 560 pounds, which is 4 times her own body weight. (Small wonder Archimedes could say that he could move the earth if given a long enough lever and a place to stand.)   ■

Focal Length of a Photographic Lens

In a camera the distance between the film and the camera lens is related to the distance between the camera lens and the object that is being focused as pictured in Figure 6.3. Each camera lens has an associated number called its focal length, and the three numbers are related by the equation

$$\frac{1}{f} = \frac{1}{p} + \frac{1}{q} \tag{6.8}$$

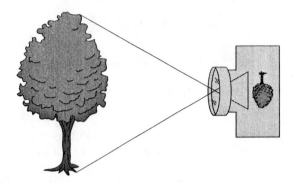

FIGURE 6.3   **Focal length of a photographic lens**

where f is the number that is called the focal length of the lens, p is the distance between the object being focused and the camera, and q is the distance between the camera lens and the camera film. When the equation is solved for the variable p, the result is the complex fraction

$$p = \cfrac{1}{\cfrac{1}{f} - \cfrac{1}{q}} \tag{6.9}$$

EXAMPLE 6   If the distance between the film and the lens is 1.75 inches and if the focal length of the lens is given by the decimal number 1.6, how far away from the camera in terms of inches is the object that is being focused?

SOLUTION $q = 1.75$ and $f = 1.6$ and we carry out decimal calculations to 5 decimal places.

$$p = \cfrac{1}{\cfrac{1}{1.6} - \cfrac{1}{1.75}} = \frac{1}{0.625 - 0.57143} = \frac{1}{0.05357} = 18.66716$$

The object is about 18.7 inches from the camera.   ■

Compound Interest Formula

When a lump sum of money is deposited in an account that earns compound interest, the future value of the account can be calculated by the formula

$$FV = PV(1 + i)^n \tag{6.10}$$

where FV is the future value, PV is the present value and is the amount originally deposited, i is the periodic interest rate and is the rate of interest (expressed as a decimal) the account earns in one time period, and the number n is the number of compounding time periods the money is left in the account.

EXAMPLE 7

Your rich aunt deposited $1,000 in an account on the day you graduated from high school. She decided to give you all the money in the account when you graduate from college as your graduation gift. If the account earns 6% interest compounded every year and if it takes you five years to graduate from college, what is the future value of your gift?

SOLUTION

At the time your aunt places the $1,000 dollars in the account, the present value of the account is $1,000. The future value FV is given by the formula where $i = 6\% = 0.06$ when expressed as a decimal and n is the number of compounding periods, which in this case is 5 years.

$$FV = 1{,}000(1 + 0.06)^5 = 1{,}000(1.06)^5 = 1{,}000(1.338225577) = 1338.8225577$$

We round this dollar amount off to the nearest penny so your gift at the time you graduate is worth $1,338.82.   ■

Effect of Inflation

The preceding formula for compound interest can be used to work backward in time. When this formula is solved for the present value variable PV, it takes on the form:

$$PV = \frac{FV}{(1 + i)^n} \tag{6.11}$$

EXAMPLE 8

Everyone knows that the value of a dollar in 1990 was more than the value of the dollar in 1980 because of the effect of inflation in the ten-year period between 1980 and 1990. Assuming an annual inflation rate of 4%, use the formula to discount the value of a 1990 dollar to determine what its value would have been in 1980.

SOLUTION

We assume the variable FV represents $1 in 1990 because this value is a future value as far as the year 1980 is concerned. By the same logic we assume the variable PV represents the answer to the question. The interest rate is 4% per year, which, expressed as a decimal, is 0.04. The time period we are working with is years and the variable n takes on the number of years between 1990 and 1980, which is 10. Substituting these values in the formula yields:

$$PV = \frac{1}{(1 + 0.04)^{10}} = \frac{1}{(1.04)^{10}} = \frac{1}{1.48024428} = 0.67556417$$

(Use a calculator with a $\boxed{y^x}$ key to calculate $(1.04)^{10}$.) Rounding the last value to the nearest penny, we find 68 cents in 1980 had the same buying power that $1 had in 1990.   ■

Area of a Triangle Using Its Perimeter

Although the formula Area $= \dfrac{1}{2}$ (base) (height) gives the area of a triangle, many cases arise in which we do not know the height of the triangle. An alternative is to use the formula

$$A = \sqrt{s(s - a)\,(s - b)\,(s - c)} \tag{6.12}$$

where the letters a, b, and c represent the lengths of the sides of the triangle and the letter s represents one-half the sum of the three values a, b, and c: $s = \dfrac{1}{2}(a + b + c)$. Thus, s is one-half the distance around the triangle. This distance is called the perimeter of the triangle, so s is one-half the perimeter. (Formula 6.12 is called either Heron's or Hero's formula.)

EXAMPLE 9

Use the formula to find the area of a triangle in which the three sides measure 8, 15, and 17, respectively. In the process use the prime factors of the numbers as demonstrated in Section 4.6 to simplify the resulting square root.

SOLUTION   We let $a = 8$, $b = 15$, and $c = 17$. We also let $s = \dfrac{1}{2}(8 + 15 + 17) = \dfrac{1}{2}(40) = 20$.

$$A = \sqrt{20(20 - 8)(20 - 15)(20 - 17)} = \sqrt{20 \cdot 12 \cdot 5 \cdot 3}$$
$$= \sqrt{2^2 \cdot 5^1 \cdot 2^2 \cdot 3^1 \cdot 5^1 \cdot 3^1} = \sqrt{2^4 \cdot 3^2 \cdot 5^2} = 2^2 \cdot 3^1 \cdot 5^1 = 60$$ ■

Arc Length of a Parabola

A parabola is a geometric curve that has many special properties. The plane figure has properties that are often exploited by 3-dimensional shapes. For example, the cross-sections on surfaces of solar collectors are parabolas; the world's largest radio telescope dish built in a mountain valley in Arecibo, Puerto Rico, has parabolic cross-sections; and at football games you may have noticed the dish-shaped microphones called *parabolic microphones*. Satellite dishes and even the reflecting plate inside the headlights on your car are all related to parabolas.

The length along the curve that is a parabola can be approximated by the formula

$$L \approx 2\sqrt{\dfrac{f^2}{4} = \dfrac{4e^2}{3}} \tag{6.13}$$

This expression contains a formula but the formula is not an equation because it has no equal sign. The calculated result approximates the answer for L. According to the labeling in Figure 6.4, e and f measure the two greatest distances across the parabola in both the vertical and horizontal directions.

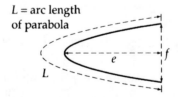

FIGURE 6.4   **Parabolic curve**

EXAMPLE 10

Use formula 6.13 to find an approximation for the length of a parabolic curve, where $f = 8$ and $e = 12$.

SOLUTION

$$L \approx 2\sqrt{\frac{8^2}{4} + \frac{4 \cdot 12^2}{3}} = 2\sqrt{\frac{64}{4} + \frac{4 \cdot 144}{3}}$$

$$= 2\sqrt{16 + \frac{576}{3}} = 2\sqrt{16 + 192} = 2\sqrt{208}$$

$$\approx 2(14.4222051) = 28.8444102 \qquad ■$$

Volume of a Spherical Cap

Figure 6.5 shows part of a sphere cut by a plane. The top section of the sphere is called a *spherical cap* and its volume is given by the formula

$$\text{spherical cap volume} = V = \frac{\pi}{3}\{2r^3 - \sqrt{r^2 - a^2}(a^2 + 2r^2)\} \qquad (6.14)$$

where r = radius of the sphere and a = radius of the cap.

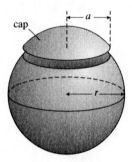

r = radius of the sphere
a = radius of the cap
V = volume of the cap

FIGURE 6.5   Volume of a spherical cap

EXAMPLE 11

If a sphere of radius 5 is such that the cap radius is 3, what is the volume of the cap? Leave your answer as a fractional multiple of π.

SOLUTION

We assign $r = 5$ and $a = 3$. Then we substitute these valuse in the above formula and simplify the answer for V. We leave π as a constant since the answer is supposed to be a multiple of π.

$$V = \frac{\pi}{3}\{2r^3 - \sqrt{r^2 - a^2}(a^2 + 2r^2)\}$$

$$= \frac{\pi}{3}\{2 \cdot 5^3 - \sqrt{5^2 - 3^2}(3^2 + 2 \cdot 5^2)\}$$

$$= \frac{\pi}{3}\{2 \cdot 125 - \sqrt{25 - 9}(9 + 2 \cdot 25)\}$$

$$= \frac{\pi}{3}\{250 - \sqrt{16}(9 + 50)\}$$

$$= \frac{\pi}{3}\{250 - 4(59)\}$$

$$= \frac{\pi}{3}\{250 - 236\}$$

$$= \frac{\pi}{3}\{14\}$$

$$= \frac{14\pi}{3}$$

The volume of the cap is $\dfrac{14\pi}{3}$ cubic units.   ■

One Swing of a Clock Pendulum

As is sometimes demonstrated in museums or planetariums, a pendulum suspended from a point moves in a periodic manner as a result of the earth rotating on its axis. The pendulums found in grandfather clocks also behave according to a predictable pattern, although such clocks are usually given some form of mechanical assistance. In fact, the following formula gives a relationship between the time for a pendulum in a clock to make a swing of one arc, the length of the pendulum, and the length of the arc.

$$T = \pi \sqrt{\frac{L}{g}\left(1 + \frac{A^2}{8L^2}\right)} \tag{6.15}$$

where T = time for one swing in seconds, L = length of the pendulum in feet, A = length of the arc of one swing in feet, and g is the constant 32 that takes into account gravity on earth.

EXAMPLE 12 Use formula 6.15 to calculate the time in seconds for one swing of the pendulum in a grandfather clock in which the length of the pendulum is $1\frac{1}{2}$ feet and the length of the arc in one swing is $\frac{1}{2}$ of a foot.

SOLUTION $L = 1.5$, $g = 32$, $A = 0.5$, and $\pi = 3.14159$

$$T = \pi\sqrt{\frac{1.5}{32}\left(1 + \frac{0.5^2}{8 \cdot 1.5^2}\right)} = \pi\sqrt{(0.046875)\left(1 + \frac{0.25}{8 \cdot (2.25)}\right)}$$

$$= \pi\sqrt{(0.046875)\left(1 + \frac{0.25}{18}\right)} = \pi\sqrt{(0.046875)(1 + 0.01388888)}$$

$$= \pi\sqrt{(0.046875)(1.01388888)} = \pi\sqrt{0.04752604} = \pi(0.21800467)$$

$$= (3.14159)(0.21800467) = 0.68488129$$

The time is approximately 0.68 seconds.   ■

PRACTICE FOR SUCCESS

Practice 1. Refer to Example 1. If $a = 14$ and $b = 17$, find the value of c rounded to the nearest ten-thousandth.

Practice 2. Refer to Example 4. Given the diameter of a basketball is 9 inches, find its volume in cubic inches. Round your answer to the nearest hundredth.

Practice 3. Refer to Example 7. What is the future value of $800 if it is placed in an account that earns 8% interest compounded every year for 3 years? Your answer should be rounded to the nearest penny.

Practice 4. Use the formula given for Example 9 to find the area of a triangle whose sides measure 9, 14, and 17. Round your answer to the nearest hundredth.

Practice 5. Given $x = -3$, $y = 6$, $z = -5$, find the value of the expression:
$$x^2 - y^2 + (x - y)^2 + z^3$$

Practice 6. Given $a = 2$ and $b = -3$, find the value of the expression:

$$\frac{a^2 + ab}{b^2 + \dfrac{a}{b}}$$

EXERCISES 6.5

In exercises 1–24, we refer to Examples 1–12 in this section. The formulas used in the examples, as well as the discussion that precedes those examples, are needed to solve the problems below.

  1. Refer to Example 1. Find the length of the third side, c, in a triangle in which $a = 12$ and $b = 24$. Round your answer to the nearest whole number.

  2. Refer to Example 1. Find the length of the third side, c, in a triangle in which $a = 20$ and $b = 21$.

  3. Refer to Example 2. Use the formula to estimate the capacity of a classroom that contains 1,600 square feet of floor space and has 45 seats.

  4. Refer to Example 2. Estimate the capacity of a room with 5,000 square feet that contains 200 seats.

  5. Refer to Example 3. If the time delay is 4.5 millionths of a second, how far away is the object? Round your answer to the nearest tenth of a mile.

  6. Refer to Example 3. To the nearest quarter of a mile, how far away is the object if the time delay is 8.25 millionths of a second?

  7. Refer to Example 4. What is the volume of a sphere of radius 8 feet? Round your answer to the nearest hundredth.

  8. Refer to Example 4. What is the volume of a sphere of radius 15 feet? Round your answer to the nearest hundredth.

9. Refer to Example 5. If the bar is 15 feet long, the person weighs 150 pounds, and she places the fulcrum 4 feet from the other end of the bar, how heavy an object can she lift?

10. Refer to Example 5. Find the value of w_2 if $w_1 = 180$, $d_1 = 25$ and $d_2 = 3$.

— 11. Refer to Example 6. How far away is the object being focused if the distance between the film and the lens is 1.8 inches and the focal length of the lens is given by the decimal 1.6?

12. Refer to Example 6. Find p if $f = 2.4$ and $q = 2.9$.

13. Refer to Example 7. Find the future value of $100 earning interest compounded monthly for 6 months at the rate of 1.5% per month.

14. Refer to Example 7. Assuming an interest rate of 6% per year, find the future value of $400 after 4 years.

15. Refer to Example 8. Assuming an inflation rate of 5% per year, find the value a 1990 dollar had in 1984.

16. Refer to Example 8. Assuming an inflation rate of 4% per year, find the value a 1988 dollar had in 1982.

17. Refer to Example 9. Find the area of a triangle whose sides measure 13, 19, and 22. Round your answer to the nearest tenth.

18. Refer to Example 9. Find the area of the triangle if the sides of the triangle measure 10, 12, and 18, respectively. Round your answer to the nearest tenth.

19. Refer to Example 10. Find the approximate arclength L of a parabola in which $f = 6$ and $e = 9$. Round your answer to hundredths.

20. Refer to Example 10. Find L when $e = 15$ and $f = 18$. Round your answer to hundredths.

21. Refer to Example 11. Find V if $r = 13$ and $a = 5$. Leave your answer as a multiple of π.

22. Refer to Example 11. Find F if $r = 17$ and $a = 8$. Leave your answer as a multiple of π.

— 23. Refer to Example 12. If the length of the pendulum is 2.5 feet and the length of the arc in one swing is 1.3 feet, find the time in seconds for 1 swing. Round your answer to hundredths.

24. Refer to Example 12. Find T if $L = 3.6$ and $A = 2.4$. Round your answer to hundredths.

In exercises 25–44, substitute the values of the variables into the expression that uses those variables and simplify the resulting expression to a single number. For each of these problems, assume the following values of the variables: $x = -2$, $y = 5$, $z = -6$, $a = 4$, $b = -10$, and $c = -3$.

25. $\dfrac{z}{x + y}$

26. $\dfrac{x^2 + y^2}{x^2 - y^2}$

27. $\dfrac{a^2 - b^2}{a^2 + b^2}$

28. $\dfrac{x^3 - y^3}{x^4 - y^2}$

29. $\dfrac{\dfrac{a}{a+b} - a}{b - \dfrac{a}{a+b}}$

30. $\dfrac{x + \dfrac{x}{y}}{x^2 - \dfrac{x^2}{y^2}}$

31. $\dfrac{x^2 + xy}{x^2 - xy}$

32. $\dfrac{ab}{a+b} + \dfrac{a+b}{ab}$

33. $\sqrt{b^2 - 4ac}$

34. $6x(y + z)^3$

35. $\dfrac{ab}{\sqrt{a^2 + b^2}}$

36. $\dfrac{6x - b(a + c)^2}{10y - z(y + z)}$

37. $\{[(3x + 5)x + 4]x - 2\}x + 6$

38. $(\{[(6z + 2)z - 1)]z + 4\}z + 2)z - 3$

39. $6(a + 6)^2 - c(a + b^2)$

40. $\dfrac{ax + by^2 + cz^3}{2bc + 4a^2}$

41. $\sqrt{-(ax + by + cz)}$

42. $\dfrac{ax^2 + bx + c}{[a(x + by) + c]z}$

43. $\dfrac{\dfrac{x}{x+y} - z}{x - \dfrac{y}{z+x}}$

44. $\dfrac{\sqrt{\left(\dfrac{c+x}{b}\right)^{-1} - c + a}}{c + \dfrac{x}{c - y}}$

Looking Back

45. Reduce $\dfrac{1{,}890}{2{,}730}$.

46. State the division check.

47. How can you tell whether a whole number is evenly divisible by 3?

48. How do you find the distance between two points on a number line?

49. What is the absolute value of 0?

50. Name the law that, under certain circumstances, can be used to transform a sum of products into a product involving a sum.

51. How does a complex fraction differ from an ordinary fraction?

52. Describe the rule that tells how many decimal places occur in the answer when two decimal numbers are multiplied.

PRACTICE-FOR-SUCCESS ANSWERS

1. $\sqrt{485} \approx 22.0227$

2. 381.70 cubic inches

3. \$1,007.77

4. $\sqrt{3{,}960} \approx 62.93$

5. -71

6. $\dfrac{-6}{25}$

SUMMARY

A variable is a symbol that can be used to represent a range of numbers. The basic terminology associated with polynomials includes the terms monomial, binomial, trinomial, coefficient, and degree — for example, the expression $5x^3 + 9x^2 - 4x + 6$ is a polynomial with four terms. The degree of this polynomial is 3, which is the largest exponent. This polynomial is written in standard form, with the powers of x decreasing from left to right. The exponent on the x term is assumed to be 1 and the constant 6 may be considered to be the coefficient of x^0, which is not normally written.

We can add and subtract polynomials by combining like terms and applying the distributive law. When subtracting polynomials, we can change the signs of all the coefficients on the polynomial being subtracted because this is equivalent to multiplying by -1. Then we can add the like terms—for example,

$$8x^3 + 2x^2 - 3x - (4x^3 + 9x^2 - 3x) = 8x^3 + 2x^2 - 3x - 4x^3 - 9x^2 + 3x$$

$$= 8x^3 - 4x^3 + 2x^2 - 9x^2 - 3x + 3x$$

$$= (8x^3 - 4x^3) + (2x^2 - 9x^2) + (-3x + 3x)$$

$$= 4x^3 - 7x^2$$

We can multiply two binomials by applying the distributive law four times. An acronym for this technique is FOIL; multiply the First, Outer, Inner, and Last terms. For example,

$$\underset{\textbf{First}}{} \quad \underset{\textbf{Outer}}{} \quad \underset{\textbf{Inner}}{} \quad \underset{\textbf{Last}}{}$$

$$(3x^2 + 8) \cdot (-4x^3 + 2x) = (3x^2) \cdot (-4x^3) + (3x^2) \cdot (2x) + (8) \cdot (-4x^3) + (8) \cdot (2x)$$

$$= -12x^5 + 6x^3 + (-32x^3) + 16x$$

$$= -12x^5 - 26x^3 + 16x$$

The distributive law also applies when dividing a polynomial by a monomial — for example,

$$\frac{18x^6 + 12x^5 - 4x^2}{-2x^2} = \frac{18x^6}{-2x^2} + \frac{12x^5}{-2x^2} + \frac{-4x^2}{-2x^2} = -9x^4 - 6x^3 + 2$$

We can also substitute values for variables in literal formulas and expressions. Given $x = 3$ and $y = -2$ and $z = -5$, we can find the value of the expression $\dfrac{x^2 + y^2 - z}{\sqrt{z^2 + y + yz + x}}$.

$$\frac{3^2 + (-2)^2 - (-5)}{\sqrt{(-5)^2 + (-2) + (-2)(-5) + 3}} = \frac{9 + 4 + 5}{\sqrt{25 + (-2) + 10 + 3}}$$

$$= \frac{18}{\sqrt{36}}$$

$$= \frac{18}{6}$$

$$= 3$$

CHAPTER 6 REVIEW PROBLEMS

In problems 1–8, classify each expression as a polynomial or not. For those expressions that are polynomials, give their degree and further classify them as monomials, binomials, or trinomials.

1. $8x^2 - 5x + 2$

2. $x + 2$

3. -7

4. $x^{-3} + x^{-2}$

5. $17 - 35x^3 + x^5$

6. $9 + x^4$

7. $x^3 - 8x^2 + 3x^{-1}$

8. $\sqrt{x + 5}$

Add or subtract the polynomials in problems 9–22.

9. $(5x^2 - 9x) - (-3x^2 - 4)$

10. $(8x + 10) + (3x^2 + 5x + 2)$

11. $(x^3 + x^8) - (x^8 + x^3)$

12. $(-3x^4 + 5x^2) - (4x^2 + 4x^4)$

13. $(x^2 - 13x + 5) + (7x - 5x^2 - 6)$

14. $(17x^3 - 12x^4 + 33x^2) + (-9x^4 + 3x^3 - 10x^2)$

15. $(14x^5 - 8x^3 - 10x) - (9x^5 - 9x^3 + 8x)$

16. $(a^9 - 13a^7 - 2a^5) - (-12a^9 + 14a^7 + 7a^5)$

17. $(-5a^3b^2 - 7a^2b^3 + 11ab^3) + (9a^2b^3 + a^3b^2 - 16ab^3)$

18. $(16x^4y^2 - 2x^3y^5 + 2x^4y^3) - (17x^4y^2 - 11x^3y^5 - 19x^4y^3)$

19. $(-4x^2yz^3 - 19x^3y^4z^2) - (16x^3y^4z^2 - 6x^2yz^3)$

20. $(-13a^5b^3c^2 + 14a^3b^2c^5 - 7a^2b^5c^3) - (-6a^2b^5c^3 + 19a^3b^2c^5 - 5a^5b^3c^2)$

21. $(-12x^2y^4z - 2x^4yz^2 - 19xy^2z^4) + (-15x^4yz^2 - 11xy^2z^4 + 10x^2y^4z)$

22. $(2x^5 - 9x^3 + 16x^2) - (3x^4 - 5x - 8)$

In problems 23–38, first use the distributive law to perform the multiplication and division operations. Then if any addition or subtraction operations remain, add or subtract any like terms and write your final answers without negative exponents.

23. $3x^3(6x^2 - 8x)$

24. $(-4x^2)(5x^3 - 12x^2 + 9x)$

25. $(16x^5 + 12x^4 - 20x^3) \div (4x^3)$

26. $(-3a^3)(a^5 - 7a^4 - 5a^2)$

27. $(2y^3 - 8y + 6)(-10y^4)$

28. $(42x^6 - 24x^5 + 18x^3) \div (-6x^4)$

29. $(21a^5 - 14a^3 + 35a^2) \div (-7a^4)$

30. $\dfrac{50x^3y^{-2}z^5}{10x^5y^3z^{-2}}$

31. $(-4x^2y^3)(5x^5y^2 - 4x^3y^2 - 6x^4y^6)$

32. $\dfrac{20x^7 + 56x^5 - 24x^3}{-4x^4}$

33. $\dfrac{18x^5y^2 - 12x^7y^3 - 27x^3y^{-2}}{-3x^{-2}y^{-3}}$

34. $3x(8x^2 + 5x) + 5x^2(x^3 - 2x^2)$

35. $(10x^3 + 6x^2)(4x^3) + (-7x^6 - x^3)(-2x^2)$

36. $(-6x^3)(4x^4 - 3x^2) + (-4x^5)(x^2 - 9)$

37. $(16x^6 + 36x^4) \div (4x^2) + (-26x^8 - 32x^6) \div (-2x^4)$

38. $(35x^{10} + 60x^7) \div (5x^4) + (-2x^4 - x)(-6x^2)$

In problems 39–52, substitute the following values and then simplify the resulting expressions to single numbers: $x = -3$, $y = 5$, $a = -1$, $b = -4$.

39. $\dfrac{a^3 + x^2}{x^3 - a^2}$

40. $6x^2y(a^2 + ab)$

41. $\sqrt{x^2 + y^2 + ab - 2}$

42. $\dfrac{x^2 - \sqrt{-(xy - 1)}}{|a^3|}$

43. $\dfrac{\dfrac{x}{2a + b}}{\dfrac{a^2 + b^2 - 2}{y}}$

44. $\dfrac{5x - b(x + a)^2}{2}$

45. $\dfrac{xy}{a + b} + \dfrac{1}{2}ax^2$

46. $\{[(5x + 3)x + (-2)]x + 7\}x + 2$

47. $\dfrac{(x - y)^2}{(b + 2a)^2}$

48. $x^2 - y^2 + (x - y)^2$

49. $\dfrac{3x^2 + 8x + 2}{4b^2 - 5b + 6}$

50. $\dfrac{b^2 + 3b + 1}{5x^2 - 6x + 2}$

51. $\sqrt{x^3 + |x| - b^3 + x^2}$

52. $\dfrac{b^3 + (y - a)^3}{\sqrt{-(x^2 - |-y|^2)}}$

Solve problems 53–60 by substituting the appropriate values into the formula; then simplify the result to a single number.

53. A torus is a 3-dimensional mathematical object that is in the shape of a donut. The volume of such an object is given by the formula

$$V = 2\pi^2(R + r)r^2$$

where R is the radius of the hole in the donut and r is the radius of the circle that forms the tubular part of the donut. What is the volume of a donut with a hole of radius 6 inches and a tubular radius of 3 inches? Use $\pi = 3.14$ and round your answer to the nearest hundredth.

54. The specific gravity of an object is the ratio of the weight of the object in air divided by the difference between the weight of the object in air and the weight of the object when it is immersed in water. If S represents the specific gravity, A represents the weight of the object in air, and W represents the weight of the object in water, then the corresponding formula is

$$S = \dfrac{A}{A - W}$$

What is the specific gravity of an object that weighs 8 pounds when in water but weighs 12 pounds when out of water?

55. The area of a trapezoid is given by the formula
$$A = \frac{h(b_1 + b_2)}{2}$$
where h is the height and the two subscripted variables b_1 and b_2 are the lengths of the top and bottom bases. Find the area of a trapezoid whose height is 10 and whose bases measure 13 and 15.

56. A pyramid with a square base that measures b on a side and that has vertical height of h and a slant height of s has a surface area A given by the formula
$$A = 2b\sqrt{s^2 - \frac{b^2}{4}} + b^2$$
Find the surface area of a square pyramid whose base is 8 and whose slant height is 10. Round your answer to the nearest tenth.

57. The surface area of a cone is given by the formula $A = \pi rs + \pi r^2$ where A is the surface area, r is the radius of the base, and s is the slant height. Find the surface area of a cone whose base radius is 10 and whose slant height is 8. Do not substitute a decimal value for π; leave your final answer as a multiple of π.

58. Use the formula $FV = PV(1 + i)^n$ to find the future value of $1,000 that is deposited in an account that earns compound interest at a rate of 1.3% per month. Assume the money is left in the account for 4 months. (See Example 9 in Section 6.5.)

59. The formula
$$V = \frac{\pi}{3}\{2r^3 - \sqrt{r^2 - a^2}(a^2 + 2r^2)\}$$
gives the volume of a spherical cap in which r is the radius of the sphere and a is the radius of the cap. (See Example 7 in Section 6.5.) Find the volume when the radius of the cap is 35 and the radius of the sphere is 37. Leave your answer as a multiple of π; do not replace π with a decimal.

60. The formula
$$T = \pi\sqrt{\frac{L}{g}\left(1 + \frac{M^2}{8L^2}\right)}$$
gives the length of time for a pendulum in a clock to make 1 swing of one arc. T is the time and g is the constant 32. Assume L and M are the length of the pendulum and the length of the arc, respectively. Use the formula to find the time it takes a pendulum to swing one arc if the length of the pendulum is 4.1 and the length of the arc is 3 feet. Use $\pi = 3.14$ and round your answer to the nearest tenth.

Use the FOIL method to multiply the binomials in problems 61–66.

61. $(3x - 9) \cdot (2x + 7)$ 62. $(4x - 5) \cdot (3x - 5)$

63. $(5 - 2x) \cdot (7x - 4)$ 64. $(m - n) \cdot (p + q)$

65. $(5a + 7b) \cdot (4a - 9b)$ 66. $(2x - 7y) \cdot (3x - 8y)$

Use the vertical form to multiply the polynomials in problems 67–74.

67. $(9x^2 - 8x + 4) \cdot (3x + 5)$

68. $(5x^2 + 4x - 6) \cdot (2x - 5)$

69. $(-8x^2 - 2x + 3) \cdot (4x - 3)$

70. $(6x^3 - 8x^2 + 4x) \cdot (3x - 2)$

71. $(9x^4 - 12x^3 + 2x^2) \cdot (4x^2 - 3x)$

72. $(-5a^4 + 3a^3 - 4a^2) \cdot (2a^3 - 5a^2)$

73. $(5x^2 - 8x + 3) \cdot (2x^2 - 4x - 5)$

74. $(4x^2 - 7x - 2) \cdot (3x^2 - 8x - 4)$

CHAPTER 6 PRACTICE TEST

In problems 1–6, classify each expression as a polynomial or not. For those expressions that are polynomials, give their degree and further classify them as monomials, binomials, or trinomials.

1. $x^4 - 5x^3 + 8x$

2. $x^5 + x^{-2}$

3. 0

4. $10x^3 + 8x^5 - 4x^2$

5. $\sqrt{x^2 + 5x}$

6. $x^3 - x^6$

Add or subtract the polynomials in problems 7–13.

7. $(6x^3 - 5x^2) + (3x^2 - 9x^3)$

8. $(x^4 + 5x^5) - (3x^5 - 6x^4)$

9. $(10x^5 + 8x^4) - (6x^5 + 8x^4)$

10. $(6x^7 - 5x^3) + (5x^3 - 6x^7)$

11. $(23x^5 - 19x^3 + 6x^2) - (-3x^2 + 10x^3 - 2x^5)$

12. $(-6a^4b^3 + 3a^5b^2 - 7a^2b^3) - (8a^5b^2 - 2a^2b^3 - 5a^4b^3)$

13. $(12x^5y^3 - 8x^2y^3 - 9x^3y^5) - (10x^2y^3 - 3x^3y^5 - 13x^5y^3)$

In problems 14–19, perform the multiplication and division operations. Write your answers without negative exponents.

14. $(-3x^4)(6x^5 - 2x^3 - 7x^2)$

15. $(-10a^4 + 3a^3 - 2a^2)(-2a^5)$

16. $\dfrac{-42x^5y^{-3}z^{-1}}{7x^{-2}y^{-4}z^3}$

17. $(56x^7 - 40x^5 + 24x^3) \div (-8x^4)$

18. $\dfrac{45a^6 - 35a^4 + 20a^3}{-5a^3}$

19. $\dfrac{18x^2y^5 - 33x^3y^{-3} + 42xy^2}{3x^{-3}y^4}$

In problems 20–23, substitute the following values and then simplify the resulting expressions to single numbers: $x = -3$, $y = 5$, $z = 0$, $a = -1$, $b = -4$.

20. $\dfrac{\sqrt{bx - a^2b}}{-|b| + a^2 - y}$

21. $\dfrac{x^2y - |b|x}{\sqrt{z^2} + |b^2 + ax|}$

22. $\dfrac{\dfrac{x}{y+z}}{b^2-4a-y^2}$

23. $3ax^3 - |x+xy| \div (b-a)^2$

Use the FOIL method to multiply the binomials in problems 24 and 25.

24. $(2x^2 - 8x) \cdot (5x - 4)$

25. $(5a^2 - 3b^2) \cdot (4b - 2a)$

Use the vertical method to multiply the polynomials in problems 26 and 27.

26. $(3x^4 - 5x^3 + 2x) \cdot (4x^2 - 3x)$

27. $(7a^3 - 4a^2 - 5a) \cdot (3a^2 - 2a)$

Solve problems 28 and 29 by substituting the appropriate values into the formula; then simplify the result to a single number.

28. The volume V of the frustum (the part near the base formed by bisecting the cone with a plane, parallel to the base) of a right circular cone with base radii a and b and height h is given by the formula

$$V = \frac{1}{3}\pi h(a^2 + ab + b^2)$$

Find the volume where the height is 12 and base radii are 4 and 9. Do not use a decimal approximation for π. Write your final answer as a multiple of π.

29. If x denotes the length of a side of a regular polygon inscribed in a circle of radius r, then the following formula gives the length y of a side in the regular polygon with twice as many sides:

$$y = \sqrt{2r^2 - r\sqrt{(2r)^2 - x^2}}$$

Find the value for y when x is 6 and r is 5. Leave your answer for y as the square root of a whole number.

SOLVING EQUATIONS

Solving equations is an essential skill for success in algebra. Being able to set up and solve equations is necessary in order to determine the solutions to more difficult word problems. For example, imagine that 17,000 people attended a rock concert. The admission price was $30 for floor seats and $25 for all other seating. If the total gate receipts were $432,500, how many of each type of ticket were sold? This problem could be done with considerable guesswork using arithmetic, but the solution is found more easily by writing an equation and solving it. In addition to solving equations and word problems, we will learn to solve inequalities.

7.1   INTRODUCTION TO EQUATIONS AND ALGEBRAIC EXPRESSIONS

OBJECTIVES

- To learn to check solutions to equations
- To understand conditional equations and identities
- To translate written expressions into algebraic expressions
- To translate algebraic expressions into written expressions

Equations

An **equation** is a mathematical statement that two expressions are equal: for example,

$$x + 11 = 9 \quad 4x + 3 = -5 \quad 7x + 22 = -10x - 12 \quad x^2 = 4$$

Each of these equations has three components: an expression on the left side, an equal sign, and an expression on the right side. Each of the equations is neither a true nor a false statement. Each can be compared to an English statement such as "I wear glasses": The statement will be true depending on who is speaking, that is, who we substitute for "I." If the speaker wears glasses and says "I wear glasses," then the statement is true.

If the speaker does not wear glasses and says "I wear glasses," then the statement is false.

Just as we can make the English statement "I wear glasses" true or false by whom we substitute for "I," we can substitute numbers for the variable in an equation to make it a true or false mathematical statement. Those numbers that make the equation a true statement are called the **solutions** to the equation. In the first three out of the four equations we just listed, the solution is -2 because -2 can be substituted for the variable x to make the equation a true statement.

$$x + 11 = 9$$
$$-2 + 11 = 9 \qquad \text{Substitute } -2 \text{ for } x.$$
$$9 = 9 \qquad \text{True.}$$
$$4 \cdot x + 3 = -5$$
$$4 \cdot (-2) + 3 = -5 \qquad \text{Substitute } -2 \text{ for } x.$$
$$-8 + 3 = -5 \qquad \text{Multiply before adding.}$$
$$-5 = -5 \qquad \text{True.}$$
$$7 \cdot x + 22 = -10 \cdot x - 12$$
$$7 \cdot (-2) + 22 = -10 \cdot (-2) - 12 \qquad \text{Substitute } -2 \text{ for } x.$$
$$-14 + 22 = 20 - 12 \qquad \text{Simplify both sides of the equation.}$$
$$8 = 8 \qquad \text{True.}$$

The equation $x^2 = 4$ has two solutions because both -2 and 2 can replace x to make a true mathematical statement.

$$x^2 = 4 \qquad\qquad x^2 = 4$$
$$2^2 = 4 \qquad\qquad (-2)^2 = 4 \qquad \text{Substitute 2 or } -2 \text{ for } x.$$
$$4 = 4 \qquad\qquad 4 = 4$$

An equation may have one solution, two solutions, three or more solutions, or even an infinite number of solutions, depending on the type of equation it is. The equation

$$(x + 2)(x + 3) - 6 = x(x + 5)$$

has an infinite number of solutions because it is true for all real numbers. (You might try checking a few numbers.) Some equations have no solutions at all. The equation $\sqrt{x} = -2$ has no solution because no real number exists to substitute for the variable to make the equation a true statement.

All equations can be divided into classes. **Identities** are equations that are true for all values of the variable for which the expressions in the equation are defined: $5(x + 9) = 5x + 45$ is an identity. **Conditional equations** are equations that are true for some values of the variable and false for other values. Most of the equations we will study in this chapter, such as $3x + 4 = 19$, are conditional equations.

Checking Solutions

Imagine that a classmate tells you that -5 is a solution to the equation $x^2 - 7x + 10 = 0$ and you want to check if that is true. To check if the given number -5 is a solution, substitute -5 for x into the equation.

$$x^2 - 7x + 10 = 0$$
$$(-5)^2 - 7 \cdot (-5) + 10 \stackrel{?}{=} 0 \qquad \text{Substitute } -5 \text{ for } x.$$
$$25 + 35 + 10 \stackrel{?}{=} 0 \qquad \text{Use the order of operations to simplify.}$$
$$60 \neq 0$$

Therefore, -5 is *not* a solution.

CHECKING A SOLUTION TO AN EQUATION

1. **Substitute the number for each occurrence of the variable.**
2. **Simplify the expressions on both sides of the equal sign as needed.**
3. **If a true mathematical statement results, the number is a solution. If a false mathematical statement results, the number is not a solution.**

EXAMPLE 1

Check to see if the given number is a solution to the equation.

a. $3x + 17 = -46 + 8$; $x = -19$

b. $9x - (2 - 7x) = 12x - 10$; $x = -2$

c. $4x^2 = -24x + 13$; $x = \dfrac{1}{2}$

d. $0.3x - 0.7x + 7.42 = 5(0.8x - 0.1)$; $x = 1.8$

e. $\dfrac{4}{x - 5} = \dfrac{3}{4x - 10}$; $x = 5$

f. $3x + 7 = 3(x + 1) + 4$; $x = 9$

SOLUTION   To check, substitute the value for each occurrence of the variable. If the value is negative, enclose it in parentheses so that the negative sign will not be misinterpreted.

a.
$$3x + 17 = -46 + 8$$
$$3 \cdot (-19) + 17 \stackrel{?}{=} -46 + 8 \qquad \text{Replace } x \text{ with } -19.$$
$$-57 + 17 \stackrel{?}{=} -38 \qquad \text{Simplify both sides.}$$
$$-40 \neq -38$$

Therefore, -19 is not a solution.

b.
$$9x - (2 - 7x) = 12x - 10$$
$$9 \cdot (-2) - (2 - 7 \cdot (-2)) \stackrel{?}{=} 12 \cdot (-2) - 10 \qquad \text{Replace } x \text{ with } -2.$$
$$-18 - (2 + 14) \stackrel{?}{=} -24 - 10$$
$$-18 - 16 \stackrel{?}{=} -24 - 10$$
$$-18 + (-16) \stackrel{?}{=} -24 + (-10) \qquad \text{Change to adding the opposite.}$$
$$-34 = -34$$

Therefore, -2 is a solution.

c.
$$4x^2 = -24x + 13$$

$$4 \cdot \left(\frac{1}{2}\right)^2 \stackrel{?}{=} -24 \cdot \left(\frac{1}{2}\right) + 13 \qquad \text{Replace } x \text{ with } \frac{1}{2}.$$

$$4 \cdot \left(\frac{1}{4}\right) \stackrel{?}{=} -24 \cdot \left(\frac{1}{2}\right) + 13 \qquad \text{Do the exponentiation.}$$

$$1 \stackrel{?}{=} -12 + 13$$

$$1 = 1$$

Therefore, $\frac{1}{2}$ is a solution.

d.
$$0.3x - 0.7x + 7.42 = 5(0.8x - 0.1)$$

$$0.3 \cdot (1.8) - 0.7 \cdot (1.8) + 7.42 \stackrel{?}{=} 5(0.8 \cdot (1.8) - 0.1) \qquad \text{Replace } x \text{ with } 1.8.$$

$$0.54 - 1.26 + 7.42 \stackrel{?}{=} 5(1.44 - 0.10)$$

$$-0.72 + 7.42 \stackrel{?}{=} 5(1.34)$$

$$6.7 = 6.7$$

Therefore, 1.8 is a solution.

e.
$$\frac{4}{x - 5} = \frac{3}{4x - 10}$$

$$\frac{4}{5 - 5} \stackrel{?}{=} \frac{3}{4 \cdot 5 - 10} \qquad \text{Replace } x \text{ with } 5.$$

$$\frac{4}{0} \stackrel{?}{=} \frac{3}{20 - 10}$$

$$\text{Undefined} \stackrel{?}{=} \frac{3}{10}$$

Because substituting 5 causes the fraction on the left side to be undefined, 5 is not a solution to the equation. Any number substituted into an equation that causes any part of the equation to be undefined makes the equation meaningless; therefore, that number is not a solution to the equation.

f.
$$3x + 7 = 3(x + 1) + 4$$

$$3 \cdot 9 + 7 = 3(9 + 1) + 4 \qquad \text{Replace } x \text{ with } 9.$$

$$27 + 7 = 3(10) + 4$$

$$34 = 34 \qquad \text{True.}$$

Therefore, 9 is a solution.

If we use the distributive law to simplify the expression on the right side of the equal sign at the beginning of (f), we get

$$3x + 7 = 3x + 3 \cdot 1 + 4$$

$$3x + 7 = 3x + 7$$

Both sides of the equation are identical so any real number that we substitute into the equation will make it true; this equation is an identity.

■

Writing Algebraic Expressions

Many word problems or application problems can be solved using equations. If we can translate the problem into **algebraic expressions,** we can more easily solve the problem. Algebraic expressions are expressions that may contain numbers, variables, symbols for operations, and grouping symbols. In Section 7.2 we will learn to combine those expressions to make an equation that we can use to solve the problem.

Imagine that we are to translate the written expression "the sum of a number and twenty" into an algebraic expression. In the expression we designate a variable, usually the letter x, to represent the unknown number. Recall that finding the sum indicates the operation of addition: We then translate the written expression "the sum of a number and twenty" into the algebraic expression $x + 20$. The accompanying table contains some key vocabulary terms and demonstrates written expressions translated into algebraic expressions.

English Expression	Algebraic Expression
Addition Phrases	
The sum of fifty and a number	$x + 50$
A number increased by negative seven	$x + (-7)$
Ninety-two more than a number	$x + 92$
Subtraction Phrases	
The difference between a number and eight	$x - 8$
A number decreased by 12.5	$x - 12.5$
One-third less than a number	$x - \dfrac{1}{3}$
Four subtracted from a number	$x - 4$
Multiplication Phrases	
Seven times a number	$7x$
The product of a number and forty-two	$42x$
Twice a number	$2x$
One-half of a number	$\dfrac{1}{2}x$
Division Phrases	
The quotient of twenty-eight and a number	$\dfrac{28}{x}$
A number divided by eighty-six	$\dfrac{x}{86}$
The reciprocal of a number	$\dfrac{1}{x}$
Exponentiation Phrases	
A number squared	x^2
The cube of a number	x^3
A number riased to the seventh power	x^7
Miscellaneous Phrases	
The square root of a number	$\sqrt{x}$
The opposite of a number	$-x$
The absolute value of a number	$|x|$

Most of the expressions in the table are translated in the same order as the written English. The expression "the difference of a number and 8" is translated as $x - 8$. Expressions in which the translation is in reverse order from the English contain the vocabulary "more than," "less than," and "subtracted from." For example, the expression "four subtracted from a number" translates as $x - 4$. The "product of a number and forty-two" also translates in reverse order as $42x$ because the numerical coefficient usually precedes the variable in mathematical expressions.

| EXAMPLE 2 | Translate the following written expressions into algebraic expressions. Use x as the variable to represent the unknown number. |

a. Ninety-six more than a number

b. Twenty-three less than a number

c. A number subtracted from 0.2

d. The product of a number and negative ninety-nine

e. Twelve times the sum of fifteen and a number

f. Four times a number subtracted from the reciprocal of a number

g. The quotient of a number and the number raised to the fifth power

h. The opposite of the product of five and the square of the number

i. One-half of the difference of a number and twenty-eight

SOLUTION
a. Ninety-six more than a number can be interpreted as a number increased by ninety-six.
$x + 96$ Reverse the order.

b. Twenty-three less than a number can be interpreted as a number decreased by twenty-three.
$x - 23$ Reverse the order.

c. A number subtracted from 0.2
$0.2 - x$ Reverse the order.

d. The product of a number and negative ninety-nine
$-99x$ The numerical coefficient precedes the variable.

e. Twelve times the sum of fifteen and a number
$12(15 + x)$ When the expression "the sum of" is located somewhere within a written expression that contains a multiplication, parentheses are needed.

f. Four times a number subtracted from the reciprocal of a number
$\dfrac{1}{x} - 4x$ Reverse the order.

g. The quotient of a number and the number raised to the fifth power
$\dfrac{x}{x^5}$ The quotient indicates division is the operation.

h. The opposite of the product of five and the square of the number
$-(5x^2) = -5x^2$ The parentheses may be omitted.

i. One-half of the difference of a number and twenty-eight

$\frac{1}{2}(x - 28)$ — When the expression "the difference of" is located somewhere within a written expression that contains a multiplication, parentheses are needed. ■

| **EXAMPLE 3** | Translate the following algebraic expressions into written expressions. |

a. $x^3 - 125$ **b.** $x + \sqrt{x}$ **c.** $-7|x|$ **d.** $\dfrac{9(x + 20)}{5}$

SOLUTION   Each of the above algebraic expressions could be translated into many written expressions. In each example two possible written expressions are given for each algebraic expression.

a. $x^3 - 125$

"The difference between a number cubed and 125" or "125 subtracted from a number to the third power"

b. $x + \sqrt{x}$

"The sum of a number and the square root of the same number" or "A number increased by its own square root"

c. $-7|x|$

"The product of -7 and the absolute value of a number" or "-7 times the absolute value of a number"

d. $\dfrac{9(x + 20)}{5}$

"9 times the sum of a number and 20, with this result divided by 5"
The phrase "with this result" is added so the reader does not interpret that only 20 is divided by 5. ■

PRACTICE FOR SUCCESS

Practice 1.   Check to see if -4 is a solution to $-4x + 7 = 15 - 2x$.

Practice 2.   Check to see if $\frac{1}{3}$ is a solution to $6x + 3x - 15 = -39x$.

Practice 3.   Translate the written expression "nine times the sum of a number and forty" into an algebraic expression.

Practice 4.   Translate the written expression "twelve more than the quotient of fourteen and a number" into an algebraic expression.

Practice 5.   Translate $9 - x^2$ into a written expression.

EXERCISES 7.1

In exercises 1–30, check to see if the given number is a solution to the equation.

1. $x + 12 = 26; x = 14$

2. $17 - x = -35; x = -18$

3. $8x = 3(15 - 7x); x = 3$

4. $10x = 5(12 - 4x); x = 2$

5. $8x - (3 - 12x) = -42; x = -2$

6. $6x - (17x - 14) = -20; x = -3$

7. $8x = 30; x = \dfrac{5}{2}$

8. $13x = \dfrac{-91}{2}; x = -\dfrac{7}{2}$

9. $\dfrac{3}{4} + x = \dfrac{17}{12}; x = \dfrac{2}{3}$

10. $-\dfrac{9}{10} + x = -\dfrac{27}{20}; x = -\dfrac{3}{4}$

11. $\dfrac{3x + 8}{5} + \dfrac{1}{2} = \dfrac{15}{2} - x; x = 4$

12. $\dfrac{7x + 4}{6} + \dfrac{1}{3} = \dfrac{55}{3} - x; x = 8$

13. $9.4 - 4x = -0.6; x = 2.5$

14. $6x + 12.42 = -0.28; x = -2.1$

15. $0.45x - 2.6 = 0.27x - 3.4; x = -3$

16. $0.88x + 4.8 = 0.42x + 0.4; x = -4$

17. $x^2 - 3x - 4 = 0; x = 1$

18. $x^2 - 11x - 12 = 0; x = -12$

19. $\sqrt{x} + 23 = 34; x = 121$

20. $\sqrt{x} - 44 = -12; x = 484$

21. $\dfrac{x}{9} + \dfrac{x}{3} + \dfrac{x}{6} = -\dfrac{11}{18}; x = -1$

22. $\dfrac{x}{12} + \dfrac{2x}{3} = \dfrac{x}{6} + \dfrac{7}{3}; x = -2$

23. $4(x - 3) + 3(x - 4) = -20; x = 0$

24. $8(x - 5) + 7(x - 4) = -143; x = -5$

25. $x^3 + 22x^2 + 14x - 7 = 0; x = -1$

26. $x^3 - 16x = -75; x = -3$

27. $8x - 3x - 3.72 = 11x - 7.44; x = 0.62$

28. $-4x - 7x - 2.96 = -3x - 8.64; x = 0.71$

29. $7(x + 0.84) + 13 = 7x + 5.88 + 13; x = -\dfrac{3}{2}$

30. $9\left(x + \dfrac{7}{10}\right) - 19 = 9x + \dfrac{63}{10} - 19; x = -0.2$

In exercises 31–56, translate the written expressions into algebraic expressions. Use *x* as the variable to represent the unknown number.

31. The sum of the cube of a number and eight

32. Nine more than the square of a number

33. A number raised to the fourth power subtracted from one hundred

34. Ninety-nine less than one-half of a number

35. The difference between twice a number and seven

36. Five-sevenths times the sum of twenty-eight and a number

37. Six less than the reciprocal of a number

38. The product of the absolute value of a number and twenty

39. Negative six multiplied by the sum of eighty-four and a number

40. Eight times the difference of a number squared and nine

41. The quotient of a number raised to the sixth power and six

42. The opposite of the product of twenty-two and the cube of a number

43. Subtract negative two from one-half of a number

44. Four less than the square root of a number

45. The product of negative four and a number, all divided by the same number squared

46. The difference of a number and negative three, all divided by three times the number

47. The sum of a number and five, all raised to the third power

48. The difference between eight and a number, all raised to the fourth power

49. Twice a number subtracted from negative nine

50. The quotient of five and the difference between a number and fifteen

51. Three times a number subtracted from ten more than twice the same number

52. Five times a number added to the sum of the same number and five

53. The product of six times the sum of negative twelve and a number, all subtracted from three times the difference of the same number and four

54. Seven times the difference of a number and one, all divided by the product of the same number cubed and three

55. Eight times the difference of a number and two, with this result subtracted from sixteen more than twice a number

56. Five multiplied times the sum of a number and twenty-five, with this result divided by the absolute value of negative ten

In exercises 57–66, translate the algebraic expressions into written expressions.

57. $3x^2$

58. $8 - 2x$

59. $\frac{1}{4}(x + 8)$

60. $\dfrac{x - 8}{16}$

61. $x^3 - x^2$

62. $\left(\dfrac{2}{3}x\right)^3$

63. $3(4 - x)$

64. $-\left(\dfrac{x}{10}\right)$

65. $4(x + 6) - 2(x - 7)$

66. $3(x - 7) + 8(2x - 10)$

 ## Looking Back

67. Classify $x^2 + 2x + 1$ as a monomial, binomial, or trinomial.

68. Add $(3x^3 + 2x^2 - 17x + 26) + (-3x^3 + 2x^2 + 17x - 27)$.

69. Subtract $(3x^3 + 2x^2 - 17x + 26) - (-3x^3 + 2x^2 + 17x - 27)$.

70. Multiply $-2x^2y^3 \, (-10x^2y + 20x - 32y)$.

71. Divide $\dfrac{-10x^2 + 6x - 20}{-2x^2}$.

72. Evaluate $\dfrac{x - y}{x^3 + y}$ if $x = -2$ and $y = -3$.

PRACTICE-FOR-SUCCESS ANSWERS

1. -4 is a solution.　　**2.** $\frac{1}{3}$ is a solution.　　**3.** $9(x + 40)$

4. $\dfrac{14}{x} + 12$　　**5.** A number squared subtracted from nine

---

| 7.2 | **SOLVING LINEAR EQUATIONS** |

OBJECTIVES

☐ To use the concept of *basic operation* to solve an equation

☐ To solve linear equations with one variable using one operation

☐ To solve linear equations with one variable using two operations

In the previous section we checked to see if a given number was a solution to an equation. In this section our goal will be to learn how to solve **linear**

equations in one variable. Linear equations in one variable are equations in which the variable has an exponent of 1. In the next chapter the connection will be made to explain why they are called *linear*.

Solving Equations Using Addition

To solve an equation containing one variable we have to isolate the variable, say x, on one side of the equation and a single number on the other side of the equation. To accomplish this, in this section we will use the four fundamental operations to transform equations into other **equivalent equations:** equations that have the same solution. For example

$$9x + 22 = 67 \quad \text{and} \quad 9x = 45 \quad \text{and} \quad x = 5$$

are all equivalent equations because they all have the same solution, 5.

Equations can be transformed into other equivalent equations using addition. If we add the same number to both sides of an equation the resulting equation is equivalent. The equations

$$x = 2 + 4$$

$$x + 10 = 2 + 4 + 10 \qquad \text{10 is added to both sides.}$$

are equivalent equations because they share the same solution, 6. The addition property of equality is the general rule for adding the same number or algebraic expression to both sides of an equation.

ADDITION PROPERTY OF EQUALITY

If $a = b$, then $a + c = b + c$, where a, b, and c are algebraic expressions.

Linear equations in one variable can be solved if we know the basic operation of the expression on either side that contains the variable. In the equation $x - 3 = 19$ the basic operation of the expression that contains the variable is subtraction, so to solve this equation we "undo" the basic operation, subtraction, by using the inverse operation, addition. Here we add 3 so that the left side of the equation reads $x - 3 + 3$, which is the same as $x + 0$, which is equal to x; we have isolated the variable. However, if we add 3 to the left side of the equation, then, according to the addition property of equality, we must also add 3 to the right side of the equation so that both sides of the equation remain equal.

$$x - 3 = 19 \qquad \text{The basic operation is subtraction.}$$

$$x - 3 + 3 = 19 + 3 \qquad \text{Add 3 to both sides.}$$

$$x + 0 = 22 \qquad \text{Simplify both sides.}$$

$$x = 22$$

The original equation $x - 3 = 19$ is transformed into a sequence of equivalent equations leading to the equation $x = 22$; the number 22 is the solution. As we learned in Section 7.1, we can check to make sure that our number is a solution to the equation by substituting 22 for x in the equation as follows:

$$\textbf{Check} \quad x - 3 = 19$$

$$22 - 3 \overset{?}{=} 19 \qquad \text{Replace } x \text{ with 22.}$$

$$19 = 19 \; \checkmark$$

Therefore, we have verified that 22 is the solution to the equation $x - 3 = 19$.

EXAMPLE 1	Use the addition property of equality to solve and check the following equations.

$$\textbf{a.} \; x - 25 = 71 \qquad \textbf{b.} \; x - \frac{3}{4} = \frac{11}{12} \qquad \textbf{c.} \; 18 = x - 22$$

SOLUTION   In each of the equations, undo the basic operation on the side of the equation that contains the variable.

a.

$$x - 25 = 71 \qquad \text{The basic operation is subtraction.}$$

$$x - 25 + 25 = 71 + 25 \qquad \text{Add 25 to both sides.}$$

$$x + 0 = 96 \qquad \text{Simplify both sides.}$$

$$x = 96$$

$$\textbf{Check} \quad x - 25 = 71$$

$$96 - 25 \overset{?}{=} 71 \qquad \text{Replace } x \text{ with 96.}$$

$$71 = 71 \; \checkmark$$

b.

$$x - \frac{3}{4} = \frac{11}{12} \qquad \text{The basic operation is subtraction.}$$

$$x - \frac{3}{4} + \frac{3}{4} = \frac{11}{12} + \frac{3}{4} \qquad \text{Add } \frac{3}{4} \text{ to both sides.}$$

$$x + 0 = \frac{11}{12} + \frac{9}{12} \qquad \text{Add opposites on the left side, and expand } \frac{3}{4} \text{ to } \frac{9}{12}$$
$$\text{on the right side.}$$

$$x = \frac{20}{12} \qquad \text{Simplify the right side.}$$

$$x = \frac{5}{3} \qquad \text{Reduce to lowest terms.}$$

$$\textbf{Check} \quad x - \frac{3}{4} = \frac{11}{12}$$

$$\frac{5}{3} - \frac{3}{4} \overset{?}{=} \frac{11}{12} \qquad \text{Replace } x \text{ with } \frac{5}{3}.$$

$$\frac{20}{12} - \frac{9}{12} \overset{?}{=} \frac{11}{12}$$

$$\frac{11}{12} = \frac{11}{12} \; \checkmark$$

c. When the variable is on the right side of the equation, we can exchange the two sides of the equation (although it is not mandatory) so that the variable is on the left side. Because the quantities on either side of an equal sign are equal, we can always exchange the two sides when it is helpful to do so.

$$18 = x - 22 \qquad \text{The basic operation is subtraction.}$$

$$x - 22 = 18 \qquad \text{Exchange the two sides of the equation.}$$

$$x - 22 + 22 = 18 + 22 \qquad \text{Add 22 to both sides.}$$

$$x - 0 = 40 \qquad \text{Simplify both sides.}$$

$$x = 40$$

Check $18 = x - 22$

$$18 \stackrel{?}{=} 40 - 22 \qquad \text{Replace } x \text{ with 40.}$$

$$18 = 18 \quad \sqrt{} \qquad\qquad\qquad\qquad\qquad ■$$

Solving Equations Using Subtraction

Equations can also be transformed into other equivalent equations using subtraction. If we subtract the same number from both sides of the equation, the resulting equation is equivalent. The equations

$$x = 7 + 8$$

$$x - 12 = 7 + 8 - 12 \qquad \text{12 is subtracted from both sides.}$$

are equivalent because they share the same solution, 15. The subtraction property of equality is the general rule for subtracting the same number or algebraic expression from both sides of an equation.

SUBTRACTION PROPERTY OF EQUALITY

If $a = b$, then $a - c = b - c$, where a, b, and c are algebraic expressions.

In an equation in which the basic operation of the expression containing the variable is addition, we "undo" using the inverse operation, subtraction. In the equation $x + 20 = -15$, we subtract 20 to make the left side of the equation read $x + 20 - 20$, which is the same as $x + 0$, which is equal to x. However, if we subtract 20 on the left side of the equation, then, according to the subtraction property of equality, we must also subtract 20 on the right side of the equation so that both sides of the equation remain equal.

$$x + 20 = -15$$

$$x + 20 - 20 = -15 - 20$$

$$x + 0 = -15 + (-20)$$

$$x = -35$$

The original equation $x + 20 = -15$ is transformed into the equivalent equation $x = -35$, so the number -35 is the solution. We substitute -35 into the original equation to verify that it is the solution.

$$x + 20 = -15$$
$$-35 + 20 \stackrel{?}{=} -15$$
$$-15 = -15 \quad \checkmark$$

Therefore, -35 is the solution to the equation $x + 20 = -15$.

EXAMPLE 2

Use the subtraction property of equality to solve and check the following equations.

a. $x + 86 = -11$ **b.** $0.85 + x = 2.6$ **c.** $-46 = x + (-10)$

SOLUTION   In each of the equations, undo the basic operation on the side of the equation that contains the variable.

a.

$x + 86 = -11$	The basic operation is addition.
$x + 86 - 86 = -11 - 86$	Subtract 86 from both sides.
$x + 86 + (-86) = -11 + (-86)$	Change to adding the opposite.
$x + 0 = -97$	Simplify both sides.
$x = -97$	

Check

$x + 86 = -11$	
$-97 + 86 \stackrel{?}{=} -11$	Replace x with -97.
$-11 = -11 \quad \checkmark$	

b. Use the commutative law for addition on the left side of the equation so that the variable is on the left side of the expression. Commuting the order of the terms places x in a convenient location; then undo the basic operation.

$0.85 + x = 2.6$	The basic operation is addition.
$x + 0.85 = 2.6$	Use the commutative law on the left side.
$x + 0.85 - 0.85 = 2.6 - 0.85$	Subtract 0.85 from both sides.
$x + 0 = 1.75$	Simplify both sides.
$x = 1.75$	

Check

$0.85 + x = 2.6$	
$0.85 + 1.75 \stackrel{?}{=} 2.60$	Replace x with 1.75.
$2.60 = 2.60 \quad \checkmark$	

c. When the variable is on the right side of the equation, it is helpful to exchange the two sides of the equation so that the variable is on the left side.

$$-46 = x + (-10)$$ The basic operation is addition.

$$x + (-10) = -46$$ Exchange the two sides of the equation.

$$x + (-10) - (-10) = -46 - (-10)$$ Subtract -10 from both sides.

$$x + (-10) + (+10) = -46 + (+10)$$ Change to adding the opposite.

$$x + 0 = -36$$ Simplify both sides.

$$x = -36$$

The equation can also be solved using addition:

$$-46 = x + (-10)$$

$$x + (-10) = -46$$

$$x + (-10) + 10 = -46 + 10$$ Adding 10 is identical to subtracting -10.

$$x + 0 = -36$$

$$x = -36$$

Check $-46 = x + (-10)$

$$-46 \stackrel{?}{=} (-36) + (-10)$$

$$-46 = -46 \quad \checkmark$$ ■

Solving Equations Using Multiplication

Equations can also be transformed into other equivalent equations using multiplication. If we multiply both sides of the equation by the same non-zero number, the resulting equation is equivalent. The equations

$$x = 7$$

$$3x = 21$$

are equivalent because they share the same solution, 7. The general rule for multiplying the same number or algebraic expression on both sides of an equation is the multiplication property of equality.

MULTIPLICATION PROPERTY OF EQUALITY

If $a = b$, then $ac = bc$, where a, b, and c are algebraic expressions and $c \neq 0$.

Equations in which the basic operation of the expression containing the variable is division are "undone" using multiplication. In the equation $\frac{x}{7} = 5$, the basic operation is division, so to "undo" the division, we multiply by 7, making the left side of the equation read $7 \cdot \frac{x}{7}$, which is the same as $1 \cdot x$, which equals x. However, according to the multiplication property of equality, if we multiply by 7 on the left side of the equation we must also multiply by 7 on the right side of the equation so that both sides of the equation remain equal.

$$7 \cdot \frac{x}{7} = 7 \cdot 5$$

$$1 \cdot x = 35$$

$$x = 35$$

The original equation $\frac{x}{7} = 5$ is transformed into a sequence of equivalent equations leading to the equation $x = 35$, so the solution is 35. This can be verified by a mental check.

EXAMPLE 3

Use the multiplication property of equality to solve and check the following equations.

a. $\dfrac{x}{-12} = -9$ **b.** $0.7 = \dfrac{x}{0.03}$

SOLUTION

In each of the equations, undo the basic operation on the side of the equation that contains the variable.

a. $\dfrac{x}{-12} = -9$ The basic operation is division.

$(-12) \cdot \dfrac{x}{-12} = (-12) \cdot -9$ Multiply both sides by -12.

$1 \cdot x = 108$ Simplify both sides.

$x = 108$

Check $\dfrac{x}{-12} = -9$

$\dfrac{108}{-12} \overset{?}{=} -9$ Replace x with 108.

$-9 = -9$ √

b. Exchange the two sides of the equation for convenience so that the variable is on the left side.

$0.7 = \dfrac{x}{0.03}$ Exchange both sides.

$\dfrac{x}{0.03} = 0.7$ The basic operation is division.

$(0.03) \cdot \dfrac{x}{0.03} = (0.03) \cdot 0.7$ Multiply both sides by 0.03.

$1 \cdot x = 0.021$ Simplify both sides.

$x = 0.021$

Check $0.7 = \dfrac{x}{0.03}$

$0.7 \stackrel{?}{=} \dfrac{0.021}{0.03}$ Replace x with 0.021.

$0.7 = 0.7$ √   ■

Solving Equations Using Division

Equations can also be transformed into other equivalent equations using division. If we divide into both sides of the equation by the same nonzero number, the resulting equation is equivalent. For example,

$$3x = 30$$

$$x = 10 \quad \text{Both sides are divided by 3.}$$

are equivalent equations because they share the same solution 10. The general rule for dividing the same number or algebraic expression into both sides of an equation is the division property of equality.

DIVISION PROPERTY OF EQUALITY

If $a = b$, then $\dfrac{a}{c} = \dfrac{b}{c}$, where a, b, and c are algebraic expressions and $c \neq 0$.

Equations in which the basic operation of the expression containing the variable is multiplication are "undone" using division. In the equation $9x = -45$ we divide by 9, leaving $\dfrac{9x}{9}$, which is the same as $1 \cdot x$, which is equal to x. According to the division property of equality, if we divide by 9 on the left side of the equation we must also divide by 9 on the right side of the equation so that both sides of the equation remain equal.

$$\frac{\cancel{9}x}{\cancel{9}} = \frac{-45}{9}$$

$$1 \cdot x = -5$$

$$x = -5$$

The original equation $9x = -45$ is transformed into the equivalent equation $x = -5$ so -5 is the solution. This can be verified by checking the problem mentally.

EXAMPLE 4

Use the division property of equality to solve and check the following equations.

a. $1{,}000 = -20x$ **b.** $0.25x = 40$ **c.** $-x = -3$

SOLUTION   In each of the equations, undo the basic operation on the side of the equation that contains the variable.

a. Equations can be solved with the variable on the right side, although it is customary to put the variable on the left side.

$$1,000 = -20x$$ The basic operation is multiplication.

$$\frac{1,000}{-20} = \frac{-20x}{-20}$$ Divide both sides by -20.

$$-50 = 1 \cdot x$$ Simplify both sides.

$$-50 = x$$

The equation $-50 = x$ is equivalent to $x = -50$. In either case the equation states that the solution is -50.

Check $1,000 = -20x$

$$1,000 \stackrel{?}{=} -20 \cdot (-50)$$ Replace x with -50.

$$1,000 = 1,000 \quad \sqrt{}$$

b. $0.25x = 40$ The basic operation is multiplication.

$$\frac{0.25x}{0.25} = \frac{40}{0.25}$$ Divide both sides by 0.25.

$$1 \cdot x = 160$$ Simplify both sides.

$$x = 160$$

Check $0.25x = 40$

$$0.25 \cdot 160 = 40$$ Replace x with 160.

$$40 = 40 \quad \sqrt{}$$

c. The opposite of x, $-x$, is equal to $-1 \cdot x$. It is sometimes helpful to write $-x$ as $-1x$. Because the basic operation of the expression $-1x$ is multiplication, we can divide both sides by -1 to solve the equation.

$$-x = -3$$

$$-1x = -3$$ $-x = -1x$

$$\frac{-1x}{-1} = \frac{-3}{-1}$$ Divide both sides by -1.

$$1 \cdot x = 3$$ Simplify both sides.

$$x = 3$$

Check $-x = -3$

$$-(3) \stackrel{?}{=} -3$$ Replace x with 3.

$$-3 = -3 \quad \sqrt{}$$ ■

Sometimes equations have a fraction as the coefficient of the variable, such as $\frac{1}{2}x = 8$. Because the basic operation is multiplication, we could divide both sides by $\frac{1}{2}$. However, to avoid writing a complex fraction, we can multiply both sides by $2 = \frac{2}{1}$, which is the same as dividing by $\frac{1}{2}$. We are thus multiplying both sides by the reciprocal of the fractional coefficient. This technique can be used whenever the basic operation of the expression is multiplication and the coefficient of the variable is a fraction.

$$\frac{1}{2}x = 8 \qquad \text{The basic operation is multiplication.}$$

$$\frac{2}{1} \cdot \frac{1}{2}x = \frac{2}{1} \cdot 8 \qquad \text{Multiply both sides by the reciprocal}$$
$$\text{of the fractional coefficient } \frac{1}{2}.$$

$$1 \cdot x = 16 \qquad \text{The product of reciprocals is 1.}$$

$$x = 16$$

EXAMPLE 5

Solve and check $\frac{7}{8}x = -49$.

SOLUTION   When the basic operation is multiplication and the coefficient of the variable is a fraction, instead of dividing both sides by the fraction, multiply both sides by the reciprocal of the fraction.

$$\frac{7}{8}x = -49$$

$$\frac{8}{7} \cdot \frac{7}{8}x = \frac{8}{7} \cdot (-49) \qquad \text{Multiply both sides by the reciprocal of } \frac{7}{8}.$$

$$1 \cdot x = -56 \qquad \text{Simplify both sides.}$$
$$x = -56$$

Check $\frac{7}{8}x = -49$

$$\frac{7}{8} \cdot (-56) \stackrel{?}{=} -49 \qquad \text{Replace } x \text{ with } -56.$$

$$-49 = -49 \quad \sqrt{} \qquad\qquad\qquad\qquad ■$$

In the previous equations only one operation was necessary, but in most equations several operations may be needed. For example, $7x + 22 = 36$ can be solved by using two operations. The first operation we use, subtraction, undoes the basic operation of the expression $7x + 22$.

$$7x + 22 = 36 \qquad \text{The basic operation is addition.}$$

$$7x + 22 - 22 = 36 - 22 \qquad \text{Subtract 22 from both sides.}$$

$$7x = 14 \qquad \text{Simplify both sides.}$$

The second operation we use, division, undoes the basic operation of the resulting expression $7x$.

$$7x = 14 \qquad \text{The basic operation is multiplication.}$$

$$\frac{7x}{7} = \frac{14}{7} \qquad \text{Divide both sides by 7.}$$

$$1 \cdot x = 2 \qquad \text{Simplify both sides.}$$

$$x = 2$$

| **EXAMPLE 6** | Solve and check the following equations, which involve more than one operation. |

$$\textbf{a. } -8x + (-21) = -93 \qquad \textbf{b. } \frac{x}{7} + 20 = -32 \qquad \textbf{c. } \frac{2}{3}x - 8 = 28$$

SOLUTION In each of the equations, begin by undoing the basic operation.

a.

$-8x + (-21) = -93$	The basic operation is addition.
$-8x + (-21) - (-21) = -93 - (-21)$	Subtract -21 from both sides.
$-8x + (-21) + 21 = -93 + 21$	Change to adding the opposite.
$-8x = -72$	The basic operation is now multiplication.
$\dfrac{-8x}{-8} = \dfrac{-72}{-8}$	Divide both sides by -8.
$x = 9$	

Check

$-8x + (-21) = -93$	
$-8 \cdot 9 + (-21) \stackrel{?}{=} -93$	Replace x with 9.
$-72 + (-21) \stackrel{?}{=} -93$	
$-93 = -93 \quad \checkmark$	

b.

$\dfrac{x}{7} + 20 = -32$	The basic operation is addition.
$\dfrac{x}{7} + 20 - 20 = -32 - 20$	Subtract 20 from both sides.
$\dfrac{x}{7} = -52$	The basic operation is now division.
$7 \cdot \dfrac{x}{7} = 7 \cdot -52$	Multiply both sides by 7.
$x = -364$	Simplify both sides.

Check

$\dfrac{x}{7} + 20 = -32$	
$\dfrac{-364}{7} + 20 \stackrel{?}{=} -32$	Replace x with -364.
$-52 + 20 \stackrel{?}{=} -32$	
$-32 = -32 \quad \checkmark$	

c.

$\dfrac{2}{3}x - 8 = 28$	The basic operation is subtraction.
$\dfrac{2}{3}x - 8 + 8 = 28 + 8$	Add 8 to both sides.
$\dfrac{2}{3}x = 36$	The basic operation is now multiplication but the coefficient is a fraction, so we multiply by the reciprocal.

$$\frac{3}{2} \cdot \frac{2}{3}x = \frac{3}{2} \cdot 36$$

Multiply both sides by the reciprocal of the fractional coefficient.

$$1 \cdot x = 54$$

Simplify both sides.

$$x = 54$$

Check $\quad \frac{2}{3}x - 8 = 28$

$$\frac{2}{3} \cdot 54 - 8 \stackrel{?}{=} 28$$

Replace x with 54.

$$36 - 8 \stackrel{?}{=} 28$$

$$28 = 28 \quad \checkmark$$

■

P R A C T I C E   F O R   S U C C E S S

Solve and check the following equations.

Practice 1. $\quad x - \frac{7}{10} = -\frac{13}{40}$ **Practice 2.** $\quad 0.78 = x + 0.8$ **Practice 3.** $\quad \frac{x}{5} = -85$

Practice 4. $\quad 0.15x = 1.95$ **Practice 5.** $\quad -\frac{2}{9}x = -20$ **Practice 6.** $\quad \frac{x}{7} + 29 = 40$

Practice 7. $\quad 62 = 6x + 60$

EXERCISES 7.2

In exercises 1–58, solve and check the equations.

1. $x + 18 = 102$ **2.** $96 + x = -1{,}728$

3. $202 = x - 98$ **4.** $x - 22 = -7$

5. $-12 = \dfrac{x}{-17}$ **6.** $\dfrac{x}{-15} = 19$

7. $23x = -138$ **8.** $-42 = -8x$

9. $x + \dfrac{2}{3} = \dfrac{3}{4}$ **10.** $x + \dfrac{9}{10} = -\dfrac{7}{15}$

11. $\dfrac{3}{7} = x - \dfrac{4}{7}$ **12.** $x - \dfrac{7}{12} = -\dfrac{7}{9}$

13. $\dfrac{1}{12}x = 60$ **14.** $\dfrac{1}{9}x = -171$

15. $-75 = \dfrac{3}{5}x$ **16.** $84 = \dfrac{3}{7}x$

17. $9 = x + 0.782$ **18.** $x + 0.61 = -7.4$

19. $x - 0.898 = -10$

20. $16.992 = x - 4.6$

21. $0.28x = 67.2$

22. $-0.52x = 4.628$

23. $-27 = \dfrac{x}{0.9}$

24. $68 = \dfrac{x}{-0.0004}$

25. $9x + 21 = 3$

26. $74 = 13x - 4$

27. $4x + 7 = -93$

28. $5x + 16 = 66$

29. $\dfrac{1}{5}x + 20 = 23$

30. $\dfrac{3}{4}x - 12 = 36$

31. $-80 = 0.2x - 42$

32. $0.07x + 1.38 = -0.65$

33. $16 + 1.25x = 20$

34. $52 + 2.8x = -4$

35. $\dfrac{x}{4} + 7 = 0$

36. $\dfrac{x}{8} - 9 = 0$

37. $-x + (-42) = 42$

38. $-x + 18 = 53$

39. $17 - x = 20$

40. $101 - x = 44$

41. $108 = \dfrac{4}{5}x - 60$

42. $-74 = \dfrac{3}{7}x + (-50)$

43. $\dfrac{x}{0.6} + 7.2 = -3$

44. $-12 = \dfrac{x}{0.5} - 3.5$

45. $\dfrac{1}{2}x + 0.7 = 0.5$

46. $\dfrac{1}{3}x - 0.8 = 0.7$

47. $6x + \dfrac{1}{2} = 3\dfrac{1}{2}$

48. $-5x + 16\dfrac{1}{2} = 31\dfrac{1}{2}$

49. $0.8x + 0.008 = 0.0008$

50. $12 = 0.4x + 0.04$

51. $\dfrac{x}{-11} - 7 = 6$

52. $\dfrac{x}{9} + 8 = 1$

53. $-113 = 7x + (-22)$

54. $-44 + 15x = 16$

55. $\dfrac{1}{2}x - 0.6 = 0.28$

56. $\dfrac{1}{4}x + 2.98 = 3.07$

57. $196 = 49x - (-196)$

58. $85 = 17x - 85$

☥ Looking Back

59. Explain why 30×10^7 is not in scientific notation.

60. Explain why 2.48×10^{-3} is in scientific notation.

61. The average distance from the earth to the sun is called an astronomical unit, AU. One AU is equal to 93 million miles. Express one AU in scientific notation.

62. One AU is also equal to 150 million kilometers. Express the number of kilometers in one AU in scientific notation.

In problems 63 and 64, write the product or quotient in both scientific notation and standard notation.

63. $(3.6 \times 10^6)\,(3 \times 10^{-6})$

64. $\dfrac{2.22 \times 10^{-5}}{6 \times 10^{-6}}$

65. Explain why 4 raised to the 0 power is equal to 1.

PRACTICE-FOR-SUCCESS ANSWERS

1. $\dfrac{3}{8}$ **2.** -0.02 **3.** -425 **4.** 13 **5.** 90 **6.** 77 **7.** $\dfrac{1}{3}$

7.3 ## MORE ON SOLVING EQUATIONS

OBJECTIVES

- To solve equations by combining like terms
- To solve equations with the variable on both sides
- To solve equations containing grouping symbols
- To solve equations by clearing fractions

In the previous section we examined methods to solve equations in which the variable appeared on only one side of the equation. In this section we will continue to solve equations, but we will work with the variable on both sides of the equation. We will also solve equations that contain grouping symbols and equations that may contain one or more fractions.

Combining Like Terms

In some equations, like terms may appear on either or both sides of the equation. When this occurs we combine like terms before using any of the properties of equality to undo the basic operation. For example, in the equation $2x + 7x + 10x = 152$ we first combine the like terms on the left side of the equation, generating the following series of equivalent equations.

$$2x + 7x + 10x = 152$$
$$9x + 10x = 152$$
$$19x = 152$$

At this point we can apply the division property of equality and undo the basic operation.

$$\frac{\cancel{19}x}{\cancel{19}} = \frac{152}{19}$$

$$x = 8$$

To check the answer, we substitute 8 for x in the original equation $2x + 7x + 10x = 152$.

Check $2x + 7x + 10x = 152$

$$2 \cdot 8 + 7 \cdot 8 + 10 \cdot 8 \stackrel{?}{=} 152$$

$$16 + 56 + 80 \stackrel{?}{=} 152$$

$$72 + 80 \stackrel{?}{=} 152$$

$$152 = 152 \quad \checkmark$$

Had we substituted 8 for x in one of the subsequent equivalent equations, we would not have been checking the original equation and might have concluded that the answer was a solution when it was not.

| **EXAMPLE 1** | Solve the following equations by combining like terms. |

a. $9x + 6x - 16x = 26$

b. $29 + (-8) = 0.25x - x$

c. $11x + 5x - 12 = 65 + 21$

SOLUTION **a.** $9x + 6x - 16x = 26$

$15x - 16x = 26$ Combine like terms.

$-1x = 26$ Combine like terms again.

$$\frac{\cancel{-1}x}{\cancel{-1}} = \frac{26}{-1}$$ Divide both sides by -1.

$$x = -26$$

Check $9x + 6x - 16x = 26$

$9 \cdot (-26) + 6 \cdot (-26) - 16 \cdot (-26) \stackrel{?}{=} 26$ Replace x with -26.

$$-234 + (-156) - (-416) \stackrel{?}{=} 26$$

$$-234 + (-156) + 416 \stackrel{?}{=} 26$$

$$-390 + 416 \stackrel{?}{=} 26$$

$$26 = 26 \quad \checkmark$$

b. $29 + (-8) = 0.25x - x$

$21 = 0.25x - 1.00x$ Simplify on the left: Recall that $x = 1x = 1.00x$.

$21 = -0.75x$ Combine like terms.

$$\frac{21}{-0.75} = \frac{-0.75x}{-0.75}$$ Divide both sides by -0.75.

$$-28 = x$$

Check $29 + (-8) = 0.25x - x$

$29 + (-8) \stackrel{?}{=} 0.25 \cdot (-28) - (-28)$ Replace x with -28.

$29 + (-8) \stackrel{?}{=} 0.25 \cdot (-28) + 28$

$21 \stackrel{?}{=} 0.25 \cdot (-28) + 28$

$21 \stackrel{?}{=} -7 + 28$

$21 = 21$ $\checkmark$

c. $11x + 5x - 12 = 63 + 21$

$16x - 12 = 84$ Combine like terms on both sides.

$16x - 12 + 12 = 84 + 12$ Add 12 to both sides.

$16x = 96$ Simplify both sides.

$$\frac{\cancel{16}x}{\cancel{16}} = \frac{96}{16}$$ Divide both sides by 16.

$x = 6$

Check $11x + 5x - 12 = 63 + 21$

$11 \cdot 6 + 5 \cdot 6 - 12 \stackrel{?}{=} 84$ Replace x with 6.

$66 + 30 - 12 \stackrel{?}{=} 84$

$96 - 12 \stackrel{?}{=} 84$

$84 = 84$ $\checkmark$ ■

Equations with Variables on Both Sides

Frequently, variables appear on both sides of the equation, and when this happens our goal continues to be to isolate the variable on one side of the equation. In the equation $6x + 8 = 2x + 20$ each side has a term containing a variable, which we will call a **variable term.** One of the variable terms needs to be eliminated from either side so that only one side has an expression with the variable. When both of the variable terms have a positive coefficient, as in $6x + 8 = 2x + 20$, it is easiest to eliminate the term with the smaller coefficient, $2x$, using the subtraction property of equality as follows.

$$6x + 8 = 2x + 20$$

$$6x + 8 - 2x = 2x + 20 - 2x$$

$$4x + 8 = 20$$

We then simplify both sides of the equation by combining like terms and solve the resulting equivalent equation, which now has a variable term only on the left side. We proceed by undoing the basic operation of the algebraic expression on the left side.

$4x + 8 = 20$ The basic operation is addition.

$4x + 8 - 8 = 20 - 8$ Subtract 8 from both sides.

$4x = 12$ Simplify both sides of the equation.

$$\frac{\cancel{4}x}{\cancel{4}} = \frac{12}{4}$$ Divide both sides by 4.

$x = 3$

The reason we eliminate the variable term with the smaller coefficient is so that the coefficient of the variable term of the subsequent equivalent equation remains positive. It is not incorrect to subtract so that the isolated variable term has a negative coefficient; however, we usually arrange the equations so that the isolated variable term has a positive coefficient.

We have seen the case in which the variable terms on both sides had positive coefficients. Now we will consider variable terms that have negative coefficients, such as in $-5x + 3 = -2x + 9$. So that the isolated variable term of the subsequent equivalent equation has a positive coefficient, we eliminate the variable term with the smaller coefficient. Since $-5 < -2$ we eliminate the term $-5x$ using the addition property of equality by adding $5x$ to both sides.

$$-5x + 3 = -2x + 9$$
$$-5x + 3 + 5x = -2x + 9 + 5x$$
$$3 = 3x + 9$$

As in the previous case, by eliminating the variable term with the smaller coefficient, the subsequent equivalent equation has a variable term with a positive coefficient. Solving this equation, we find that $x = -2$.

The final case is one in which one variable term has a positive coefficient and the other has a negative coefficient, as in the equation $6x + 22 = -4x - 8$. Again, we want to eliminate the variable term with the smaller coefficient, and because a negative number is always less than a positive number we eliminate the term with the negative coefficient $-4x$ using the addition property of equality.

$$6x + 22 = -4x - 8$$
$$6x + 22 + 4x = -4x - 8 + 4x$$
$$10x + 22 = -8$$

As in all cases, because we eliminated the variable term with the smaller coefficient, the subsequent equivalent equation has a variable term with a positive coefficient. We can establish a general rule for deciding which variable term to eliminate when each side has a variable term.

DETERMINING WHICH VARIABLE TERM TO ELIMINATE

When a linear equation contains a variable term on both sides, eliminate the variable term with the smaller coefficient using either the addition or subtraction property of equality.

EXAMPLE 2

Solve and check the following equations, which have variable terms on both sides.

a. $7x + 3 = 5x - 9$

b. $-15x + 19 = 76 - 12x$

c. $8x - 2x = -12x + 36 - 72$

SOLUTION   **a.** $7x + 3 = 5x - 9$ Each side has a variable term.

$7x + 3 - 5x = 5x - 9 - 5x$ Eliminate the variable term
                                             with the smaller coefficient.

$2x + 3 = -9$ The basic operation is addition.

$2x + 3 - 3 = -9 - 3$ Subtract 3 from both sides.

$2x = -12$ The basic operation is now
                                         multiplication.

$$\frac{\cancel{2}x}{\cancel{2}} = \frac{-12}{2}$$ Divide both sides by 2.

$x = -6$

Check $7x + 3 = 5x - 9$

$7 \cdot (-6) + 3 \stackrel{?}{=} 5 \cdot (-6) - 9$ Replace x with -6.

$-42 + 3 \stackrel{?}{=} -30 - 9$

$-42 + 3 \stackrel{?}{=} -30 + (-9)$

$-39 = -39$ $\sqrt{}$

b. When each side has a variable term and either side contains a subtraction, change to adding the opposite before deciding which variable term has the smaller coefficient.

$-15x + 19 = 76 - 12x$ Each side has a variable term.

$-15x + 19 = 76 + (-12x)$ Change to adding the opposite.

$-15x + 19 + 15x = 76 - 12x + 15x$ Eliminate the variable term
                                             with the smaller coefficient.

$19 = 76 + 3x$ The basic operation is addition.

$19 - 76 = 76 + 3x - 76$ Subtract 76 from both sides.

$-57 = 3x$ The basic operation is now
                                         multiplication.

$$\frac{-57}{3} = \frac{\cancel{3}x}{\cancel{3}}$$ Divide both sides by 3.

$-19 = x$

Check $-15x + 19 = 76 - 12x$

$-15 \cdot (-19) + 19 \stackrel{?}{=} 76 - 12 \cdot (-19)$

$285 + 19 \stackrel{?}{=} 76 + 228$

$304 = 304$ $\sqrt{}$

c. When either side of an equation contains like terms, combine them first.

$8x - 2x = -12x + 36 - 72$ Each side has like terms.

$6x = -12x - 36$ Combine like terms.

$6x + 12x = -12x + 12x - 36$ Eliminate the variable term
                                         with the smaller coefficient.

$18x = -36$ The basic operation is now
                                         multiplication.

$$\frac{\cancel{18}x}{\cancel{18}} = \frac{-36}{18}$$ Divide both sides by 18.

$x = -2$

Check $6x = -12x + 36 - 72$

$6 \cdot (-2) \stackrel{?}{=} -12 \cdot (-2) + 36 - 72$ Replace x with -2.

$-12 \stackrel{?}{=} 24 + 36 - 72$

$-12 \stackrel{?}{=} 24 + 36 + (-72)$

$-12 \stackrel{?}{=} 60 + (-72)$

$-12 = -12$ ✓   ■

Equations Containing Grouping Symbols

Linear equations sometimes contain grouping symbols; in the equation $4(2x + 5) = 92$, the left side is an expression with a grouping symbol. We will solve this equation using two different methods. The first method is to undo the basic operation on the side that contains the variable. In this equation, the basic operation is multiplication by 4, so our first step is to undo this operation by dividing both sides by 4.

$4(2x + 5) = 92$ Divide both sides by 4.

$\dfrac{\cancel{4}(2x + 5)}{\cancel{4}} = \dfrac{92}{4}$ Simplify.

$2x + 5 = 23$ The basic operation is addition.
Subtract 5 from both sides.

$2x + 5 - 5 = 23 - 5$ Simplify.

$2x = 18$ Divide by 2 on both sides.

$x = 9$

An alternate method that is more commonly used is to begin by applying the distributive law, which removes the grouping symbol.

$4(2x + 5) = 92$

$4 \cdot 2x + 4 \cdot 5 = 92$ Apply the distributive law.

$8x + 20 = 92$ The basic operation is addition.

$8x + 20 - 20 = 92 - 20$ Subtract 20 from both sides.

$8x = 72$ The basic operation is multiplication.

$\dfrac{\cancel{8}x}{\cancel{8}} = \dfrac{72}{8}$ Divide both sides by 8.

$x = 9$

Which method should be used depends on the context of the problem. In most problems the variable appears more than once in the equation, and in these cases applying the distributive law first to eliminate the grouping symbols is preferable. When the variable occurs only once in the equation, the first method, which emphasizes undoing the basic operation, can be used.

SOLVING AN EQUATION CONTAINING GROUPING SYMBOLS

1. **Apply the distributive law to remove the grouping symbol on either or both sides of the equation.**
2. **Solve the resulting equivalent equation.**

| **EXAMPLE 3** | Solve and check the following equations containing grouping symbols. |

a. $8(3x - 5) - 17x = 23$

b. $12(x - 4) = -8(x + 16)$

c. $-51 = 3(2x + 7) - (x - 3)$

SOLUTION **a.** $8(3x - 5) - 17x = 23$

$$24x - 40 - 17x = 23 \qquad \text{Apply the distributive law.}$$

$$7x - 40 = 23 \qquad \text{Combine like terms.}$$

$$7x - 40 + 40 = 23 + 40 \qquad \text{Add 40 to both sides.}$$

$$7x = 63 \qquad \text{The basic operation is now multiplication.}$$

$$\frac{7x}{7} = \frac{63}{7} \qquad \text{Divide both sides by 7.}$$

$$x = 9$$

Check $8(3x - 5) - 17x = 23$

$$8(3 \cdot 9 - 5) - 17 \cdot 9 \overset{?}{=} 23 \qquad \text{Replace } x \text{ with 9.}$$

$$8(27 - 5) - 17 \cdot 9 \overset{?}{=} 23$$

$$8(22) - 17 \cdot 9 \overset{?}{=} 23$$

$$176 - 17 \cdot 9 \overset{?}{=} 23$$

$$176 - 153 \overset{?}{=} 23$$

$$23 = 23 \quad \checkmark$$

b. $12(x - 4) = -8(x + 16)$

$$12x - 48 = -8x - 128 \qquad \text{Apply the distributive law.}$$

$$12x - 48 + 8x = -8x - 128 + 8x \qquad \text{Add } 8x \text{ to both sides.}$$

$$20x - 48 = -128 \qquad \text{The basic operation is subtraction.}$$

$$20x - 48 + 48 = -128 + 48 \qquad \text{Add 48 to both sides.}$$

$$20x = -80 \qquad \text{The basic operation is now multiplication.}$$

$$\frac{20x}{20} = \frac{-80}{20} \qquad \text{Divide both sides by 20.}$$

$$x = -4$$

Check $12(x - 4) = -8(x + 16)$

$$12(-4 - 4) \overset{?}{=} -8(-4 + 16) \qquad \text{Replace } x \text{ with } -4.$$

$$12(-8) \overset{?}{=} -8(12)$$

$$-96 = -96 \quad \checkmark$$

c. Recall that 1 is a factor of any polynomial. Before we subtract polynomials, when no factor is present in front of the second polynomial, it is helpful to insert a 1 as the factor before applying the distributive law.

$$-51 = 3(2x + 7) - (x - 3)$$

$$-51 = 3(2x + 7) + -(x - 3)$$

$$-51 = 3(2x + 7) + -1(x - 3) \qquad \text{Insert the 1.}$$

$$-51 = 6x + 21 - x + 3 \qquad \text{Apply the distributive law twice.}$$

$$-51 = 5x + 24$$ The basic operation is addition.

$$-51 - 24 = 5x + 24 - 24$$ Subtract 24 from both sides.

$$-75 = 5x$$ The basic operation is now multiplication.

$$\frac{-75}{5} = \frac{\cancel{5}x}{\cancel{5}}$$ Divide both sides by 5.

$$-15 = x$$

Check $-51 = 3(2x + 7) - (x - 3)$

$$-51 \stackrel{?}{=} 3[2(-15) + 7] - (-15 - 3) \quad \text{Replace } x \text{ with } -15.$$

$$-51 \stackrel{?}{=} 3(-30 + 7) - [-15 + (-3)]$$

$$-51 \stackrel{?}{=} 3(-23) - (-18)$$

$$-51 \stackrel{?}{=} -69 - (-18)$$

$$-51 \stackrel{?}{=} -69 + (+18)$$

$$-51 = -51 \quad \sqrt{}$$ ■

Equations Containing Fractions

Linear equations sometimes contain fractions. As fractions usually cause some difficulties, we can clear the equations of fractions to make an equivalent equation that is easier to solve. Recall that the multiplication property of equality allows us to multiply both sides of the equation by the same nonzero number; to clear an equation of fractions, we can multiply both sides of the equation by the least common denominator (LCD) of the fractions in the equation.

For example, to solve the equation $\frac{x}{2} - \frac{x}{5} = 6$, we first want to eliminate the fractions so we multiply both sides by the LCD of 2 and 5, which is 10. Each denominator will divide evenly into 10 and the resulting equivalent equation will then contain no fractions.

$$\frac{x}{2} - \frac{x}{5} = 6$$ The expression on the left is a difference, which requires grouping symbols before multiplying on both sides by 10.

$$10 \cdot \left(\frac{x}{2} - \frac{x}{5}\right) = 10 \cdot 6$$ Apply the multiplication property of equality; multiply by the LCD of the fractions.

$$10 \cdot \left(\frac{x}{2}\right) - 10 \cdot \left(\frac{x}{5}\right) = 10 \cdot 6$$ Apply the distributive law.

$$\frac{10x}{2} - \frac{10x}{5} = 60$$ Multiply.

$$5x - 2x = 60$$ Simplify.

$$3x = 60$$ The basic operation is now multiplication.

$$\frac{\cancel{3}x}{\cancel{3}} = \frac{60}{3}$$ Divide both sides by 3.

$$x = 20$$

By replacing x with 20 in the original equation $\dfrac{x}{2} - \dfrac{x}{5} = 6$, we can mentally verify that 20 is the solution.

SOLVING A LINEAR EQUATION CONTAINING FRACTIONS

1. **If either side of the equation consists of a basic sum or difference, enclose that side in parentheses.**
2. **Determine the LCD of all the fractions that appear in the equation.**
3. **Multiply both sides of the equation by the LCD to clear the fractions.**
4. **Solve the resulting equivalent equation.**

EXAMPLE 4   Solve and check the following equations.

a. $\dfrac{x}{2} + \dfrac{x}{4} + \dfrac{x}{6} = -11$ **b.** $\dfrac{3}{4}x + 10 = \dfrac{7}{10}x + 6$

c. $\dfrac{1}{7}(3x + 2) = \dfrac{2}{3}$ **d.** $-\dfrac{11}{9}x = -\dfrac{33}{8}$

SOLUTION   **a.**

$$\frac{x}{2} + \frac{x}{4} + \frac{x}{6} = -11$$

$$12 \cdot \left(\frac{x}{2} + \frac{x}{4} + \frac{x}{6} \right) = 12 \cdot (-11)$$ Apply the multiplication property of equality; multiply by the LCD of the fractions.

$$12 \cdot \left(\frac{x}{2} \right) + 12 \cdot \left(\frac{x}{4} \right) + 12 \cdot \left(\frac{x}{6} \right) = 12 \cdot (-11)$$ Apply the distributive law.

$$\frac{12x}{2} + \frac{12x}{4} + \frac{12x}{6} = -132$$ Multiply.

$$6x + 3x + 2x = -132$$ Simplify fractions.

$$11x = -132$$ The basic operation is now multiplication.

$$\frac{\cancel{11}x}{\cancel{11}} = \frac{-132}{11}$$ Divide both sides by 11.

$$x = -12$$

Check $$\frac{x}{2} + \frac{x}{4} + \frac{x}{6} = -11$$

$$\frac{-12}{2} + \frac{-12}{4} + \frac{-12}{6} \overset{?}{=} -11$$ Replace x with -12.

$$-6 + (-3) + (-2) \overset{?}{=} -11$$

$$-11 = -11 \quad \checkmark$$

b.
$$\frac{3}{4}x + 10 = \frac{7}{10}x + 6$$

$$20 \cdot \left(\frac{3}{4}x + 10\right) = 20 \cdot \left(\frac{7}{10}x + 6\right)$$
    Apply the multiplication property of equality; multiply by the LCD of the fractions.

$$20 \cdot \left(\frac{3}{4}x\right) + 20 \cdot 10 = 20 \cdot \left(\frac{7}{10}x\right) + 20 \cdot 6$$
    Apply the distributive law.

$$\frac{60}{4}x + 200 = \frac{140}{10}x + 120$$
    Multiply.

$$15x + 200 = 14x + 120$$
    Simplify fractions.

$$15x + 200 - 14x = 14x + 120 - 14x$$
    Eliminate the variable term with the smaller coefficient.

$$x + 200 = 120$$
    The basic operation is now addition.

$$x + 200 - 200 = 120 - 200$$
    Subtract 200 from both sides.

$$x = -80$$

Check
$$\frac{3}{4}x + 10 = \frac{7}{10}x + 6$$

$$\frac{3}{4}(-80) + 10 \stackrel{?}{=} \frac{7}{10}(-80) + 6$$
    Replace x with -80.

$$-60 + 10 \stackrel{?}{=} -56 + 6$$

$$-50 = -50 \quad \checkmark$$

c.
$$\frac{1}{7}(3x + 2) = \frac{2}{3}$$

$$\frac{1}{7} \cdot (3x) + \frac{1}{7} \cdot (2) = \frac{2}{3}$$
    Apply the distributive law.

$$\frac{3}{7}x + \frac{2}{7} = \frac{2}{3}$$
    Multiply.

$$21 \cdot \left(\frac{3}{7}x + \frac{2}{7}\right) = 21 \cdot \left(\frac{2}{3}\right)$$
    Apply the multiplication property of equality; multiply by the LCD of the fractions.

$$21 \cdot \left(\frac{3}{7}x\right) + 21 \cdot \left(\frac{2}{7}\right) = 21 \cdot \left(\frac{2}{3}\right)$$
    Apply the distributive law.

$$\frac{63}{7}x + \frac{42}{7} = \frac{42}{3}$$
    Multiply.

$$9x + 6 = 14$$
    Simplify fractions.

$$9x + 6 - 6 = 14 - 6$$
    Subtract 6 from both sides.

$$9x = 8$$
    The basic operation is now multiplication.

$$\frac{\cancel{9}x}{\cancel{9}} = \frac{8}{9} \qquad \text{Divide both sides by 9.}$$

$$x = \frac{8}{9}$$

Check
$$\frac{1}{7}(3x + 2) = \frac{2}{3}$$

$$\frac{1}{7}\left[3 \cdot \left(\frac{8}{9}\right) + 2\right] \stackrel{?}{=} \frac{2}{3} \qquad \text{Replace } x \text{ with } \frac{8}{9}.$$

$$\frac{1}{7}\left(\frac{8}{3} + 2\right) \stackrel{?}{=} \frac{2}{3}$$

$$\frac{1}{7}\left(\frac{8}{3} + \frac{6}{3}\right) \stackrel{?}{=} \frac{2}{3} \qquad \text{Expand } \frac{2}{1} \text{ so that it has a denominator of 3.}$$

$$\frac{1}{7}\left(\frac{14}{3}\right) \stackrel{?}{=} \frac{2}{3}$$

$$\frac{2}{3} = \frac{2}{3} \quad \checkmark$$

d. When an equation has only one variable term with a fractional coefficient, it can be solved by multiplying both sides by the LCD of the fractions or by multiplying both sides by the reciprocal of the fractional coefficient. Usually, the latter will require fewer steps.

Method 1
$$-\frac{11}{9}x = \frac{-33}{8}$$

$$72 \cdot \left(-\frac{11}{9}x\right) = 72 \cdot \left(-\frac{33}{8}\right)$$

$$8 \cdot (-11x) = 9 \cdot (-33)$$

$$-88x = -297$$

$$\frac{\cancel{-88}x}{\cancel{-88}} = \frac{-297}{-88}$$

$$x = \frac{27}{8}$$

Method 2
$$-\frac{11}{9}x = -\frac{33}{8}$$

$$-\frac{9}{11} \cdot \left(-\frac{11}{9}x\right) = -\frac{9}{11} \cdot \left(-\frac{33}{8}\right)$$

$$x = \frac{27}{8}$$

Because we solved the equation with two different valid methods and each yielded $\frac{27}{8}$, we feel confident that it is the solution. Using two different valid methods to solve a math problem is another way to check our work.   ■

Solve and check the following equations.

Practice 1. $4x + 5x + 9x = 198$ **Practice 2.** $7x + 12 = -3x - 13$

Practice 3. $88 = 7(x + 4) + 3(2x + 7)$ **Practice 4.** $\dfrac{x}{8} + \dfrac{x}{3} = -22$

Practice 5. $\dfrac{2}{3}x + 12 = \dfrac{1}{4}x - 8$

EXERCISES 7.3

In exercises 1–70, solve and check the equations.

1. $-5x - 3x + 6x = 18$
2. $12x - 14x - 16x = -54$
3. $4x - 5x = 28 - 23.6$
4. $9x - 8x = 7 - (-5.1)$
5. $42 + (-16) = x - 0.6x$
6. $x - 0.35x = 13$
7. $8x + 7x - 22 = 38$
8. $17x - 20x + 42 = -9$
9. $4.3x + 6.2x + 8 = -34$
10. $26 = 9.8x - 1.8x + 2$
11. $8x - 11 = -12x - 101$
12. $7x + 15 = 13x - 75$
13. $10x + 16 = 14x + 18$
14. $19x - 22 = 12x + 139$
15. $-16x + 32 = -20x$
16. $-27x + 70 = 8x$
17. $8x + 15 + 13 = 5x - 2$
18. $x + 3x - 96 = 3x - 14$
19. $6x - 13 + 27 = 7x + 42$
20. $5x + 82 = 7x + 46 + 36$
21. $22x - 13x = -9x + 160 - 52$
22. $14x - 19x = -25x - 84 - 136$
23. $16x + 12 - x = 15 - x - 19$
24. $6x + 27 + 9x = 12 + 6x - 30$
25. $4.2x = 112 + 1.4x$
26. $-1.9x + 63.8 = -3.9x$
27. $8.7x + 49 = 6.7x + 21$
28. $12.5x - 26.3 = -12.5x - 1.3$
29. $-3.8x + 2.6 + 5.4 = 4.2x - 72$
30. $6.2x + 12.8 + 36.2 = 8x - 41$
31. $7(x + 3) = 49$
32. $9(x + 2) = -45$
33. $8(2x + 6) - 20x = 84$
34. $12(3x + 1) - 30x = 16$
35. $-5(x + 5) = -10(x + 2)$
36. $-2(x - 6) = 24x - 66$
37. $6(x + 4) + 2(x + 3) = 22$
38. $8(x + 5) + 7(x + 2) = -36$
39. $12(x + 5) + (13x + 40) = 0$
40. $18(x + 7) + (9x + 62) = 53$
41. $44 = 4(x + 30)$
42. $62 = 6(2x + 10)$
43. $8x - (x + 4) = 52$
44. $7x - (2x - 5) = 60$
45. $0.8(x + 7) = -2.4$
46. $0.04(x + 9) = -3.6$
47. $18(x + 0.2) = 14(x + 0.3)$
48. $45(x + 0.4) = 35(x + 0.8)$
49. $16.2 - (x - 4.7) = 30$
50. $94 - (98.6 - x) = 3.14$

51. $\dfrac{x}{4} - \dfrac{x}{8} = \dfrac{7}{8}$

52. $\dfrac{x}{3} - \dfrac{x}{6} = 0$

53. $\dfrac{x}{3} + \dfrac{x}{5} + \dfrac{x}{15} = 18$

54. $\dfrac{x}{4} + \dfrac{x}{8} + \dfrac{x}{11} = -41$

55. $\dfrac{2x}{3} + 7 = \dfrac{6x}{7} + 1$

56. $\dfrac{x}{2} - 4 = \dfrac{2x}{5}$

57. $\dfrac{1}{4}(8x + 3) = \dfrac{7}{16}$

58. $\dfrac{1}{2}(x + 6) = 1\dfrac{1}{4}$

59. $\dfrac{2}{3}x = \dfrac{3}{2}$

60. $\dfrac{3}{4}x = -\dfrac{4}{3}$

61. $\dfrac{1}{2}x + \dfrac{3}{4}x = 20$

62. $\dfrac{7}{8}x - \dfrac{3}{5}x = -44$

63. $\dfrac{x + 7}{12} = \dfrac{x + 3}{8}$

64. $\dfrac{x}{6} + \dfrac{x}{9} = \dfrac{x}{18}$

65. $\dfrac{5}{6}x + \dfrac{1}{5}x + \dfrac{5}{2} = \dfrac{7}{10}x$

66. $\dfrac{8}{9}x - \dfrac{2}{3}x = \dfrac{1}{18}x + 1$

67. $x + \dfrac{1}{8}x + \dfrac{5}{6}x = 141$

68. $x + \dfrac{3}{4}x + \dfrac{4}{5}x = -255$

69. $\dfrac{5}{8}(x + 22) = \dfrac{3}{4}(x + 2)$

70. $\dfrac{11}{12}(x + 60) = \dfrac{1}{3}(x + 186)$

Looking Back

71. Define and give an example of a rational number.

72. Define and give an example of an irrational number.

73. When the divisor in a division problem is a decimal, why can we move the decimal point before dividing?

74. Define and give an example of a repeating decimal.

75. Define and give and example of a terminating decimal.

76. What are the only prime factors possible in the denominator of a fraction that converts to a terminating decimal?

77. True or false: When dividing by a decimal between 0 and 1, the quotient will always be larger than the dividend.

PRACTICE-FOR-SUCCESS ANSWERS

1. $x = 11$ **2.** $x = \dfrac{5}{2}$ **3.** $x = 3$ **4.** $x = -48$ **5.** $x = -48$

INTRODUCTION TO WORD PROBLEMS

OBJECTIVES

- ☐ To solve word problems that describe relationships between numbers
- ☐ To solve word problems with two or more related quantities
- ☐ To solve consecutive integer problems

One of the main purposes for learning algebra is to be able to solve word problems that cannot be solved easily using only arithmetic. In this section we will translate parts of word problems into algebraic expressions that we will eventually combine into an equation. We will then use our equation-solving skills to solve the equation and solve the word problem. We will also learn to solve different types of problems that can be translated into linear equations.

Solving Word Problems Using Equations

We can use our ability to translate written expressions into algebraic expressions with our ability to solve equations to solve a problem such as: "The difference of a number and 17 is -5. What is the number?" The first step is to read the problem carefully and determine the unknown number. We assign a variable, usually x, to represent the unknown number.

$$\text{Let } x = \text{ the unknown number}$$

The second step is to write an algebraic expression using the variable. In this problem "The difference of a number and 17" translates as $x - 17$. The third step is to take the expressions and write an equation, so "The difference of a number and 17 is -5" translates as

$$x - 17 = -5$$

The fourth step is to solve the equation using the transformations we learned in the previous sections.

$$x - 17 = -5$$
$$x - 17 + 17 = -5 + 17$$
$$x = 12$$

The fifth step is to check your work. We can check mentally by substituting 12 for "a number" in the problem: "The difference of 12 and 17 is -5" is a true statement. The check can also be written out as follows.

$$\textbf{Check} \quad x - 17 = -5$$
$$12 - 17 = -5$$
$$-5 = -5 \quad \checkmark$$

The sixth and final step is to verify that your answer satisfies what is asked for in the problem. In this problem we write "The number is 12." The steps for solving a word problem using an equation are summarized in the accompanying box.

SOLVING A WORD PROBLEM USING EQUATIONS

1. **Read the problem to determine what is unknown in the problem. Assign a variable, usually x, to represent the unknown number in the problem and describe in English what unknown quantity the variable represents.**

2. **Write at least one algebraic expression that uses the variable selected in Step 1. If the problem has more than one unknown quantity, represent each such quantity in terms of the variable.**

3. **Two numerical quantities in the problem must be equal. First, write a statement in English that summarizes the equivalence between two quantities; then write the equation using the algebraic expressions.**

4. **Solve the equation.**

5. **Read the problem one more time and mentally check to see if the solution is reasonable. If it is not, start over again and retrace the steps. If the answer seems reasonable, check your solution by substituting it into the equation.**

6. **Write a short sentence explaining the answer.**

EXAMPLE 1   Twice the sum of a number and 36 is equal to 100. Find the number.

SOLUTION   Use the six steps to solve the word problem using an equation.

1. Let x = the unknown number

2. $x + 36$ = the sum of a number and 36

   $2(x + 36)$ = twice the sum of a number and 36

3. Twice the sum of a number and 36 = 100

   $2(x + 36) = 100$ This is the equation.

4. $2(x + 36) = 100$

   $2 \cdot x + 2 \cdot 36 = 100$ Apply the distributive law.

   $2x + 72 = 100$ Multiply.

   $2x + 72 - 72 = 100 - 72$ Subtract 72 from both sides.

   $2x = 28$ The basic operation is now multiplication.

   $\dfrac{2x}{2} = \dfrac{28}{2}$ Divide both sides by 2.

   $x = 14$

5. Substituting 14 into the original wording of the problem demonstrates that 14 is a reasonable solution: "Twice the sum of 14 and 36 is equal to 100."

Check $2(x + 36) = 100$

$2(14 + 36) \stackrel{?}{=} 100$ Replace x with 14.

$2(50) \stackrel{?}{=} 100$

$100 = 100$ $\sqrt{}$

6. The number is 14.   ▪

| **EXAMPLE 2** | When 30 is subtracted from the quotient of a number and 4, the result is 19. Find the number. |

SOLUTION   **1.** Let x = the unknown number

2. $\dfrac{x}{4}$ = the quotient of a number and 4

$\dfrac{x}{4} - 30 = 30$ subtracted from the quotient of a number and 4

3. $\dfrac{x}{4} - 30 = 19$ This is the equation.

4. $\dfrac{x}{4} - 30 = 19$ The basic operation is subtraction.

$\dfrac{x}{4} - 30 + 30 = 19 + 30$ Add 30 to both sides.

$\dfrac{x}{4} = 49$ Simplify.

$\cancel{4} \cdot \dfrac{x}{\cancel{4}} = 4 \cdot 49$ Multiply both sides by 4.

$x = 196$

5. Substituting into the original wording of the problem demonstrates that 196 is a reasonable solution: "When 30 is subtracted from the quotient of 196 and 4, the result is 19."

Check $\dfrac{x}{4} - 30 = 19$

$\dfrac{196}{4} - 30 \stackrel{?}{=} 19$ Replace x with 196.

$49 - 30 \stackrel{?}{=} 19$

$19 = 19$ $\sqrt{}$

6. The number is 196.   ▪

| **EXAMPLE 3** | If 5 times a certain number is increased by 20, the result is 6 less than 3 times the same number. Find the number. |

SOLUTION   **1.** Let x = the unknown number
2. $5x$ = five times the number

$5x + 20$ = five times the number increased by 20

$3x =$ three times the number

$3x - 6 =$ six less than three times the number

3. Five times the number increased by 20 = 6 less than 3 times the number

$5x + 20 = 3x - 6$	This is the equation.

4.

$5x + 20 = 3x - 6$	Each side has a variable term.
$5x + 20 - 3x = 3x - 6 - 3x$	Eliminate the variable term with the smaller coefficient.
$2x + 20 = -6$	The basic operation is addition.
$2x + 20 - 20 = -6 - 20$	Subtract 20 from both sides.
$2x = -26$	
$\dfrac{\cancel{2}x}{\cancel{2}} = \dfrac{-26}{2}$	
$x = -13$	

5. The number -13 appears to be a reasonable solution when we substitute it into the original wording of the problem.

Check

$$5x + 20 = 3x - 6$$

$$5 \cdot (-13) + 20 \stackrel{?}{=} 3 \cdot (-13) - 6 \qquad \text{Replace } x \text{ with } -13.$$

$$-65 + 20 \stackrel{?}{=} -39 - 6$$

$$-45 = -45 \quad \sqrt{}$$

6. The number is -13.   ■

Word Problems with Two or More Related Quantities

Often we are asked to find two numbers or quantities in a problem in which one number or quantity is related to the other. For example, a word problem might read "Roger is 6 years older than Bryan. If their combined age is 38, what are their ages?" In this problem we need to find Roger's age and Bryan's age. We let x equal Bryan's age because we know the least about it. Roger's age is related to Bryan's age; since we know that Roger is six years older than Bryan we write $x + 6$ to represent Roger's age.

Let $x =$ Bryan's age

Then $x + 6 =$ Roger's age

Writing the second quantity in terms of the first quantity is called "writing in terms of x" where the first quantity is assigned the value of x. Notice that we assigned x to Bryan's age, not to Bryan himself. Whenever we assign a variable we must make sure that it represents a mathematical quantity and not a person or object.

The problem also states that the combined age of Roger and Bryan is 38. We can write the following verbal equation to help us determine the algebraic equation.

Bryan's age + Roger's age = Total

$$x + (x + 6) = 38$$

To complete the problem, we solve the equation $x + (x + 6) = 38$. The parentheses are used to emphasize that $x + 6$ stands for a single quantity.

$$x + (x + 6) = 38$$

$(x + x) + 6 = 38$	Use the associative law of addition.
$2x + 6 = 38$	Combine like terms.
$2x + 6 - 6 = 38 - 6$	Subtract 6 from both sides.
$2x = 32$	Simplify both sides of the equation.
$\dfrac{\cancel{2}x}{\cancel{2}} = \dfrac{32}{2}$	Divide both sides by 2.
$x = 16$	

Because x represented Bryan's age, he is 16 years old.
Because $x + 6$ represented Roger's age, he is $16 + 6$ or 22 years old.

If the answer had indicated that Bryan's age was negative, then the answer would have been unreasonable because no one's age is negative. A mental check reveals that the solutions are accurate because Bryan's age, 16, and Roger's age, 22, do indeed add up to 38.

EXAMPLE 4

Amanda is going to buy a VCR and a television. If the television costs $200 more than the VCR and the total cost of both is $790, what is the cost of each item?

SOLUTION

In this example we are looking for two quantities. We know the least about the cost of the VCR so to begin we let x represent the cost of the VCR.

1. Let $x =$ the cost of the VCR
2. $x + 200 = 200$ more than the cost of the VCR
   $x + 200 =$ the cost of the television
3. Cost of VCR + Cost of TV = Total
   $x + (x + 200) = 790$
4. $\quad x + (x + 200) = 790$

$2x + 200 = 790$	Combine like terms.
$2x + 200 - 200 = 790 - 200$	Subtract 200 from both sides.
$2x = 590$	Simplify both sides of the equation.
$\dfrac{\cancel{2}x}{\cancel{2}} = \dfrac{590}{2}$	Divide both sides by 2.
$x = 295$	The cost of the VCR
$x + 200 = 495$	The cost of the television

5. **Check**

$x + (x + 200) = 790$	
$295 + (295 + 200) \stackrel{?}{=} 790$	Replace x with 295.
$295 + 495 \stackrel{?}{=} 790$	
$790 = 790 \quad \checkmark$	

6. The cost of the VCR is $295 and the cost of the television is $495.   ■

| EXAMPLE 5 | One week a computer store that sells laptop and desktop computers sold a total of 68 computers. If the number of laptop computers sold was 7 less than twice the number of desktop computers sold, how many of each type did the computer store sell? |

SOLUTION   Assign x to represent the number of desktop computers sold because we know the least about the number of those sold. Then express the number of laptop computers sold in terms of x.

1. Let x = the number of desktop computers sold

2. $2x$ = twice the number of desktop computers sold

   $2x - 7$ = 7 less than twice the number of desktop computers sold

   $2x - 7$ = the number of laptop computers sold

3. Number of desktop   Number of laptop
     computers sold   +   computers sold   = Total sold
          x + $(2x - 7)$ = 68

4. $x + (2x - 7) = 68$

   $\quad\quad 3x - 7 = 68$ Combine like terms.

   $\quad 3x - 7 + 7 = 68 + 7$ Add 7 to both sides.

   $\quad\quad\quad\quad 3x = 75$ Simplify both sides of the equation.

   $\quad\quad\quad \dfrac{\cancel{3}x}{\cancel{3}} = \dfrac{75}{3}$ Divide both sides by 3.

   $\quad\quad\quad\quad\quad x = 25$ The number of desktop computers sold

   $\quad\quad 2x - 7 = 43$ The number of laptop computers sold

5. **Check** $x + (2x - 7) = 68$

   $\quad\quad 25 + (2 \cdot 25 - 7) \stackrel{?}{=} 68$

   $\quad\quad\quad 25 + (50 - 7) \stackrel{?}{=} 68$

   $\quad\quad\quad\quad\quad 25 + 43 \stackrel{?}{=} 68$

   $\quad\quad\quad\quad\quad\quad 68 = 68$ $\checkmark$

6. The computer store sold 25 desktop computers and 43 laptop computers.

■

Consecutive Integer Problems

Next we use our problem-solving skills with word problems that involve **consecutive integers.** The word *consecutive* means "following in order." For example, 3 and 4 are consecutive integers because 4 follows 3 on the number line and is 1 greater. The integers -7, -6, and -5 are also consecutive integers because each is 1 greater than the one before it.

Even and odd integers are consecutive when they follow in order as well. The consecutive even integers are $\{..., -6, -4, -2, 0, 2, 4, 6, ...\}$; each even integer is 2 greater than the previous one. If we assign the variable x to represent any even integer, then the next or second consecutive even integer must be 2 greater and would be represented as $x + 2$. The third consecutive even integer would be represented as $x + 2 + 2$ or $x + 4$. The third consecutive even integer is 4 greater than the integer with which we started. This is illustrated by the consecutive even integers 20, 22, and 24; the integer 24 is 4 greater than 20.

The consecutive odd integers are {..., -5, -3, -1, 1, 3, 5, ...}. If we assign the variable x to represent any odd integer, then the next consecutive odd integer must be 2 greater and would also be represented as $x + 2$. Notice that consecutive odd integers are found by adding 2 (an even number) in the same way that consecutive even integers are found. The integers 13 and 15 are consecutive odd integers because 15 is 2 greater than 13.

| **EXAMPLE 6** | Find two consecutive odd integers whose sum is 76. |

SOLUTION   Consecutive odd integers are found by adding 2 to the previous odd integer.

1. Let x = the first odd integer

2. Then $x + 2$ = the second odd integer

3. First odd integer + Second odd integer = Sum

$$x \quad + \quad (x + 2) \quad = 76$$

4. $x + (x + 2) = 76$

$2x + 2 = 76$	Combine like terms.
$2x + 2 - 2 = 76 - 2$	Subtract 2 from both sides.
$2x = 74$	Simplify both sides of the equation.
$\dfrac{2x}{2} = \dfrac{74}{2}$	Divide both sides by 2.
$x = 37$	The first odd integer
$x + 2 = 39$	The second odd integer

5. The problem asked us to find two consecutive odd integers whose sum was 76. The integers 37 and 39 are indeed consecutive odd integers and mentally adding 37 and 39 we get a sum of 76.

Check $x + (x + 2) = 76$

$$37 + (37 + 2) \stackrel{?}{=} 76 \qquad \text{Replace } x \text{ with 37.}$$

$$37 + 39 \stackrel{?}{=} 76$$

$$76 = 76 \quad \checkmark$$

6. The first odd integer is 37 and the second odd integer is 39.   ■

| **EXAMPLE 7** | Find three consecutive even integers whose sum is -24. |

SOLUTION   Consecutive even integers are found by adding 2 to the previous even integer.

1. Let x = the first even integer

2. Then $x + 2$ = the second even integer

Then $x + 4$ = the third even integer

3. First even   Second even   Third even

    integer +   integer   +   integer = Sum

      x + $(x + 2)$ + $(x + 4)$ = -24

4. $x + (x + 2) + (x + 4) = -24$

$$3x + 6 = -24 \qquad \text{Combine like terms.}$$
$$3x + 6 - 6 = -24 - 6 \qquad \text{Subtract 6 from both sides.}$$
$$3x = -30 \qquad \text{Simplify both sides of the equation.}$$
$$\frac{3x}{3} = \frac{-30}{3} \qquad \text{Divide both sides by 3.}$$
$$x = -10 \qquad \text{The first even integer}$$
$$x + 2 = -8 \qquad \text{The second even integer}$$
$$x + 4 = -6 \qquad \text{The third even integer}$$

5. The problem asked us to find three consecutive even integers whose sum was -24. The integers -10, -8, and -6 are indeed consecutive even integers. Mentally adding -10, -8, and -6 we get a sum of -24.

Check $x + (x + 2) + (x + 4) = -24$

$$-10 + (-10 + 2) + (-10 + 4) \overset{?}{=} -24 \qquad \text{Replace } x \text{ with } -10.$$
$$-10 + (-8) + (-6) \overset{?}{=} -24$$
$$-24 = -24 \quad \checkmark$$

6. The first even integer is -10, the second even integer is -8, and the third even integer is -6.   ■

P R A C T I C E   F O R   S U C C E S S

Practice 1.   When twice a number is increased by 48, the sum is 104. Find the number.

Practice 2.   When 4 times a number is decreased by 28, the result is equal to 14 more than seven times a number. What is the number?

Practice 3.   A mother is 25 years older than her daughter. If the sum of their ages is 67, what are the ages of the mother and daughter?

Practice 4.   A college lecture hall seats 1,000 students. If the hall is full and the number of women is 200 less than twice the number of men, how many men and how many women are sitting in the lecture hall?

Practice 5.   Find three consecutive even integers whose sum is 126.

Practice 6.   Find three consecutive integers so that the sum of the first and second is 12 less than the third.

EXERCISES 7.4

In exercises 1–60, solve the word problems using equations.

1. The sum of $-3\frac{1}{2}$ and a number is -10. Find the number.

2. The difference of a number and $7\frac{3}{4}$ is $-2\frac{1}{2}$. Find the number.

3. Eighty-six more than a number is 22. Find the number.

4. Seven less than a number is the same as 23. Find the number.

5. 6.23 subtracted from a number is -5.9. What is the number?

6. Eighty-seven is equal to a number decreased by 17.5. What is the number?

7. Nine times a number is the same as -198. What is the number?

8. The quotient of a number and -6 is the same as 30. What is the number?

9. When 16 is added to twice a number, the sum is 42. Find the number.

10. Eighteen less than three times a number is equal to 6. Find the number.

11. Seven times a number, increased by 66 is equal to -25. Find the number.

12. Twenty-nine is the same as 5 times a number decreased by 16. Find the number.

13. Two is equal to four-fifths of a number. Find the number.

14. A number added to two-thirds of a number is equal to 10. Find the number.

15. When 3 times a number is subtracted from -26, the difference is 124. Find the number.

16. Sixteen more than three-sevenths of a number is equal to the product of 28 and 4. Find the number.

17. If 8 times a certain number is increased by 5, the result is 12 times the number increased by 21. Find the number.

18. Eight times a number decreased by 29 is the same as twice a number subtracted from 61. Find the number.

19. Nine times a number is 88 more than a number. Find the number.

20. Three times a number increased by 4 times the same number is 24 less than the number. Find the number.

21. Four times the difference of a number and 10 is -92. Find the number.

22. Seven times the sum of a number and 138 is 980. Find the number.

23. Three times the sum of a number and 17 is 19 more than the number. Find the number.

24. Eleven times the difference of a number and 42 is the same as the number increased by 138. Find the number.

25. One-fifth of a number subtracted from one-third of a number is 6. Find the number.

26. One-eighth of a number decreased by one-tenth of a number is −1. Find the number.

27. One-half of a number decreased by three-fourths is 15 more than one-eighth of a number. Find the number.

28. Find the number so that the sum of one-third of it, one-fourth of it, and one-sixth of it is equal to 9.

29. The larger of two numbers is 7 more than 4 times the smaller number. Find the numbers if their sum is 62.

30. The sum of two numbers is −9. If the larger number is 12 more than twice the smaller number, what are the two numbers?

31. Jennie and Carrie are sisters. Jennie is 3 years younger than Carrie. If their combined age is 25, how old is each girl?

32. The grandfather is 12 times as old as his grandson. If their combined age is 78, how old is the grandson?

33. Mercedes is twice as old as Reyna. Antonia is 5 years older than Mercedes. If their combined age is 60, how old is each person?

34. Karen is 7 years more than twice as old as Victoria. If their combined age is 61, how old is each person?

35. An office photocopier costs 10 times as much as a home photocopier. If it costs $5,500 to buy both, what is the cost of each?

36. A computer and a printer cost $1,800. If the computer costs $950 more than the printer, what is the cost of each?

37. Two cars are traveling on a freeway. One car is traveling 10 miles slower than the other car and they are going at a combined speed of 114 miles per hour. What is the speed of the slower car?

38. A history textbook costs $7 less than a sociology textbook. If the two textbooks cost $73, what is the cost of the history textbook?

39. A prealgebra class contains 45 students. If the number of women is 3 less than twice the number of men, how many women and how many men are in the class?

40. A box of candy contains 28 pieces. If the number of pieces of light chocolate is 4 less than 3 times the number of pieces of dark chocolate, how many pieces of each are there?

41. A nurse worked 3 more hours on Wednesday than on Thursday and twice as many hours on Friday as on Thursday. If he worked 23 hours, how many hours did he work each day?

42. Sherell purchased $6.99 worth of school supplies for her math class. She bought a binder, paper, and a package of pencils. If the paper cost 3 times as much as the package of pencils, and the binder cost 27¢ more than the paper, what was the cost of each item?

43. A Coke and a roast beef sandwich cost $3.75. If the Coke costs $1.95 less than the roast beef sandwich, what is the cost of the Coke?

44. Two cheese pizzas and 3 pepperoni pizzas are purchased for a party. If 1 pepperoni pizza costs $1.50 more than a cheese pizza and the total cost of the pizzas is $47, find the cost of a cheese pizza.

45. Find two consecutive integers whose sum is 289.

46. Find two consecutive even integers whose sum is 58.

47. The sum of two consecutive odd integers is 136. Find the integers.

48. The sum of three consecutive integers is 87. Find the integers.

49. Find three consecutive even integers whose sum is 258.

50. Find three consecutive odd integers whose sum is −3.

51. The sum of two consecutive even integers is −270. Find the integers.

52. The sum of two consecutive integers is −611. Find the integers.

53. Find three consecutive integers so that the sum of the first and third integer is 60.

54. Find four consecutive even integers so that the sum of the second and fourth integer is 0.

55. Find three consecutive integers so that twice the first added to the second is 11 more than the third.

56. Find three consecutive integers so that the sum of the second and the third is 16 more than the first.

57. Find two consecutive even integers so that twice the first increased by 5 times the second is equal to 66.

58. Find two consecutive even integers so that 4 times the first decreased by 7 times the second is equal to −50.

59. When the smaller of two consecutive integers is added to 3 times the larger, the result is 75. Find the smaller integer.

60. If 6 times the smaller of two consecutive integers is added to 4 times the larger, the result is 254. Find the smaller integer.

61. If 29 is added to the largest of three consecutive odd integers, the answer equals the sum of the first and second integers. Find the integers.

62. Find four consecutive even integers such that the sum of 5 times the first and 2 times the fourth is equal to 16 more than six times the third.

👁 Looking Back

63. Write the word name for 2,083.0097.

64. Which is greater, −0.67 or −0.667?

65. Estimate the product of 7.4 and −4.1 and then find the exact product.

66. Round 29.9972 to the nearest tenth.

67. Divide −532 by 0.07.

68. Find $\sqrt{-121}$.

69. Find $\left(\dfrac{3}{4}\right)^{-2}$.

1. $x = 28$
2. $x = -14$
3. The mother is 46 years old and the daughter is 21 years old.
4. The lecture hall contains 400 men and 600 women.
5. The three consecutive even integers are 40, 42, and 44.
6. The three consecutive integers are -11, -10, and -9.

7.5 SOLVING RATIO, PROPORTION, AND PERCENT PROBLEMS

OBJECTIVES

- To solve a proportion
- To solve word problems involving proportions
- To solve word problems involving ratios
- To solve word problems involving percent

In this section we will solve some different types of word problems using ratios, proportions, and percent. In each type of problem we will continue to use the six steps to solve word problems in algebra:

1. Read the problem and assign a variable to represent the unknown number.
2. Write algebraic expressions using the variable. (In the percent problems, which have more than one variable, we will assign values to the other variables.)
3. Write an equation using the ratio or proportion in the problem. (We will first write a proportion using the units.)
4. Solve the equation.
5. Read the problem one more time and check the work.
6. Write a short sentence explaining the answer.

Ratios and Rates

A **ratio** is the comparison of two numbers or quantities, usually written as a quotient. The ratio of the number a to the number b may be written in the following ways:

$$\frac{a}{b} \quad \text{or} \quad a{:}b \quad \text{or} \quad a \text{ to } b$$

For example, we could write the ratio of the number of hours we sleep to the number of hours in a day as

$$\frac{8 \text{ hours}}{24 \text{ hours}} = \frac{8}{24} \quad \text{or} \quad 8{:}24 \quad \text{or} \quad 8 \text{ to } 24$$

Because the units are identical, they are divided out similarly to the way a fraction is reduced to lowest terms by dividing out common factors. Ratios are normally written in lowest terms, so the ratio of the number of hours we sleep (8) to the number of hours during the day (24) is reduced to the ratio $\frac{1}{3}$ as follows.

$$\frac{8 \text{ hours}}{24 \text{ hours}} = \frac{2 \cdot 2 \cdot 2}{2 \cdot 2 \cdot 2 \cdot 3} = \frac{1}{3} \quad \text{or} \quad 1{:}3 \quad \text{or} \quad 1 \text{ to } 3$$

Ratios are most frequently written in the rational number form $\frac{a}{b}$, simplified to lowest terms. Of the three forms used to represent ratio, we will use the form $\frac{a}{b}$ in this book. For example, we will use $\frac{1}{3}$ instead of 1:3 or "1 to 3" to represent the ratio of the number of hours of sleep to the number of hours in the day. This ratio indicates that for every hour you sleep, there are 3 hours in the day.

Not all ratios have the same units. We may say a college has a certain ratio of men to women, which are certainly different units. Because the units are different they cannot be divided out and so are included in the answer. Ratios that have different units are called **rates.** We often use the word *per* in expressing a rate, as in such well-known rates as miles per hour, dollars per hour, cents per pound, percent per year, and miles per gallon.

Proportions

A **proportion** is a statement that two ratios are equal. For example,

$$\frac{4}{5} = \frac{8}{10} \quad \text{and} \quad \frac{25}{30} = \frac{5}{6}$$

are proportions.

Proportions are usually written in the form $\frac{a}{b} = \frac{c}{d}$. The numbers a, b, c, and d are called the *terms* of the proportion. The first and fourth terms, a and d, are called the **extremes** and the second and third terms, b and c, are called the **means.**

Proportions can be true or false. The proportion $\frac{1}{2} = \frac{3}{7}$ is an example of a false proportion because $\frac{1}{2}$ and $\frac{3}{7}$ do not reduce to the same equivalent fraction or ratio. The proportion $\frac{5}{9} = \frac{10}{18}$ is an example of a true proportion since $\frac{5}{9}$ and $\frac{10}{18}$ both reduce to the same equivalent ratio, $\frac{5}{9}$.

If the proportion $\dfrac{a}{b} = \dfrac{c}{d}$ is a true proportion, we can multiply both sides by the least common denominator of the two to write an equivalent equation. The least common denominator of b and d is $b \cdot d$.

$$\frac{a}{b} = \frac{c}{d}$$

$$\cancel{b}d \cdot \frac{a}{\cancel{b}} = b\cancel{d} \cdot \frac{c}{\cancel{d}} \qquad \text{Multiply by } bd, \text{ the LCD.}$$

$$d \cdot a = b \cdot c \qquad \text{Simplify the expressions.}$$

$$a \cdot d = b \cdot c \qquad \begin{array}{l}\text{Apply the commutative law of} \\ \text{multiplication on the left side.}\end{array}$$

The products ad and bc can be found by multiplying in a diagonal direction as well. Multiplying diagonally in a proportion is called **cross multiplication,** and the values $a \cdot d$ and $b \cdot c$ are called the **cross products** (see Figure 7.1).

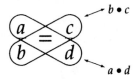

FIGURE 7.1   Cross multiplication

FUNDAMENTAL PROPERTY OF PROPORTIONS

If $\dfrac{a}{b} = \dfrac{c}{d}$, then $a \cdot d = b \cdot c$, where $b \neq 0$ and $d \neq 0$.

In a true proportion, cross products are equal.

We have seen that a proportion has four terms. If any three of these four terms are known, then the fourth term in the proportion can be found by using the fundamental property of proportions and solving the resulting equivalent equation.

EXAMPLE 1

Solve and check the following proportions.

a. $\dfrac{12}{15} = \dfrac{x}{60}$ **b.** $\dfrac{x}{3x + 4} = \dfrac{7}{25}$

SOLUTION   **a.** $\dfrac{12}{15} = \dfrac{x}{60}$

$12 \cdot 60 = 15 \cdot x$ — Apply the fundamental property of proportions.

$720 = 15x$ — Multiply.

$\dfrac{720}{15} = \dfrac{\cancel{15}x}{\cancel{15}}$ — Divide both sides by 15.

$48 = x$

Check $\dfrac{12}{15} = \dfrac{x}{60}$

$\dfrac{12}{15} \overset{?}{=} \dfrac{48}{60}$ Replace x with 48.

$720 = 720$ √   Apply the fundamental property of proportions.

b. $\dfrac{x}{3x + 4} = \dfrac{7}{25}$

$25 \cdot x = 7(3x + 4)$ Apply the fundamental property of proportions.

$25 \cdot x = 7 \cdot 3x + 7 \cdot 4$ Apply the distributive law.

$25x = 21x + 28$ Multiply.

$25x - 21x = 21x + 28 - 21x$ Eliminate the variable term with the smaller coefficient.

$4x = 28$ The basic operation is now multiplication.

$\dfrac{4x}{4} = \dfrac{28}{4}$ Divide both sides by 4.

$x = 7$

Check $\dfrac{x}{3x + 4} = \dfrac{7}{25}$

$\dfrac{7}{3 \cdot 7 + 4} \overset{?}{=} \dfrac{7}{25}$ Replace x with 7.

$7 \cdot 25 \overset{?}{=} 7(3 \cdot 7 + 4)$ Apply the fundamental property of proportions.

$7 \cdot 25 \overset{?}{=} 7(21 + 4)$

$7 \cdot 25 \overset{?}{=} 7 \cdot 25$

$175 = 175$ √   ■

Word Problems Involving Proportions

Proportions occur in many word problems. We will solve them using the six-step method but instead of writing algebraic expressions, we will write a proportion using the units in the problem. A problem might read: "On a road map drawn to scale, 1 inch represents 63 miles. How many inches would represent a distance of 189 miles?" To solve this problem, the first step is to represent the unknown.

Let x = the number of inches representing 189 miles

The second step in writing algebraic expressions is usually not necessary in a proportion problem. The third step is to write the proportion using only the units and then insert the numerical information from the problem into the proportion.

$$\frac{\text{inches}}{\text{miles}} = \frac{\text{inches}}{\text{miles}}$$

$$\frac{1}{63} = \frac{x}{189}$$

The fourth step is to solve the proportion using the fundamental property of proportions.

$$\frac{1}{63} = \frac{x}{189}$$

$$189 = 63x$$

$$\frac{189}{63} = \frac{\cancel{63}x}{\cancel{63}}$$

$$3 = x$$

The fifth step is to ask if 3 is a reasonable solution and then check it.

$$\frac{1}{63} = \frac{x}{189}$$

$$\frac{1}{63} \overset{?}{=} \frac{3}{189} \qquad \text{Replace } x \text{ with 3.}$$

$$189 = 189 \qquad \text{Cross multiply.}$$

The sixth step is to write a sentence explaining your answer.

Three inches represent 189 miles on the road map.

| EXAMPLE 2 | The Chicago Cubs will win 12 of their first 18 games played next season. At this rate the team will win a record 108 games. How many games will they play during the season? |

SOLUTION   **1.** Let $x =$ the number of games played in a season

3. $\dfrac{\text{games won}}{\text{games played}} = \dfrac{\text{games won}}{\text{games played}}$

$$\frac{12}{18} = \frac{108}{x}$$

4. $\dfrac{12}{18} = \dfrac{108}{x}$

$12x = 1{,}944$ \qquad Apply the fundamental property of proportions.

$\dfrac{\cancel{12}x}{\cancel{12}} = \dfrac{1{,}944}{12}$ \qquad Divide both sides by 12.

$x = 162$

5. 162 is a reasonable answer because the professional baseball season is exactly 162 games in length.

Check $\qquad \dfrac{12}{18} = \dfrac{108}{x}$

$\dfrac{12}{18} \overset{?}{=} \dfrac{108}{162}$ \qquad Replace x with 162.

$1{,}944 = 1{,}944 \quad \checkmark$

6. The Chicago Cubs will play 162 games during the season. ■

| **EXAMPLE 3** | Suppose that the amount of material needed to make 12 quilts is 63 yards more than the amount needed for 9 quilts. How many yards of material is needed for 9 quilts? |

SOLUTION   In this problem we need to write an algebraic expression. After assigning x to represent the number of yards of material for 9 quilts, the algebraic expression $x + 63$ will then represent the number of yards of material for 12 quilts.

1. Let x = the number of yards of material for 9 quilts

2. Let $x + 63$ = the number of yards of material for 12 quilts

3. $\dfrac{\text{yards of material}}{\text{quilts}} = \dfrac{\text{yards of material}}{\text{quilts}}$

$$\frac{x}{9} = \frac{x + 63}{12}$$

4. $$\frac{x}{9} = \frac{x + 63}{12}$$

$12x = 9(x + 63)$	Apply the fundamental property of proportions.
$12x = 9 \cdot x + 9 \cdot 63$	Apply the distributive law.
$12x = 9x + 567$	Multiply.
$12x - 9x = 9x + 567 - 9x$	Eliminate the term with the smaller coefficient.
$3x = 567$	Combine like terms.
$\dfrac{\cancel{3}x}{\cancel{3}} = \dfrac{567}{3}$	Divide both sides by 3.
$x = 189$	The number of yards of material for 9 quilts.
$x + 63 = 252$	The number of yards of material for 12 quilts.

5. **Check** $\dfrac{x}{9} = \dfrac{x + 63}{12}$

$\dfrac{189}{9} \overset{?}{=} \dfrac{252}{12}$ Replace x with 189.

$2{,}268 = 2{,}268$ √

6. For 9 quilts, 189 yards of material are needed.   ▪

Equations Involving Percent

Three key quantities are involved in a percent problem: the *amount* (*A*) which is a part of the total, the *total* (*T*), and the *percent* (*P*). The percent proportion can be used to solve percent problems.

PERCENT PROPORTION

$$\frac{A}{T} = \frac{P}{100}$$

where *A* is the amount, *T* is the total, and *P* is the percent.

The percent proportion can be used to solve a problem of the form: "Rosa received a score of 90% on a math exam that had 20 problems. How many problems did she answer correctly?" To solve this problem, the first step is to represent the unknown.

Let A = the number of problems Rosa answered correctly out of 20

In proportion problems the second step is to assign values to the other two of the three quantities: the amount, the total, and the percent. Since we have already assigned A to represent the amount, we need to assign values to the total and the percent.

The total number of problems (T) is 20

The percent (P) is 90

The third step is to write the percent proportion and then insert the information from the first two steps.

$$\frac{A}{T} = \frac{P}{100}$$

$$\frac{A}{20} = \frac{90}{100} \qquad \text{Substitute } T = 20 \text{ and } P = 90.$$

The fourth step is to solve the proportion using the fundamental property of proportions.

$$\frac{A}{20} = \frac{90}{100}$$

$$100A = 1{,}800 \qquad \text{Cross multiply to clear the fractions.}$$

$$\frac{\cancel{100}A}{\cancel{100}} = \frac{1{,}800}{100}$$

$$A = 18$$

The highest possible score Rosa could have earned on the exam is 100%, and to earn that score she would have had to answer all 20 problems correctly. Since 90% is less than 100%, Rosa must have answered fewer than 20 problems correctly; therefore, 18 is a reasonable solution.

Check $\qquad \dfrac{A}{20} = \dfrac{90}{100}$

$$\frac{18}{20} \overset{?}{=} \frac{90}{100}$$

$$1{,}800 = 1{,}800 \quad \checkmark$$

The sixth step is to write a sentence explaining your answer.

Rosa answered 18 problems correctly.

EXAMPLE 4	Solve the following problems by using the percent proportion. **a.** 62 is 25% of what number?　　**b.** 30 is what percent of 150?
SOLUTION	**a.** To solve a percent problem using the percent proportion, we need to determine the amount, the total, and the percent. One of the three quantities

will be unknown, so we assign the related variable in the percent proportion to it. A helpful hint is that usually the total follows the word *of* and the amount usually precedes the word *is* in a number problem.

1. Let T = the total

2. The amount $(A) = 62$ and the percent $(P) = 25$

3. $\dfrac{A}{T} = \dfrac{P}{100}$ Write the percent proportion.

   $\dfrac{62}{T} = \dfrac{25}{100}$ Substitute into the percent proportion.

4. $\dfrac{62}{T} = \dfrac{25}{100}$

   $6{,}200 = 25T$

   $\dfrac{6{,}200}{25} = \dfrac{25\,T}{25}$

   $248 = T$

5. Another method of checking a solution in a proportion is to reduce the fractions on both sides of the equation. If the reduced fractions are equal, then the proportion is true and, therefore, the solution is valid.

   Check $\dfrac{62}{T} = \dfrac{25}{100}$

   $\dfrac{62}{248} \overset{?}{=} \dfrac{25}{100}$

   $\dfrac{1}{4} = \dfrac{1}{4}$ $\checkmark$

6. The number is 248.

b. 1. Let P = the percent

   2. The amount $(A) = 30$ and the total $(T) = 150$

   3. $\dfrac{A}{T} = \dfrac{P}{100}$ Write the percent proportion.

      $\dfrac{30}{150} = \dfrac{P}{100}$ Substitute into the percent proportion.

   4. $\dfrac{30}{150} = \dfrac{P}{100}$

      $\dfrac{1}{5} = \dfrac{P}{100}$ Fractions on either side of the equation can be reduced before cross multiplying. Generally it is helpful to reduce, when possible.

      $100 = 5P$

      $\dfrac{100}{5} = \dfrac{5P}{5}$

      $20 = P$

   5. The check is left for the reader.

   6. The percent is 20%.   ■

Discount problems are a type of percent problem that can be solved using the percent proportion. The amount A in this type of problem is usually the discount, the amount that a retail outlet lowers the regular price of a product for a sale. The total T is the regular price of the product. The percent P is the discount rate, the discount expressed as a percent of the regular price. Once any two of the three are known, the third number can be determined using the percent proportion. Once the amount of the discount is determined, the sale price can then be found by subtracting the amount of the discount from the regular price.

| EXAMPLE 5 | A suit is going on sale at a discount of 15.5%. If the regular price is $200, determine the amount of the discount and the sale price. |

SOLUTION
1. Let A = the amount of the discount
2. The total $T = 200$ and the percent $P = 15.5$

3. $\dfrac{A}{T} = \dfrac{P}{100}$ Write the percent proportion.

   $\dfrac{A}{200} = \dfrac{15.5}{100}$ Substitute into the percent proportion.

4. $\dfrac{A}{200} = \dfrac{15.5}{100}$

   $100A = 3{,}100$

   $\dfrac{\cancel{100}A}{\cancel{100}} = \dfrac{3{,}100}{100}$

   $A = 31$

5. **Check** $\dfrac{A}{200} = \dfrac{15.5}{100}$

   $\dfrac{31}{200} \overset{?}{=} \dfrac{15.5}{100}$

   $3{,}100 = 3{,}100$ ✓

6. The amount of the discount is $31 and the sale price is $169, which is calculated by subtracting the amount of the discount ($31) from the regular price ($200). ■

| EXAMPLE 6 | Natasza gets a raise from $10.50 to $11.97 per hour. What was the percent of increase in her salary per hour? |

SOLUTION   To calculate the percent of increase or decrease, determine the amount A the original number has either increased or decreased. In this example Natasza's salary increase of $1.47 is the amount A. In percent increase or decrease problems, the total T is always the original number. In this example Natasza's original salary of $10.50 per hour is the total T.

1. Let P = the percent
2. The amount $A = 1.47$ and the total $T = 10.50$

3. $\dfrac{A}{T} = \dfrac{P}{100}$ Write the percent proportion.

$\dfrac{1.47}{10.50} = \dfrac{P}{100}$ Substitute into the percent proportion.

4. $\dfrac{1.47}{10.50} = \dfrac{P}{100}$

$147 = 10.5P$

$\dfrac{147}{10.5} = \dfrac{10.5P}{10.5}$

$14 = P$

5. 14% is a reasonable answer (although most salary increases are considerably less).

Check $\dfrac{1.47}{10.50} = \dfrac{P}{100}$

$\dfrac{1.47}{10.50} \stackrel{?}{=} \dfrac{14}{100}$

$147 = 147$ √

6. Natasza's salary increased 14%.   ■

Word Problems Involving Ratios

EXAMPLE 7   Two numbers have a ratio of 2 to 3. If their sum is 25, what are the numbers?

SOLUTION   If two numbers have a sum of 25, the first number might be 5 and the second number 20, or the first number might be 8 and the second number 17. How we determine the second number each time is to subtract the first number from the sum. Because we do not know what the first number in this problem is, we assign x to represent the first number. The second number is then represented by the algebraic expression $25 - x$, which is the first number subtracted from the sum.

1. Let $x =$ the first number

2. Then $25 - x =$ the second number

3. $\dfrac{\text{first number}}{\text{second number}} = \dfrac{2}{3}$ ←The ratio

$\dfrac{x}{25 - x} = \dfrac{2}{3}$

4. $\dfrac{x}{25 - x} = \dfrac{2}{3}$

$3x = 2(25 - x)$ Apply the fundamental property of proportions.

$3x = 2 \cdot 25 - 2 \cdot x$ Apply the distributive law.

$3x = 50 - 2x$ Multiply.

$$3x + 2x = 50 - 2x + 2x \qquad \text{Eliminate the variable term with the smaller coefficient.}$$

$$5x = 50 \qquad \text{The basic operation is now multiplication.}$$

$$\frac{\cancel{5}x}{\cancel{5}} = \frac{50}{5} \qquad \text{Divide both sides by 5.}$$

$$x = 10 \qquad \text{The first number}$$

$$25 - x = 15 \qquad \text{The second number}$$

5. In this type of ratio problem, we must first determine if the answers are in the correct ratio. We see that, in this example, 10 and 15 are in the correct ratio, 2 to 3.

$$\frac{10}{15} = \frac{2 \cdot \cancel{5}}{3 \cdot \cancel{5}} = \frac{2}{3}$$

Then we check to see if the answers add up to 25.

$$10 + 15 = 25 \quad \checkmark$$

6. The numbers are 10 and 15.   ■

| **EXAMPLE 8** | Two families rented a van for one week. One family used the van for 5 days and the other family used the van for 2 days. If the cost of renting the van including tax, gasoline, and insurance was \$385, how much money should each family pay? |

SOLUTION   Because one family used the van for 5 days and the other family used the van for 2 days, a fair method to determine how much each family should pay would be to split the bill using the ratio 5 to 2. Because the total spent by both families was \$385, the cost for one family can be represented by x and the cost for the other family can be represented by $385 - x$, the cost for the first family subtracted from the total.

1. Let $x =$ the cost for the first family

2. Then $385 - x =$ the cost for the second family

3. $\dfrac{\text{cost for first family}}{\text{cost for second family}} = \dfrac{5}{2}$ ←The ratio.

$$\frac{x}{385 - x} = \frac{5}{2}$$

4. $\dfrac{x}{385 - x} = \dfrac{5}{2}$

$$2x = 5(385 - x) \qquad \text{Apply the fundamental property of proportions.}$$

$$2x = 5 \cdot 385 - 5 \cdot x \qquad \text{Apply the distributive law.}$$

$$2x = 1{,}925 - 5x \qquad \text{Multiply.}$$

$$2x + 5x = 1{,}925 - 5x + 5x \qquad \text{Eliminate the variable term with the smaller coefficient.}$$

$$7x = 1{,}925 \qquad \text{The basic operation is now multiplication.}$$

$$\frac{\cancel{7}x}{\cancel{7}} = \frac{1{,}925}{7} \qquad \text{Divide both sides by 7.}$$

$$x = 275 \qquad \text{The cost for the first family}$$

$$385 - x = 110 \qquad \text{The cost for the second family}$$

5. Now we check that the dollar amounts $275 and $110 are in the ratio 5 to 2.

$$\frac{\$275}{\$110} = \frac{\cancel{5} \cdot 5 \cdot \cancel{11}}{2 \cdot \cancel{5} \cdot \cancel{11}} = \frac{5}{2}$$

and that the dollar amounts add up to $385.

$$\$275 + \$110 = \$385 \quad \sqrt{}$$

6. The family renting the van for 5 days pays $275 and the family renting the van for 2 days pays $110. ■

P R A C T I C E F O R S U C C E S S

Practice 1. Solve and check $\dfrac{4}{x} = \dfrac{8}{x-2}$.

Practice 2. Three quarts of yogurt are needed to make 11 yogurt shakes. How many quarts of yogurt are needed to make 121 shakes?

Practice 3. 75 is what percent of 225?

Practice 4. A dress is going on sale at a discount of 25%. If the regular price is $75, determine the amount of the discount and the sale price.

Practice 5. An amusement park raises its price per ticket for an adult from $38.50 to $42.00. Find the percent increase in price to the nearest tenth of a percent.

Practice 6. Two numbers have a ratio of 7 to 10. If their sum is 68, what are the numbers?

Practice 7. Anela and Tollie divided the profits from a sale of one of their businesses in a ratio of 3:5. If the total profits from the sale were $71,200, how much money did each business partner get?

EXERCISES 7.5

In exercises 1–10, solve the proportions using cross multiplication.

1. $\dfrac{7}{18} = \dfrac{x}{144}$

2. $\dfrac{108}{x} = \dfrac{9}{17}$

3. $\dfrac{x}{25} = \dfrac{132}{275}$

4. $\dfrac{19}{21} = \dfrac{57}{x}$

5. $\dfrac{x}{7} = \dfrac{x+30}{49}$

6. $\dfrac{x+2}{x+3} = \dfrac{24}{27}$

7. $\dfrac{x-2}{x+3} = \dfrac{1}{2}$

8. $\dfrac{3x+4}{10} = \dfrac{17x+10}{50}$

9. $\dfrac{15}{22} = \dfrac{x-1}{2x-10}$

10. $\dfrac{x}{x-5} = \dfrac{60}{35}$

In exercises 11–70, solve the word problems.

11. If a quarterback completes 5 out of every 11 passes, how many passes will he complete if he throws 44 passes in one game?

12. A recycling center pays 5¢ for every 2 aluminum cans. If Terry brings 432 aluminum cans to the recycling center, how much money will she receive?

13. Five out of 9 people who participated in a taste test preferred Diet Cola A over Diet Cola B. If 75 people preferred Diet Cola A, how many people participated in the taste test? How many preferred Diet Cola B?

14. On a map of Utah $\dfrac{1}{2}$ inch represents 31.5 miles. If two cities are $2\dfrac{1}{2}$ inches apart, what is the actual distance between them?

15. A secretary who does word processing earns \$13 for every two pages completed. How much money does he earn if he completes 182 pages?

16. One mile is approximately equal to 1.6 kilometers. If a runner participates in a 10-kilometer race, how many miles does she run?

17. Rodney rides his bicycle every day and each week he rides a total of 546 miles to prepare for races. How many miles does he ride Monday through Friday?

18. On a trip a man drives his car 315 miles in 7 hours. At this rate how many hours will it take him to reach his destination 495 miles away from his current location?

19. A diagram of a plane is drawn to the scale of 0.5 inch equals 40 feet. If the wingspan of the plane in the diagram is 1.5 inches, what is the actual wingspan of the plane?

20. If a light flashes once every 5 seconds, how many times will it flash in 30 minutes? (*Hint:* convert minutes to seconds.)

21. If Kevin Brown, a pitcher for the Los Angeles Dodgers, gave up 28 earned runs in 126 innings, how many earned runs did he give up every 9 innings?

22. A van went 127.5 miles on 8.5 gallons of gas. At this rate how many gallons of gasoline would be needed to go 195 miles?

23. A quality-control inspector examined 300 light bulbs and found 24 defective. At this rate how many defective light bulbs would be found in a lot of 24,600?

24. Mary Lois sells a house for \$175,000 and receives a commission of \$12,250. At the same commission rate, how much commission would Mary Lois receive for selling a house at \$125,000?

25. The Milburn family spends $294 for food during a 14-day period. If they continue to spend at the same rate, how long will it take them to spend $651 for food?

26. If it takes 1.5 cups of sugar to make 36 cookies, how many cups of sugar would be needed to make 90 cookies?

27. The number of gallons of gasoline needed to travel 125 miles is 3 gallons less than the number needed to travel 200 miles. How many gallons of gasoline are needed to travel 200 miles?

28. The dosage of medication required for a person who weighs 175 pounds is 0.5 ounce more than the dosage of medication required for a person who weighs 125 pounds. What is the dosage of medication required for a person who weighs 125 pounds?

29. The amount of material needed to make 7 sundresses is 7.5 yards more than the amount needed to make 4 sundresses. How many yards of material are needed to make 4 sundresses?

30. The number of gallons of paint needed to cover 800 square feet is 3 less than the number needed to cover 1,400 square feet. How many gallons of paint are needed to cover 1,400 square feet?

31. Thirty-seven is what percent of 50?

32. What percent of 176 is 88?

33. What number is 96% of 25?

34. Seven is 3.5% of what number?

35. Seventy-five percent of what number is 12?

36. Forty-five percent of what number is 18?

37. What number is $5\frac{1}{2}$% of 500?

38. What number is $6\frac{3}{4}$% of 200?

39. Thirty is what percent of 45?

40. Sixty is what percent of 72?

41. In a prealgebra class 30% of the students earned Bs. If 15 students earned Bs, how many students are in the class?

42. Marvin received a score of 95% on a chemistry exam. If he answered 38 questions correctly, how many questions were on the exam?

43. Nina purchased a watch for $30. If she must pay a 7% sales tax, how much tax will she pay?

44. Your bill for dinner at a restaurant is $21.40 and you add a 15% tip to the bill. Calculate the tip and the total bill.

45. A company plans to spend $300,000 to develop a new product. Of the $300,000, $180,000 is set aside for research. What percent of the budget is for research?

46. An inspector found that 8 out of 1,000 microchips inspected were defective. What percent of the microchips were defective?

47. A television station shows commercials 29% of every hour. How many minutes of commercials are shown during a 1-hour situation comedy?

48. In a basketball game Cheryl attempted 28 free throws. If she made 75% of them, how many free throws did she make?

49. A sport coat normally selling for $220 is reduced by $44. What is the rate of discount?

50. Jeanne earned $30,000 last year and she saved $5,400. What percent of the money did she save?

51. A fax machine was sold at a reduction or discount of $209. If the rate of discount was 22%, what was the regular price of the fax machine?

52. Lance paid $2.52 in sales tax when he bought a pair of tennis shoes. If the sales tax was 6%, what was the price of the tennis shoes before tax?

53. Christian paid $12,200 for a car. If the car is now worth $11,102, what is the percent decrease in value?

54. After going on a diet, Jim found his weight dropped from 180 pounds to 153 pounds. What was his percent decrease in weight?

55. The price of a condominium went up from $80,000 to $102,400. What is the percent increase in the price of the condominum?

56. A rare coin from the nineteenth century increases in value from $2,500 to $2,950. What is the percent increase in the value of the coin?

57. A suit that regularly costs $300 goes on sale for 32% off. Find the discount and the sale price.

58. A tube of lipstick that regularly costs $5 goes on sale for 12% off. Find the discount and the sale price.

59. Dale paid $3.99 for a nonaerosol bottle of hair spray. If the sales tax was 6%, what was the tax and the total cost of the hair spray?

60. Roy bought a graphite tennis racket on sale at a reduction or discount of $19.80. If the rate of discount was 20%, what was the regular price of the tennis racket?

61. Two numbers have a ratio of 7 to 9. If their sum is 128, find the numbers.

62. Two numbers have a ratio of 19 to 11. If their sum is 240, find the numbers.

63. Two numbers have a ratio of 16 to 5. If their sum is −84, find the numbers.

64. Two numbers have a ratio of 6 to 5. If their sum is −22, find the numbers.

65. Two families rented a condo for one week. One family used the condo 3 days and the other family used the condo for 4 days. If the cost of renting the condo was $679 dollars, how much money should each family pay?

66. Selena wants to invest $10,000 in stocks and partnerships in a ratio of 2 to 3. How much money should she invest in stocks and how much in partnerships?

67. In an elementary algebra class the ratio of men to women is 5 to 4. If the class size is 45, how many men and how many women are in the class?

68. At a community college the ratio of nonsmokers to smokers is 7 to 2. If the community college has 18,900 students, how many students are nonsmokers and how many are smokers?

69. Two friends start a cabinetry business. The first week, one friend works 32 hours and the other friend works 40 hours. If their income for the week is $1,980, how much is each friend's share?

70. A brother and a sister inherit $28,000 to be divided up in the ratio of 2 to 5. How much money is each going to inherit?

 Looking Back

71. Is 2,896,452 divisible by 3?

72. Write the prime factorization 14,014.

73. Find the LCM and GCF of 10, 18, and 32.

74. Define the basic operation of an expression.

75. Which is larger, $\dfrac{7}{8}$ or 0.872?

76. True or false: If an expression containing only multiplications has an odd number of negative signs, the product is positive.

77. True or false: $(-5)^4 = -5^4$.

PRACTICE-FOR-SUCCESS ANSWERS

1. $x = -2$ **2.** 33 quarts of yogurt

3. $33\dfrac{1}{3}\%$ **4.** The discount is $18.75 and the sale price is $56.25.

5. 9.1%   **6.** The numbers are 28 and 40.

7. Anela gets $26,700 and Tollie gets $44,500.

7.6   SOLVING LITERAL EQUATIONS

OBJECTIVES

☐ To solve literal equations for a specified variable

☐ To solve word problems that involve literal equations

Each equation we've solved so far in this chapter contained only one variable. To solve that kind of equation, we use the various properties of equality to create a series of equivalent equations that eventually lead to the solution. In this section we will use the same properties of equality to find the solution but for the first time our equations will have more than one variable. We will solve these equations for a chosen variable and the solutions will usually be algebraic expressions instead of numbers.

Literal Equations

In the equation $2x + 4 = x + 6$, we solve the equation for x because it is the only variable. However, some equations have more than one variable and they are called **literal equations.** Some examples are:

$$2x + 6y = 12$$

$$S = R - D$$

Formulas are expressed in the form of literal equations. For example, the formula length · width = area is written

$$L \cdot W = A$$

and has three variables L, W, and A. The formula is currently *solved for A.* This means that if we know the values of L and W, we can find A because it is isolated on one side of the equation.

Using the area formula we can derive two other formulas by solving for either L or W. We might have many problems in which we are asked to find the length of a rectangle, so having a formula to find the length would be beneficial. We can solve the formula $L \cdot W = A$ for the variable L and create a new formula. To solve a formula for a particular variable, we undo the basic operation of the expression containing that variable, isolating it on one side.

$$L \cdot W = A \qquad \text{The basic operation is multiplication.}$$

$$\frac{L \cdot \cancel{W}}{\cancel{W}} = \frac{A}{W} \qquad \text{Divide by } W \text{, assuming } W \neq 0.$$

$$L = \frac{A}{W} \qquad \text{The equation is now solved for } L.$$

We started with a formula for the area of a rectangle and derived a formula for the length of a rectangle, thus solving the literal equation for L. We "undid" the basic operation of the expression containing L just as we would have in an equation containing only one variable.

SOLVING A LITERAL EQUATION FOR A SPECIFIED VARIABLE

1. **Locate the specified variable.**
2. **Solve the equation for the specified variable using the same properties used to solve linear equations.**

EXAMPLE 1	Solve the literal equation $P = 2W + 2L$ for W.

SOLUTION　A good first step in solving a literal equation in which the specified variable is on the right side of the equation is to exchange the sides of the equation.

$$P = 2W + 2L$$

$2W + 2L = P$	Exchange the sides of the equation.
$2W + 2L - 2L = P - 2L$	Subtract $2L$ from both sides.
$2W = P - 2L$	The basic operation is now multiplication.
$\dfrac{2W}{2} = \dfrac{P - 2L}{2}$	Divide both sides by 2.
$W = \dfrac{P - 2L}{2}$	The variable W is now isolated. ■

EXAMPLE 2	Solve the literal equation $N = \dfrac{A - 6.7S}{6.25}$ for A.

SOLUTION　This formula, as mentioned in Section 6.5, calculates the capacity of a room. By solving for A we will derive a formula that will calculate the area of a room containing S seats and a maximum of N people.

$$N = \frac{A - 6.7S}{6.25}$$

$\dfrac{A - 6.7S}{6.25} = N$	Exchange the sides of the equation. The basic operation is division.
$6.25\left(\dfrac{A - 6.7S}{6.25}\right) = 6.25 \cdot N$	Multiply both sides by 6.25.
$A - 6.7S = 6.25N$	Simplify.
$A - 6.7S + 6.7S = 6.25N + 6.7S$	Add $6.7S$ to both sides.
$A = 6.25N + 6.7S$	Simplify. ■

EXAMPLE 3	Solve the literal equation $F = \dfrac{9}{5}C + 32$ for C.

SOLUTION　The formula $F = \dfrac{9}{5}C + 32$ can be used to convert from degrees Celsius to degrees Fahrenheit. By solving for C, we are deriving a second formula for converting from degrees Fahrenheit to degrees Celsius.

$$F = \frac{9}{5}C + 32$$

$\dfrac{9}{5}C + 32 = F$	Exchange the sides of the equation.
$\dfrac{9}{5}C + 32 - 32 = F - 32$	Subtract 32 from both sides.

$$\frac{9}{5}C = F - 32 \qquad \text{Simplify.}$$

$$\frac{\cancel{5}}{\cancel{9}} \cdot \frac{\cancel{9}}{\cancel{5}}C = \frac{5}{9}(F - 32) \qquad \text{Multiply both sides by the reciprocal } \frac{5}{9}.$$

$$C = \frac{5}{9}(F - 32) \qquad \text{The variable } C \text{ is now isolated.} \qquad ■$$

| **EXAMPLE 4** | Solve the literal equation $A = a + (n - 1)d$ for d. |

SOLUTION

$$A = a + (n - 1)d$$

$$a + (n - 1)d = A \qquad \text{Exchange the sides of the equation.}$$

$$a + (n - 1)d - a = A - a \qquad \text{Subtract } a \text{ from both sides.}$$

$$(n - 1)d = A - a \qquad \text{Simplify.}$$

$$\frac{(n - 1)d}{(n - 1)} = \frac{A - a}{(n - 1)} \qquad \text{Divide both sides by } (n - 1).$$

$$d = \frac{A - a}{n - 1} \qquad \text{Simplify.} \qquad ■$$

Word Problems Using Formulas

Formulas expressed as literal equations often help us solve word problems. Formulas can be used to solve such problems as how fast a vehicle is going, what the area of a geometric figure is, and how much interest we have to pay. They are a valuable asset in many word problems. The seven steps listed in the box can be used to solve a word problem when the formula is known.

SOLVING WORD PROBLEMS USING LITERAL EQUATIONS

1. **Identify which variable is unknown and which variables are known.**
2. **Write the literal formula.**
3. **Solve the literal formula for the variable that is unknown.**
4. **Substitute the values for the known variables in the last equation.**
5. **Simplify the numerical expression that remains on one side of the last equation.**
6. **Check to see if the answer for the unknown variable is reasonable.**
7. **Write a short sentence explaining the answer.**

Formulas can be used to solve interest problems. When a person puts money in a bank or a savings and loan, the institution pays the person for the use of the money. The additional money the person receives is called *interest*. Also, when a person borrows money from a lending institution, the person pays the institution for the use of the money. The additional money the person must pay back is also interest.

Interest that is calculated using only the initial amount of money borrowed or invested is called *simple interest*. (Most banks and savings and loans use *compound interest* to calculate interest, which requires a more complicated formula as explained in Section 6.5.) To calculate simple interest, we use the simple interest formula.

SIMPLE INTEREST FORMULA

$$I = PRT$$

where I is the interest amount paid or received, P is the principal amount borrowed or invested, R is the annual interest rate, and T is the length of time in years.

EXAMPLE 5

If you borrow $500 from a friend and you agree to pay back the money at the end of 6 months and your friend says that the interest amount you will have to pay back is $20, what annual interest rate is your friend charging you?

SOLUTION   Apply the seven steps.

1. Let R = the annual interest rate. Because we are being asked to find the interest rate, R is the unknown variable. We know I = $20. The time T is always expressed in years so we must convert 6 months into years. Then

   $$T = \frac{1}{2} \text{ because } \frac{6}{12} = \frac{1}{2}.$$

2. $I = PRT$ Write the literal formula.

3. $PRT = I$ Switch the sides of the equation to get R on the left.

   $$\frac{\cancel{P}R\cancel{T}}{\cancel{P}\cancel{T}} = \frac{I}{PT}$$ Divide both sides by PT to isolate R.

   $$R = \frac{I}{PT}$$ Simplify.

4. $R = \dfrac{20}{500 \cdot \dfrac{1}{2}}$ Substitute the known values.

5. $R = \dfrac{20}{250}$ Simplify the denominator.

   $$R = \frac{2}{25}$$ Reduce the fraction.

   $R = 0.08$ Divide to get a decimal.

   $R = 8\%$ Convert the decimal to a percent.

6. Check using the original formula.

    Check $I = PRT$

          $20 \stackrel{?}{=} (500)(0.08)(0.5)$

          $20 \stackrel{?}{=} (40)(0.5)$

          $20 = 20$ √

7. The annual interest rate charged by your friend is 8%.   ■

Another formula that can be used to solve word problems is the formula rate · time = distance.

RATE, TIME, DISTANCE FORMULA

$$r \cdot t = d$$

where r is the rate of travel, t is the time spent traveling, and d is the distance traveled.

Units are associated with the variables in this formula. If the rate is in miles per hour then the distance must be in miles and the time must be in hours. For example, if you ride your bicycle at a rate of 9 miles per hour for 30 minutes, how far have you gone? You cannot have gone 270 miles; the minutes are converted to hours because the units for the rate are *miles per hour*. Because 30 minutes is equal to $\frac{1}{2}$ hour, the distance you have gone is

$(9)\left(\frac{1}{2}\right) = 4\frac{1}{2}$ miles.

EXAMPLE 6   Diane went on a trip from Los Angeles to San Francisco by car. She traveled at 55 miles per hour and her odometer showed that the length of the trip was 385 miles. How many hours did the trip take?

SOLUTION   **1.** Let t = the time spent traveling, r = 55 miles per hour, d = 385 miles.

    2. $r \cdot t = d$

    3. $\dfrac{\cancel{r} \cdot t}{\cancel{r}} = \dfrac{d}{r}$ Divide both sides by r to isolate t.

    4. $t = \dfrac{d}{r}$

    5. $t = \dfrac{385}{55}$ Substitute the known values.

          $t = 7$ Simplify.

    6. Check $rt = d$

          $55(7) \stackrel{?}{=} 385$

          $385 = 385$ √

    7. The trip took 7 hours.   ■

| EXAMPLE 7 | The formula for the surface area of a tin can is $S = 2\pi rh + 2\pi r^2$, where r is the radius of the circular part of the can and h is the height of the can. If the surface area S is 100 π square inches and the radius is 2 inches, what is the height of the can? (In this problem do not convert π to a decimal, but work with π as a constant.) |

SOLUTION

1. Let $h =$ the height of the can. We are given $S = 100\pi$ and $r = 2$.

2. $S = 2\pi rh + 2\pi r^2$

3.
$$2\pi rh + 2\pi r^2 = S \qquad \text{Exchange both sides of the equation.}$$
$$2\pi rh + 2\pi r^2 - 2\pi r^2 = S - 2\pi r^2 \qquad \text{Subtract } 2\pi r^2 \text{ from both sides.}$$
$$2\pi rh = S - 2\pi r^2 \qquad \text{Simplify.}$$
$$\frac{2\cancel{\pi} r h}{2\cancel{\pi} r} = \frac{S - 2\pi r^2}{2\pi r} \qquad \text{Divide both sides by } 2\pi r \text{ to isolate } h.$$
$$h = \frac{S - 2\pi r^2}{2\pi r}$$

4. $h = \dfrac{100\pi - 2\pi(2)^2}{2\pi(2)^2}$ \qquad Substitute the known values.

5. $h = \dfrac{100\pi - 8\pi}{4\pi}$

$h = \dfrac{92\pi}{4\pi}$ \qquad Combine the like terms 100π and 8π.

$h = 23$ \qquad Divide 4 into 92 and divide π by itself.

6. **Check** $S = 2\pi rh + 2\pi r^2$

$100\pi \overset{?}{=} 2\pi(2)(23) + 2\pi(2)^2$

$100\pi \overset{?}{=} 92\pi + 8\pi$

$100\pi = 100\pi \quad \checkmark$

7. The height of the tin can is 23 inches. ■

PRACTICE FOR SUCCESS

Practice 1. Solve $x + 3y = 8$ for y.

Practice 2. Solve $A = P + PRT$ for T.

Practice 3. Solve $A = \dfrac{1}{2}(b + B)h$ for b. $\left(\textit{Hint:} \text{ Begin by multiplying both sides by the reciprocal of } \dfrac{1}{2}.\right)$

Practice 4. Jack lent Lee \$2,000 at 11% per year and expected to make \$330 in interest. How many months did Lee have to pay back Jack?

Practice 5. Sepi went on a 1,925-mile flight traveling at a speed of 550 miles per hour. How many hours was she in the air?

Practice 6. The area of a triangle is 30 square inches. If the base is 15 inches, find the height.

EXERCISES 7.6

In exercises 1–20, solve the formulas for the specified variable.

1. $P = 4s$ for s 2. $F = ma$ for a

3. $d = rt$ for t 4. $I = PRT$ for R

5. $P = a + b + c$ for b 6. $P = 2W + 2L$ for L

7. $PV = nRT$ for T 8. $E = mc^2$ for m

9. $y = mx + b$ for m 10. $y = mx + b$ for x

11. $V = \pi r^2 h$ for h 12. $V = LWH$ for L

13. $C = \dfrac{5}{9}(F - 32)$ for F 14. $A = \dfrac{1}{2}bh$ for b

15. $P = \dfrac{R - C}{n}$ for R 16. $P = \dfrac{R - C}{n}$ for C

17. $S = 2\pi rh + 2\pi r^2$ for h 18. $A = a + (n - 1)d$ for n

19. $A = P + Prt$ for P 20. $s = \dfrac{1}{2}at^2 + vt$ for a

In exercises 21–50, solve using literal equations.

21. June invested \$750 at 12% for 2 years. How much simple interest will she receive at the end of the 2 years?

22. Paul borrowed \$480 at 11% for 3 months. How much simple interest will he have to pay at the end of the 3 months?

23. Ray borrowed \$700 at 10% and is told that the simple interest he will have to pay is \$105. In how many months will he have to pay back the principal and interest?

24. Joan invested \$3,000 at 13% and is told that the simple interest she will receive is \$260. In how many years will she receive the interest?

25. A family borrows \$20,000 to make home improvements. If the simple interest on the loan is \$9,000 and they are to pay the lender over a 5-year period, what rate of interest did the lender charge the family?

26. Liz deposits \$800 in an account and is told that she will receive \$33 in interest at the end of 9 months. What is the account's rate of interest?

27. Chuck invests money at 15% and will earn \$1,200 in simple interest at the end of 2 years. How much money will he invest to receive the \$1,200 in interest?

28. A farmer borrows money at 13% to buy a truck. If the interest is \$780 after 6 months, how much did the farmer borrow?

29. If you ride a stationary bike for 50 minutes and the odometer says that you have "traveled" 10 miles, how fast are you riding the bike in miles per hour?

30. If you drive a speedboat going 88 miles per hour for 2 hours and 45 minutes, how far do you travel?

31. Sandy travels from Bozeman to Billings, Montana. If she travels for $7\frac{1}{2}$ hours at 55 miles per hour, how far apart are the two cities?

32. Lonnie travels from Clarksville to Memphis, Tennessee. If he travels for 2 hours and 16 minutes at 60 miles per hour, how far apart are the two cities?

33. A runner completes a 6-mile run in 48 minutes. What is her rate in miles per hour?

34. A long-distance swimmer swims 1 mile in 45 minutes. What is his rate in miles per hour?

35. Imagine that you are in the Indianapolis 500-mile race and the rate of your car is 160 miles per hour. How long will it take you to finish the race?

36. A trip by train between Paris and Lyon, France, is about 312 miles. If the rate of the train is 144 miles per hour, how long does the trip take?

37. Ashley bicycles from Asheville to Hickory, North Carolina, in 6 hours, 15 minutes. If the trip is 75 miles in length, how fast did she ride in miles per hour?

38. A trip from San Francisco to Oahu is 2,394 miles. If the trip takes 5 hours and 4 minutes, what is the speed of the airplane in miles per hour?

39. A rectangle has an area of 33.48 square feet. If the length of the rectangle is 6.2 feet, what is the width? (Use the formula $A = LW$.)

40. If the circumference of a circle is 87.92 inches, what is the radius of the circle? (Use the formula $C = 2\pi r$ and use 3.14 for the value of π.)

41. If the circumference of a circle is 138.16 inches, what is the diameter of the circle? (Use the formula $C = \pi d$ and use 3.14 for the value of π.)

42. A triangle has an area of 52 square feet. If the base of the triangle is 6.5 feet, what is the height of the triangle? (Use the formula $A = \frac{1}{2}bh$.)

43. A trapezoid has an area of 30 square inches. If the shorter base is 8 inches and the longer base is 12 inches, what is the height of the trapezoid? [Use the formula $A = \frac{1}{2}(b + B)h$.]

44. The perimeter of an acre (a square unit of measure) is approximately 278 yards. What is the length of a side of an acre? (Use the formula $P = 4s$.)

45. How heavy an object can a 200-pound man lift with a bar that is 12 feet long if he uses a fulcrum that is positioned 2 feet along the bar from the object at one end, and he stands with all of his weight at the other end of the bar? (Use the formula $w_1d_1 = w_2d_2$.)

46. Find the length of a shoe box if its volume is 360 cubic inches, its height is 5 inches, and its width is 6 inches. (Use the formula $V = LWH$.)

47. The average temperature in Santa Monica, California, is 68°F. Find the average temperature in degrees Celsius.

48. An oven is set at 200°C. Convert the temperature of the oven to degrees Fahrenheit.

49. If the surface area of a tin can is 100 π square inches and the radius is 5 inches, what is the height of the can? (Use the formula $S = 2\pi rh + 2\pi r^2$. Do not convert π to a decimal, but work with π as a constant.)

50. If the volume of an ice cream cone is 2π cubic inches and the radius is 1 inch, what is the height of the ice cream cone? (Use the formula $V = \frac{1}{3}\pi r^2 h$. Do not convert π to a decimal, but work with π as a constant.)

Looking Back

51. Subtract 7,984 from 10,000.

52. Evaluate $-17\{6 - [4(7 - 10) + 1]\}$.

53. Simplify $\dfrac{\frac{3}{4} - \frac{7}{10}}{\frac{2}{3} - \frac{4}{5}}$.

54. Evaluate $\sqrt{4{,}840}$. Round to the nearest thousandth.

55. Evaluate $\dfrac{7^{-5}}{7^{-7}}$.

56. Multiply $x^5 y^4 z^7 (x^2 - 2xy + y^2)$.

57. Multiply $(2x + 5)(3x^2 + 8x - 22)$.

58. True or false: $7x + 2x + 3 = x + 6x + 10 - 4$ is an identity.

PRACTICE-FOR-SUCCESS ANSWERS

1. $y = \dfrac{8 - x}{3}$ 2. $T = \dfrac{A - P}{PR}$ 3. $b = \dfrac{2A - Bh}{h}$

4. 18 months 5. 3.5 hours 6. 4 inches

7.7 SOLVING INEQUALITIES

OBJECTIVES

☐ To learn which basic operations preserve and which reverse inequalities
☐ To solve single inequalities with linear expressions
☐ To graph the solution to an inequality on a number line

In previous sections we learned how to solve linear equations. In this section we are going to change from equations to **inequalities.** Equations are statements that use the $=$ sign to convey the fact that two expressions are equal in value. Inequalities use the symbols $<, >, \leq$, and $\geq$ to convey the fact that one expression is larger or smaller than another. With one notable exception, all the techniques and concepts we learned to solve equations apply to solving inequalities. In particular the key idea of undoing the basic operation to isolate the variable still applies.

To solve an equation means to find any and all values of the variable that make the equation true. The same may be said about inequalities, but whereas most of the linear equations we have solved have had only one correct answer for the variable, most inequalities that we will solve will have an infinite number of solutions. Consider the inequality

$$2x + 3 < 11$$

Just as an equation has sides to the left and right of the $=$ symbol, an inequality has sides to the left and right of the $<$ symbol. The variable x is on the left side and the basic operation is addition; to undo the addition of 3 we subtract 3.

As we do with equations, if we subtract 3 on the left side we must also subtract 3 on the right side. Subtracting 3 from both sides does not change the solution to the inequality. We say the operation of subtracting 3 on both sides of $<$ *preserves* the inequality.

$$2x + 3 < 11$$
$$2x + 3 - 3 < 11 - 3 \quad \text{Subtract 3 from both sides.}$$
$$2x < 8 \qquad\qquad \text{Simplify.}$$

Now the basic operation is multiplication, so to further isolate the variable we divide by 2 on both sides of the inequality. This operation preserves the inequality and it isolates the variable and makes the final answer clear.

$$2x < 8$$
$$\frac{2x}{2} < \frac{8}{2} \quad \text{Divide by 2 on both sides.}$$
$$x < 4 \quad \text{Simplify.}$$

If x is any number less than 4, then x should make the original inequality $2x + 3 < 11$ true. We can even partially check this answer by choosing two numbers, one less than 4 and one not less than 4, say $x = 3$ and $x = 5$. Substituting these values in the original inequality shows

$2x + 3 < 11$	$2x + 3 < 11$
$2 \cdot 3 + 3 \overset{?}{<} 11$	$2 \cdot 5 + 3 \overset{?}{<} 11$
$6 + 3 \overset{?}{<} 11$	$10 + 3 \overset{?}{<} 11$
$9 < 11$	$13 < 11$
True	False

To say $x < 4$ is the solution means that every number x strictly less than 4 makes $2x + 3 < 11$ true. It also means every number x greater than or equal to 4 makes $2x + 3 < 11$ false. This is what we mean when we find any and all solutions to an inequality. Inequalities like this one have an infinite number of solutions.

Graphing the Solution

In addition to showing a solution in the algebraic form $x < 4$, we can use a diagram on a number line to convey a geometric picture of an inequality solution. We draw and label a number line and shade all the parts on the number line whose corresponding coordinates satisfy the inequality. The graphical solution to $2x + 3 < 11$ is shown in Figure 7.2.

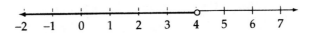

FIGURE 7.2   **Graphical solution to $2x + 3 < 11$**

When graphing an inequality such as $x < 4$ on a number line, we show a hollow dot on the line where $x = 4$ to indicate that the point corresponding to $x = 4$ is not part of the solution. When an inequality uses $\le$ or $\ge$, we graph the starting point with a solid dot to indicate the point is part of the solution.

Operations with Inequalities

Analogous to the addition and subtraction properties of equations are addition and subtraction properties of inequalities; in fact, for addition and subtraction the analogy is exact. The $=$ symbol in an equation may be replaced by any one of the inequality symbols: $<$, $>$, $\le$, or $\ge$. We state the fundamental property using the $<$ symbol.

ADDITION AND SUBTRACTION PROPERTY OF INEQUALITIES

If $a < b$ and c is any expression, then $a + c < b + c$.

If $a < b$ and c is any expression, then $a - c < b - c$.

The properties hold when the inequality symbol $<$ is replaced by any one of $>$, $\le$, and $\ge$.

Multiplication and division must be treated more carefully. For example, $-2 < 5$, and if we multiply the left and right sides by the same number, say -3, we may be tempted to write

$$(-2) \cdot (-3) \overset{?}{<} 5 \cdot (-3)$$

$$6 \overset{?}{<} -15$$

This last inequality is false but if we reverse the inequality it becomes true.

$$6 > -15$$

Next, consider $25 > -40$. Suppose we divide both sides by 5.

$$\frac{25}{5} \overset{?}{>} \frac{-40}{5}$$

$$5 > -8$$

In this example the inequality remains true without reversing the > symbol.

The multiplication and division properties for equations also hold for inequalities, but only when the multiplier or divisor is positive. When the multiplier or divisor is negative, a new property for inequalities applies, summarized in the accompanying rules.

MULTIPLICATION AND DIVISION PROPERTIES OF INEQUALITIES

If $a < b$ and $c > 0$, then $a \cdot c < b \cdot c$ and $\dfrac{a}{c} < \dfrac{b}{c}$.

If $a < b$ and $c < 0$, then $a \cdot c > b \cdot c$ and $\dfrac{a}{c} > \dfrac{b}{c}$.

Whenever we multiply or divide both sides of an inequality by a negative number we reverse the sense of the inequality to preserve a true statement.

The multiplication and division rules hold when the symbols comparing the terms with a and b are replaced by any one of $>$, $\geq$, and $\leq$. For example,

$$\text{if } a \leq b \text{ and } c < 0, \text{ then } a \cdot c \geq b \cdot c \text{ and } \frac{a}{c} \geq \frac{b}{c}.$$

The justification for reversing the sense of an inequality when both sides are multiplied or divided by a negative number can be appreciated by considering the role of opposites on a number line. In Figure 7.3 we show two points a and b to the right of zero where $a < b$. We also show and label the corresponding points on the opposite side of zero, which are $-a$ and $-b$. Since a is closer to zero than b, $-a$ is closer to zero than $-b$; but on a number line, smaller numbers lie on the left. So if $a < b$ we also have $-a > -b$. If we multiply or divide both sides of $a < b$ by -1, we must also reverse the inequality.

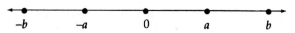

FIGURE 7.3   Number line showing points a and b and $-a$ and $-b$ where $0 < a < b$

EXAMPLE 1   Solve the inequality $4x - 7 > 13$ and graph your solution on a number line.

SOLUTION   The basic operation on the side that contains the variable is subtraction. Undo the subtraction by adding 7 to both sides. Whenever adding or subtracting, the inequality symbol does not change.

$$4x - 7 > 13$$
$$4x - 7 + 7 > 13 + 7 \quad \text{Add 7 to both sides.}$$
$$4x > 20 \quad\quad \text{Simplify.}$$

$$\frac{\cancel{4}x}{\cancel{4}} > \frac{20}{4}$$ Since 4 is positive, the $>$ symbol is not reversed when we divide by 4.

$$x > 5$$

In Figure 7.4 we graph the solution on a number line by shading all points greater than 5. The point at $x = 5$ is graphed with a hollow dot to indicate that $x = 5$ is not part of the solution.   ■

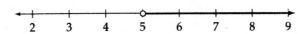

2   3   4   5   6   7   8   9

FIGURE 7.4   Graphical solution to $4x - 7 > 13$

| **EXAMPLE 2** | Solve the inequality $14 \le -3x + 8$ and graph your solution on a number line. |

SOLUTION   The basic operation on the side with the variable is addition.

$$14 \le -3x + 8$$
$$14 - 8 \le -3x + 8 - 8$$ Subtract 8 from both sides.
$$6 \le -3x$$ Simplify.
$$\frac{6}{-3} \ge \frac{-\cancel{3}x}{-\cancel{3}}$$ Since we are dividing by a negative, $\le$ is replaced by $\ge$.
$$-2 \ge x$$ Simplify.
$$x \le -2$$ Write the final answer using $\le$.

When graphing, we may find it easiest to write all inequalities with $<$ or $\le$ symbols because that way the expressions will line up left to right as they will appear when graphed. In Figure 7.5 we rewrite the last inequality as $x \le -2$ and graph the solution by shading all points to the left of the number -2. The point at $x = -2$ is graphed with a solid dot to include that point as part of the solution.   ■

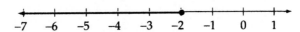

-7   -6   -5   -4   -3   -2   -1   0   1

FIGURE 7.5   Graphical solution to $14 \le -2x + 8$

| **EXAMPLE 3** | Solve the inequality $-\frac{2}{3}x + \frac{20}{3} < 7$ and graph your solution on a number line. |

SOLUTION   The basic operation on the side with the variable is addition so we undo the addition by subtracting $\frac{20}{3}$ from both sides.

$$-\frac{2}{3}x + \frac{20}{3} < 7$$

$$-\frac{2}{3}x + \frac{20}{3} - \frac{20}{3} < 7 - \frac{20}{3}$$ Subtract $\frac{20}{3}$ from both sides.

$$-\frac{2}{3}x < \frac{1}{3}$$ Simplify $7 - \frac{20}{3} = \frac{1}{3}$.

$$\left(-\frac{3}{2}\right) \cdot \left(-\frac{2}{3}x\right) > \left(-\frac{3}{2}\right) \cdot \left(\frac{1}{3}\right)$$ Multiply by $-\frac{3}{2}$ and reverse the inequality.

$$x > -\frac{1}{2}$$ Simplify $\left(-\frac{3}{2}\right) \cdot \left(-\frac{2}{3}\right) = 1$ and $\left(-\frac{3}{2}\right) \cdot \left(\frac{1}{3}\right) = -\frac{1}{2}$.

$$-\frac{1}{2} < x$$ Rewrite using $<$.

We prefer to leave the answer with the $<$ symbol even though the variable ends up on the right side of the inequality. In Figure 7.6 we graph the solution by shading all points to the right of the number $-\frac{1}{2}$. The point at $x = -\frac{1}{2}$ is graphed with a hollow dot to indicate that that point is not part of the solution. ■

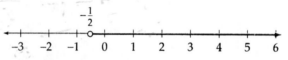

FIGURE 7.6 Graphical solution to $-\frac{2}{3}x + \frac{20}{3} < 7$

EXAMPLE 4 Solve the inequality $(2.5)\,[2.8 - 2.4x] < -4x + 2$ and graph your solution on a number line.

SOLUTION We begin by analyzing both sides that contain the variable. On the left side we first apply the distributive law and simplify.

$$(2.5)\,[2.8 - 2.4x] < -4x + 2$$

$$(2.5) \cdot (2.8) - (2.5) \cdot (2.4x) < -4x + 2$$ Apply the distributive law.

$$7 - 6x < -4x + 2$$ Multiply and simplify.

$$7 - 6x + 6x < -4x + 2 + 6x$$ Add $6x$ to both sides.

$$7 < 2x + 2$$ Simplify.

$$7 - 2 < 2x + 2 - 2$$ Subtract 2 from both sides.

$$5 < 2x$$ Simplify.

$$\frac{5}{2} < \frac{2x}{2}$$ Divide by 2 and preserve the inequality since $2 > 0$.

$$2.5 < x$$ Since the problem began with decimals, we write the final answer in decimal form.

We graph the solution in Figure 7.7 by shading all points to the right of the number 2.5. The hollow dot at $x = 2.5$ indicates that x must be strictly greater than 2.5. ■

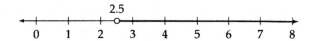

FIGURE 7.7   **Graphical solution to (2.5) [2.8 − 2.4x] < −4x + 2**

PRACTICE FOR SUCCESS

Practice 1.   Solve and graph your solution to the inequality $-5x + 18 > -12$.

Practice 2.   Solve and graph your solution to the inequality $-8 + 2x \leq 6 - 5x$.

Practice 3.   Explain the difference between the addition and subtraction properties of inequalities and the multiplication and division properties of inequalities.

Practice 4.   Solve and graph your solution to the inequality $-3[2x - 10] > 2[12 + 3x]$.

EXERCISES 7.7

Solve the inequalities in exercises 1–22 and graph your solutions on a number line.

1. $5x - 9 < 6$ **2.** $3x + 10 < 4$

3. $4x - 7 \geq 17$ **4.** $-3x - 4 \leq 5$

5. $-5x + 8 < 8$ **6.** $-5x - 28 \leq -3$

7. $-x + 13 < 3x + 5$ **8.** $-2x + 17 > x + 5$

9. $-2x > -5x + 6$ **10.** $-6x + 10 \geq -7x + 9$

11. $8x < 2(3x + 5)$ **12.** $3(7x + 4) \leq 6x + 27$

13. $4(-3x + 4) > 2(4x + 8)$ **14.** $5.3x + 1.4 < 14 + 3.2x$

15. $\dfrac{13}{3}x + \dfrac{5}{3} < \dfrac{8}{3} + 4x$ **16.** $4.5x + 2.7 < 3(x + 4.9)$

17. $\dfrac{4}{3}x + 4 < \dfrac{17}{3} + \dfrac{2}{3}x$ **18.** $\dfrac{3}{4}\left(\dfrac{5}{2}x - \dfrac{2}{3}\right) < \dfrac{3}{2}\left(-\dfrac{7}{12} + \dfrac{3}{4}x\right)$

19. $2(5.1x + 2.1) \geq 12.7 + 6.8x$ **20.** $2.5(6.5x + 8.5) \leq 0.5(27.5x + 63.5)$

21. $15\left(-\dfrac{2}{3}x + \dfrac{1}{5}\right) + 3x > 3(x + 6)$

22. $5(0.7x + 1.3) < 0.5(3 + 5x) + 6.5$

👁 Looking Back

23. Explain the difference between a ratio and a proportion.

24. State the Pythagorean theorem.

25. Solve for x: $\dfrac{2x + 3}{5} = 9y + 2z$.

26. Explain the difference between an expression and a term.

27. Name four undefined mathematical operations.

28. The combined cost of a computer, a printer, and a fax machine was $2,200. The printer cost $500 less than the computer and the computer cost $600 more than the fax machine. What was the cost of the computer?

29. Name four special properties of the number 0.

30. When converted to decimal form, is the fraction $\dfrac{5}{19}$ a repeating or a terminating decimal? Why?

PRACTICE-FOR-SUCCESS ANSWERS

1. $x < 6$

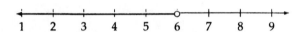

FIGURE 7.8 **Graphical solution to** $-5x + 18 > -12$

2. $x \leq 2$

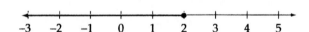

FIGURE 7.9 **Graphical solution to** $-8 + 2x \leq 6 - 5x$

3. The only difference occurs when multiplying or dividing by a negative number; in this case we must reverse the inequality symbol.

4. $x < \dfrac{1}{2}$

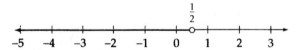

FIGURE 7.10 **Graphical solution to** $-3(2x - 10) > 2(12 + 3x)$

SUMMARY

An equation is a mathematical statement that two expressions are equal. Some equations such as $5(x + 3) = 5x + 15$ are called identities because they are true for all values of the variable. However, most equations encountered in algebra are conditional equations, such as $2(x - 7) = 9x + 22 - 5x$, and these equations are true for only certain values of the variable. To solve an equation means to find all the values of the variable that make the equation true. For the most part, all the equations we studied had at most one solution.

The steps used to solve any equation involve writing equivalent equations until the variable in the equation appears on only one side and is isolated. The equation $2(x - 7) = 9x + 22 - 5x$ will be used to illustrate the basic steps. Because the variable appears on both sides of the equals sign we begin by simplifying the left and right sides using two instances of the distributive law.

$2(x - 7) = 9x + 22 - 5x$	
$2x - 14 = 4x + 22$	Apply the distributive law on each side.
$2x - 14 - 2x = 4x + 22 - 2x$	Subtract $2x$ from both sides.
$-14 = 2x + 22$	Simplify to eliminate the smallest variable term.
$2x + 22 = -14$	Exchange left and right sides to get the variable on the left.
$2x + 22 - 22 = -14 - 22$	Undo the basic operation on the left. Subtract 22 from both sides.
$2x = -36$	Except for the coefficient 2, the variable is almost isolated.
$\dfrac{2x}{2} = \dfrac{-36}{2}$	Undo the basic operation on the left by dividing both sides by 2.
$x = -18$	The final solution appears after simplifying.

The last step is to check if this solution satisfies the original equation. We substitute $x = -18$ and simplify both sides of the original equation.

Check	$2(x - 7) = 9x + 22 - 5x$	
	$2((-18) - 7) \overset{?}{=} 9(-18) + 22 - 5(-18)$	Substitute $x = -18$.
	$2(-25) \overset{?}{=} -162 + 22 + 90$	
	$-50 \overset{?}{=} -162 + 112$	
	$-50 = -50 \;\surd$	It checks.

Word problems can be solved using the skills of manipulating equations with the following steps.

1. Read the problem, identify the unknown quantity, and identify the variable.

2. Write one or more expressions that make use of the variable, representing any other unknown quantities in terms of the variable.

3. Write in words the statement that summarizes the equality of two expressions. Then write the equation using the expressions from Step 2.

4. Solve the equation.

5. Check the solution by substituting back into the equation and verify that it seems reasonable.

6. Answer the question asked in the problem.

A ratio is a quotient of two quantities, and a rate is a special kind of ratio in which the two quantities have different units. Miles per hour is an example of a rate. A proportion is a statement that two ratios are equal and can be solved using cross multiplication.

Literal equations are equations that contain more than one variable. The steps for solving a literal equation for one of its variables are basically the same as those for solving any other equation. We form equivalent equations and isolate the desired variable on one side. These same steps also apply to solving inequalities; but when solving an inequality, we reverse the sense of the inequality whenever we multiply or divide by a negative number.

CHAPTER 7 REVIEW PROBLEMS

In problems 1–6, check to see if the given number is a solution to the equation.

1. $2x + 19 = -38 + 27; x = -15$

2. $8x - (6 - 8x) = 13x - 15; x = -3$

3. $9x^2 = -36x + 8; x = \dfrac{1}{2}$

4. $0.4x - 0.8x + 2.8 = 4(6x - 2.35); x = 0.5$

5. $\dfrac{8 - x}{32} = \dfrac{3 + x}{28}; x = 4$

6. $9x + 31 = 3(3x + 2) + 29; x = -8$

In problems 7–10, translate the written expressions into algebraic expressions. Use x as the variable to represent the unknown number.

7. Fifty-five subtracted from twice a number

8. Ninety-two times the difference of a number and sixty

9. Eighty-six more than the reciprocal of a number

10. Four times the sum of a number and twenty-two, added to the quotient of the number and six

In problems 11–30, solve and check the equations.

11. $x - \dfrac{3}{4} = -\dfrac{11}{5}$

12. $x + 2.782 = 3$

13. $-92 = \dfrac{4}{3}x$

14. $-0.008x = -34$

15. $\dfrac{x}{8} = -56$

16. $9x - 4 = -67$

17. $89 = \dfrac{x}{7} + 12$

18. $\dfrac{3}{5}x - 17 = 34$

19. $36 = -7x + 32\dfrac{1}{2}$

20. $\dfrac{2}{5}x + 0.236 = 0.22$

21. $9x + x + 12x = -242$

22. $87 + 14 = 19x - 7x + 5$

23. $3x + 4x - 23 = 9x + 17$

24. $16x + 82 + 20x = -42x - 74$

25. $22 - 4(x + 13) = 102$

26. $19(x - 6) = 13(x - 3)$

27. $\dfrac{x}{3} + \dfrac{x}{5} + \dfrac{x}{10} = -19$

28. $\dfrac{3}{4}x + \dfrac{2}{3}x = -17$

29. $\dfrac{x + 5}{7} = \dfrac{2x - 5}{4}$

30. $\dfrac{x - 10}{6} = \dfrac{2x - 7}{8}$

In problems 31–36, solve the literal equations for the specified variable.

31. $C = 2\pi r$ for r

32. $N = \dfrac{A - 6.7S}{6.25}$ for A

33. $d = \dfrac{tc}{2}$ for t

34. $h = vt - 16t^2$ for v

35. $A = \pi rs + \pi r^2$ for s

36. $y = a(x - h)^2 + k$ for a

In problems 37–60, solve the word problems.

37. Seven times a number added to 9 times a number is the same as 12 times a number subtracted from 28. Find the number.

38. The sum of two numbers is 46. If the larger is 14 less than 3 times the smaller number, what are the two numbers?

39. In a family of four the brother is 8 years older than his baby sister. The mother of the two children is 3 times as old as her son and the father is 3 years older than his wife. If the combined age of the family members is 83, how old is each family member?

40. A mother is 4 times as old as her daughter. If their combined age is 35, how old is the daughter?

41. A dining room set consists of a table and four chairs. If the table costs $327 more than a chair and the dining room set costs $577, what is the cost of a chair?

42. A tent costs $62 more than a sleeping bag. If the cost of 2 sleeping bags and a tent is $145.97, what is the cost of a sleeping bag?

43. Find 3 consecutive even integers whose sum is 204.

44. Find 2 consecutive odd integers so that twice the second subtracted from the first is equal to -11.

45. The Cincinnati Reds win 60 of their first 100 games. If they continue winning at the same rate, how many games will they win if they play 160 games?

46. If the average family has 2.3 people per family, how many people are in 80 families?

47. Suppose that the amount of money needed to buy 6 tires is $78 more than the amount needed to buy 4 tires. How much money is needed to buy 4 tires?

48. Two numbers have a ratio of 5 to 8. If their sum is 104, what are the numbers?

49. What percent of 70 is 45?

50. What is 150% of 28?

51. Sixty-two percent of what is 217?

52. A watch goes on sale for 25% off. If the regular price is $24.99, find the discount and the sale price. (*Hint:* Round off the discount to the nearest cent.)

53. A belt bag regularly priced at $7.99 is on sale for $5.59. Determine the rate of discount. (*Hint:* Round the rate of discount to the nearest percent.)

54. The price of unleaded gasoline went up from $1.08 to $1.13 per gallon. What is the percent increase to the nearest tenth of a percent?

55. Arlene borrowed $2,500 and agreed to pay the money back plus interest at the end of 3 months. If Arlene was to pay back $81.25 in interest, what was the rate of interest?

56. Juan borrowed $750 from a credit union for 9 months at 14%. What was the simple interest due on the loan?

57. The earth travels around the sun at 18.5 miles per second. At this rate how far does the earth travel in 1 hour?

58. A sports car in a race travels at a speed of 114 miles per hour. At this rate how long will it take the sports car to travel 171 miles?

59. The perimeter of a room is 280 feet. Find the width of the room if the length of the room is 75 feet.

60. If the height of a triangle is 5 inches and the area is 36 square inches, find the base of the triangle.

Solve the inequalities in problems 61–64 and graph your solutions on a number line.

61. $-11x < 12 - 8x$

62. $10 - 6x \geq -x$

63. $x - 8 + 2x - 3x < -3x - 5 + 2(x - 4)$

64. $3(x - 5) + 4x \geq (3x - 15) + 28$

CHAPTER 7 PRACTICE TEST

In problems 1 and 2, check to see if the given number is a solution to the equation.

1. $4x + 26 - 7x = 9x + 2; x = 2$

2. $6x^2 + 3x + 7 = 10; x = -1$

In problems 3 and 4, translate the written expressions into algebraic expressions. Use *x* as the variable to represent the unknown number.

3. Five times a number subtracted from the square of a number

4. The quotient of a number and 6 decreased by two-thirds of the sum of a number and 12

In problems 5–14, solve and check the equations.

5. $3x - 13 = -28$ **6.** $\dfrac{x}{4} + 12 = -12$

7. $-\dfrac{4}{3}x = -64$ **8.** $12x - 7x - 6x = 100$

9. $6x + 22 = -8x - 20$ **10.** $4(2x - 7) - (-7x - 2) = 0$

11. $\dfrac{x}{5} + \dfrac{x}{10} + \dfrac{x}{15} = 22$ **12.** $\dfrac{2x + 7}{5} = \dfrac{10x - 4}{10}$

13. $\dfrac{3}{4}(x + 8) = -42$ **14.** $25(x + 0.4) = 21(x + 0.2)$

In problems 15–16, solve the literal equations for the specified variable.

15. $A = \dfrac{1}{2}bh$ Solve for b.   **16.** $A = P + PRT$ Solve for R.

In problems 17–25, solve the word problems.

17. When 5 times a number is increased by 30, the result is equal to 22 subtracted from 3 times the number. Find the number.

18. A chemistry lab seats 40 people. If the lab is full and the number of women is 7 more than twice the number of men, how many men are in the lab?

19. Find 3 consecutive odd integers whose sum is -105.

20. A family tries to conserve 9 gallons of water every 2 days. How many gallons of water will they conserve in the month of April, a 30-day month?

21. Mike's weight decreased from 200 pounds to 172 pounds. What was Mike's percent decrease in weight?

22. Wendy and Thad inherit $45,000 and the money is to be divided up in a ratio of 5 to 4. How much money is each going to inherit?

23. Carrie deposits $1,000 in an account and is told that she will receive $41 in simple interest at the end of six months. What is the account's rate of interest?

24. Guadalupe went on a 2,340-mile flight traveling at 520 miles per hour. How many hours was she in the air?

25. If the surface area of a tin can is 78π square inches and the radius is 3 inches, what is the height of the can? (Use the formula $S = 2\pi rh + 2\pi r^2$. Do not convert π to a decimal, but work with π as a constant.)

Solve the inequalities in problems 26 and 27 and graph your solutions on a number line.

26. $5 \le -5x + 20$ **27.** $-3x - 5(2x - 3) > 27 - 10x$

A BRIEF INTRODUCTION TO ANALYTIC GEOMETRY

This chapter presents a combination of algebra and geometry as an introduction to **analytic geometry**, invented by the French mathematician and philosopher René Descartes (1596-1650). Analytic geometry differs from plane geometry in that equations can be used to describe and analyze geometric figures. In this chapter we will restrict our discussion and analysis to lines and triangles. The subject of analytic geometry is important because most examples of relationships between variables can be graphed and then understood in a geometric fashion, and this understanding in turn helps us comprehend algebraic methods of reasoning. The wedding between algebra and geometry is rich in ideas and relationships; in later math courses you will discover more about analytic geometry than what we present in this book.

8.1 RECTANGULAR COORDINATE SYSTEM

OBJECTIVES

- To understand the foundations of the rectangular coordinate system
- To understand the concept of a signed distance from an axis and the concept of an ordered pair
- To learn some associated terminology, including the names of the axes, the quadrant names, and the name *origin*
- To plot a given ordered pair
- To read the ordered pair coordinates of a plotted point
- To calculate either the vertical or horizontal distance between two points on the same line

Rectangular Coordinate System

We previously introduced the concept of the real number line as a mechanism for realizing relationships between negative, zero, and positive numbers. In this section we are going to combine two such number lines; one has the usual horizontal orientation but the other has a vertical orientation in which the positive numbers appear above zero and the negative numbers appear below zero. The horizontal number line is called the x-axis and the vertical number line is called the y-axis. We label the positive and negative directions on each axis with the axis letter name followed by the corresponding sign. The arrows at the axes' extremes indicate that the axes continue forever in the indicated direction. The two lines are depicted in Figure 8.1.

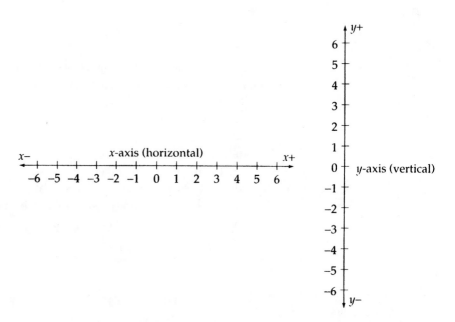

FIGURE 8.1   Separate vertical and horizontal axes shown before their combination

When we cross the two axes so that their 0-point origins coincide, the resulting two-dimensional figure is called the $x-y$ coordinate plane. Every point that appears in this plane is given two coordinates: one relative to the y-axis and one relative to the x-axis. (See Figure 8.2.)

In Figure 8.3 we have marked the coordinates of several points that are in the coordinate plane. Each point is given a pair of coordinates that are written between parentheses and separated by a comma. Such pairs are called **ordered pairs** and the order of the coordinates is crucial. The first number in each pair is called the x-coordinate and the second number in each pair is called the y-coordinate.

On first reading it may sound contradictory, but the **x-coordinate** denotes the signed distance of the point from the y-axis and the **y-coordinate** denotes the signed distance of the point from the x-axis. The notion of a signed distance and its relationship to ordered pairs can be understood by examining the points in Figure 8.3 labeled P, Q, R, S, and T.

Point P's x-coordinate is the number 4, and we can see point P lies four units to the right of the y-axis. At the same time, P's y-coordinate is the number 3, and we can see point P lies three units above the x-axis. Point Q is two units to the right of the y-axis and is five units above the x-axis. A

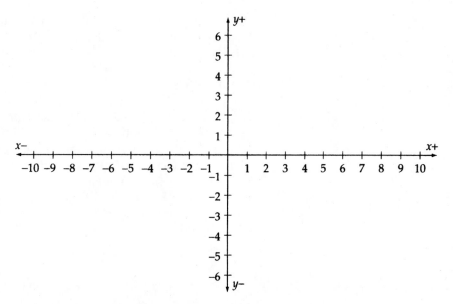

FIGURE 8.2 The *x−y* coordinate axes combined and the *x−y* plane

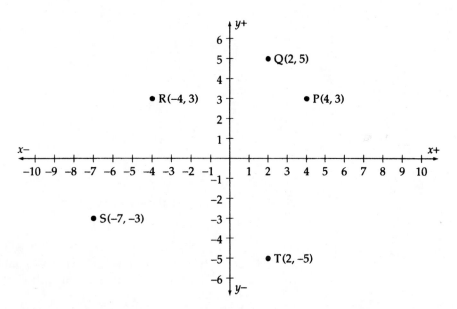

FIGURE 8.3 Sample points plotted and labeled with their ordered pair coordinates

positive *x*-coordinate always denotes a point that lies to the right of the *y*-axis, and a positive *y*-coordinate always denotes a point that lies above the *x*-axis.

To understand the signed distance concept when a coordinate is negative, study the coordinates of point T. The *y*-coordinate of point T is −5; thus, point T lies below the *x*-axis because the *y*-coordinate gives the position of a point relative to the *x*-axis. Point S has negative numbers for both of its coordinates, and, thus, point S lies to the left of the *y*-axis and below the *x*-axis. Only one of point R's coordinates is negative. Since it is the *x*-coordinate that is negative, R lies to the left of the *y*-axis. In every case, the actual distance that a point lies away from an axis is the absolute value of its corresponding coordinate.

To help further clarify the signs of the coordinates and the relative positions of points in the plane, names have been given to the sections of the plane whose coordinates all have the same signs. The plane can be considered to be divided into four sections, each of which is called a **quadrant**. The quadrants are traditionally numbered using Roman numerals that increase in a counterclockwise direction, starting with quadrant I as the quadrant in which both coordinates are positive. (See Figure 8.4.) Thus, a point that lies in Quadrant III will have a negative *y*-coordinate and a negative *x*-coordinate. A point with a negative *x*-coordinate but a positive *y*-coordinate must lie in Quadrant II.

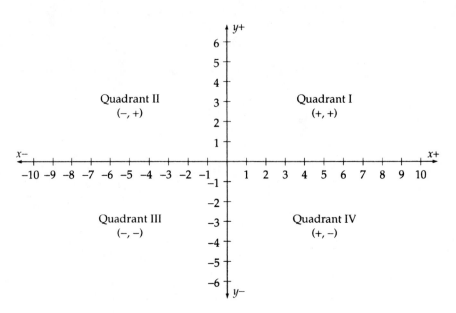

FIGURE 8.4   Four quadrants of the x−y coordinate system

In each of Figures 8.2, 8.3, and 8.4 we have only labeled a limited portion of the *x−y* coordinate plane. This plane extends an infinite distance in all directions, but of course we can only show a limited portion on any given page.

There are coordinate systems used for marine navigation and aviation that differ from the coordinate system shown here. However, the *x−y* coordinate system is the most fundamental of all coordinate systems and is usually the first type of coordinate system one studies. The *x−y* coordinate system is also called the **rectangular coordinate system** for the following reason. The point at which the two axes cross has the special coordinates (0,0) and is called the **origin**. Now consider Figure 8.5 in which point P is shown again. If we draw horizontal and vertical lines from P to each of the coordinate axes, the resulting figure is a rectangle. Thus, every point in each of the four quadrants determines a rectangle and constitutes one corner, the opposite corner of which is the origin.

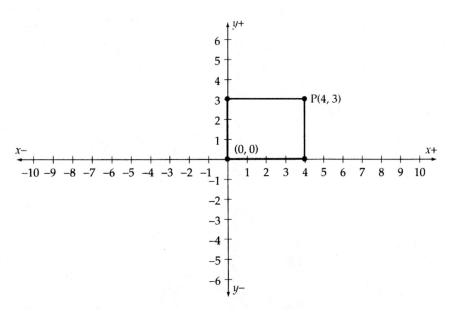

FIGURE 8.5   Point P shown with the rectangle its coordinates determine

Although we prefer to use the terms x-coordinate and y-coordinate, sometimes the x- and y-coordinates of a point are referred to as the **abscissa** and the **ordinate**. The abscissa is the x or the horizontal coordinate and the ordinate is the y or the vertical coordinate. The rectangular coordinate system is sometimes referred to as the **Cartesian coordinate system**, in honor of Descartes.

| **EXAMPLE 1** | Figure 8.6 (see p. 472) shows an x–y coordinate system in which points labeled A–F with integer coordinates have already been graphed. Write the ordered pair coordinates for each of the points. |

SOLUTION $A = (3,2)$ $B = (2,4)$ $C = (-4,5)$

$D = (-8, -4)$ $E = (1, -5)$ $F = (5, -3)$ ■

| **EXAMPLE 2** | Name the quadrant occupied by each of the points labeled A–F in Example 1. |

SOLUTION   A: Quadrant I   B: Quadrant I   C: Quadrant II

D: Quadrant III   E: Quadrant IV   F: Quadrant IV   ■

There is a one-to-one correspondence between ordered pairs and points in the coordinate plane. Every point in the plane determines a unique ordered pair and every ordered pair determines a unique point in the plane. Fundamental to the concept of an ordered pair is the fact that two ordered pairs are considered equal if and only if both x- and y-coordinates are identical. More formally,

$$(a,b) = (c,d) \text{ if and only if } a = c \text{ and } b = d$$

Thus, the point (2,3) is different from the point (3,2): $(2,3) \neq (3,2)$.

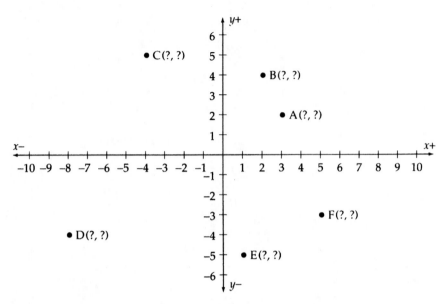

FIGURE 8.6   Example 1 points

Another useful observation is that if a point lies on one of the coordinate axes, that point must have a zero for one of its coordinates. Remember that the x-coordinate is the signed distance from the y-axis and the y-coordinate is the signed distance from the x-axis. So if a point lies on the y-axis its x-coordinate must be zero; if a point lies on the x-axis its y-coordinate must be zero. The coordinates of the origin are (0,0) and this is the only point that lies on both axes simultaneously.

EXAMPLE 3   Plot and label the following points in an $x-y$ coordinate system.

A: (3,5)   B: (−5,2)   C: (2, −4)   D: (−6, −5)

E: (−5, −4)   F: (−4,4)   G: (7,0)   H: (0, −3)

SOLUTION   The solution appears in Figure 8.7.

Horizontal and Vertical Distances

Earlier we introduced the expression $|a - b|$ to represent the distance between two points, say A and B, whose coordinates on a number line were a and b. We also remarked that the distance from A to B is the same as the distance from B to A so $|a - b| = |b - a|$. In this section we will extend this idea to calculate the distance between two points that lie on the same vertical or horizontal line, and in Section 8.2 we will develop a more general distance formula that will give the distance between any two points in the $x-y$ coordinate plane.

Consider points A and B as shown in Figure 8.8. If you were standing on point A and decided to walk to point B, how far would you have to walk? Since A and B have the same y-coordinate, these two points lie on a

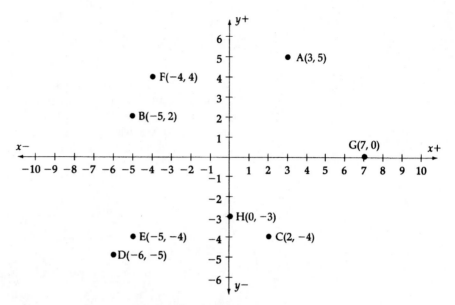

FIGURE 8.7   Points showing the ordered pair coordinate answers to Example 3

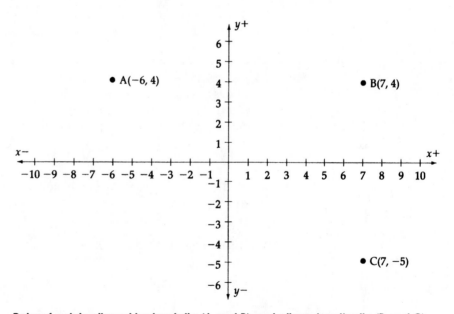

FIGURE 8.8   Pairs of points aligned horizontally (A and B) and aligned vertically (B and C)

horizontal line that connects them. We use the notation $d(A, B)$ to represent the distance from point A to point B, read as "the distance from point A to point B."

Since point A has coordinates $(-6,4)$ and point B has coordinates $(7,4)$ we take the absolute value of the difference between the x-coordinates to find the horizontal distance between A and B.

$$d(A,B) = \left| -6 - 7 \right| = \left| -13 \right| = 13$$

This also could be calculated by reversing the subtraction within the absolute value expression.

$$d(A,B) = |7-(-6)| = |13| = 13$$

Next, consider the vertical distance between points B and C. Because B and C are the same signed distance from the y-axis, B and C have the same x-coordinate. The coordinates of points B and C differ only in their y-coordinates, and the vertical distance between B and C is given by the absolute value of the difference between their y-coordinates.

$$d(B,C) = |4 - (-5)| = |4 + (+5)| = |9| = 9$$

CALCULATING VERTICAL AND HORIZONTAL DISTANCE BETWEEN POINTS

Assume A has coordinates (x_1,y_1) and B has coordinates (x_2,y_2).

If $y_1 = y_2$, then A and B are horizontally aligned points, and the horizontal distance between A and B $= |x_1 - x_2|$.

If $x_1 = x_2$, then A and B are vertically aligned points, and the vertical distance between A and B $= |y_1 - y_2|$.

EXAMPLE 4

Plot points A and B in the same coordinate system and then use absolute values to calculate the vertical distance between A and B. Then plot points C and D in the same coordinate system and use absolute values to calculate the horizontal distance between C and D.

A: (3,5)   B: (3, −2)   C: (−6, −6)   D: (4, −6)

SOLUTION   We do not show the graph of the plotted points, but the distance calculations are given:

The vertical distance between A and B is $d(A,B) = |5 - (-2)| = |7| = 7$.

The horizontal distance between C and D is
$d(C,D) = |-6 - 4| = |-10| = 10$.   ■

P R A C T I C E   F O R   S U C C E S S

Practice 1.   Assume that all the points in Figure 8.9 have integer coordinates and read the graph to determine the ordered pair coordinates of points A, B, C, D, E, and F.

Practice 2.   Name the quadrant occupied by each of the points labeled A–F in Figure 8.9.

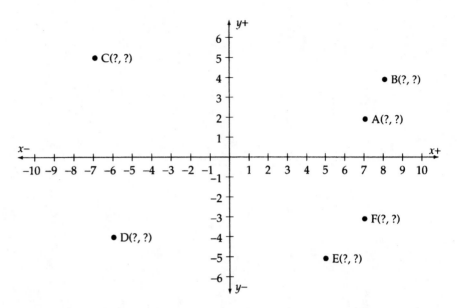

FIGURE 8.9   Practice 1 exercise points

Practice 3.   Plot and label the following points in an $x-y$ coordinate system.
A: $(-6,2)$ B: $(8, -5)$ C: $(0, -3)$
D: $(-7, -4)$ E: $(9,4)$ F: $(-6,0)$

Practice 4.   Use absolute value to determine the horizontal distance between the point A$(-25,35)$ and the point B$(17,35)$.

Practice 5.   Use absolute value to determine the vertical distance between the point C$(37, -29)$ and the point D$(37, -42)$.

Practice 6.   If a point is such that its signed distance from the x-axis is -3 units and its signed distance from y-axis is $+7$ units, in what quadrant does the point lie?

EXERCISES 8.1

In exercises 1–15, use Figure 8.10 to determine the ordered pair coordinates of each corresponding point.

1. A	**2.** B
3. C	**4.** D
5. E	**6.** F
7. G	**8.** H
9. I	**10.** J
11. K	**12.** L
13. M	**14.** N
15. O	

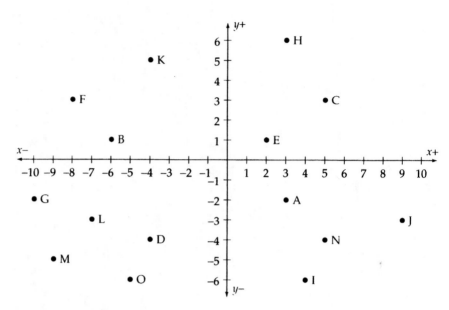

FIGURE 8.10   Points A–O used in exercises 1-20

In exercises 16–20, use the points in Figure 8.10 and name the quadrant of the indicated points.

16. B   **17.** D
18. H   **19.** M
20. N

Use one coordinate system graph to plot all the points in exercises 21–32. Label each point in your graph with both its letter and its ordered pair coordinates.

21. A(6,1)   **22.** B(−4,4)
23. C(5, −6)   **24.** D(1, −9)
25. E(−9, −6)   **26.** F(0, −4)
27. G(−6,8)   **28.** H(9, −4)
29. I(0,0)   **30.** J(8, −8)
31. K(−2,0)   **32.** L(0, −3)

In exercises 33–42, you are given two points that are either vertically or horizontally aligned. Name the type of alignment and use absolute value to determine the corresponding distance between the points. Graphing the points is not necessary.

33. A(27, −48)   B(27,30)   **34.** C(−34, −47)   D(−31, −47)
35. A(5, −13)   B(17,−13)   **36.** C(29, −33)   D(29,25)
37. C(8,25)   D(−18,25)   **38.** A(9,0)   B(9,22)
39. C(21,10)   D(32,10)   **40.** A(−20,36)   B(36,36)
41. A(−31,0)   B(5,0)   **42.** C(0, −12)   D(−27, −12)

👁 Looking Back

43. Apply the distributive law to the expression: $5x^3 + 5y^2 + 5z$.

44. Multiply $(-5x^4 + 6x^3 - 9x) \cdot (4x + 3)$.

45. Solve for x: $3x - 8 = 5x + 2$.

46. Simplify the complex fraction $\dfrac{\dfrac{3}{5} + \dfrac{1}{2}}{\dfrac{1}{6} - \dfrac{8}{15}}$.

47. Reduce $\sqrt{720}$.

48. Simplify $\left(\dfrac{1}{3}\right)^3 \div (-3)^{-3}$.

49. Subtract $(8x^5 - 7x^4 + 6x^3) - (10x^5 - 5x^4 + 7x^3)$.

50. Multiply $-5x^4y^2(3x^2y^3 - 6xy^4 + 2x^3y)$.

PRACTICE-FOR-SUCCESS ANSWERS

1. A(7,2)   B(8,4)   C(−7,5)   D(−6, −4)   E(5, −5)   F(7, −3)

2. A is in quadrant I.   B is in quadrant I.   C is in quadrant II.
D is in quadrant III.   E is in quadrant IV.   F is in quadrant IV.

3.

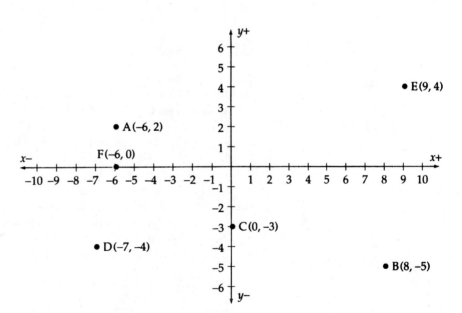

FIGURE 8.11   Points A–F used in Practice exercise 3

4. The horizontal distance from A to B is $d(A,B) = |-25 - 17| = |-42| =$ 42.

5. The vertical distance from C to D is $d(C,D) = |-29 - (-42)| = |13| =$ 13.

6. The point has coordinates $(7, -3)$ and, thus, the point lies in the fourth quadrant IV.

8.2	**DISTANCE FORMULA AND GRAPHING LINEAR EQUATIONS**

OBJECTIVES

☐ To develop the general distance formula

☐ To apply the distance formula

☐ To use the y-intercept to graph a linear equation

☐ To use both x-intercept and y-intercept points to graph an equation

---

In the previous section we gave two formulas to calculate the horizontal and vertical distances between two points that were aligned either horizontally or vertically. In this section we are going to expand that development to derive a formula to calculate the distance between any two points in the $x-y$ coordinate plane, even if those two points are not aligned horizontally or vertically. We are also going to illustrate the connection between an equation using x and y variables and a graph in the $x-y$ plane.

Distance Formula

The development of the formula that gives the distance between any two points in the $x-y$ coordinate plane is based on the Pythagorean theorem introduced in Section 4.5 and on the horizontal and vertical distance formulas developed in Section 8.1. To find the distance between two points that are *not* aligned either horizontally or vertically, such as between A and B in Figure 8.12, we first draw the vertical and horizontal line segments from points A and B that connect at point C; the point opposite the hypotenuse in a right triangle. The hypotenuse of the right triangle is the line segment that connects point A with point B. Point C is given the same y-coordinate as point A and the same x-coordinate as point B; thus, point C is horizontally aligned with point A and vertically aligned with point B. Note the vertical and horizontal distance calculations:

$$d(A,C) = |-7 - 3| = |-10| = 10$$
$$d(C,B) = |5 - 2| = |3| = 3$$

According to the Pythagorean theorem, the square of the hypotenuse AB is equal to the sum of the squares of line segments AC and CB.

$$d(A,B)^2 = d(A,C)^2 + d(C,B)^2$$

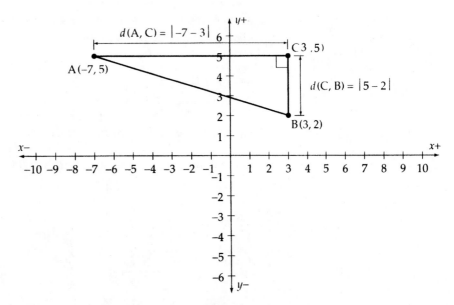

FIGURE 8.12   Right triangle with line segment AB as the hypotenuse

or

$$d(A,B) = \sqrt{d(A,C)^2 + d(C,B)^2}$$
$$= \sqrt{|-7 - 3|^2 + |5 - 2|^2}$$
$$= \sqrt{10^2 + 3^2}$$
$$= \sqrt{109}$$
$$\approx 10.44030651$$

We see that the straight-line distance from A to B is a little more than 10 units; use a ruler to verify that this calculation matches the distance shown in Figure 8.12.

An argument similar to the one just given can be used to find the distance between any two points, say $P(x_1,y_1)$ and $Q(x_2,y_2)$. The expressions $|x_1 - x_2|$ and $|y_1 - y_2|$ always give the vertical and horizontal distances between P and Q, whether or not these points are horizontally or vertically aligned. In general we have

$$d(P,Q) = \sqrt{|x_1 - x_2|^2 + |y_1 - y_2|^2}$$

However, this is not the way the formula is usually written. The squares of the absolute values can be simplified to the squares of the coordinate differences without the absolute values because

$$|a - b|^2 = (a - b)^2$$

To better understand this simplification, consider the example using the horizontal distance between A and C in Figure 8.12.

$$|-7 - 3|^2 = |-10|^2 = 10^2 = 100 \text{ whereas } (-7 - 3)^2 = (-10)^2 = 100$$

So $|-7 - 3|^2 = (-7 - 3)^2$ and this second form is usually considered simpler because it does not use absolute values. When squaring, we arrive at the same answer whether we write the absolute value bars or not, so the absolute value bars are optional. Without the squaring operation, the absolute value bars are necessary.

Because distances are never negative, the absolute value bars were required in Section 8.1; there we were calculating simple horizontal and vertical distances and the absolute values prevented the answers from being negative. There were no squaring operations in Section 8.1, but because squaring operations are part of the Pythagorean theorem we can replace $|x_1 - x_2|^2$ with $(x_1 - x_2)^2$ and we can replace $|y_1 - y_2|^2$ with $(y_1 - y_2)^2$. The general distance formula is a slight variation of the formula

$$d(P,Q) = \sqrt{|x_1 - x_2|^2 + |y_1 - y_2|^2}$$

DISTANCE FORMULA FOR TWO POINTS IN THE $x-y$ PLANE

If points P and Q have coordinates $P(x_1,y_1)$ and $Q(x_2,y_2)$, then

$$d(P,Q) = \sqrt{(x_1 - x_2)^2 + (y_1 - y_2)^2}$$

EXAMPLE 1

Use the distance formula to calculate the distances between the following pairs of points P and Q.

a. P(13, 15) and Q(8, 3)   **b.** P(−3, 6) and Q(4, −9)
c. P(8, −5) and Q(10, −5)   **d.** P(−6, 7) and Q(−6, 11)

SOLUTION   **a.** $d(P,Q) = \sqrt{(13 - 8)^2 + (15 - 3)^2} = \sqrt{5^2 + 12^2}$
$= \sqrt{25 + 144} = \sqrt{169} = 13$

b. $d(P,Q) = \sqrt{(-3 - 4)^2 + [6 - (-9)]^2} = \sqrt{(-7)^2 + 15^2}$
$= \sqrt{49 + 225} = \sqrt{274} \approx 16.55294536$

c. $d(P,Q) = \sqrt{(8 - 10)^2 + [-5 - (-5)]^2} = \sqrt{(-2)^2 + 0^2}$
$= \sqrt{4 + 0} = \sqrt{4} = 2$

Note that P and Q are horizontally aligned because P and Q have the same y-coordinate. The y-coordinate difference is 0 and there is no right triangle, so in this case the horizontal distance between P and Q is simply the expression $|8 - 10| = 2$, as it would have been calculated in Section 8.1. The distance formula yields the same answer because

$$\sqrt{(8 - 10)^2} = \sqrt{|8 - 10|^2} = |8 - 10|$$

d. $d(P,Q) = \sqrt{(-6 - (-6))^2 + (7 - 11)^2} = \sqrt{0^2 + (-4)^2}$
$= \sqrt{0 + 16} = \sqrt{16} = 4$

Note that in this case P and Q were vertically aligned because P and Q have the same x-coordinate. In this case there is no right triangle because the difference in the x-coordinates is 0.   ■

Graphing Equations of the Form $y = mx + b$

We have already seen examples of formulas in Section 6.5. One of the benefits of introducing analytic geometry is that it allows us to see a geometric picture of a formula. Consider the equation $y = \frac{1}{3}x - 2$. This equation has two variables, x and y, and we can associate points in the plane with this equation by agreeing to the following rule.

> Point $P(x,y)$ will be plotted if and only if the x and y coordinates of P satisfy the equation.

We will usually find it convenient to select various values of x and use the formula to calculate the corresponding y-values. For example, when $x = 3$, $y = \frac{1}{3} \cdot 3 - 2 = 1 - 2 = -1$; so the ordered pair $(3, -1)$ satisfies the equation. If $x = -6$, then the corresponding value of y is calculated as $y = \frac{1}{3} \cdot (-6) - 2 = -2 - 2 = -4$; so two different ordered pairs that satisfy the equation $y = \frac{1}{3}x - 2$ are $(3, -1)$ and $(-6, -4)$.

The equation $y = \frac{1}{3}x - 2$ is an open sentence. For each value of x there is a corresponding value of y that makes the equation true. The graph of the equation is the set of all ordered pairs (x,y) that satisfy the equation. Only one pair of coordinates can satisfy this equation at a time, but there are an infinite number of such pairs because x can take on an infinite number of different values.

Although it is not necessary or even possible to plot every point, one device that can help organize the calculations of the x and y coordinates is to make a table of values. The table is most conveniently made by labeling two columns that are separated by a cross symbol; one label is for the column of x-values and the other label is for the column of y-values. In the table below we have placed the x and y values in two horizontal rows, rather than two vertical columns. All of the pairs in this table satisfy the equation $y = \frac{1}{3}x - 2$, but not all the pairs that satisfy this equation are shown in the table.

x	-6	-3	-2	0	1	2	3	4	6	9
y	-4	-3	$-2\frac{2}{3}$	-2	$-1\frac{2}{3}$	$-1\frac{1}{3}$	-1	$-\frac{2}{3}$	0	1

Some of the calculations involve fractions, and points with fractional coordinates are plotted by approximating where the fractional parts lie between the unit marks on the axes. For example, when $x = 4$ then $y = -\frac{2}{3}$, so when this point is plotted the x-coordinate is directly over a grid mark but the y-coordinate is one third of a unit above the -1 grid mark.

When we plot all of these points in an $x-y$ coordinate system, a pattern of dots appears; the points all seem to lie on one line. The graph of the equation $y = \frac{1}{3}x - 2$ is a line. In the graph shown in Figure 8.13 we have plotted all the points with integer coordinates between -10 and 10.

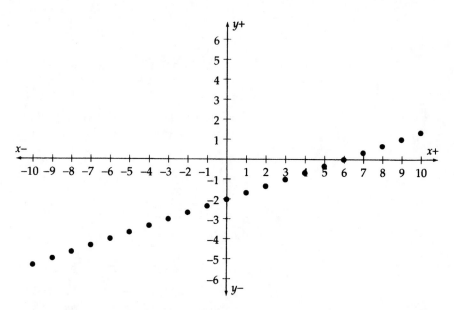

FIGURE 8.13   Sampling of integer x-values between -10 and 10 for the equation

$$y = \frac{1}{3}x - 2$$

Given that the pattern of dots continues, when we plot the graph of the equation $y = \frac{1}{3}x - 2$, we simply fill in a solid line that connects all the points. Filling in the line as a solid line is equivalent to plotting all of the infinite number of points that lie on the line.

Any equation of the form $y = mx + b$ is always a graph that is a line. The coefficient of x is the constant number called m, and the number b is the constant that is added. For the example equation $y = \frac{1}{3}x - 2$, we would say $m = \frac{1}{3}$ and $b = -2$, since subtracting 2 is the same as adding -2.

Figure 8.14 shows the solid line that is the graph of the equation $y = \frac{1}{3}x - 2$. We have drawn arrows on the line to indicate that the line extends beyond that portion of the $x-y$ plane that can be shown in the graph.

In the remainder of this section we will first explore the graphs of equations of the form

$$y = mx + b \qquad \text{where } m \text{ and } b \text{ are constants}$$

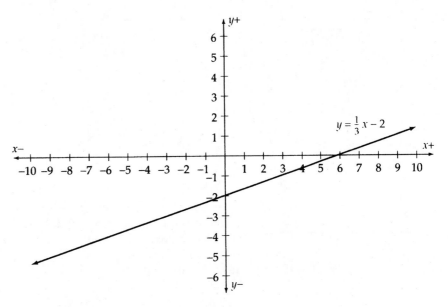

FIGURE 8.14   Solid line graph for the equation $y = \dfrac{1}{3}x - 2$

and then we will explore equations of the form

$$ax + by = c \qquad \text{where } a, b, \text{ and } c \text{ are constants}$$

Equations in either of these two forms have graphs that are straight lines. We can simplify the graphing process because only two distinct points are required to determine any line. Note that to plot two points requires calculating four coordinates.

y-Intercept Point and y-Intercept Coordinates

One point that always satisfies the equation $y = mx + b$ has coordinates $(0, b)$; that is, when $x = 0$ then $y = b$. Substitute $x = 0$ in this equation and calculate y:

$$\text{when } x = 0, \qquad y = m \cdot 0 + b = 0 + b = b$$

Because a point is on the y-axis whenever its x-coordinate is 0, the point $(0, b)$ always lies on the y-axis. This point is given a special status and is called the **y-intercept**. Actually, the term *y-intercept* is ambiguous because sometimes we refer to the y-intercept as a point (remember a point has two coordinates) and sometimes we refer to the y-intercept as the number that is the y-coordinate.

If you look back at both Figure 8.13 and Figure 8.14, you should find that the point that lies on the y-axis has coordinates $(0, -2)$ and this corresponds to the equation $y = \dfrac{1}{3}x - 2$ in which $b = -2$; when $x = 0$ then $y = -2$.

EXAMPLE 2

Find the y-intercept point coordinates for the following linear equations.

a. $y = -5x + 7$ **b.** $y = 3x - 10$

SOLUTION
a. When $x = 0$ we calculate y to find the y-intercept as a number.

$y = -5 \cdot 0 + 7 = 7$. The y-intercept point has coordinates $(0, 7)$.

b. When $x = 0$ we calculate y to find the y-intercept as a number.

$y = 3 \cdot 0 - 10 = -10$. The y-intercept point has coordinates $(0, -10)$.

■

EXAMPLE 3

Graph the equation $y = -2x + 4$ by first plotting the y-intercept point and then plotting two other points, say when $x = 3$ and when $x = 5$.

SOLUTION
The following short table is all that is required.

x	y
0	4
3	-2
5	-6

When these points are plotted as in Figure 8.15, they all lie along the same line that determines the graph of the equation.

■

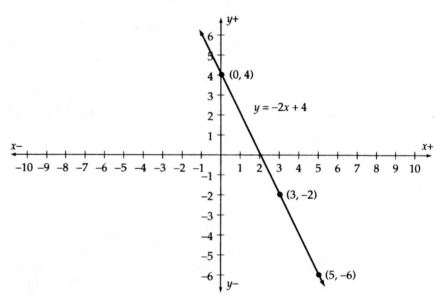

FIGURE 8.15   Graph for the equation $y = -2x + 4$

x-Intercept Point and x-Intercept Coordinates

The process of setting $x = 0$ and solving for y to find the y-intercept has an analog for finding where a graph crosses the x-axis. The point (or x-coordinate) where a line crosses the x-axis is called the **x-intercept**. The following rules are based on the fact that when a point's x-coordinate is zero that point must be on the y-axis, and when a point's y-coordinate is zero the point must be on the x-axis.

Usually only the y-intercept is convenient for equations of the form $y = mx + b$. However, for equations of the form $ax + by = c$ it is often convenient to calculate and plot both the x- and y-intercepts.

FINDING THE x- AND y-INTERCEPTS

To find the y-intercept of the graph of any equation, set $x = 0$ in that equation and then solve for y.
To find the x-intercept of the graph of any equation, set $y = 0$ in that equation and then solve for x.

Graphing Equations of the Form $ax + by = c$

Another form for equations of lines is $ax + by = c$. An equation in this form can be graphed most easily by finding both the x-intercept and y-intercept points.

EXAMPLE 4 | Graph the equation $3x + 5y = 15$ by plotting both the x-intercept and y-intercept points.

SOLUTION | Since two points determine a line, we need only find the x- and y-intercept points, which requires calculating four coordinates. Setting $x = 0$, the equation reduces to $5y = 15$, so $y = 3$ when $x = 0$. Setting $y = 0$, the equation reduces to $3x = 15$, so $x = 5$ when $y = 0$. We plot the two points $(0,3)$ and $(5,0)$ and then draw the line connecting them, as shown in Figure 8.16. ■

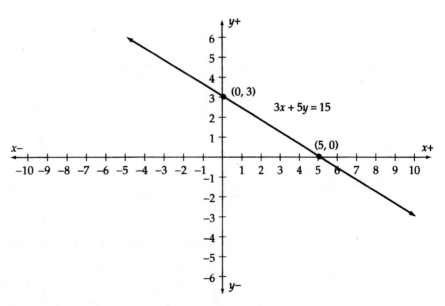

FIGURE 8.16   Graph for the equation $3x + 5y = 15$, showing its x- and y-intercepts

| **EXAMPLE 5** | Transform the equation $-3x + 8y = 24$ into the form $y = mx + b$ and then identify the values of m and b. |

SOLUTION   First we solve the equation for y in terms of x.

$$-3x + 8y = 24$$
$$8y = 3x + 24 \qquad \text{Add } 3x \text{ to both sides.}$$
$$\frac{8y}{8} = \frac{3x + 24}{8}$$
$$y = \frac{3x}{8} + \frac{24}{8}$$
$$y = \frac{3}{8}x + 3$$

Since m is the coefficient on x and b is the constant that is added to the x-term, we have $m = \dfrac{3}{8}$ and $b = 3$. This example shows how to convert from the general form of the equation of a line to the slope-intercept form.   ▪

P R A C T I C E   F O R   S U C C E S S

Practice 1.   Plot the points A$(-5, -4)$ and B$(6, 6)$ and use the distance formula to find the straight line distance between A and B. Then use a ruler to measure the distance and verify that your calculation matches the graph.

Practice 2.   Without plotting the points, use the distance formula to find $d(A, B)$ with A$(-7, 5)$ and B$(-10, 13)$.

Practice 3.   Make a table of six values for the equation $y = -\dfrac{1}{2}x + 3$ using $x = -6$, $x = -4$, $x = 0$, $x = 2$, $x = 4$, $x = 6$. Then plot the points in the table.

Practice 4.   Graph the equation $y = -3x + 6$ by first finding the y-intercept and then choosing $x = 2$ and $x = 3$ as two other points. Fill in the graph as a solid line.

Practice 5.   Graph the equation $-5x - 8y = 40$ by plotting both the x-intercept and y-intercept points.

Practice 6.   Transform the equation $8x - 4y = 20$ into the form of $y = mx + b$ and then identify the values of m and b.

EXERCISES 8.2

In exercises 1–10, use the distance formula to compute the distance between the points P and Q.

1. P$(-3, 2)$ Q$(5, 1)$ **2.** P$(6, 4)$ Q$(-2, 1)$
3. P$(-8, 17)$ Q$(-1, -7)$ **4.** P$(-14, 13)$ Q$(-3, -47)$

5. P(1, −4)   Q(−7, 11)   **6.** P(18, −18)   Q(9, 22)

7. P(0, 0)   Q(20, 21)   **8.** P(−4, −2)   Q(4, −17)

9. P(25, −10)   Q(20,2)   **10.** P(−15, 18)   Q(−13, 22)

Graph the equations in exercises 11–20 by first finding the y-intercept and then choosing x = −3 and x = 3 as two other points. Fill in each graph as a solid line.

11. $y = -2x + 2$

12. $y = \dfrac{5}{3}x - 2$

13. $y = \dfrac{1}{3}x + 5$

14. $y = \dfrac{2}{3}x - 3$

15. $y = \dfrac{1}{2}x + \dfrac{5}{2}$

16. $y = -\dfrac{1}{3}x + 2$

17. $y = -x + 6$

18. $y = -2x - 3$

19. $y = \dfrac{1}{6}x + \dfrac{1}{2}$

20. $y = -\dfrac{5}{6}x + \dfrac{5}{2}$

Graph the equations in exercises 21–30 by first finding both the x-intercept and the y-intercept.

21. $4x + 6y = 12$

22. $6x + 9y = 72$

23. $-5x + 10y = 30$

24. $-8x - 10y = -40$

25. $-12x + 3y = -24$

26. $15x - 25y = 75$

27. $6x + 10y = -30$

28. $9x - 12y = 144$

29. $14x + 7y = 42$

30. $-8x + 18y = -72$

Transform the equations in exercises 31–40 into equations in the form of y = mx + b and then identify the values of m and b.

31. $13x + 6y = 5$

32. $4x + 11y = -6$

33. $-12x - 4y = 16$

34. $6x - 14y = 10$

35. $-9x + 11y = 99$

36. $3x - 15y = 75$

37. $26x - 39y = 52$

38. $x + 8y = 20$

39. $-3x - y = 54$

40. $-12x - 10y = 48$

 Looking Back

41. Simplify $x^{13} \div x^{-8}$ to a single power of x.

42. What is the basic operation for the expression $5x + \sqrt{9 - (-7)} - 3x^3$.

43. How is a binomial defined?

44. What is the LCM of 36 and 42?

45. State the divisibility test for 3.

46. Are the equations $x = \sqrt{49}$ and $x = 7$ equivalent equations?

47. What is the definition of an integer?

48. Name four undefined operations in mathematics.

PRACTICE-FOR-SUCCESS ANSWERS

1. $d(A, B) = \sqrt{(-5 - 6)^2 + (-4 - 6)^2} = \sqrt{221} \approx 14.86606875$.
   See Figure 8.17.

2. $d(A, B) = \sqrt{[-7 - (-10)]^2 + (5 - 13)^2} = \sqrt{3^2 + (-8)^2}$
   $= \sqrt{9 + 64} = \sqrt{73} \approx 8.544003745$

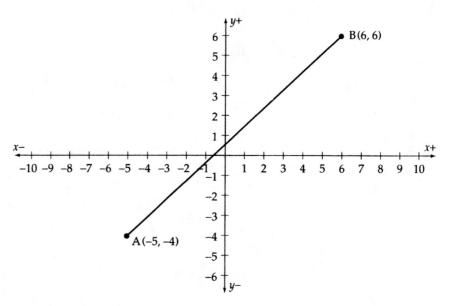

FIGURE 8.17   Practice 1 exercise

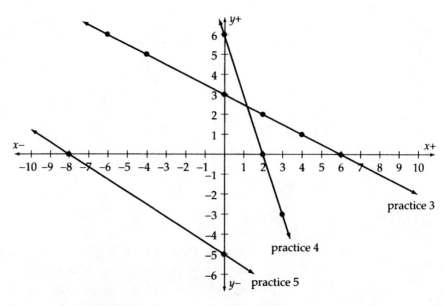

FIGURE 8.18   Line graph answers to Practice exercises 3, 4, and 5

3. x	y
-6	6
-4	5
0	3
2	2
4	1
6	0

4. x	y
0	6
2	0
3	-3

5. x	y
0	-5
-8	0

The graphs for Practice problems 3, 4, and 5 are all shown together in Figure 8.18.

6. $y = 2x - 5$. $m = 2$ and $b = -5$.

8.3

SLOPES OF LINES AND GEOMETRY OF SIMILAR TRIANGLES

OBJECTIVES

☐ To develop and show the applications of the notations Δx and Δy

☐ To recognize similar triangles and their relationships to slopes of lines

☐ To recognize the relationship between the slope of a line, equivalent fractions, and similar triangles

Δx and Δy Notations

If A and B denote any two points in the coordinate plane, we consider A to be the first point and B to be the second point. If we start at point A and move to point B, there will be a change in our coordinates. This change has both a horizontal and vertical component that will be called the *change in x* and the *change in y,* respectively. As an example, consider the two points shown in Figure 8.19, where A has coordinates $(-5, 4)$ and B has coordinates $(3, 2)$.

Moving from point A to point B our x-coordinate changes from -5 to 3. What is called the change in x, which is denoted by Δx, is the difference between 3 and -5 which is the quantity

$$\Delta x = 3 - (-5) = 3 + (+5) = 8 \qquad \Delta x \text{ is read as "delta } x\text{"}$$

When x changes from its original value of -5 at A to its new value of 3 at B, the amount of the change is 8.

The original x + the change in x = the new value of x

$$-5 + \Delta x = 3$$

Similarly, we calculate the change in the y-coordinates by subtracting the new value from the original value. The change in y is denoted by Δy and is calculated as

$$\Delta y = 2 - 4 = -2$$

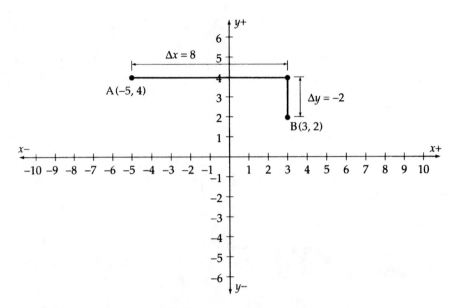

FIGURE 8.19   Graph showing Δx and Δy, starting from point A and moving to point B

So when y starts with an original value of 4 at A and changes to the new value 2 at B, the change in the y-value is -2.

The original y + the change in y = the new value of y

$$4 + \Delta y = 2$$

If point A has coordinates (x_1, y_1) and point B has coordinates (x_2, y_2), and if point A is considered the initial point and point B is considered the new point, then we can define

$$\Delta x = x_2 - x_1 \text{ and } \Delta y = y_2 - y_1$$

The Δ-values are related to the horizontal and vertical distances that are labeled in Figure 8.19.

Another way of describing Δx and Δy is to say that they represent the *signed* horizontal and vertical distances between point A and point B. Since the Δx and Δy values are just differences between coordinate values, Δx and Δy can be negative numbers. In the preceding example Δy was negative.

EXAMPLE 1   Given A(14, −40) and B(−10, −25) and assuming A is the starting point, find the Δx and Δy changes in the coordinates if we were to move from point A to point B.

SOLUTION $\Delta x = -10 - 14 = -24$
$\Delta y = -25 - (-40) = -25 + 40 = 15$
Note that the change in x is negative but the change in y is positive, even though both of the y-coordinates were negative. The move from A to B would be a move to the left and up, with the signs of Δx and Δy giving clues as to the horizontal and vertical directions involved in the move. The absolute values of Δx and Δy determine the lengths of the moves.   ■

| **EXAMPLE 2** | Imagine we are standing in the $x-y$ coordinate plane on the point A$(-5, 7)$. We move to a new point by going down 3 units and then to the left 5 units. What are the coordinates of our new position and what values of Δx and Δy are associated with this move? |

SOLUTION   Our y-coordinate starts at 7 and drops down 3 units; our new y-coordinate is 4 and $\Delta y = 4 - 7 = -3$.

Our original x-coordinate is -5 and the horizontal movement to the left by 5 units makes our new x-coordinate -10. $\Delta x = -10 - (-5) = -10 + 5 = -5$. Whenever we calculate Δy or Δx we take the new value minus the original value.   ■

Another Form of the Distance Formula

We will introduce two applications of the Δx and Δy notations. The first application is sometimes considered a simplification of the distance formula already given in Section 8.2. If A(x_1, y_1) and B(x_2, y_2) are any two points in the $x-y$ coordinate plane, then

$$d(\text{A, B}) = \sqrt{(x_1 - x_2)^2 + (y_1 - y_2)^2} = \sqrt{\Delta x^2 + \Delta y^2}$$

Because of the squaring operation, it doesn't matter which point, A or B, is considered the original point. But in general, whenever the Δx and Δy notations are used, consideration must be given as to which point is considered the "original point" and which point is considered the "new point."

The Δ-notations are another example of writing adjacent mathematical symbols that do *not* contain an implied multiplication between them. Just as the future value variable FV contains two symbols that make one name, Δx should be considered the name of a single quantity. Thus, when we write the square of Δx we are not squaring x and multiplying by Δ; $\Delta x^2 = (\Delta x)^2$, and since the parentheses are not necessary they may be omitted.

| **EXAMPLE 3** | Use the distance formula with the Δx and Δy notations to find the distance between the two points in Example 1. |

SOLUTION   Refer back to Example 1 where we calculated $\Delta x = -24$ and $\Delta y = 15$. Then,

$$d(\text{A, B}) = \sqrt{\Delta x^2 + \Delta y^2} = \sqrt{(-24)^2 + (15)^2} = \sqrt{801} \approx 28.3019$$ ■

Slope of a Line

The second application of the Δx and Δy notations is in the calculation of what is called the **slope of a line.** Intuitively the slope of a line is a number that measures the steepness of the line. In this sense the slope of a line may be compared to the slope of a roof on a house; the "larger" the slope, the more steep is the slant of the line. The stated definition of the slope of a line makes this idea more concrete.

DEFINITION	SLOPE OF A LINE

If $A(x_1, y_1)$ and $B(x_2, y_2)$ are any two points on a line, where $x_1 \neq x_2$, the slope of the line is denoted by the number m and

$$\text{the slope of the line} = m = \frac{\Delta y}{\Delta x}$$

When $x_1 = x_2$, the slope of the line is undefined.

In actual calculations slope is usually arrived at by considering either of the following two fractions:

$$m = \frac{y_2 - y_1}{x_2 - x_1} \text{ or } m = \frac{y_1 - y_2}{x_1 - x_2}$$

To understand why the second fraction is the same as the first, consider that $\frac{\Delta y}{\Delta x} = \frac{(-1) \cdot \Delta y}{(-1) \cdot \Delta x}$ and apply the distributive law in both the numerator and denominator.

$$m = \frac{\Delta y}{\Delta x} = \frac{(-1) \cdot (y_2 - y_1)}{(-1) \cdot (x_2 - x_1)} = \frac{-y_2 + y_1}{-x_2 + x_1} = \frac{y_1 + (-y_2)}{x_1 + (-x_2)} = \frac{y_1 - y_2}{x_1 - x_2}$$

Note the ordering of the subscripts in the two fractions for calculating slope. We can perform either the 1s minus the 2s or the 2s minus the 1s, but we must subtract in the same order in both the numerator and denominator.

To better understand the subscript order, consider the following two fractions, which are the wrong calculations for slope.

$$m \neq \frac{y_2 - y_1}{x_1 - x_2} \text{ and } m \neq \frac{y_1 - y_2}{x_2 - x_1}$$

If we are inconsistent with the ordering of the subscripts between the numerator and denominator, we will calculate the negative of the answer for slope that we should get.

The reason for requiring $x_1 \neq x_2$ in the definition of slope is so we do not divide by 0. If $x_1 = x_2$ then $\Delta x = x_2 - x_1 = 0$ and $m = \frac{\Delta y}{\Delta x} \stackrel{?}{=} \frac{\Delta y}{0}$; this last fraction is undefined.

EXAMPLE 4	A line goes through the two points $A(-6, 8)$ and $B(10, 20)$. Use Δx and Δy to find the slope m of the line.

SOLUTION   Assuming A is the first point, $\Delta y = 20 - 8 = 12$ and $\Delta x = 10 - (-6) = 16$. So $m = \frac{\Delta y}{\Delta x} = \frac{20 - 8}{10 - (-6)} = \frac{12}{16} = \frac{3}{4}$ when reduced.   ■

There are several aspects to understanding the slope of a line. Using the fraction definition for slope is only a first step toward comprehending slope.

Similar Triangles to Understand Slope

Consider the step pattern shown in Figure 8.20. The horizontal steps in Figure 8.20 all have Δx as their horizontal runs and Δy as their vertical rises; the little triangles that make up the steps are all the same shape. In geometry, triangles that have the same shape but possibly different sizes are called **similar triangles.**

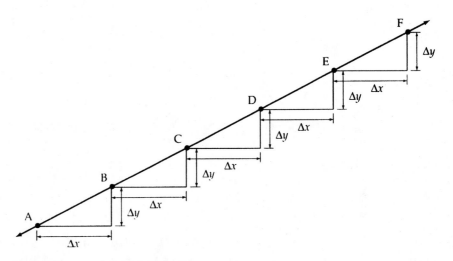

FIGURE 8.20   **Step pattern associated with a line**

The slope of the line in Figure 8.20 would be defined as $m = \dfrac{\Delta y}{\Delta x}$. In actually building a staircase or a roof on a house, carpenters use the terms *rise* and *run* to refer to the vertical and horizontal changes. In fact, the slope m may also be defined as any of the ratios

$$m = \frac{\Delta y}{\Delta x} = \frac{\text{rise}}{\text{run}} = \frac{\text{vertical change}}{\text{horizontal change}}$$

There is a strong connection between equivalent fractions and making larger or smaller similar triangles that fit a step pattern in a line. Note that

$$\frac{\Delta y}{\Delta x} = \frac{2 \cdot \Delta y}{2 \cdot \Delta x} = \frac{3 \cdot \Delta y}{3 \cdot \Delta x}$$

So if we draw triangles that are twice as large or three times as large as those shown in Figure 8.20 we should still have the same slope on the line. A geometric and visual feeling for this concept can be gained by studying Figure 8.21 and comparing it with Figure 8.20.

When we write the equation $m = \dfrac{2}{3} = \dfrac{\Delta y}{\Delta x}$, we are not saying $\Delta y = 2$ and $\Delta x = 3$. In fact, Δy and Δx can be as small or as large as we like and they could both be negative. Only their ratio remains constant and this is the idea behind defining the slope of a line as the quantity m, which is a ratio. The m remains constant no matter how large or small either Δx or Δy become.

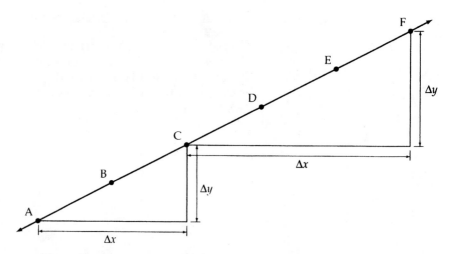

FIGURE 8.21   **Same line as in Figure 8.20 with different and larger step sizes**

Armed with the knowledge of the slope of a line and given a point on a line, we can determine any number of other points on that same line because the slope of a line is constant all along the line. The equation $m = \dfrac{\Delta y}{\Delta x}$ can be thought of as implying that every time the y-coordinate changes by the amount Δy, the x-coordinate must change by the amount Δx in order for the new coordinates to make a point on the line.

EXAMPLE 5   Given that the slope of a line is $\dfrac{3}{5}$ and that the point P($-4,7$) is on the line, find the coordinates of four other points on the line.

SOLUTION   Note that finding four points requires calculating eight coordinates. Since the slope is $\dfrac{3}{5}$, we know that every time the y-coordinate increases by 3 the x-coordinate increases by 5. Starting at P we will simultaneously increase y by 3 and increase x by 5; thus, the first new point on the line has coordinates (1, 10). To get another point on the line we again increase y by 3 and increase x by 5; the next point has coordinates (6, 13). Continuing to consistently change x- and y-coordinates following the slope, we find that the next two points have coordinates (11, 16) and (16, 19). Using Δy and Δx to move from one point to another along the line in this example matches what is depicted in Figure 8.20.   ■

When the slope of a line is given as a fraction we can make Δy and Δx changes that differ from either the numerator or denominator, but the ratio of Δy divided by Δx must be equivalent to the fractional slope.

EXAMPLE 6	A line has slope $\dfrac{-2}{3}$. If we are standing at a point on this line and our y-coordinate decreases by 8, what is the corresponding change in our x-coordinate, if we remain on the line?

SOLUTION   We are given $\Delta y = -8$ and we are asked to find Δx. Using the value for the slope we have $\dfrac{\Delta y}{\Delta x} = \dfrac{-8}{\Delta x} = \dfrac{-2}{3}$. We cross multiply and solve the last equation for Δx.

$-24 = -2\Delta x$; $\Delta x = 12$. The x-coordinate must increase by 12.   ■

Imagine that you are walking along a line but then decide to take a detour by making a move that is either purely horizontal or purely vertical. Once you stray off a given line, how do you get back to the line? The answer is that you refer back to the last known point on the line and use your current position and the slope of the line to determine how to move to get back on the line.

EXAMPLE 7	You are walking along a line with slope $m = \dfrac{2}{3}$. You leave the line by walking 8 units in a purely vertical direction up from the point P(5,9), which is known to be on the line. To get back to the line requires walking in a horizontal direction. In which horizontal direction should you move and how far? When you follow this direction and get back to the line, what are your new coordinates on the line?

SOLUTION   Your last known point on the line was P(5,9), from which you went up 8 units. So your current position is at a point, say Q, where Q has coordinates (5, 17); you have just made a Δy change of 8. We want to know the value of Δx that will put you back on the line: $\dfrac{\Delta y}{\Delta x} = \dfrac{8}{\Delta x} = \dfrac{2}{3}$. We cross multiply in the last equation, $24 = 2\Delta x$ and solve for Δx; $\Delta x = 12$. From Q we change our x-coordinate by 12, so we should move horizontally 12 units to the right, and when we get back on the line our new coordinates will be (17, 17).   ■

EXAMPLE 8	You are walking along a line with slope $m = \dfrac{-4}{5}$. You leave the line by walking 10 units in a purely horizontal direction to the right from point P(-6, -10), which is known to be on the line. To get back to the line requires walking in a vertical direction. In which vertical direction should you move and how far? When you follow this direction and get back to the line, what are your new coordinates on the line?

SOLUTION Your last known point on the line was P(−6, −10), from which you moved right 10 units. Your current position is at a point, say Q, where Q has coordinates (4, −10); you have just made a Δx change of 10. Because we want to know the value of Δy that will put you back on the line $\dfrac{\Delta y}{\Delta x} = \dfrac{\Delta y}{10} = \dfrac{-4}{5}$ we cross multiply in the equation $5\Delta y = -40$ and solve for Δy; $\Delta y = \Delta y = -8$. From Q we change our y-coordinate by −8, so we should move vertically down 8 units and when we get back on the line our new coordinates will be (4, −18).   ▪

P R A C T I C E   F O R   S U C C E S S

Practice 1. If A has coordinates (−5,9) and B has coordinates (7, −3) and if A is the starting point, what are the Δy and Δx changes in going from A to B?

Practice 2. Use the distance formula with the Δy and Δx notations to find the distance between the points A and B in Practice Problem 1.

Practice 3. Use Δy and Δx to find the slope of the line that contains points A and B in Practice Problem 1.

Practice 4. Given P(3, −5) is on a line with slope $\dfrac{-3}{4}$, find the coordinates of 3 other points on that same line.

Practice 5. A line has slope $\dfrac{-5}{8}$. If you are at a point on this line and your x-coordinate changes by 24, how does your y-coordinate change if you remain on the line?

Practice 6. The point P(−6, −14) is known to be on a line with slope $\dfrac{-5}{6}$. If you move 12 units to the left of P, you will move off the line. In which direction and how far should you then move to get back on the line? What will be your new coordinates on the line?

Practice 7. The point P(9, −20) is known to be on a line with slope $\dfrac{-7}{12}$. If you move 21 units up from P you will move off the line. In which direction and how far should you then move to get back on the line? What will be your new coordinates on the line?

EXERCISES 8.3

In exercises 1–10, use the calculations of Δy and Δx to find the slope of the lines that contain the points P and Q.

1. P(−9,12)   Q(5, −14)   2. P(−16,−22)   Q(−9,−28)
3. P(−5,−8)   Q(0,5)   4. P(26,−14)   Q(23,−12)

5. P(3,9)	Q(3,−10)	**6.** P(2,0)	Q(−18,−18)
7. P(1,−25)	Q(−24,−27)	**8.** P(9,26)	Q(0,10)
9. P(0,0)	Q(−28,0)	**10.** P(16,18)	Q(16,−7)

In exercises 11–20, use the calculations of Δy and Δx to find the straight line distance between the points P and Q.

11. P(−13,22)	Q(−15,18)	**12.** P(20,2)	Q(25,−10)
13. P(4,−17)	Q(−4,−2)	**14.** P(20,21)	Q(0,0)
15. P(9,22)	Q(18, −18)	**16.** P(−7,11)	Q(1,−4)
17. P(−3,−47)	Q(−14,13)	**18.** P(−1,−7)	Q(−8,17)
19. P(−2,1)	Q(6,4)	**20.** P(5,1)	Q(−3,2)

In exercises 21–30, you are given the coordinates of a point P which is on a line with the given slope m. Find the coordinates of three other points that are all on the line containing P.

21. P(6,5)	$m = \dfrac{3}{4}$	**22.** P(−8,2)	$m = \dfrac{4}{5}$
23. P(9,−22)	$m = \dfrac{-2}{7}$	**24.** P(19,11)	$m = \dfrac{-10}{7}$
25. P(24,−6)	$m = \dfrac{-13}{8}$	**26.** P(12,−24)	$m = \dfrac{5}{6}$
27. P(−24,−7)	$m = \dfrac{11}{4}$	**28.** P(−16,−2)	$m = \dfrac{-9}{14}$
29. P(7,−20)	$m = \dfrac{-7}{2}$	**30.** P(13,1)	$m = \dfrac{-3}{8}$

31. A line has slope $\dfrac{5}{6}$. If you are at a point on this line and your y-coordinate changes by 30, how does your x-coordinate change if you remain on the line?

32. A line has slope $\dfrac{-7}{2}$. If you are at a point on this line and your x-coordinate changes by −14, how does your y-coordinate change if you remain on the line?

33. A line has slope $\dfrac{-7}{9}$. If you are at a point on this line and your x-coordinate changes by 27, how does your y-coordinate change if you remain on the line?

34. A line has slope $\dfrac{8}{3}$. If you are at a point on this line and your y-coordinate changes by −24, how does your x-coordinate change if you remain on the line?

35. A line has slope $\dfrac{-3}{13}$. If you are at a point on this line and your y-coordinate changes by 12, how does your x-coordinate change if you remain on the line?

36. A line has slope $\dfrac{-9}{4}$. If you are at a point on this line and your x-coordinate changes by 28, how does your y-coordinate change if you remain on the line?

37. The point P(21,10) is known to be on a line with slope $\dfrac{7}{3}$. If you move 15 units to the left of P you will move off the line. In which direction and how far should you then move to get back on the line? What will be your new coordinates on the line?

38. The point P(1, −21) is known to be on a line with slope $\dfrac{-2}{15}$. If you move 6 units up from P you will move off the line. In which direction and how far should you then move to get back on the line? What will be your new coordinates on the line?

39. The point P(−10,−1) is known to be on a line with slope $\dfrac{9}{4}$. If you move 20 units to the right of P you will move off the line. In which direction and how far should you then move to get back on the line? What will be your new coordinates on the line?

40. The point P(0, −14) is known to be on a line with slope $\dfrac{6}{17}$. If you move 18 units down from P you will move off the line. In which direction and how far should you then move to get back on the line? What will be your new coordinates on the line?

41. The point P(−13, −11) is known to be on a line with slope $\dfrac{-15}{2}$. If you move 10 units to the left of P you will move off the line. In which direction and how far should you then move to get back on the line? What will be your new coordinates on the line?

42. The point P(25, −19) is known to be on a line with slope $\dfrac{14}{3}$. If you move 42 units up from P you will move off the line. In which direction and how far should you then move to get back on the line? What will be your new coordinates on the line?

Looking Back

43. Solve for x: $\dfrac{4}{5}x - \dfrac{1}{3} = \dfrac{2}{15}$

44. If a car burns $\dfrac{3}{4}$ quart of oil when it is driven 800 miles, how much oil will have been burned after the car is driven 2,800 miles? Write your answer as an exact decimal.

45. If on a map $\dfrac{3}{5}$ inch represents 25 miles, how many inches would be used to represent 80 miles? Write your answer as an exact decimal.

46. Convert 0.025% into a number in scientific notation.

47. Solve the equation $\dfrac{ax + by}{c} = d$ for the variable y.

48. Are the numbers 42 and 39 relatively prime?

49. Is $\sqrt{605}$ reduced?

50. Is there a real number that is neither a rational number nor an irrational number?

PRACTICE-FOR-SUCCESS ANSWERS

1. $\Delta y = -12, \Delta x = 12$ **2.** $d(A,B) = 12\sqrt{2}$

3. $m = -1$ **4.** $(7,-8), (11,-11), (15,-14)$

5. $\Delta y = -15$ **6.** Move up 10 units; $(-18,-4)$

7. Move left 36 units; $(-27,1)$

SUMMARY

Horizontal and vertical number lines may be combined to form the x–y coordinate axes system. The x-coordinate of a point describes the signed distance from the vertical y-axis to that point, and the y-coordinate describes the signed distance from the horizontal x-axis to the point. The two coordinate axes intersect at the point with coordinates $(0,0)$, called the origin; and the two axes divide the plane into four distinct regions called quadrants.

The quadrants are numbered with Roman numerals in a counterclockwise direction, with all points in the first quadrant having both coordinates positive. The point $(5,3)$, for example, lies in the first quadrant; the point $(-5,3)$ lies in the second quadrant because its x-coordinate is negative and its y-coordinate is positive. All points in the third quadrant have both coordinates negative, so $(-5, -3)$ lies in the third quadrant; and the point $(5, -3)$ lies in the fourth quadrant because it has a positive x-coordinate and a negative y-coordinate. Given its coordinates, we can plot any point; or given any point, we can read its approximate coordinates from a graph.

We can calculate the distance between two points in the plane using the distance formula — for example, the distance between the points $A(-2,7)$ and $B(3, -4)$ is given by

$$d(A,B) = \sqrt{(-2 - 3)^2 + (7 - (-4))^2} = \sqrt{(-5)^2 + 11^2} = \sqrt{146}$$

We can graph equations of lines by finding their x-axis and y-axis intercepts—for example, to graph $4x + 6y = 12$, we set $x = 0$ and solve for the y-intercept, which is 2. We set $y = 0$ and solve for the x-intercept, which is 3. We then graph the line that contains the points $(0,2)$ and $(3,0)$.

We can also transform equations into the form $y = mx + b$. For example, the equation $6x + 9y = 33$ can be solved for y and rewritten in the form $y = -\frac{2}{3}x + \frac{11}{3}$, where $m = -\frac{2}{3}$ and $b = \frac{11}{3}$.

We also examined the notations Δx and Δy. If an original point is A$(-7,9)$ and the new point is B$(-5,3)$, then $\Delta x = -5 - (-7) = 2$ and $\Delta y = 3 - 9 = -6$. The slope of a line through two given points is given by the formula $m = \dfrac{\Delta y}{\Delta x}$. Thus, the slope of the line that contains the points A and B just given is $\dfrac{-6}{2} = \dfrac{-3}{1} = -3$. We can interpret these numbers as saying every time y changes by -6, x must change by 2. Or, every time y changes by -3, x must change by 1. When $\Delta x = 0$ the slope of the line is undefined.

If a line through point A$(-2,5)$ has slope $\dfrac{-3}{7}$, we can find several other points on the line by continuously changing y by -3 at the same time we change x by 7. For example, three other points on the line would have coordinates $(5,2)$, $(12, -1)$, and $(19, -4)$. If we were standing on point A and decided to move vertically down 15 units, then to get back to the line we should move to the right 35 units:

$$\frac{-3}{7} = \frac{-3 \cdot 5}{7 \cdot 5} = \frac{-15}{35} = \frac{\Delta y}{\Delta x}$$

So if $\Delta y = -15$, then $\Delta x = 35$. If we were standing on point A and decided to move left 14 units, then to get back to the line we should move up vertically 6 units:

$$\frac{-3}{7} = \frac{-3 \cdot (-2)}{7 \cdot (-2)} = \frac{6}{-14} = \frac{\Delta y}{\Delta x}$$

So if $\Delta x = -14$, then $\Delta y = 6$.

CHAPTER 8 REVIEW PROBLEMS

Determine the quadrant in which each of the points lies in problems 1–12.

1. P$(7, -10)$ **2.** Q$(-3,8)$

3. R$(1,1)$ **4.** S$(-9, -1)$

5. P$(-8, -5)$ **6.** Q$(3,6)$

7. R$(-4,2)$ **8.** S$(3, -5)$

9. The point is such that its signed distance from the y-axis is -6 and its signed distance from the x-axis is -2.

10. The point is such that its signed distance from the y-axis is 8 and its signed distance from the x-axis is -4.

11. The point is such that its signed distance from the x-axis is 3 and its signed distance from the y-axis is -9.

12. The point is such that its signed distance from the x-axis is -1 and its signed distance from the y-axis is -1.

In problems 13–18, you are given two points that are either vertically or horizontally aligned. Name the type of alignment and use absolute value to determine the distance between the points.

13. $A(-3,9)$ $B(-3, -12)$ **14.** $P(17,2)$ $Q(-3,2)$

15. $C(-3, -3)$ $D(3, -3)$ **16.** $R(5,4)$ $S(-6,4)$

17. $A(-2, -1)$ $B(-2, -10)$ **18.** $P(6, -9)$ $Q(6, -11)$

In problems 19–24, use the distance formula to compute the distance between points P and Q.

19. $P(-3, -6)$ $Q(-6, -2)$ **20.** $P(4, -9)$ $Q(9, 3)$

21. $P(10, -7)$ $Q(18, 8)$ **22.** $P(-3, -15)$ $Q(4, 9)$

23. $P(27, -23)$ $Q(15, 12)$ **24.** $P(6, 28)$ $Q(-5, -32)$

Graph the equations in problems 25–30 by finding the x–intercept and y–intercept points.

25. $-3x + 9y = 18$ **26.** $6x - 18y = 54$

27. $-5x + 15y = 45$ **28.** $8x - 14y = 112$

29. $9x + 15y = 135$ **30.** $-34x + 17y = 68$

Transform the equations in problems 31–38 into the form $y = mx + b$ and identify the values of m and b.

31. $-4x + 3y = 17$ **32.** $9x - 2y = 14$

33. $-8x + 5y = 16$ **34.** $12x - 110y = 24$

35. $5x + 16y = 31$ **36.** $6x + 8y = 23$

37. $-5x + 7y = 20$ **38.** $3x - 4y = 10$

In problems 39–44, assume A is the first point, B is the second point, and calculate Δy and Δx between points A and B; also calculate the slope of the line through A and B.

39. $A(6, -4)$ $B(-2, -11)$ **40.** $A(12,8)$ $B(-3,6)$

41. $A(-7,8)$ $B(2, -15)$ **42.** $A(-9,12)$ $B(-12,15)$

43. $A(3, -7)$ $B(-5, -14)$ **44.** $A(-19,15)$ $B(-14,25)$

45. A line has slope $\dfrac{-3}{11}$. If you are at a point on this line and your x-coordinate changes by 33, how does your y-coordinate change if you remain on the line?

46. A line has slope $\dfrac{10}{13}$. If you are at a point on this line and your y-coordinate changes by 40, how does your x-coordinate change if you remain on the line?

47. The point P(-3, 15) is known to be on a line with slope $\frac{-5}{4}$. If you move 24 units to the left of P you will move off the line. In which direction and how far should you then move to get back on the line? What will be your new coordinates on the line?

48. The point P(10, -8) is known to be on a line with slope $\frac{-12}{5}$. If you move 60 units down from P you will move off the line. In which direction and how far should you then move to get back on the line? What will be your new coordinates on the line?

49. A line has slope $\frac{8}{9}$. If you are at a point on this line and your x-coordinate changes by 36, how does your y-coordinate change if you remain on the line?

50. A line has slope $\frac{6}{17}$. If you are at a point on this line and your y-coordinate changes by -24, how does your x-coordinate change if you remain on the line?

51. The point P(9, -14) is known to be on a line with slope $\frac{-9}{5}$. If you move 25 units to the left of P you will move off the line. In which direction and how far should you then move to get back on the line? What will be your new coordinates on the line?

52. The point P(-13, 1) is known to be on a line with slope $\frac{-12}{23}$. If you move 36 units down from P you will move off the line. In which direction and how far should you then move to get back on the line? What will be your new coordinates on the line?

CHAPTER 8 PRACTICE TEST

Name the quadrant in which each of the points in problems 1–6 lies.

1. P(-3, 5)   **2.** Q(4, -7)

3. R(-7, -7)   **4.** S(3, 13)

5. The point is such that its signed distance from the x-axis is -5 and its signed distance from the y-axis is 4.

6. The point is such that its signed distance from the y-axis is -5 and its signed distance from the x-axis is 3.

In problems 7–10, you are given two points that are either vertically or horizontally aligned. Name the type of alignment and use absolute values to determine the distance between the points.

7. A(-6,8)   B(-5, 8)   **8.** P(5, 13)   Q(5, -6)

9. C(9, -10)   D(-7, -10)   **10.** R(-7, -7)   S(-9, -7)

In problems 11 and 12, use the distance formula to compute the distance between points P and Q.

11. $P(-4, -7)$ $Q(-7, -11)$ **12.** $P(10, -9)$ $Q(15,3)$

Graph the equations in problems 13 and 14 by finding the *x*–intercept and *y*–intercept points.

13. $-7x + 8y = 56$ **14.** $12x - 14y = 84$

Transform the equations in problems 15 and 16 into the form $y = mx + b$ and identify the values of *m* and *b*.

15. $-5x + 9y = 25$ **16.** $12x - 16y = 32$

In problems 17 and 18, assume A is the first point, B is the second point, and calculate Δy and Δx between points A and B; also calculate the slope of the line through A and B.

17. $A(-7, -8)$ $B(-3, -10)$ **18.** $A(-13,12)$ $B(-12,13)$

19. A line has slope $\dfrac{-13}{9}$. If you are at a point on this line and your *x*-coordinate changes by 27, how does your *y*-coordinate change if you remain on the line?

20. A line has slope $\dfrac{8}{15}$. If you are at a point on this line and your *y*-coordinate changes by 40, how does your *x*-coordinate change if you remain on the line?

21. The point $P(-6,9)$ is known to be on a line with slope $\dfrac{-2}{3}$. If you move 24 units to the left of P you will move off the line. In which direction and how far should you then move to get back on the line? What will be your new coordinates on the line?

22. The point $P(8, -5)$ is known to be on a line with slope $\dfrac{-6}{13}$. If you move 12 units down from P you will move off the line. In which direction and how far should you then move to get back on the line? What will be your new coordinates on the line?

FINAL EXAM PRACTICE TEST

1. Give the place value of the digit 8 in 938,443,121,030.
2. Write the number 63,257 in an expanded form.
3. Write the number 2,007,081 in words.
4. Write the following number in standard form: Twenty-five million, five thousand, sixteen.
5. Round 3,789,956,669 to the nearest hundred thousand.
6. Divide $5,043 \div 27$. Give the quotient and the remainder.

7. Simplify 3^5 and identify which number is the base and which number is the exponent.

8. Simplify $2^4 \cdot 5^2 \cdot 7$.

9. Simplify $[(84 + 96 \div 16) + 10] \div 25 - 30$.

10. What is the basic operation for the expression in problem 9?

11. Is the number 495,762,511,239 evenly divisible by 3?

12. Find the prime factorization of 15,600.

13. Is the number 511 a composite number?

14. Calculate the LCM of the numbers 120 and 440.

15. Calculate the GCF of the numbers 2,560 and 560.

In problems 16–20, an equation is given in which the left and right sides are mathematically the same. A single instance of either the commutative law, associative law, or distributive law has been made in transforming the left side into the right side. Identify which law applies to each problem and in the case of the commutative or associative laws, state the corresponding operation.

16. $[(20 + 13) + 31] \cdot 3 = [20 + (13 + 31)] \cdot 3$

17. $[85 \cdot (17 \cdot 34) + 19 \cdot 52] = [(85 \cdot 17) \cdot 34 + 19 \cdot 52]$

18. $6 \cdot (32 + 19 \cdot 27) + 39 - 16 = 6 \cdot (32 + 27 \cdot 19) + 39 - 16$

19. $13 + (18 + 30 \cdot 76 + 75 \div 25) = 13 + (18 + 76 \cdot 30 + 75 \div 25)$

20. $[59 \cdot 81 + 97 \cdot 46 + 8 \cdot (9 + 3)] = (59 \cdot 81 + 97 \cdot 46 + 8 \cdot 9 + 8 \cdot 3)$

21. What is the basic operation for $[70 \div 14 + 3^5] \cdot 6 \div (2^4)$?

22. Simplify the expression in problem 21 according to the rules for the order of operations.

23. Simplify $\left| -(-7) \right|^2 - \left| -(-5) \right|$.

24. Is $-35 \le \left| -35 \right|$ true or false?

25. Is $-391 < -390$ true or false?

26. Simplify $-39 - \left| -26 \right| + (-3)^3 + (-9)$.

27. Write an expression using absolute value that gives the distance between two points on a number line whose coordinates are -38 and -117.

28. Subtract -56 from -93.

29. Simplify $(-180 \div 15) \div (-6) \cdot \left| -2 \right|$.

30. Simplify $[-280 \div 40 - (9 - 12)^2] \cdot \left| -3 \right| \div (-6)$.

31. Simplify $\dfrac{-(-2)^3 - (56 - 6 \div 2) + -\left| -12 \right|}{\left| -28 \right| - (-3)^2}$.

32. Write an expression corresponding to the following description and then simplify the expression to a single number: Negative three plus the quotient thirty-six divided by negative nine, all divided by negative seven.

33. Write $\dfrac{19}{21}$ as a fraction with a denominator of 84.

34. Write $\dfrac{17}{24}$ as a fraction with a numerator of 85.

35. Reduce $\dfrac{560}{448}$ to lowest terms.

36. Convert $-3\dfrac{3}{5}$ to an improper fraction.

37. Convert $\dfrac{-588}{23}$ to a mixed number.

38. Simplify $\dfrac{4}{3} + \left(\dfrac{-7}{15}\right) - \left(3\dfrac{1}{2}\right)$ and write your answer as a reduced fraction.

39. True or false: $-3\dfrac{5}{21} < -3\dfrac{7}{24}$.

40. Simplify $\dfrac{-3}{4} \div \dfrac{-5}{6} \div \dfrac{-2}{3}$.

41. What is $\dfrac{7}{9}$ of $5\dfrac{2}{3}$?

42. Simplify $\dfrac{3}{8} \div \left(\dfrac{-3}{2}\right)^2 + \left(3\dfrac{1}{2}\right) \cdot \left[-2 - \left(\dfrac{-2}{3}\right)\right]$.

43. Write the division check as an equation using the words *dividend, quotient, remainder,* and *divisor*.

44. Simplify the complex fraction $\dfrac{\dfrac{2}{3} + \dfrac{5}{6}}{\dfrac{7}{8} - \dfrac{9}{16}}$.

45. What is the basic operation of the expression in problem 42?

46. Write the number 83.561 in words.

47. Convert 0.0325 to a reduced fraction.

48. True or false: $-72.365 < -72.36$.

49. Simplify $[26 - (26 - 0.25)] - (9.2 - 13.5)$.

50. To purchase a stereo system, the buyer can pay $675 in cash or she can make monthly payments of $42.50 for a year and a half. What is the savings if she pays in cash?

51. Convert $\dfrac{37}{40}$ to a decimal.

52. Is $\sqrt{9}$ a rational or an irrational number?

53. Use estimation to find the whole number that is nearest to $\sqrt{250}$.

54. Simplify $\sqrt{169} - \sqrt{121} + 7 \cdot \sqrt{36}$.

55. Reduce $\sqrt{2^3 \cdot 5^2 \cdot 7^4}$.

56. Reduce $\sqrt{560}$.

57. Convert 5.6% to a reduced fraction.

58. Convert $\dfrac{17}{20}$ to a percent.

59. Convert 0.00245 to a percent.

60. Convert 23.6% to a decimal.

61. Simplify $(-2)^{-3}$.

62. Simplify $\left(\dfrac{3}{4}\right)^{-2}$.

63. Simplify $\dfrac{4^{-6} \div 4^{-2}}{4^{-7} \cdot 4^{3}}$.

64. Rewrite $(8^{-4})^{-6}$ as an exponential expression with the base 8 and a single exponent.

65. Convert 72.69×10^{-5} to standard notation.

66. Convert 283.5×10^{2} to scientific notation.

67. Simplify $\dfrac{(3.6 \times 10^{-3}) \cdot (1.5 \times 10^{5})}{2.7 \times 10^{-4}}$ and write your answer in scientific notation.

68. Simplify $[(3^{-2}) \div (3^{3})]^{-2}$ and write the answer with base 3 and a single exponent.

69. What is the degree of the polynomial $5x^{4} + 3x^{6} - 2x^{2}$?

70. Is the polynomial in problem 69 a monomial, binomial, trinomial, or none of these?

71. Subtract $5x^{3} + 9x^{2} - 6x$ from $4x^{3} - 3x^{2} - 10x$.

72. Multiply $-5x^{2}y^{3}(7x^{3}y^{4} - 3x^{2}y^{5} - 6x^{4}y^{3})$.

73. Multiply $(-3x^{2} + 2x)(5x - 3)$.

74. Multiply $(6x^{3} - 5x^{2})(x^{4} - 3x^{3} + 8x^{2})$.

75. Divide $\dfrac{52x^{-3}y^{2} + 65x^{2}y^{4}}{-13x^{4}y^{-5}}$.

76. Substitute $x = -3$, $y = 4$, and $z = -2$ into the expression $\dfrac{x^{2} - xy + z^{-3}}{z(y^{2} - 5x)}$ and simplify. Leave your answer as a reduced fraction.

77. Solve for x: $8x - 5(3x - 2) = 31$.

78. Solve for x: $\dfrac{3}{4}(6x - 5) = \dfrac{x}{8} + 3x + 12\dfrac{3}{4}$.

79. One car is traveling at a speed of 15 miles per hour less than twice the speed of another car. If the combined speed of both cars is 90 miles per hour, what is the speed of the slower car?

80. If it requires 6 gallons of gasoline to travel 162 miles, how many gallons would be required to travel 351 miles?

81. The dosage of a certain medication is based on physical weight. If a person who weighs 145 pounds takes 4.5 ounces, how many ounces should a person who weighs 203 pounds take?

82. Solve $y = mx + b$ for the variable m.

83. Solve $\dfrac{3 - 9x}{2} = y^2$ for the variable x.

84. Name the quadrant in which the point P($-3,5$) lies.

85. True or false: If a point lies in the third quadrant, both of its coordinates must be negative.

86. Find the distance between P($-2, -8$) and the point Q($10, -3$). Simplify your answer to a single number.

87. What is the y-intercept of the linear equation $y = -3x + 5$?

88. What are the x-intercept and the y-intercept of the linear equation $-5x + 2y = -40$?

89. What is the slope of the line that contains the points P and Q in problem 86?

90. Solve the inequality and graph your solution on a number line: $-6x + 17 > -3x + 5$.

91. Solve the inequality and graph your solution on a number line: $-21 + 2x > 6x - 9$.

92. Convert 0.00357 km to meters.

93. Convert 350 mℓ to kℓ.

TABLES

PRIME FACTORS, SQUARES, AND SQUARE ROOTS

The table starting on the following page contains a list of numerical information about the whole numbers between 1 and 300. This information includes the prime factorization for each number, the value of the square of each number, and a decimal approximation of the square root of each number. Each nonperfect square root value is given with 10 significant digits. To demonstrate how to use this table, consider the following four questions about the number 250.

1. What is the prime factorization of 250?
2. What number is 250^2?
3. What is the prime factorization of 250^3?
4. What is a decimal approximation of $\sqrt{250}$?

To answer these questions, look down the column labeled n until you find the number 250 and then read the information going across. For convenience, the information you should find in the table is reproduced below:

n	primes	n^2	$\sqrt{n}$
250	$2 \cdot 5^3$	62500	15.811388301

Under the column labeled "primes" is the prime factorization of the number n in the leftmost column; thus, $250 = 2 \cdot 5^3$. We can also read the exact value of 250^2 from the table by looking for the value under the column labeled n^2; thus, $250^2 = 62,500$. To find the prime factorization of 250^3, triple the exponents on the primes in the factorization of 250; thus, $250^3 = 2^3 \cdot 5^9$.

The value of $\sqrt{250}$ is the decimal number under the column labeled $\sqrt{n}$, so reading the value from the table we find $\sqrt{250} \approx 15.811388301$ which means $15.811388301^2 \approx 250$. Remember the symbol $\approx$ is read as "is approximately equal to." In this table approximate square root values are shown with a decimal point, whereas exact square root values are shown without a decimal point. For example, we should think $\sqrt{25} = 5$ and not $\sqrt{25} \approx 5$ and we avoid writing $\sqrt{25} = 5.0000000000$.

n	primes	n^2	$\sqrt{n}$	n	primes	n^2	$\sqrt{n}$
1		1	1	51	$3 \cdot 17$	2601	7.1414284285
2	2	4	1.4142135624	52	$2^2 \cdot 13$	2704	7.2111025509
3	3	9	1.7320508076	53	53	2809	7.2801098893
4	2^2	16	2	54	$2 \cdot 3^3$	2916	7.3484692284
5	5	25	2.2360679775	55	$5 \cdot 11$	3025	7.4161984871
6	$2 \cdot 3$	36	2.4494897428	56	$2^3 \cdot 7$	3136	7.4833147735
7	7	49	2.6457513111	57	$3 \cdot 19$	3249	7.5498344353
8	2^3	64	2.8284271247	58	$2 \cdot 29$	3364	7.6157731059
9	3^2	81	3	59	59	3481	7.6811457479
10	$2 \cdot 5$	100	3.1622776602	60	$2^2 \cdot 3 \cdot 5$	3600	7.7459666924
11	11	121	3.3166247904	61	61	3721	7.8102496759
12	$2^2 \cdot 3$	144	3.4641016151	62	$2 \cdot 31$	3844	7.8740078740
13	13	169	3.6055512755	63	$3^2 \cdot 7$	3969	7.9372539332
14	$2 \cdot 7$	196	3.7416573868	64	2^6	4096	8
15	$3 \cdot 5$	225	3.8729833462	65	$5 \cdot 13$	4225	8.0622577483
16	2^4	256	4	66	$2 \cdot 3 \cdot 11$	4356	8.1240384046
17	17	289	4.1231056256	67	67	4489	8.1853527719
18	$2 \cdot 3^2$	324	4.2426406871	68	$2^2 \cdot 17$	4624	8.2462112512
19	19	361	4.3588989435	69	$3 \cdot 23$	4761	8.3066238629
20	$2^2 \cdot 5$	400	4.4721359550	70	$2 \cdot 5 \cdot 7$	4900	8.3666002653
21	$3 \cdot 7$	441	4.5825756950	71	71	5041	8.4261497732
22	$2 \cdot 11$	484	4.6904157598	72	$2^3 \cdot 3^2$	5184	8.4852813742
23	23	529	4.7958315233	73	73	5329	8.5440037453
24	$2^3 \cdot 3$	576	4.8989794856	74	$2 \cdot 37$	5476	8.6023252670
25	5^2	625	5	75	$3 \cdot 5^2$	5625	8.6602540379
26	$2 \cdot 13$	676	5.0990195136	76	$2^2 \cdot 19$	5776	8.7177978871
27	3^3	729	5.1961524227	77	$7 \cdot 11$	5929	8.7749643874
28	$2^2 \cdot 7$	784	5.2915026221	78	$2 \cdot 3 \cdot 13$	6084	8.8317608663
29	29	841	5.3851648071	79	79	6241	8.8881944173
30	$2 \cdot 3 \cdot 5$	900	5.4772255751	80	$2^4 \cdot 5$	6400	8.9442719100
31	31	961	5.5677643628	81	3^4	6561	9
32	2^5	1024	5.6568542495	82	$2 \cdot 41$	6724	9.0553851381
33	$3 \cdot 11$	1089	5.7445626465	83	83	6889	9.1104335791
34	$2 \cdot 17$	1156	5.8309518948	84	$2^2 \cdot 3 \cdot 7$	7056	9.1651513899
35	$5 \cdot 7$	1225	5.9160797831	85	$5 \cdot 17$	7225	9.2195444573
36	$2^2 \cdot 3^2$	1296	6	86	$2 \cdot 43$	7396	9.2736184955
37	37	1369	6.0827625303	87	$3 \cdot 29$	7569	9.3273790531
38	$2 \cdot 19$	1444	6.1644140030	88	$2^3 \cdot 11$	7744	9.3808315197
39	$3 \cdot 13$	1521	6.2449979984	89	89	7921	9.4339811321
40	$2^3 \cdot 5$	1600	6.3245553203	90	$2 \cdot 3^2 \cdot 5$	8100	9.4868329805
41	41	1681	6.4031242374	91	$7 \cdot 13$	8281	9.5393920142
42	$2 \cdot 3 \cdot 7$	1764	6.4807406984	92	$2^2 \cdot 23$	8464	9.5916630466
43	43	1849	6.5574385243	93	$3 \cdot 31$	8649	9.6436507610
44	$2^2 \cdot 11$	1936	6.6332495807	94	$2 \cdot 47$	8836	9.6953597148
45	$3^2 \cdot 5$	2025	6.7082039325	95	$5 \cdot 19$	9025	9.7467943448
46	$2 \cdot 23$	2116	6.7823299831	96	$2^5 \cdot 3$	9216	9.7979589711
47	47	2209	6.8556546004	97	97	9409	9.8488578018
48	$2^4 \cdot 3$	2304	6.9282032303	98	$2 \cdot 7^2$	9604	9.8994949366
49	7^2	2401	7	99	$3^2 \cdot 11$	9801	9.9498743711
50	$2 \cdot 5^2$	2500	7.0710678119	100	$2^2 \cdot 5^2$	10000	10

n	primes	n^2	$\sqrt{n}$	n	primes	n^2	$\sqrt{n}$
101	101	10201	10.049875621	151	151	22801	12.288205727
102	$2 \cdot 3 \cdot 17$	10404	10.099504938	152	$2^3 \cdot 19$	23104	12.328828006
103	103	10609	10.148891565	153	$3^2 \cdot 17$	23409	12.369316877
104	$2^3 \cdot 13$	10816	10.198039027	154	$2 \cdot 7 \cdot 11$	23716	12.409673646
105	$3 \cdot 5 \cdot 7$	11025	10.246950766	155	$5 \cdot 31$	24025	12.449899598
106	$2 \cdot 53$	11236	10.295630141	156	$2^2 \cdot 3 \cdot 13$	24336	12.489995997
107	107	11449	10.344080433	157	157	24649	12.529964086
108	$2^2 \cdot 3^3$	11664	10.392304845	158	$2 \cdot 79$	24964	12.569805090
109	109	11881	10.440306509	159	$3 \cdot 53$	25281	12.609520213
110	$2 \cdot 5 \cdot 11$	12100	10.488088482	160	$2^5 \cdot 5$	25600	12.649110641
111	$3 \cdot 37$	12321	10.535653753	161	$7 \cdot 23$	25921	12.688577540
112	$2^4 \cdot 7$	12544	10.583005244	162	$2 \cdot 3^4$	26244	12.727922061
113	113	12769	10.630145813	163	163	26569	12.767145335
114	$2 \cdot 3 \cdot 19$	12996	10.677078252	164	$2^2 \cdot 41$	26896	12.806248475
115	$5 \cdot 23$	13225	10.723805295	165	$3 \cdot 5 \cdot 11$	27225	12.845232579
116	$2^2 \cdot 29$	13456	10.770329614	166	$2 \cdot 83$	27556	12.884098727
117	$3^2 \cdot 13$	13689	10.816653826	167	167	27889	12.922847983
118	$2 \cdot 59$	13924	10.862780491	168	$2^3 \cdot 3 \cdot 7$	28224	12.961481397
119	$7 \cdot 17$	14161	10.908712115	169	13^2	28561	13
120	$2^3 \cdot 3 \cdot 5$	14400	10.954451150	170	$2 \cdot 5 \cdot 17$	28900	13.038404810
121	11^2	14641	11	171	$3^2 \cdot 19$	29241	13.076696831
122	$2 \cdot 61$	14884	11.045361017	172	$2^2 \cdot 43$	29584	13.114877049
123	$3 \cdot 41$	15129	11.090536506	173	173	29929	13.152946438
124	$2^2 \cdot 31$	15376	11.135528726	174	$2 \cdot 3 \cdot 29$	30276	13.190905958
125	5^3	15625	11.180339888	175	$5^2 \cdot 7$	30625	13.228756555
126	$2 \cdot 3^2 \cdot 7$	15876	11.224972160	176	$2^4 \cdot 11$	30976	13.266499161
127	127	16129	11.269427670	177	$3 \cdot 59$	31329	13.304134696
128	2^7	16384	11.313708499	178	$2 \cdot 89$	31684	13.341664064
129	$3 \cdot 43$	16641	11.357816692	179	179	32041	13.379088160
130	$2 \cdot 5 \cdot 13$	16900	11.401754251	180	$2^2 \cdot 3^2 \cdot 5$	32400	13.416407865
131	131	17161	11.445523142	181	181	32761	13.453624047
132	$2^2 \cdot 3 \cdot 11$	17424	11.489125293	182	$2 \cdot 7 \cdot 13$	33124	13.490737563
133	$7 \cdot 19$	17689	11.532562595	183	$3 \cdot 61$	33489	13.527749258
134	$2 \cdot 67$	17956	11.575836903	184	$2^3 \cdot 23$	33856	13.564659966
135	$3^3 \cdot 5$	18225	11.618950039	185	$5 \cdot 37$	34225	13.601470509
136	$2^3 \cdot 17$	18496	11.661903790	186	$2 \cdot 3 \cdot 31$	34596	13.638181697
137	137	18769	11.704699911	187	$11 \cdot 17$	34969	13.674794331
138	$2 \cdot 3 \cdot 23$	19044	11.747340124	188	$2^2 \cdot 47$	35344	13.711309201
139	139	19321	11.789826123	189	$3^3 \cdot 7$	35721	13.747727085
140	$2^2 \cdot 5 \cdot 7$	19600	11.832159566	190	$2 \cdot 5 \cdot 19$	36100	13.784048752
141	$3 \cdot 47$	19881	11.874342087	191	191	36481	13.820274961
142	$2 \cdot 71$	20164	11.916375288	192	$2^6 \cdot 3$	36864	13.856406461
143	$11 \cdot 13$	20449	11.958260743	193	193	37249	13.892443989
144	$2^4 \cdot 3^2$	20736	12	194	$2 \cdot 97$	37636	13.928388277
145	$5 \cdot 29$	21025	12.041594579	195	$3 \cdot 5 \cdot 13$	38025	13.964240044
146	$2 \cdot 73$	21316	12.083045974	196	$2^2 \cdot 7^2$	38416	14
147	$3 \cdot 7^2$	21609	12.124355653	197	197	38809	14.035668848
148	$2^2 \cdot 37$	21904	12.165525061	198	$2 \cdot 3^2 \cdot 11$	39204	14.071247279
149	149	22201	12.206555616	199	199	39601	14.106735980
150	$2 \cdot 3 \cdot 5^2$	22500	12.247448714	200	$2^3 \cdot 5^2$	40000	14.142135624

n	primes	n^2	$\sqrt{n}$	n	primes	n^2	$\sqrt{n}$
201	$3 \cdot 67$	40401	14.177446879	251	251	63001	15.842979518
202	$2 \cdot 101$	40804	14.212670404	252	$2^2 \cdot 3^2 \cdot 7$	63504	15.874507866
203	$7 \cdot 29$	41209	14.247806849	253	$11 \cdot 23$	64009	15.905973721
204	$2^2 \cdot 3 \cdot 17$	41616	14.282856857	254	$2 \cdot 127$	64516	15.937377451
205	$5 \cdot 41$	42025	14.317821063	255	$3 \cdot 5 \cdot 17$	65025	15.968719423
206	$2 \cdot 103$	42436	14.352700094	256	2^8	65536	16
207	$3^2 \cdot 23$	42849	14.387494570	257	257	66049	16.031219542
208	$2^4 \cdot 13$	43264	14.422205102	258	$2 \cdot 3 \cdot 43$	66564	16.062378404
209	$11 \cdot 19$	43681	14.456832295	259	$7 \cdot 37$	67081	16.093476939
210	$2 \cdot 3 \cdot 5 \cdot 7$	44100	14.491376746	260	$2^2 \cdot 5 \cdot 13$	67600	16.124515497
211	211	44521	14.525839046	261	$3^2 \cdot 29$	68121	16.155494421
212	$2^2 \cdot 53$	44944	14.560219779	262	$2 \cdot 131$	68644	16.186414056
213	$3 \cdot 71$	45369	14.594519519	263	263	69169	16.217274740
214	$2 \cdot 107$	45796	14.628738838	264	$2^3 \cdot 3 \cdot 11$	69696	16.248076809
215	$5 \cdot 43$	46225	14.662878299	265	$5 \cdot 53$	70225	16.278820596
216	$2^3 \cdot 3^3$	46656	14.696938457	266	$2 \cdot 7 \cdot 19$	70756	16.309506430
217	$7 \cdot 31$	47089	14.730919863	267	$3 \cdot 89$	71289	16.340134638
218	$2 \cdot 109$	47524	14.764823060	268	$2^2 \cdot 67$	71824	16.370705544
219	$3 \cdot 73$	47961	14.798648587	269	269	72361	16.401219467
220	$2^2 \cdot 5 \cdot 11$	48400	14.832396974	270	$2 \cdot 3^3 \cdot 5$	72900	16.431676725
221	$13 \cdot 17$	48841	14.866068747	271	271	73441	16.462077633
222	$2 \cdot 3 \cdot 37$	49284	14.899664426	272	$2^4 \cdot 17$	73984	16.492422502
223	223	49729	14.933184523	273	$3 \cdot 7 \cdot 13$	74529	16.522711642
224	$2^5 \cdot 7$	50176	14.966629547	274	$2 \cdot 137$	75076	16.552945357
225	$3^2 \cdot 5^2$	50625	15	275	$5^2 \cdot 11$	75625	16.583123952
226	$2 \cdot 113$	51076	15.033296378	276	$2^2 \cdot 3 \cdot 23$	76176	16.613247726
227	227	51529	15.066519173	277	277	76729	16.643316977
228	$2^2 \cdot 3 \cdot 19$	51984	15.099668871	278	$2 \cdot 139$	77284	16.673332001
229	229	52441	15.132745950	279	$3^2 \cdot 31$	77841	16.703293089
230	$2 \cdot 5 \cdot 23$	52900	15.165750888	280	$2^3 \cdot 5 \cdot 7$	78400	16.733200531
231	$3 \cdot 7 \cdot 11$	53361	15.198684154	281	281	78961	16.763054614
232	$2^3 \cdot 29$	53824	15.231546212	282	$2 \cdot 3 \cdot 47$	79524	16.792855624
233	233	54289	15.264337522	283	283	80089	16.822603841
234	$2 \cdot 3^2 \cdot 13$	54756	15.297058541	284	$2^2 \cdot 71$	80656	16.852299546
235	$5 \cdot 47$	55225	15.329709717	285	$3 \cdot 5 \cdot 19$	81225	16.881943016
236	$2^2 \cdot 59$	55696	15.362291496	286	$2 \cdot 11 \cdot 13$	81796	16.911534525
237	$3 \cdot 79$	56169	15.394804318	287	$7 \cdot 41$	82369	16.941074346
238	$2 \cdot 7 \cdot 17$	56644	15.427248621	288	$2^5 \cdot 3^2$	82944	16.970562749
239	239	57121	15.459624834	289	17^2	83521	17
240	$2^4 \cdot 3 \cdot 5$	57600	15.491933385	290	$2 \cdot 5 \cdot 29$	84100	17.029386366
241	241	58081	15.524174696	291	$3 \cdot 97$	84681	17.058722109
242	$2 \cdot 11^2$	58564	15.556349186	292	$2^2 \cdot 73$	85264	17.088007491
243	3^5	59049	15.588457268	293	293	85849	17.117242769
244	$2^2 \cdot 61$	59536	15.620499352	294	$2 \cdot 3 \cdot 7^2$	86436	17.146428199
245	$5 \cdot 7^2$	60025	15.652475843	295	$5 \cdot 59$	87025	17.175564037
246	$2 \cdot 3 \cdot 41$	60516	15.684387141	296	$2^3 \cdot 37$	87616	17.204650534
247	$13 \cdot 19$	61009	15.716233646	297	$3^3 \cdot 11$	88209	17.233687940
248	$2^3 \cdot 31$	61504	15.748015748	298	$2 \cdot 149$	88804	17.262676502
249	$3 \cdot 83$	62001	15.779733838	299	$13 \cdot 23$	89401	17.291616466
250	$2 \cdot 5^3$	62500	15.811388301	300	$2^2 \cdot 3 \cdot 5^2$	90000	17.320508076

TABLE OF COMMON FRACTIONS
AND DECIMAL EQUIVALENTS

Fractions					Decimal	Fractions					Decimal
1/64					0.015625	33/64					0.515625
2/64	1/32				0.03125	34/64	17/32				0.53125
3/64					0.046875	35/64					0.546875
4/64	2/32	1/16			0.625	36/64	18/32	9/16			0.5625
5/64					0.078125	37/64					0.578125
6/64	3/32				0.09375	38/64	19/32				0.59375
7/64					0.109375	39/64					0.609375
8/64	4/32	2/16	1/8		0.125	40/64	20/32	10/16	5/8		0.625
9/64					0.140625	41/64					0.640625
10/64	5/32				0.15625	42/64	21/32				0.65625
11/64					0.171875	43/64					0.671875
12/64	6/32	3/16			0.1875	44/64	22/32	11/16			0.6875
13/64					0.203125	45/64					0.703125
14/64	7/32				0.21875	46/64	23/32				0.71875
15/64					0.234375	47/64					0.734375
16/64	8/32	4/16	2/8	1/4	0.25	48/64	24/32	12/16	6/8	3/4	0.75
17/64					0.265625	49/64					0.765625
18/64	9/32				0.28125	50/64	25/32				0.78125
19/64					0.296875	51/64					0.796875
20/64	10/32	5/16			0.3125	52/64	26/32	13/16			0.8125
21/64					0.328125	53/64					0.828125
22/64	11/32				0.34375	54/64	27/32				0.84375
23/64					0.359375	55/64					0.859375
24/64	12/32	6/16	3/8		0.375	56/64	28/32	14/16	7/8		0.875
25/64					0.390625	57/64					0.890625
26/64	13/32				0.40625	58/64	29/32				0.90625
27/64					0.421875	59/64					0.921875
28/64	14/32	7/16			0.4375	60/64	30/32	15/16			0.9375
29/64					0.453125	61/64					0.953125
30/64	15/32				0.46875	62/64	31/32				0.96875
31/64					0.484375	63/64					0.984375
32/64	16/32	8/16	4/8	2/4	0.5	64/64	32/32	16/16	8/8	4/4	1.000000

TABLE OF COMMON MEASUREMENTS

Area

144 square inches = 1 square foot
9 square feet = 1 square yard
1 acre = 43,560 square feet
640 acres = 1 square mile

Circular Measure

360 degrees = 1 circumference
1 radian ≈ 57.29577951 degrees
1 degree ≈ 0.017453292 radian
60 minutes = 1 degree
60 seconds = 1 minute

Fluid Measure

1 teaspoon = $\dfrac{1}{3}$ tablespoon

1 tablespoonful = $\dfrac{1}{2}$ fluid ounce

16 fluid ounces = 1 pint

Mathematical Constants

$\pi \approx 3.14159265359$
$e \approx 2.71828182846$
Golden ratio = $\dfrac{1 + \sqrt{5}}{2}$
≈ 1.61803398875

Length

1 printer's point ≈ 0.013837 inch
1 inch = 2.54 centimeters
12 inches = 1 foot
3 feet = 1 yard
6 feet = 1 fathom
5,280 feet = 1 mile
1,760 yards = 1 mile
1 meter = 100 centimeters ≈ 39.37008 inches
1 kilometer = 1,000 meters ≈ 0.6214 mile
1 mile ≈ 1.609344 kilometers
1 astronomical unit = 93,000,000 miles

Volume

1,728 cubic inches = 1 cubic foot
27 cubic feet = 1 cubic yard
2 pints = 1 quart
4 quarts = 1 gallon
1 gallon = 231 cubic inches
1 cubic foot ≈ 7.48 gallons
31.5 gallons = 1 barrel

Weight

16 ounces = 1 pound
2,000 pounds = 1 ton
1 kilogram ≈ 2.205 pounds
1 gram ≈ 0.035 ounce
1 pound ≈ 0.493827 kilogram

Miscellaneous Physical Constants

Equatorial radius of the earth ≈ 3,963.34 miles
Acceleration due to gravity ≈ 32.1725 feet/second^2
Velocity of sound in air ≈ 1,087.1 feet/second
Velocity of sound in water ≈ 4,823 feet/second
Avogadro's number ≈ 6.02257×10^{23} grams/mole
Density of the earth ≈ 344.7 lbs/feet^3
Density of water ≈ 62.425 lbs/feet^3
Density of air ≈ 0.0807 lb/feet^3
1 gallon of water weighs 8.337 lbs
Speed of light ≈ 186,282.397 miles/second
1 light year ≈ 5.8746×10^{12} miles (approximate)
Distance from earth to the moon ≈ 238,857 miles (average)
Distance from earth to the sun ≈ 92,900,000 miles (average)
Diameter of the moon ≈ 2,160 miles
Diameter of the sun ≈ 864,000 miles
Diameter of the planet Jupiter ≈ 88,000 miles
Diameter of the planet Mars ≈ 4,200 miles

TABLE OF COMMON MEASUREMENTS
(continued)

Time

60 seconds = 1 minute
60 minutes = 1 hour
24 hours = 1 day
7 days = 1 week
365 days = 1 common year
12 months = 1 year
10 years = 1 decade
100 years = 1 century
1,000 years = 1 millennium

Metric System Equivalents

2.54 centimeters = 1 inch
1 meter ≈ 39.37 inches ≈ 3.28084 feet
1 kilometer ≈ 0.6214 mile
1 are ≈ 1,076.39 square feet ≈ 119.599 square yards ≈ 0.024711 acre
1 liter ≈ 61.024 cubic inches ≈ 0.26417 gallon ≈ 1.0567 quarts
1 gram ≈ 0.035 ounce
1 kilogram ≈ 2.205 pounds

TABLE OF GEOMETRIC FORMULAS

2-DIMENSIONAL FIGURES

Rectangle

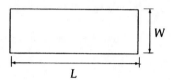

Perimeter $= 2 \cdot L + 2 \cdot W$
Area $= L \cdot W$

Triangle

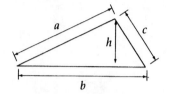

b = base length
h = vertical height
Perimeter $= a + b + c$
Area $= \dfrac{1}{2} \cdot b \cdot h$

Parallelogram

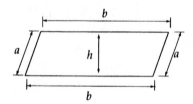

a = slant height
b = base length
h = vertical height
Perimeter $= 2 \cdot a + 2 \cdot b$
Area $= b \cdot h$

Trapezoid

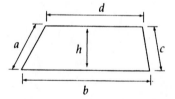

a and c are the nonparallel side lengths
b and d are the parallel side lengths
h = vertical height
Perimeter $= a + b + c + d$
Area $= \dfrac{1}{2} \cdot (b + d) \cdot h$

Circle

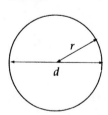

r = radius of the circle
d = diameter of the circle $= 2 \cdot r$
Circumference $= 2 \cdot \pi \cdot r = \pi \cdot d$
Area $= \pi \cdot r^2$

3-DIMENSIONAL FIGURES

Rectangular Box

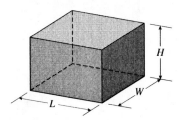

Volume $= L \cdot W \cdot H$

Surface Area $= 2 \cdot (L \cdot W + L \cdot H + W \cdot H)$

Right Circular Cylinder

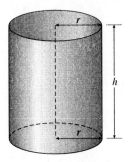

r = radius of circular top and bottom

h = vertical height

Volume $= \pi \cdot r^2 \cdot h$

Surface area $= 2 \cdot \pi \cdot r \cdot (r + h)$

Cone

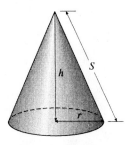

s = slant height

h = vertical height

r = radius of circular base

$r^2 + h^2 = s^2$

Volume $= \dfrac{1}{3} \cdot \pi \cdot r^2 \cdot h$

Surface area $= \pi \cdot r \cdot s + \pi \cdot r^2$

Pyramid (Square Base)

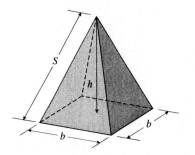

s = slant height

h = vertical height

b = base width

$2 \cdot h^2 + b^2 = 2 \cdot s^2$

Volume $= \dfrac{1}{3} \cdot b^2 \cdot h$

Surface area $= 2 \cdot b \cdot \sqrt{s^2 - \dfrac{b^2}{4}} + b^2$

Sphere

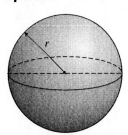

r = radius of sphere

Volume $= \dfrac{4}{3} \cdot \pi \cdot r^3$

Surface area $= 4 \cdot \pi \cdot r^2$

Torus (Donut)

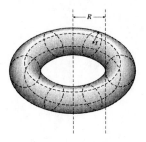

R = radius of hole

r = circular radius of donut

Volume $= 2 \cdot \pi^2 \cdot (R + r) \cdot r^2$

Surface area $= 4 \cdot \pi^2 \cdot (R + r) \cdot r$

3-DIMENSIONAL FIGURES *(continued)*

Spherical Cap

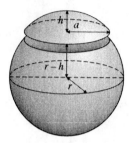

r = radius of sphere
a = cap radius
h = cap height
$a^2 + h^2 = 2 \cdot r \cdot h$

Cap volume $= \dfrac{1}{6} \cdot \pi \cdot h \cdot (3a^2 + h^2)$

$\qquad\quad = \dfrac{\pi}{3}\{2r^3 - \sqrt{r^2 - a^2}\,(a^2 + 2r^2)\}$

Cap surface area $= \pi \cdot (a^2 + h^2)$

Spherical Segment

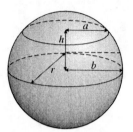

r = radius of sphere
h = segment height
a = segment upper radius
b = segment lower radius

Segment volume $= \dfrac{\pi \cdot h}{6}(3 \cdot a^2 + 3 \cdot b^2 + h^2)$

Segment surface area $= 2 \cdot \pi \cdot r \cdot h$

GLOSSARY OF SPECIAL
SYMBOLS AND ABBREVIATIONS

Symbol	Name	Meaning/Use
,	comma	period separator for whole numbers
.	decimal point	denotes the start of the decimal part of a number
×	times	denotes multiplication, especially in scientific notation
·	raised dot	denotes multiplication, avoids confusing × with x
+	plus	addition or positive
−	minus	subtraction, negative, or the opposite of
÷	divide	one of three notations used for division
—	fraction bar	denotes division and fractions (see also *vinculum*)
=	equal	denotes that two quantities have exactly the same value
≠	not equal	denotes that two quantities differ in value
≈	approximately =	denotes that two quantities have nearly the same value
√	square root	denotes the square root of a number
( )	parentheses	aggregation symbols to group parts of expressions
{ }	curly braces	aggregation symbols to group parts of expressions
[ ]	square brackets	aggregation symbols to group parts of expressions
π	pi	denotes the constant number pi ≈ 3.14159265359
)	division brace	denotes long division
| |	absolute value bars	denotes the absolute value operation
GCD	GCD	acronym for greatest common divisor
GCF	GCF	acronym for greatest common factor
LCM	LCM	acronym for least common multiple
LCD	LCD	acronym for least common denominator
<	less than	denotes that one quantity is less than another
≤	less than or equal	denotes that one quantity is less than or equal to another
>	greater than	denotes that one quantity is greater than another
≥	greater than or equal	denotes that one quantity is greater than or equal to another
±	plus or minus	denotes the same or opposite sign of a quantity
—	vinculum	aggregation symbol to cover repeating part of a decimal
%	percent	used to denote the number of parts per 100
FOIL	foil	acronym for First Outer Inner Last, used to multiply binomials
°	degree	denotes either temperature or angle measure in geometry

Symbol	Name	Meaning/Use
. . .	ellipsis	denotes a pattern to be continued
x_2	subscripted variable	x can be any variable letter, 2 can be any whole number
(x, y)	ordered pair	represents points in the x–y coordinate plane
$d(\text{A, B})$	distance A–B	represents the distance from point A to point B
Δx	delta x	horizontal change in point coordinates, new x – old x
Δy	delta y	vertical change in point coordinates, new y – old y
PV	present value	standard financial variable name called the present value
PMT	payment	standard financial variable name for a periodic payment
FV	future value	standard financial variable name called the future value
km	kilometer	km is an abbreviation for kilometer
m	meter	m is an abbreviation for meter
cm	centimeter	cm is an abbreviation for centimeter
mm	millimeter	mm is an abbreviation for millimeter
$k\ell$	kiloliter	kl is an abbreviation for kiloliter
ℓ	liter	l is an abbreviation for liter
ml	milliliter	ml is an abbreviation for milliliter
cc	cubic centimeter	cc is an abbreviation used for cubic centimeter
kg	kilogram	kg is an abbreviation for kilogram
g	gram	g is an abbreviation for gram
cg	centigram	cg is an abbreviation for centigram
mg	milligram	mg is an abbreviation for milligram
a	are	a is an abbreviation for are
○	hollow dot	indicates a point excluded from a graph on a number line
●	solid dot	indicates a point included in a graph on a number line

GLOSSARY OF SIGNIFICANT TERMS

The following is an alphabetical listing of significant terms defined and used in this book.

Abscissa   An alternate name for a horizontal or x-coordinate. *See also* Ordinate; x-coordinate.

Absolute value $|x|$ denotes the absolute value of the number x or the distance between the two points on a number line that correspond to the numbers x and 0.

Addition   One of the four fundamental mathematical operations. If $a = b$, then $a + c = b + c$; and if $a < b$, then $a + c < b + c$.

Addition rule for exponents $b^m b^n = b^{m+n}$ where m and n may be any integers and b is any nonzero real number. If $b = 0$, then m and n must be positive integers.

Aggregation symbols   Symbols used to group or contain other objects. Examples include curly braces, parentheses, and square brackets. These symbols always appear in left-right pairs. The vinculum, fraction bar, and radical sign are other symbols of aggregation that may appear singly. Absolute value bars also occur in pairs.

Analytic geometry   A branch of mathematics that makes use of a combination of the traditional subjects known as geometry and algebra. In two dimensions, analytic geometry studies properties of graphs in the x–y coordinate plane. *See also* Cartesian coordinate system.

Area   The fundamental unit of area is the square. Other nonsquare figures such as rectangles, triangles, and circles have areas determined by fitting a number of smaller square units inside the given figure. *See also* Perimeter; Volume.

Associative laws   Two operations satisfy their associative law equations:

$$(a + b) + c = a + (b + c) \qquad \text{Addition is associative.}$$
$$(a \cdot b) \cdot c = a \cdot (b \cdot c) \qquad \text{Multiplication is associative.}$$

However, subtraction, division, and exponentiation are not associative.

Average   The average of a group of numbers is the single number that is derived by taking the sum of all the values and then dividing by the number of numbers.

Base   The lower number in an exponential expression. For example, in 2^3 the base is 2 and the exponent is 3.

Basic operation for an expression   The basic operation for an expression is the last operation that would be performed according to the order of operations agreement when the expression is simplified to a single number.

Binomial   The sum (difference) of two monomials. $x^2 - 8x$ is a binomial. $x^2 - 8x = x^2 + (-8x)$. *See also* Monomial; Polynomial; Trinomial.

Cartesian coordinate system   The coordinate system most often applied in the study of analytic geometry. The name is in honor of the French mathematician René Descartes.

Circle   The set of all points in a plane that are equidistant from a given point. The constant distance is called the radius of the circle. *See also* Diameter; Radius; Sphere.

Coefficient   In a product of two or more factors, any factor is considered the coefficient of the remaining factors. In $5x^3y^4$, the coefficient of y^4 is $5x^3$.

Common denominator   For two or more fractions, a common denominator is any common multiple of the individual denominators. Common denominators are required for addition or subtraction of fractions, but neither multiplication nor division requires a common denominator. *See also* Least common denominator; Least common multiple.

Common factor   For two or more whole numbers, a common factor is any divisor of all the whole numbers. The common factors of 24, 36, and 60 are 2, 3, 6, and 12.

Common multiple   For two or more whole numbers, a common multiple is any whole number that is simultaneously divisible by all those numbers.

Commutative laws   Two operations satisfy their commutative law equations:

$$a + b = b + a \qquad \text{Addition is commutative.}$$
$$a \cdot b = b \cdot a \qquad \text{Multiplication is commutative.}$$

However, subtraction, division, and exponentiation are not commutative.

Complex fraction   Any fraction that contains another fraction as part of either its numerator, denominator, or both is called a complex fraction.

Composite number   Any whole number greater than 1 that is not a prime number. Composite numbers always have at least three distinct divisors. Neither 0 nor 1 is composite.

Compound interest formulas   Formulas that can be used to compute the future value of money that earns interest on top of interest. The basic formula for a one-time deposit is $FV = PV \cdot (1 + i)^n$, where FV is the future value, PV is the present value, i is the periodic interest rate, and n is the number of compounding time periods.

Conditional equation   An equation with at least one variable such that some values of the variables make the equation true and other values of the variables make the equation false. *See also* Equation; Identity.

Constant   A symbol that represents a single number. That number is not allowed to change or vary. For example, π represents the constant value 3.141592654.

Cross multiplication   A method used to change a proportion of the form $\dfrac{a}{b} = \dfrac{c}{d}$ into the form $a \cdot d = b \cdot c$. *See also* Fundamental property of proportions; Proportion; Rate; Ratio.

Curly braces   Denoted by { and }. They are aggregation symbols used to enclose a quantity in a mathematical expression. *See also* Aggregation symbols.

Degree of a polynomial   The degree of a polynomial in one variable is the largest power of the variable. The degree of $5x^3 + 6x^2 - 9x$ is 3.

Denominator   The name of the part of a rational number or fraction that occurs below the fraction bar symbol. The denominator of the fraction $\dfrac{5}{8}$ is the number 8.

Diameter   Either a line segment or the length of a line segment that contains the center and connects two points on a circle or on a sphere. The diameter is always twice the radius.

Distance between two points on a number line   The absolute value of the difference between the numbers on the number line that correspond to those two points. If the numbers a and b correspond to the points named A and B, then $d(A, B) = |a - b| = |b - a|$.

Distance formula   The formula used in the Cartesian coordinate system to find the straight line distance between two points. If points A and B have coordinates (x_1, y_1) and (x_2, y_2), then $d(A, B) = \sqrt{(x_1 - x_2)^2 + (y_1 - y_2)^2}$.

Distributive law   A fundamental property of numbers that can be used to convert a sum or difference of factors into a factor with a sum or difference. If a, b, and c represent any three numbers: $a(b \pm c) = ab \pm ac$.

Dividend   Refers to the number being divided into when the process of division is applied. In the expression $45 \div 8$, the dividend is 45 and the divisor is 8, *See also* Division check.

Divisibility test   Any method for quickly determining when one number is divisible by another. A number is divisible by 2 if it is an even number; by 3 if the number that is the sum of its digits is divisible by 3; by 5 if its digit in the ones place is either 0 or 5.

Divisible (evenly)   An integer a will be called evenly divisible by an integer b if another integer c exists such that $c = \dfrac{a}{b}$ or, equivalently, $a = b \cdot c$. *See also* Divisibility test.

Division   One of the four fundamental mathematical operations. Three notations are used to indicate division—that is $\div$, a fraction bar, and a square brace. If $a = b$ and $c \neq 0$, then $a \div c = b \div c$. If $a < b$ and $c > 0$, then $a \div c < b \div c$. If $a < b$ and $c < 0$, then $a \div c > b \div c$. Division by the number 0 is impossible.

Division by zero   Division by zero is impossible. There are two cases to be considered: $\dfrac{a}{0}$, where $a \neq 0$, and $\dfrac{0}{0}$. The division check fails to hold for the case $\dfrac{a}{0}$; whereas an infinite number of answers check out for the case $\dfrac{0}{0}$. Since neither of these two cases produces a unique acceptable answer, we conclude that division by zero is impossible.

Division check   The statement used to check whether the answer to a division problem is correct or not. In general, quotient $\times$ divisor + remainder = dividend.

Divisor   The name of the number that is used to divide with. In the problem $29 \div 6$, the number 6 is called the divisor.

Ellipsis   The symbol, consisting of three dots (...), used to indicate a repeated pattern in mathematics. For example, to list the numbers from 1 to 500, we would write 1, 2, 3,..., 500. It is a shortcut notation.

Equality of ordered pairs $(a, b) = (c, d)$ if and only if $a = c$ and $b = d$.

Equation   A statement that two mathematical expressions (which use at least one variable) are equal in value. All equations can be classified as being either identities or conditional equations.

Equivalent equations   Two equations are equivalent equations if every solution of one equation is a solution of the other equation and vice versa.

Equivalent fractions   Two fractions $\dfrac{a}{b}$ and $\dfrac{c}{d}$ are equivalent fractions if they represent the same value.

Even number   An integer is called an even number if it is evenly divisible by the number 2. The number 0 is also an even number since $0 = 0 \cdot 2$. The ones place digit of an even number is always 0, 2, 4, 6, or 8.

Expanded forms of a number   Any decimal number may be written in one of several expanded forms. For example,

$$5{,}237 = 5 \cdot 1{,}000 + 2 \cdot 100 + 3 \cdot 10 + 7 \cdot 1 = 5 \cdot 10^3 + 2 \cdot 10^2 + 3 \cdot 10^1 + 7 \cdot 10^0$$

$$0.623 = \frac{6}{10} + \frac{2}{100} + \frac{3}{1{,}000} = 6 \cdot 10^{-1} + 2 \cdot 10^{-2} + 3 \cdot 10^{-3}$$

Exponent   The raised number in an exponential expression. For example, in 2^3 the exponent is 3 and the base is 2.

Exponential notation   A notation used to write numbers that make use of exponents. For example, $8 = 2^3$. *See also* Expanded forms of a number; Scientific notation; Standard notation.

Exponentiation   A higher-level operation compared to the standard four operations of addition, subtraction, multiplication, and division. The basic operation for $(2 + 3)^5$ is exponentiation.

Expression   An expression is either a single term or a sum or difference of several terms. *See also* Term.

Factor (noun)   When used as a noun, factor indicates one of the numbers in a product. For example, since $15 = 3 \cdot 5$, we can say 3 and 5 are factors of 15. *See also* Factor (verb); Prime number; Zero product property.

Factor (verb)   When used as a verb, factor means "to write as a product."

Finite decimal   Refers to a decimal number with a finite number of decimal digits to the right of the decimal point. For example, $\frac{1}{4} = 0.25$ is a finite decimal; but $\frac{1}{3} = 0.33\overline{3}$ is not a finite decimal. The denominator of a fraction determines whether the fraction is a finite or infinite decimal. Only those denominators with prime factors of 2 and 5 are finite decimals. *See also* Irrational number; Terminating decimal.

FOIL   Acronym standing for **First Outer Inner Last**. In the product $(a + b) \cdot (c + d)$ the **First** terms make $a \cdot c$, the **Outer** terms make $a \cdot d$, the **Inner** terms make $b \cdot c$, and the **Last** terms make $b \cdot d$. $(a + b) \cdot (c + d) = a \cdot c + a \cdot d + b \cdot c + b \cdot d$.

Fraction   A quotient of two numbers in which the divisor is required to be nonzero. A number of the form $\frac{a}{b}$ where $b \neq 0$. The fraction $\frac{a}{b}$ is said to be in lowest terms if the greatest common factor of a and b is the number 1. *See also* Equivalent fractions; Rational number.

Fundamental property of proportions   The proportion $\frac{a}{b} = \frac{c}{d} (b \neq 0, d \neq 0)$ can be stated equivalently as $a \cdot d = b \cdot c$. *See also* Cross multiplication; Rate.

Fundamental theorem of arithmetic   Every whole number greater than 1 can be written in essentially only one way as a product of powers of prime numbers.

Future value   A term applied to an amount of money relative to an earlier time called the present value, usually applied when money earns some form of interest. *See also* Compound interest formulas; Present value.

General form (for the equation of a line)   The equation $ax + by = c$ can be used to represent any line in the x–y coordinate plane. *See also* Linear equation; Point-slope form; Slope-intercept form.

Gram   The fundamental unit of mass in the metric system. A gram (or g) is equivalent to 0.002205 pounds or about the weight of a standard paper clip.

Greater than   The symbol for greater than is ">". To say $a > b$ means the points A and B that lie on a number line and correspond to the numbers a and b are such that B is to the left of A.

Greatest common divisor   For two or more whole numbers, the greatest common divisor (or GCD), which is sometimes called the greatest common factor (or GCF), is the largest of all the common divisors. For example, the GCD of 36 and 60 is 12. *See also* Least common multiple.

Greatest common factor   *See* Greatest common divisor.

Grouping symbols   Symbols used to group or contain parts of mathematical expressions. The most common form of grouping symbols are parentheses, square brackets, and curly braces. The fraction bar, square root symbol, and absolute value bars also act as grouping symbols. *See also* Aggregation symbols.

Horizontal line equation   In the Cartesian coordinate system, the equation of a horizontal line is always of the form $y = c$, where c is a constant. Horizontal lines always have slope 0.

Horizontally aligned points   Two points, $A(x_1, y_1)$ and $B(x_2, y_2)$, will be called horizontally aligned if they lie on the same horizontal line, which only happens if $y_1 = y_2$.

Hypotenuse   The name given to the longest side in a right triangle. A triangle in which one angle measures 90 degrees is called a right triangle. The side which is opposite this 90-degree angle is called the hypotenuse. *See also* Pythagorean theorem; Right triangle.

Identity   A special kind of equation that is true for all values of the variable (variables) for which the expression in the equation are defined. For example, $x^2 + 5x + 6 = (x + 2)(x + 3)$. *See also* Conditional equation; Equation; Solution (to an equation).

Implicit coefficient   An implied coefficient that is not explicitly written. In the polynomial expression $6x^5 + x^4 + 9x^3$, the implicit coefficient on the x^4 term is the number 1.

Implicit operation   An implied operation that is not explicitly written. In the monomial $5x^3$, there is an implied operation of multiplication between 5 and x^3.

Implicit power   An implied power that is not explicitly written. In $7x^2 + 6x + 5$, the implicit powers of x are 1 and 0, which can be explicitly written as $7x^2 + 6x^1 + 5x^0$.

Improper fraction   A fraction of the form $\dfrac{m}{n}$ is called an impropoer fraction if $|m| > |n|$. For example, $\dfrac{-8}{5}$ is an improper fraction. *See also* Mixed number; Proper fraction.

Inequality   A statement that two quantities differ in value. Usually inequalities are expressed using one of the ordering relations: $>, \geq, <, \leq$. *See also* Order relations.

Integer   Any whole number, written with or without a sign. The number 0 is an integer even though 0 does not have a sign. *See also* Whole number.

Inverse operations   The operations of addition and subtraction are called inverse operations because each undoes the other. Similarly, multiplication and division with a nonzero number are inverse operations.

Irrational number   Any number that cannot be written as a simple fraction. The only examples of irrational numbers given in this book are the number π and the square roots of nonperfect square numbers. Irrational numbers are always nonrepeating infinite decimals.

Least common denominator   For two fractions the least common denominator (or LCD) is the number that is the least common multiple of the two denominators. *See also* Least common multiple.

Least common multiple   For two or more whole numbers, the least common multiple (or LCM) is the smallest of all the common multiples. For example, the LCM of 6 and 8 is 24. *See also* Greatest common divisor.

Less than   The symbol for less than is "<". To say $a < b$ means the points A and B that lie on a number line and correspond to the numbers a and b are such that A is to the left of B.

Like terms   Any two terms with a common factor. Two monomials are called like terms if they consist of exactly the same variables with the same powers. For example, $8x^2y^3$ and $13x^2y^3$ are like terms, but $6x^3y^4$ and $11a^3b^4$ are not like terms.

Linear equation   Any equation with the variables x and y that can be used to represent a line in the $x-y$ coordinate plane is called a linear equation in the two variables x and y. *See also* General form; Point-slope form; Slope-intercept form.

Liter   The fundamental unit of volume in the metric system. A liter (or l) is defined to be 1,000 cm^3 and is equivalent to 61.02 cubic inches.

Literal equation   An equation with more than one variable is called a literal equation. $P = 2L + 2W$ and $I = P \cdot R \cdot T$ are literal equations. *See also* Conditional equation.

Meter   The fundamental unit of length in the metric system. A meter (or m) is equivalent to 39.37 inches.

Mixed number   A number that is a combination of a whole number and a fraction. For example, $4\frac{3}{5}$ is a mixed number. *See also* Division check; Improper Fraction; Reduced fraction.

Monomial   A mathematical term that consists of a numerical coefficient times a product of whole number powers of one or more variables. *See also* Binomial; Polynomial; Trinomial.

Multiplication   One of the four fundamental mathematical operations. Both the $\times$ symbol and the raised dot $\cdot$ are used to indicate multiplication. If $a = b$ then $a \cdot c = b \cdot c$. If $a < b$ and $c > 0$ then $a \cdot c < b \cdot c$. If $a < b$ and $c < 0$ then $a \cdot c > b \cdot c$.

Multiplication rule for exponents $(b^m)^n = b^{m \cdot n}$, where m and n may be integers and b is any nonzero number. *See also* Addition rule for exponents; Subtraction rule for exponents.

Negative exponent   An exponent that is a negative number. When n is positive and $b \neq 0$, we may define $b^{-n} = \frac{1}{b^n}$. For example, $2^{-3} = \frac{1}{2^3} = \frac{1}{8}$. *See also* Zero exponent.

Negative number   Any number that lies to the left of zero on a number line. Negative numbers can be associated with "signed distances" on a number line.

Nonrepeating decimal   A decimal number that is either a finite decimal or an irrational number. Square roots of nonperfect squares are the most common form of nonrepeating decimals. The number π is also an example of a nonrepeating decimal.

Number line   A line with uniformly spaced scale marks extending to the left and right of a special point called the origin, which corresponds to the number 0. The numbers to the right of 0 are the positive numbers, those to the left of 0 are the negatives. Every real number corresponds to some point on the line, and every point on the line corresponds to some real number. The number line gives a geometric way of realizing positive and negative numbers.

Numerator   The name of the part of a rational number or fraction that occurs above the fraction bar symbol. The numerator of the fraction $\frac{5}{8}$ is the number 5.

Numerical coefficient   Refers to the number that is usually written at the beginning of a monomial. For example, the numerical coefficient of the monomial $6x^3y^5$ is the number 6.

Odd number   An integer is called an odd number if it leaves a remainder of 1 when divided by the number 2. The ones place digit of an odd number must be one of the digits 1, 3, 5, 7, or 9.

Opposite of a number   Used to refer to the number that lies on the opposite side of 0 on a number line. For example, the opposite of -3 is $+3$ and the opposite of $+10$ is -10. If x denotes any number, then $-x$ denotes the opposite of x.

Ordered pair   A form of notation used to denote the coordinates of a point in a two-dimensional coordinate system. For example, (a, b) is an ordered pair. *See also* Equality of ordered pairs.

Order of operations   A collection of rules that allows mathematical expressions to be written with a minimum number of grouping symbols. The rules state that exponents are to be performed before multiplications or divisions, which are also performed before additions or subtractions. All of these operations are carried out within each grouping symbol pair, starting with the innermost set of grouping symbols. *See also* Expression; Term.

Order relations   Refers to the $>$, $\geq$ and $<$, $\leq$ notations as they relate to the ordering of the numbers on a number line. *See also* Greater than; Less than.

Ordinary notation   The notation that is usually used to represent numbers. For example, $250 = 2.5 \times 10^2$. The first form is ordinary or standard notation; the second form is scientific notation. *See also* Standard notation.

Ordinate   An alternate name for a vertical or y-coordinate. *See also* Abscissa; y-coordinate.

Origin   Any point in a coordinate system that is considered the starting point. On a single-line axis, the origin is the point whose coordinate is 0. In the $x-y$ plane, the origin is the point whose coordinates are (0,0). *See also* Number line; Ordered pair.

Parabola   A special kind of geometric figure that is a plane curve. Parabolas have a reflecting property that can be used to focus light or sound. Satellite dishes and certain kinds of antennae are designed using parabolic curves.

Parentheses   Aggregation symbols (and), used to enclose a quantity in a mathematical expression. *See also* Aggregation symbols.

Percent   Literally means "to divide by 100." The most common use of percent is to describe ratios based on counts of 100.

Perfect square   A whole number is called a perfect square if its square root is another whole number. An equivalent description is that the exponents in the prime factorizations of perfect squares are even numbers only. For example, the numbers 36 and 400 are perfect squares; $36 = 2^2 \cdot 3^2$ and $400 = 2^4 \cdot 5^2$.

Perimeter   Refers to the distance around the outside of a plane geometric figure. Linear units measure perimeter. *See also* Area; Volume.

Periods   Refers to the names of the three-digit groupings of the digits of numbers that are separated by commas. In the number 567,892,143 the first set of three digits refers to the millions; the second group of three digits refers to thousands. Millions and thousands are examples of periods. *See also* Place value.

Pi   The constant number denoted by the special symbol π, which may be defined as the ratio of circumference to diameter in any circle. The number π is an irrational number and may be approximated by the decimal 3.141592654.

Place value An attribute of a number system which has the property that the positions of the symbols for individual numbers determine the value of the numbers. For example, the "2" in the number 20 has a different place value from the "2" in the number 2,000. *See also* Periods; Rounding.

Point-slope form The name given to a linear equation when written in the form $(y - y_1) = m(x - x_1)$. This line has slope m and goes through the point (x_1, y_1). *See also* General form; Linear equation; Slope-intercept form.

Polynomial Refers to special kinds of mathematical expressions. It is a sum or difference of several (one or more) monomials. *See also* Binomial; Monomial; Trinomial

Positive number Any number on the number line that lies to the right of the origin number 0. *See also* Negative number; Number line; Opposite of a number.

Present value A term applied to an amount of money relative to a later time called the future value. *See also* Compound interest formulas; Future value.

Prime factorization Refers to the process of writing a number in terms of products of powers of prime numbers. For example, the prime factorization of the number 1,500 is the expression $2^2 \cdot 3^1 \cdot 5^3$. *See also* Fundamental theorem of arithmetic; Prime number.

Prime number Any whole number greater than 1 whose only divisors are itself and 1. Neither the number 0 nor the number 1 is a prime number. *See also* Composite number; Divisibility test; Fundamental theorem of arithmetic; Prime factorization

Principle for reducing a square root If n is an even whole number and $b \geq 0$, then $\sqrt{b^n} = b^{(1/2)n}$.

Principle of dividing by one For any number x, $\dfrac{x}{1} = x$.

Principle of dividing a nonzero number into itself If $x \neq 0$, then $\dfrac{x}{x} = 1$.

Principle of dividing into 0 If $x \neq 0$, then $\dfrac{0}{x} = 0$. *See also* Division by zero; Undefined operations

Principle of multiplying by one For any number x, $x \cdot 1 = x$.

Principle of multiplying by 0 If x is any real number, then $x \cdot 0 = 0$. *See also* Zero product property of numbers.

Product property of square roots $\sqrt{a \cdot b} = \sqrt{a} \cdot \sqrt{b}$ provided $a \geq 0$, $b \geq 0$.

Product rule for exponents If $b \neq 0$ and m and n are any integers, then $(b^m)^n = b^{m \cdot n}$

Proper fraction A fraction of the form $\dfrac{m}{n}$ is called a proper fraction when $|m| < |n|$. For example, $\dfrac{-5}{8}$ is a proper fraction. *See also* Improper fraction.

Proportion A proportion is a statement that two ratios are equal. *See also* Cross multiplication; Fundamental property of proportions; Rate; Ratio.

Pythagorean theorem If a, b, and c represent the three sides of a triangle in which the angle opposite side c is a right angle, then $a^2 + b^2 = c^2$ or $c = \sqrt{a^2 + b^2}$. Side c is called the hypotenuse. *See also* Hypotenuse; Right angle; Right triangle.

Quadrant A name given to one of the four sections of the two-dimensional coordinate system that are sectioned off by the coordinate axes. Two points belong to the same quadrant if and only if the signs of their x- and y-coordinates are the same. In quadrant I both x and y are positive. In quadrant II x is negative but y is positive. In quadrant III both x and y are negative. In quadrant IV x is positive and y is negative.

Quotient   The answer to a division problem. If $a \div b = c$, then the number c is the quotient of the division. The number a is the dividend and b is the divisor. *See also* Dividend; Division; Division check; Divisor; Remainder.

Radical symbol   The symbol for a square root, $\sqrt{}$. *See also* Irrational number; Nonrepeating decimal; Square root.

Radius   For a circle or a sphere, the radius is the distance from the center to any point on the circle or on the sphere. The radius is always half of the diameter. *See also* Circle; Diameter; Sphere.

Raised dot   A special symbol used to denote multiplication. Using a dot for multiplication avoids confusion of the multiplication symbol $\times$ with the letter x.

Rate   A special kind of ratio. A ratio is the quotient of any two quantities. When the two quantities are measured in different units, the ratio is called a rate. For example, a ratio of distance divided by time is a rate that could be measured in terms of miles per hour.

Ratio The quotient of any two quantities, usually expressed as a fraction in the form $\frac{a}{b}$, where $b \neq 0$. Either one or both of a and b may be measured in terms of units. For example, if $a = 165$ miles and $b = 3$ hours, the ratio $\frac{a}{b} = \frac{165 \text{ miles}}{3 \text{ hours}} = 55$ miles per hour. A proportion is a statement that two ratios are equal. *See also* Cross multiplication; Proportion.

Rational number   Any number that can be written as a quotient of two integers. Thus, every rational number is a fraction, but there are numbers that can be written in fractional form that are not rational numbers. Every finite decimal and every infinite repeating decimal is a rational number. Square roots of nonperfect square whole numbers are not rational numbers.

Real number   Any number that can be thought of as corresponding to the position of a point on a number line. Real numbers can be broken down into the two major categories of rational and irrational numbers.

Reciprocal   If x is a nonzero real number, then the reciprocal of x is the number represented by the expression $\frac{1}{x}$. Every real number except zero has a reciprocal. If $x > 1$, then $\frac{1}{x} < x$, but if $0 < x < 1$, then $\frac{1}{x} > x$. The reciprocal of the fraction $\frac{a}{b}$ is the fraction $\frac{b}{a}$.

Rectangular coordinate system   The name given to a coordinate system in which perpendicular axes form the basis for the system and coordinates are determined by computing signed perpendicular distances from those axes. All points not on either axis determine a rectangle, one of whose corners is the point itself. The opposite diagonal corner of the rectangle is the origin. *See also* Cartesian coordinate system; x-coordinate; y-coordinate.

Reduced fraction   The fraction $\frac{a}{b}$ is called reduced if the greatest common factor of a and b is the number 1. For example, $\frac{8}{5}$ is a reduced fraction. *See also* Greatest common factor; Improper fraction.

Reduced square root   The radical $\sqrt{b}$ is called reduced if in the prime factorization of b all the primes have an exponent of 1. Thus, $\sqrt{10}$ is reduced since $10 = 2^1 \cdot 5^1$, but $\sqrt{18}$ is not reduced since $18 = 2^1 \cdot 3^2$. *See also* Principle for reducing a square root.

Relatively prime Two whole numbers a and b are called relatively prime if their greatest common factor is 1. Another characterization is that the prime factorizations of a and b do not have any common prime factors.

Remainder One of the four numbers that occur in division. For example, when 25 is divided by 9, the remainder is 7.

Repeating decimal A repeating decimal always represents a rational number, although some fractions are also finite decimals. Irrational numbers are nonrepeating infinite decimals.

Right angle An angle whose measure in degrees is 90°. A right angle is half of a straight angle. Lines that are perpendicular form right angles; sometimes a corner bracket symbol is used to denote that an angle is a right angle.

Right triangle A triangle that has a right angle for one of its angles. A triangle cannot have more than one right angle, if it has any. *See also* Hypotenuse; Pythagorean theorem.

Rounding (of numbers) Numbers can be rounded to a given decimal place or to other kinds of numbers. For example, rounded to the nearest hundred, the number 81 becomes the number 100; rounded to the nearest multiple of 25, the number 81 becomes 75; rounded to the nearest thousandth, the number 0.2368 becomes 0.237. *See also* Place value.

Round-off error Refers to calculational inaccuracies that arise when calculations are done on a computer or calculator. For example, a calculator may show $\sqrt{5} = 2.236067978$ and yet $(2.236067978)^2 = 5.000000002$ so the square of the square root does not make 5 exactly. The small decimal is an indication of round-off error.

Rule of signs for products and quotients The product or quotient of two positive numbers is a positive number. The product or quotient of a positive and a negative number is a negative number. The product or quotient of two negative numbers is a positive number. So like signs determine a positive answer and unlike signs determine a negative answer.

Scientific notation A number is said to be written in scientific notation when it is written as a signed number larger than or equal to one but less than ten times an integer power of 10. Usually, scientific notation is used only when a number is very large or very small. For example, $0.000645 = 6.45 \times 10^{-4}$. *See also* Ordinary notation; Standard notation.

Signed distance A method of describing the position of a point relative to another point on a line. The actual distance is always nonnegative. Signed distances are sometimes called directed distances since the sign is used to determine the direction. In a horizontal sense, negative and positive signs refer to directions left and right, respectively. In a vertical sense, negative and positive signs refer to directions down and up, respectively.

Signed fraction A fraction can be written most simply with a sign in one of three positions. For example, $-\frac{2}{3} = \frac{-2}{3} = \frac{2}{-3}$. The last form is less common.

Signed number A number written with either a $+$ sign or a $-$ sign. The number 0 does not have a sign and it is the only real number without a sign. Otherwise a real number must be positive or negative. If a number is written without an explicit sign, the number is assumed to be positive.

Similar triangles Triangles that have the same shape but possibly different sizes. Any stair-step pattern obtained by drawing vertical and horizontal line segments to and from a fixed line makes similar triangles. The ratios of corresponding sides in similar triangles are always proportional.

Simple interest formula The formula $I = P \cdot R \cdot T$. Interest equals principle times rate times time. *See also* Compound interest formulas; Future value; Present value.

Slope-intercept form   The name given to an equation of the form $y = mx + b$, since the number m is the slope of the line and the point with coordinates $(0, b)$ is the line's intercept with the y-axis. *See also* General form; Linear equation; Point-slope form.

Slope of a line   A number that measures the steepness of the tilt of a line. A line's slope can be obtained by choosing two points on the line and calculating the fraction that is the ratio between the difference of the x and y coordinates of those two points. Usually the number called m refers to the slope of a line in which m is defined by $m = \dfrac{\Delta y}{\Delta x}$, where $\Delta x \neq 0$. Only nonvertical lines have slope. Horizontal lines have slope 0. More intuitively, slope is the ratio of rise over run.

Solution (to an equation)   The set of values of the variable (variables) that make an equation true. *See also* Conditional equation; Equation; Identity.

Sphere   A three-dimensional shape that is a perfectly round ball. More precisely, the set of all points in three dimensions that are equidistant from a given point that is the center of the sphere. The constant distance is called the radius of the sphere. *See also* Circle; Diameter; Radius.

Square brackets   The aggregation symbols [and].

Square root   If x is a nonnegative number, then $\sqrt{x}$ denotes the square root of x. If $y^2 = x$ and $y \geq 0$, then y is called the square root of x and we can write $y = \sqrt{x}$. *See also* Perfect square; Reduced square root.

Standard notation   Numbers are usually written in what is called ordinary or standard notation. Scientific notation is an alternate form of denoting a number.

Subscripted variable   A variable written with a whole number subscript. For example, x_2 is a subscripted variable. Even though the variable letter may be the same, different subscripts represent different variables.

Subtraction   One of the four fundamental mathematical operations. The symbol $-$ is used to denote the subtraction operation. If $a = b$, then $a - c = b - c$. If $a < b$, then $a - c < b - c$.

Subtraction rule for exponents $b^m \div b^n = b^{m-n}$, where m and n may be any integers and $b \neq 0$.

Subtraction rule for signed numbers   The rule for expressing subtraction of signed numbers is $a - b = a + (-b)$. For example, $5 - 13 = 5 + (-13) = -8$.

Term   Either a single number or a mathematical expression in which the basic operation is either multiplication or division. *See also* Basic operation for an expression; Expression; Factor; Order of operations.

Terminating decimal   A finite decimal. *See also* Finite decimal; Irrational number; Nonrepeating decimal; Repeating decimal.

Trinomial   A special name for a polynomial that is a combination of three monomials. *See also* Binomial; Monomial; Polynomial.

Undefined operations   Several mathematical operations are undefined because they are impossible to perform. In this book, the following four operations are undefined: (1) Division by zero; $\dfrac{x}{0}$ is undefined, even if $x = 0$. (2) Zero raised to the power of 0; 0^0 is undefined. (3) Zero raised to a negative power. If n is a positive number, 0^{-n} is undefined. (4) The square root of a negative number. If n is positive, then $\sqrt{-n}$ is undefined.

Unlike terms   Terms that are not like terms. Only like terms may be added or subtracted. Like or unlike terms can be multiplied or divided. *See also* Like terms.

Variable   A symbol used to denote any one number from a specified set of numbers. In algebra, variables are usually single letters chosen from the end of the alphabet. If not specified, the set of replacement numbers is the real numbers. *See also* Constant; Subscripted variable.

Vertical line equation   In the Cartesian coordinate system the equation of a vertical line is always of the form $x = c$, where c is a constant. Vertical lines do not have slope and cannot be written using the slope-intercept form or the point-slope form.

Vertically aligned points   Two points, $A(x_1, y_1)$ and $B(x_2, y_2)$, are called vertically aligned if they lie on the same vertical line, which only happens if $x_1 = x_2$.

Vinculum   A special aggregation symbol used to denote the repeating part of a repeating decimal. In $\dfrac{7}{88} = 0.079545\overline{454}$ the vinculum covers the digits 54.

Volume   In contrast to plane figures, which have area and perimeter, only three-dimensional geometric solids are said to have volume. Cubic units measure volume, square units measure area, and linear units measure perimeter.

Whole number   Whole numbers are used to count whole parts. The number zero is also considered to be a whole number. The number of whole numbers is infinite and whole numbers are always positive, rational, and real. Signed whole numbers are called integers. A given whole number is either even or odd.

x-axis   The name usually reserved for the horizontal axis in a two-dimensional rectangular coordinate system. *See also* y-axis; y-coordinate.

x-coordinate   The number that represents the signed distance of a point from the y-axis. *See also* Abscissa; Ordered pair; Signed distance; y-coordinate.

x-intercept   Either the point or the number that is the x-coordinate of the point where a graph crosses the x-axis. *See also* y-intercept.

y-axis   The name usually reserved for the vertical axis in a two-dimensional rectangular coordinate system. *See also* x-axis; x-coordinate.

y-coordinate   The number that represents the signed distance of a point from the x-axis. *See also* Ordered pair; Ordinate; Signed distance; x-coordinate.

y-intercept   Either the point or the number that is the y-coordinate of the point where a graph crosses the y-axis. *See also* Slope-intercept form; x-intercept.

Zero   The name of a number that corresponds to the origin on a number line. The number 0 has no sign, 0 added to a number leaves the number unchanged, 0 multiplied by any number is always 0, and you cannot divide by 0. *See also* Number line; Origin; Zero product property of numbers.

Zero exponent   If the base b is nonzero, then we can define $b^0 = 1$. When the base b is 0, 0^0 is undefined. *See also* Negative exponent.

Zero product property of numbers   If a and b are any two real numbers and if $a \cdot b = 0$, then either $a = 0$, $b = 0$, or both a and b are zero. This rule is a consequence of the rule of signs for products of numbers. *See also* Principle of multiplying by 0.

ANSWERS TO ODD-NUMBERED EXERCISES

CHAPTER 1

EXERCISES 1.1

1. hundred thousands 3. thousands

5. hundreds 7. ten thousands

9. billions 11. tens 13. hundred trillions

15. hundred thousands

17. $340{,}875 = 3 \cdot 100{,}000 + 4 \cdot 10{,}000 + 8 \cdot 100$
$+ 7 \cdot 10 + 5 \cdot 1$
$= 300{,}000 + 40{,}000 + 800 + 70 + 5$

19. $5{,}602{,}809 = 5 \cdot 1{,}000{,}000 + 6 \cdot 100{,}000$
$+ 2 \cdot 1{,}000 + 8 \cdot 100 + 9 \cdot 1$
$= 5{,}000{,}000 + 600{,}000 + 2{,}000$
$+ 800 + 9$

21. $1 = 1$ (there is really only one expanded form for this number)

23. $54{,}663 = 5 \cdot 10{,}000 + 4 \cdot 1{,}000 + 6 \cdot 100$
$+ 6 \cdot 10 + 3 \cdot 1$
$= 50{,}000 + 4{,}000 + 600 + 60 + 3$

25. $45{,}072{,}190 = 4 \cdot 10{,}000{,}000 + 5 \cdot 1{,}000{,}000$
$+ 7 \cdot 10{,}000 + 2 \cdot 1{,}000$
$+ 1 \cdot 100 + 9 \cdot 10$
$= 40{,}000{,}000 + 5{,}000{,}000 + 70{,}000$
$+ 2{,}000 + 100 + 90$

27. forty-five thousand, one

29. one million, two hundred ninety-four thousand, five hundred forty-three

31. five hundred ninety-nine thousand

33. five billion, six hundred twenty-one million, three hundred forty-five thousand, seven hundred seventy-two

35. forty-four

37. two million, two thousand, nine

39. five hundred forty-two billion, six hundred thirty-six million, one hundred nineteen thousand, four

41. 2,579 43. 2,001 45. 24,020,004,013

47. 509,099 49. 900,084 51. 244,000,000,000

53. 910 55. 3,303 57. 2,000

59. 9,876,600 61. 4,000,000 63. 1,000,000

65. 120,000,000

EXERCISES 1.2

1. 475,883 3. 1,073,802 5. 3,764,452

7. 615,334 9. 459,139,627 11. 7,358,948

13. 891,216 15. 30,114 17. 2,883,004

19. 11,112,046 21. 11,755,463

23. 195,777,688 25. 127,871 dog registrations

27. 18,085,000,000 gallons

29. 543,104,313 people

31. $1,053,315 per carat

33. 1,678 missed free throws

35. 22,142 total days

37. $1,799,521,622

39. 589,792 square miles

41. ten millions 43. 3,006,014

45. 8,000,000

EXERCISES 1.3

1. 21,072 3. 15,015 5. 3,742,782

7. 3,292,258 9. 6,164,000 11. 5,373,108

13. 3,562,592 15. 774,639 17. 96 R1

19. 4,527   **21.** 104 R9   **23.** 2,039 R22

25. 40 R52   **27.** 4,416 R64   **29.** 200 R78

31. 9,360 square inches   **33.** 1,760 yards

35. $242 per stockholder   **37.** 304 cases

39. 1,080 books   **41.** $194,100

43. 502 hours   **45.** 21 times

47. 154,000 total holes

49. 22 times larger with 400,000 people left over

51. 8,959,335   **53.** 1,051,000 square miles

EXERCISES 1.4

1. 8   **3.** 9   **5.** 1,024   **7.** 625

9. 216   **11.** 729   **13.** 2,187   **15.** 343

17. 27   **19.** 256   **21.** 3,125   **23.** 46,656

25. 2,048   **27.** 1   **29.** 0   **31.** 1

33. 10,000,000,000   **35.** 1,000,000

37. 1,000,000,000   **39.** 8,000

41. 1,000,000,000,000   **43.** 1,024   **45.** 2,187

47. 2,048   **49.** 2,025   **51.** 64   **53.** 1,960

55. 541   **57.** 300   **59.** 2,646   **61.** 4,840

63. 729   **65.** 22,932 **67.** 2,200

69. 32,256   **71.** 602

73. five hundred four million, forty-four thousand, ninety-six

75. 4 times with 45,500 miles left over

EXERCISES 1.5

1. 14   **3.** 16   **5.** 204   **7.** 990   **9.** 28

11. 6,627   **13.** 34   **15.** 64   **17.** 64

19. 532   **21.** 16,632 **23.** 126   **25.** 21

27. 0   **29.** 67   **31.** 137   **33.** 13,133

35. 2,081   **37.** 7,564   **39.** 62,275 **41.** 21

43. 12 **45.** 6   **47.** 8   **49.** 282 **51.** 8,180

53. 3,724   **55.** 96   **57.** addition

59. division   **61.** division   **63.** subtraction

65. subtraction **67.** subtraction

69. multiplication   **71.** exponentiation

73. 7,508 R0   **75.** 0   **77.** 2,809 R0

79. ones   **81.** 7,286,000

EXERCISES 1.6

1. prime   **3.** composite   **5.** prime

7. composite   **9.** composite   **11.** prime

13. neither prime nor composite

15. composite

17. divisible by 3: $5,637 = 3 \cdot 1,879$

19. divisible by 5: $3,695 = 5 \cdot 739$

21. divisible by 2 and 5:
$2,510 = 2 \cdot 1,255$ $2,510 = 5 \cdot 502$

23. divisible by 2, 3, and 5:
$8,280 = 2 \cdot 4,140$ $8,280 = 3 \cdot 2,760$
$8,280 = 5 \cdot 1,656$

25. divisible by 3: $243 = 3 \cdot 81$

27. divisible by 5: $13,145 = 5 \cdot 2,629$

29. divisible by 2: $4,672 = 2 \cdot 2,336$

31. divisible by 2, 3, and 5:
$6,000 = 2 \cdot 3,000$ $6,000 = 3 \cdot 2,000$
$6,000 = 5 \cdot 1,200$

33. not divisible by any of 2, 3, or 5

35. divisible by 5: $140,725 = 5 \cdot 28,145$

37. divisible by 3: $252,689,241 = 3 \cdot 84,229,747$

39. $1,050 = 2^1 \cdot 3^1 \cdot 5^2 \cdot 7^1$ **41.** $221 = 13^1 \cdot 17^1$

43. $4,500 = 2^2 \cdot 3^2 \cdot 5^3$ **45.** $120 = 2^3 \cdot 3^1 \cdot 5^1$

47. $15,400 = 2^3 \cdot 5^2 \cdot 7^1 \cdot 11^1$

49. $2,695 = 5^1 \cdot 7^2 \cdot 11^1$ **51.** $286 = 2^1 \cdot 11^1 \cdot 13^1$

53. $442 = 2^1 \cdot 13^1 \cdot 17^1$ **55.** $500 = 2^2 \cdot 5^3$

57. $437 = 19^1 \cdot 23^1$ **59.** $53 = 53^1$

61. $178 = 2^1 \cdot 89^1$ **63.** $34,300 = 2^2 \cdot 5^2 \cdot 7^3$

65. $5,915 = 5^1 \cdot 7^1 \cdot 13^2$ **67.** $493 = 17^1 \cdot 29^1$

69. $1,023 = 3^1 \cdot 11^1 \cdot 31^1$

71. $3,451 = 7^1 \cdot 17^1 \cdot 29^1$

73. $2,691 = 3^2 \cdot 13^1 \cdot 23^1$

75. $100,320 = 2^5 \cdot 3^1 \cdot 5^1 \cdot 11^1 \cdot 19^1$

77. 122   **79.** division   **81.** 729

EXERCISES 1.7

1. $LCM = 105 = 7 \cdot 15 = 3 \cdot 35$

3. $LCM = 144 = 4 \cdot 36 = 3 \cdot 48$

5. $LCM = 25,200 = 12 \cdot 2,100 = 35 \cdot 720$

7. $LCM = 252 = 9 \cdot 28 = 7 \cdot 36$

9. $LCM = 576 = 32 \cdot 18 = 9 \cdot 64$

11. $LCM = 120 = 5 \cdot 24 = 3 \cdot 40$

13. $LCM = 460 = 10 \cdot 46 = 23 \cdot 20$

15. $LCM = 9,000 = 25 \cdot 360 = 6 \cdot 1,500$

17. $LCM = 300 = 5 \cdot 60 = 6 \cdot 50$

19. $LCM = 3,000 = 25 \cdot 120 = 6 \cdot 500$

21. $GCF = 140$: $1,680 = 140 \cdot 12$
$4,900 = 140 \cdot 35$

23. $GCF = 6$: $150 = 6 \cdot 25$ $504 = 6 \cdot 84$

25. GCF = 11: 2,002 = 11 · 182
    2,805 = 11 · 255

27. GCF = 80: 400 = 80 · 5   560 = 80 · 7

29. GCF = 105: 525 = 105 · 5   2,205 = 105 · 21

31. GCF = 168: 4,704 = 168 · 28
    7,560 = 168 · 45

33. GCF = 45: 315 = 45 · 7   495 = 45 · 11

35. GCF = 55: 385 = 55 · 7   605 = 55 · 11

37. GCF = 35: 3,500 = 35 · 100   455 = 35 · 13

39. GCF = 336: 1,680 = 336 · 5
    3,696 = 336 · 11

41. LCM = 72 = 6 · 12 = 3 · 24 = 2 · 36
    GCF = 12: 12 = 12 · 1   24 = 12 · 2
    36 = 12 · 3

43. LCM = 960 = 24 · 40 = 20 · 48 = 15 · 64
    GCF = 8: 40 = 8 · 5   48 = 8 · 6   64 = 8 · 8

45. LCM = 29,400 = 245 · 120 = 120 · 245
    = 98 · 300
    GCF = 5: 120 = 5 · 24   245 = 5 · 49
    300 = 5 · 60

47. LCM = 1,540 = 77 · 20 = 44 · 35 = 28 · 55
    GCF = 5: 20 = 5 · 4   35 = 5 · 7
    55 = 5 · 11

49. LCM = 1,001 = 143 · 7 = 91 · 11 = 77 · 13
    GCF = 1: 7 = 1 · 7   11 = 1 · 11
    13 = 1 · 13

51. LCM = 80,080 = 1,001 · 80 = 1,456 · 55
    = 880 · 91
    GCF = 1: 80 = 1 · 80   55 = 1 · 55
    91 = 1 · 91

53. LCM = 5,460 = 195 · 28 = 105 · 52 = 91 · 60
    GCF = 4: 28 = 4 · 7   52 = 4 · 13
    60 = 4 · 15

55. LCM = 2,184 = 28 · 78 = 52 · 42 = 21 · 104
    GCF = 2: 78 = 2 · 39   42 = 2 · 21
    104 = 2 · 52

57. 91 is composite: 91 = 7 · 13

59. $114{,}954 = 2^1 \cdot 3^1 \cdot 7^2 \cdot 17^1 \cdot 23^1$

61. 749,632   **63.** 622,521

EXERCISES 1.8

1. associative law for addition

3. distributive law

5. associative law for multiplication

7. associative law for addition

9. commutative law for multiplication

11. distributive law

13. commutative law for addition

15. associative law for addition

17. distributive law

19. distributive law

21. associative law for multiplication

23. commutative law for multiplication

25. distributive law

27. commutative law for multiplication

29. distributive law

31. Subtraction is not associative.

33. Subtraction is not associative.

35. Division is not associative.

37. Subtraction is not associative.

39. Distributive law is violated.

41. 5 · 8 + 5 · 6   **43.** 48 · (5 + 3)

45. 9 · (3 + 5 + 7)   **47.** 5 · (8 + 12 + 20)

49. 24 · (5 + 9 + 10 + 18)

51. 19 · 8 + 19 · 17 + 19 · 19 + 19 · 23

53. 15 · (7 + 23 + 2 + 8)

55. 8 · 11 + 8 · 32 + 8 · 8 + 8 · 17

57. LCM = 19,656   GCF = 156

59. exponentiation

61. No; 119 is composite; 119 = 7 · 17

63. 675,543 = 6 · 100,000 + 7 · 10,000 + 5 · 1,000
        + 5 · 100 + 4 · 10 + 3 · 1
    = 600,000 + 70,000 + 5,000 + 500
        + 40 + 3

CHAPTER 1 REVIEW PROBLEMS

1. hundreds   **3.** millions

5. ten thousands   **7.** hundred billions

9. 96,127 = 9 · 10,000 + 6 · 1,000 + 1 · 100
        + 2 · 10 + 7 · 1
    = 90,000 + 6,000 + 100 + 20 + 7

11. 79,548 = 7 · 10,000 + 9 · 1,000 + 5 · 100
        + 4 · 10 + 8 · 1
    = 70,000 + 9,000 + 500 + 40 + 8

13. 203,080 = 2 · 100,000 + 3 · 1,000 + 8 · 10
    = 200,000 + 3,000 + 80

15. four hundred fifty-four thousand, four hundred seven

17. fifty-five thousand, six hundred sixty

19. Twenty-two billion, three hundred thirty-two million, two hundred twenty-two thousand, two hundred thirty-nine

21. 2,934,527   **23.** 17,005   **25.** 6,072,015

27. $833   **29.** 1,008 passengers

31. 165 crates   **33.** $972,000

35. 150 television sets   **37.** 134   **39.** 140

41. 1,105   **43.** 9   **45.** 14,432   **47.** 84

49. $2^3 \cdot 5^2$ **51.** $2^1 \cdot 13^2 \cdot 17^1$

53. $5^1 \cdot 7^1 \cdot 11^1 \cdot 13^1$ **55.** $11^1 \cdot 31^1$

57. $7^2 \cdot 13^1$
  GCF = 120: $360 = 120 \cdot 3$
  $1,200 = 120 \cdot 10$

59. LCM = 3,600 = $4 \cdot 900 = 15 \cdot 240$
  GCF = 60: $900 = 60 \cdot 15$ $240 = 60 \cdot 4$

61. LCM = 25,025 = $13 \cdot 1,925 = 55 \cdot 455$
  GCF = 35: $1,925 = 35 \cdot 55$ $455 = 35 \cdot 13$

63. LCM = 4,760 = $7 \cdot 680 = 5 \cdot 952$
  GCF = 136: $680 = 136 \cdot 5$ $952 = 136 \cdot 7$

65. LCM = 192 = $4 \cdot 48 = 3 \cdot 64 = 2 \cdot 96$
  GCF = 16: $48 = 16 \cdot 3$ $64 = 16 \cdot 4$
  $96 = 16 \cdot 6$

67. commutative law for addition

69. associative law for multiplication

71. associative law for addition

73. commutative law for multiplication

75. distributive law

77. associative law for addition

79. $6 \cdot 7 + 6 \cdot 5$ **81.** $7 \cdot (3 + 17)$

83. $5 \cdot (2 + 21 + 7)$ **85.** $23 \cdot (7 + 5 + 18)$

87. $56 \cdot (23 + 17 + 20)$ **89.** addition

91. addition   **93.** division

95. subtraction   **97.** multiplication

CHAPTER 1 PRACTICE TEST

1. 1 is in the ten thousands place, 4 is in the hundred millions place, 8 is in the ten billions place

2. 56,198 = $5 \cdot 10,000 + 6 \cdot 1,000 + 1 \cdot 100$
    $+ 9 \cdot 10 + 8 \cdot 1$
    $= 50,000 + 6,000 + 100 + 90 + 8$

3. sixty-three billion, one hundred fifty-four million, forty-four thousand, nine hundred nine

4. 99,083 total points

5. 286 crates   **6.** 529   **7.** 317   **8.** 95

9. 155   **10.** 900

11. A prime number is any whole number greater than 1 that is divisible only by itself and 1.

12. $3^3 \cdot 31^1$ **13.** $2^5 \cdot 3^2 \cdot 29^1$

14. LCM stands for Least Common Multiple. The LCM of two nonzero whole numbers is the smallest whole number that both numbers divide into evenly. GCF stands for Greatest Common Factor. The GCF of two nonzero whole numbers is the smallest number that divides evenly into both whole numbers.

15. LCM = 14,000 = $4 \cdot 3,500 = 5 \cdot 2,800$

16. GCF = 18: $1,674 = 18 \cdot 93$
  $4,176 = 18 \cdot 232$

17. commutative law for multiplication

18. associative law for multiplication

19. commutative law for addition

20. distributive law

21. associative law for multiplication

22. addition   **23.** subtraction

24. division   **25.** subtraction

CHAPTER 2
EXERCISES 2.1

1. -17 **3.** -350 **5.** $+45$ **7.** -2

9. -35 **11.** -13 **13.** -1 **15.** 500

17. $-600,000$ **19.** -7 **21.** -12 **23.** -16

25. $+50$ **27.** -2 **29.** -7 **31.** $+7$

33. -7 **35.** $+9$ **37.** $+9$ **39.** $+5$ **41.** 0

43. $+16$ **45.** $+84$ **47.** 0   **49.** $+62$

51. $+524$ **53.** $0 > -7$ **55.** $16 > 0$

57. $-82 > -93$ **59.** $-134 > -135$

61. $353 > |-352|$ **63.** $85 < +93$

65. $18 > -27$ **67.** -62

69. $+146$ **71.** $+638$ **73.** $+1,071$

75. $+23$ **77.** $+27$ **79.** $+181$

81. $+2,234$ **83.** LCM = 62,530   GCF = 13

85. Addition and multiplication are commutative; subtraction and division are not commutative.

87. The LCM = 48 and the GCF = 4: $48 \cdot 4 = 192$ and $12 \cdot 16 = 192$.

EXERCISES 2.2

1. −21	**3.** −3	**5.** +21	**7.** 0
9. +30	**11.** +1	**13.** +30	**15.** −18
17. +7	**19.** +12	**21.** +24	**23.** +13
25. −6	**27.** −29	**29.** −35	**31.** +18
33. +57	**35.** −9	**37.** −80	**39.** +119
41. −86	**43.** −538	**45.** 39	**47.** 106
49. 6	**51.** 21	**53.** 25	**55.** 30
57. −14	**59.** 19	**61.** −100	**63.** 90
65. 439	**67.** 65	**69.** 167	**71.** −118
73. 582	**75.** 166		

77. $250 + (−25) + (−30) + (+18) + (−25) =$ +188. The gambler has $188.

79. $0 + (−1) + (−2) + (+1) + (+1) = −1$. She is 1 under par.

81. $42 + (−15) + (+35) + (−20) + (+32) = +74$. Your score is 74 points.

83. $175 + (−8) + (+10) + (−12) + (+7) + (−7) = +165$. He weighs 165 pounds.

85. In terms of inches, $60 + 4 + 4 + 3 + (−4) + (−4) = 63$ inches, or 5 feet 3 inches.

87. LCM = 728   GCF = 14

89. $13 \cdot 14 + 13 \cdot 82$

EXERCISES 2.3

1. +53	**3.** −17	**5.** +29	**7.** 0
9. −60	**11.** +36	**13.** +38	**15.** −78
17. +79	**19.** +60	**21.** +24	**23.** +41
25. +14	**27.** 36	**29.** −76	**31.** +166
33. +98	**35.** −800	**37.** 77	**39.** −69
41. 107	**43.** 77	**45.** 1,599	**47.** −1,215
49. −117	**51.** 0	**53.** 1	**55.** 98
57. 72	**59.** 98	**61.** 36	**63.** −28
65. 412	**67.** 77	**69.** 215	
71. −416	**73.** 35	**75.** 104	**77.** 137
79. 18	**81.** 12	**83.** 1,346	**85.** 162°

87. 500 feet below sea level   **89.** $89 per share

91. 6 quarts   **93.** 508,400 barrels

95. LCM = 37,228   GCF = 2

97. "to write as a product"

99. No; 0 is neither positive nor negative.

EXERCISES 2.4

1. −14	**3.** −7	**5.** −13	**7.** −75
9. 0	**11.** −13	**13.** +84	**15.** +99
17. −132	**19.** +32	**21.** +110	**23.** −154
25. +14	**27.** −182	**29.** −156	**31.** −117
33. 0	**35.** +117	**37.** −98	**39.** 80
41. −840	**43.** −120	**45.** 14	**47.** −780
49. +130	**51.** 100	**53.** 1,440	**55.** 572
57. 192	**59.** 15	**61.** −2,002	**63.** −5
65. 16	**67.** −4	**69.** 5,040	

71. −5,760   **73.** *undefined*   **75.** 0

77. −180°   **79.** $33 gain per share

81. 29,778,476 gallons of fuel

83. 2,145 seconds or 35 minutes and 45 seconds

85. 806,400 cubic inches of sawdust

87. 990 feet   **89.** −61

91. The verb *to factor* means "to write as a product," whereas the noun *factor* names one of the parts in a product.

93. Only one number, the number 0, is both non-negative and nonpositive.

EXERCISES 2.5

1. −270	**3.** +22	**5.** −209	**7.** −128
9. −27	**11.** 0	**13.** −1,281	**15.** +521
17. −3,206	**19.** +914	**21.** −130	
23. −461	**25.** −134	**27.** −882	
29. −1,726	**31.** 525	**33.** +94	**35.** −81
37. 0	**39.** −72	**41.** −26,565	**43.** 0
45. 14,874	**47.** −731	**49.** −3,789	
51. −126			

53. $(−68 + 92) \cdot [73 + (−78)] = −120$

55. $−132 ÷ (−12) + (−54) ÷ (27) = 9$

57. $−140 ÷ (−28) + 18 = 23$

59. $5 \cdot [−68 ÷ 17 + (−12) \cdot 15] = −920$

61. $[(−48) ÷ 16 + |−12| \cdot 4] + 25 = 70$

63. It is the distance on a number line between the points corresponding to the number and zero.

65. GCF = 8   LCM = 19,352

67. A whole number is divisible by 5 if and only if the ones place digit in the number is 5 or 0.

CHAPTER 2 REVIEW PROBLEMS

1. -4 3. $+8$ 5. -88 7. -12
9. 0 11. -4 13. $+64$ 15. -47
17. -14 19. $+318$ 21. -160 23. $+140$
25. -144 27. $+254$ 29. -938 31. $+304$
33. $+3$ 35. $+160$ 37. -2 39. $+25$
41. $+378$ 43. -2 45. $+543$ 47. 72
49. -255 51. $+155$ 53. $+165$
55. $-1,540$ 57. $-28 < 27$ 59. $43 < 44$
61. $-18 > -19$ 63. $78 > -2$
65. $-51 < -49$ 67. $-7 < 0$ 69. 78
71. 130 73. 35 75. 110 77. 365
79. 225 81. 31
83. $2 + 3 \cdot [75 \div (-10 + 35)] = 11$
85. $|-10| \cdot (-3)^2 - 7 = 83$
87. $7 \cdot [-(-10) + (-8) \cdot 9] = -434$
89. $9 \cdot [-14 - 33 \div (-11)] = -99$
91. $(-6) \cdot [11 - (-11) \cdot (-8)] = 462$
93. $|-80 - (26 - (-328))| = 434$

CHAPTER 2 PRACTICE TEST

1. $<$ 2. $>$ 3. $>$ 4. $<$ 5. $>$
6. $>$ 7. 137 8. 205 9. 12 10. 13
11. 97 12. 87 13. -148 14. -264
15. 36 16. -296 17. 226 18. 266
19. -10 20. 140 21. -1 22. -104
23. 4 24. -173 25. -4 26. -33
27. 672 28. $-3,168$ 29. -168
30. -686 31. 230 32. $2,226$

CHAPTER 3

EXERCISES 3.1

1. $\dfrac{3}{7}$ 3. $\dfrac{17}{24}$ 5. $\dfrac{1}{2}$ 7. $\dfrac{5}{23}$ 9. $\dfrac{5}{6}$

11. $\dfrac{3}{4}$ 13. $\dfrac{1}{4}$ 15. $\dfrac{5}{6}$ 17. $\dfrac{1}{3}$ 19. $\dfrac{1}{3}$

21. $\dfrac{2}{5}$ 23. $\dfrac{1}{3}$ 25. $\dfrac{17}{34}$ 27. $\dfrac{48}{84}$ 29. $\dfrac{52}{116}$

31. $\dfrac{104}{448}$ 33. $\dfrac{49}{91}$ 35. $\dfrac{25}{185}$ 37. 60

39. 13 41. 64 43. 5 45. 72 47. 236

49. 41 51. 138 53. 32 55. 52 57. 72

59. $\dfrac{11}{12}$ 61. $\dfrac{162}{161}$ 63. $\dfrac{34}{325}$ 65. $\dfrac{53}{172}$

67. $\dfrac{1}{4}$ 69. $\dfrac{3}{7}$ 71. $\dfrac{6}{11}$ 73. $\dfrac{2}{7}$ 75. $\dfrac{3}{7}$

77. $\dfrac{6}{11}$ 79. $\dfrac{8,000}{12,000} = \dfrac{2}{3}$ 81. $\dfrac{150}{200} = \dfrac{3}{4}$

83. $\dfrac{50}{235} = \dfrac{10}{47}$ 85. $\dfrac{185}{15} = \dfrac{37}{3}$ 87. $\dfrac{106}{100} = \dfrac{53}{50}$

89. Third powers are called cubes because the formula for the volume of a cube is Volume = length × width × height. A cube is such that length = width = height. For example, if length = width = height = 6, then the volume would be $6 \times 6 \times 6 = 6^3$.

91. An expression is a series of one or more terms connected by addition and subtraction operations. A term is a series of one or more numbers connected by multiplications and/or divisions.

93. A composite number is any nonzero whole number which has more than two divisors.

EXERCISES 3.2

1. $-\dfrac{4}{7}$ 3. $-\dfrac{8}{19}$ 5. $\dfrac{5}{77}$ 7. $\dfrac{-41}{53}$

9. $\dfrac{67}{16}$ 11. $-\dfrac{77}{75}$ 13. $\dfrac{24}{43}$ 15. $\dfrac{37}{57}$

17. $\dfrac{9}{67}$ 19. $-\dfrac{41}{36}$ 21. $\dfrac{13}{10}$ 23. $\dfrac{56}{39}$

25. $9\dfrac{4}{5}$ 27. $-3\dfrac{1}{3}$ 29. $-3\dfrac{1}{4}$ 31. $21\dfrac{2}{3}$

33. $4\dfrac{7}{8}$ 35. $-7\dfrac{3}{4}$ 37. -7 39. $5\dfrac{2}{13}$

41. $-2\dfrac{14}{17}$ 43. $15\dfrac{1}{5}$ 45. $\dfrac{15}{2}$ 47. $-\dfrac{28}{3}$

49. $\dfrac{43}{4}$ 51. $-\dfrac{32}{9}$ 53. $\dfrac{113}{13}$ 55. $\dfrac{76}{15}$

57. $\dfrac{34}{3}$ 59. $-\dfrac{99}{7}$ 61. $\dfrac{93}{5}$ 63. $>$ 65. $<$
67. $>$ 69. $>$ 71. $<$ 73. $<$ 75. $<$

77. When the word *factor* is used as a noun, it names one part in a product—for example, when we write $15 = 5 \cdot 3$, we can say 3 is a

factor of 15. When the word *factor* is used as a verb, it means to write as a product—for example, to factor the number 54 we can write $54 = 6 \cdot 9$.

79. The fundamental theorem of arithmetic says that every whole number greater that 1 can be written as a product of powers of prime numbers. Moreover, except for their order of appearance, the primes and their powers are unique. Each whole number greater than 1 has only one prime factorization.

81. Take the absolute value of the difference between the two numbers—for example, if the two numbers are called x and y, the distance is given by the expression $|x - y|$.

83. Two fractions are called equivalent if they represent the same numerical value—for example, $\frac{3}{6}$ and $\frac{4}{8}$ are equivalent fractions since they both represent the same number, namely $\frac{1}{2}$.

EXERCISES 3.3

1. $\frac{1}{2} = \frac{3}{6}$ and $\frac{2}{3} = \frac{4}{6}$

3. $\frac{-5}{14} = \frac{-10}{28}$ and $\frac{5}{4} = \frac{35}{28}$

5. $\frac{-85}{66} = \frac{-170}{132}$ and $\frac{17}{4} = \frac{561}{132}$

7. $-\frac{-108}{78} = \frac{108}{78}$ and $\frac{5}{6} = \frac{65}{78}$

9. $-\frac{-21}{-24} = \frac{-105}{120}$ and $\frac{39}{-40} = \frac{-117}{120}$

11. $-\frac{65}{-24} = \frac{130}{48}$ and $\frac{-21}{16} = \frac{-63}{48}$

13. $\frac{-17}{15} = \frac{-68}{60}$ and $\frac{91}{-4} = \frac{-1,365}{60}$

15. $\frac{-75}{18} = \frac{-300}{72}$ and $\frac{19}{-24} = \frac{-57}{72}$

17. $-\frac{25}{18} = \frac{-175}{126}$ and $\frac{7}{9} = \frac{98}{126}$

and $\frac{32}{21} = \frac{192}{126}$

19. $-\frac{46}{-39} = \frac{92}{78}$ and $\frac{1}{6} = \frac{13}{78}$ and $\frac{7}{-13} = \frac{-42}{78}$

21. $\frac{-75}{-32} = \frac{375}{160}$ and $\frac{-31}{10} = \frac{-496}{160}$ and $\frac{79}{-80} = \frac{-158}{160}$

23. $9\frac{1}{3}$ 25. $-\frac{11}{78}$ 27. $-1\frac{13}{30}$ 29. $1\frac{1}{180}$

31. $-\frac{19}{108}$ 33. $\frac{49}{200}$ 35. $\frac{63}{160}$ 37. $\frac{1}{58}$

39. $3\frac{11}{90}$ 41. $-\frac{41}{72}$ 43. $-\frac{1}{200}$ 45. $5\frac{1}{4}$

47. $-2\frac{5}{72}$ 49. $\frac{39}{140}$ 51. $-\frac{21}{22}$ 53. $\frac{5}{12}$

55. $-\frac{7}{90}$ 57. $-11\frac{1}{33}$ 59. $1\frac{11}{20}$ 61. $1\frac{1}{24}$

63. $3\frac{29}{40}$ 65. $\frac{137}{140}$ 67. $1\frac{7}{48}$ 69. $\frac{43}{110}$

71. $-1\frac{6}{7}$ 73. $30\frac{9}{20}$ hours   75. $8\frac{19}{120}$ acres

77. $6\frac{17}{24}$ cups of ingredients

79. $\frac{1,870}{4,180} = \frac{2 \cdot 5 \cdot 11 \cdot 17}{2 \cdot 2 \cdot 5 \cdot 11 \cdot 19} = \frac{17}{38}$

81. -20 83. LCM $= 2,970$

85. By applying the division check, the remainder is 16.

EXERCISES 3.4

1. $\frac{11}{20}$ 3. $\frac{-23}{45}$ 5. $-2\frac{13}{24}$ 7. $\frac{67}{100}$

9. $\frac{-15}{28}$ 11. $\frac{-15}{16}$ 13. $\frac{1}{18}$ 15. $1\frac{23}{78}$

17. $\frac{-5}{14}$ 19. $\frac{-64}{69}$ 21. $1\frac{7}{120}$ 23. $\frac{13}{42}$

25. $-3\frac{8}{21}$ 27. $3\frac{3}{14}$ 29. $\frac{-61}{110}$ 31. $2\frac{13}{210}$

33. $2\frac{34}{99}$ 35. $-2\frac{1}{6}$ 37. $-1\frac{39}{80}$

39. $-4\frac{5}{38}$ **41.** $-2\frac{3}{4}$ **43.** $\frac{-125}{126}$

45. $-1\frac{19}{42}$ **47.** $\frac{-101}{108}$ **49.** $\frac{-97}{108}$ **51.** $3\frac{35}{102}$

53. $17\frac{11}{24}$ inches **55.** $\frac{23}{24}$ cups short

57. $54\frac{7}{24}$ points

59. The supports may move another $\frac{5}{6}$ of an inch.

61. quotient = 13; divisor = 75;
dividend = 1,026; remainder = 51

63. addition **65.** 1,009 **67.** distributive law

69. $9 \cdot (97 + 3)$

EXERCISES 3.5

1. $\frac{9}{10}$ **3.** $\frac{-1}{2}$ **5.** $\frac{-4}{11}$ **7.** $1\frac{22}{41}$

9. $2\frac{19}{73}$ **11.** 1 **13.** 1 **15.** $1\frac{1}{3}$

17. -11 **19.** $\frac{-1}{9}$ **21.** $5\frac{3}{7}$ **23.** $-3\frac{11}{21}$

25. $-1\frac{7}{25}$ **27.** $\frac{-27}{59}$ **29.** $\frac{-39}{50}$ **31.** $\frac{-29}{36}$

33. $\frac{39}{50}$ **35.** $4\frac{15}{32}$ **37.** $\frac{19}{105}$ **39.** $20\frac{5}{8}$

41. $-1\frac{17}{118}$ **43.** $\frac{7}{36}$ **45.** $\frac{-13}{165}$ **47.** $\frac{-15}{16}$

49. $-621\frac{3}{5}$ **51.** $\frac{52}{97}$ **53.** $\frac{-56}{95}$ **55.** $2\frac{4}{15}$

57. $\frac{16}{33}$ **59.** $-1\frac{5}{52}$ **61.** 3 **63.** $\frac{5}{12}$

65. $4\frac{8}{15}$ **67.** 80 **69.** 57 **71.** 1 **73.** $\frac{35}{48}$

75. The word *period* refers to the grouping of decimal digits taken 3 at a time. The names of the first few periods are ones, thousands, millions, and billions.

77. False. $|0| = 0$ **79.** $-\frac{4}{5} = \frac{-4}{5} = \frac{4}{-5}$

EXERCISES 3.6

1. $\frac{14}{45}$ **3.** 0 **5.** 3 **7.** $1\frac{18}{25}$ **9.** 2

11. $12\frac{21}{32}$ **13.** -2 **15.** $-17\frac{1}{3}$ **17.** $2\frac{9}{49}$

19. $1\frac{7}{36}$ **21.** -7 **23.** $-6\frac{11}{14}$ **25.** $\frac{-1}{20}$

27. -9 **29.** $-3\frac{1}{3}$ **31.** $-4\frac{63}{92}$ **33.** 1

35. $5\frac{163}{216}$ **37.** $1\frac{10}{21}$ **39.** $1\frac{1}{2}$

41. reduction amount = \$1,040; final selling price = \$4,160

43. 18 whole strips with $\frac{15}{32}$ of a strip left over

45. \$712 **47.** 4,400 workers **49.** \$2,100

51. $30\frac{7}{8}$ miles apart **53.** 17 hours

55. You cannot divide by 0.

57. subtraction, negative, opposite of

59. The two integers are opposites.

61. division

63. There is only one possible choice for the divisor and quotient: dividend = 68; remainder = 8; divisor = 15; quotient = 4

EXERCISES 3.7

1. $\frac{8}{9}$ **3.** $\frac{14}{33}$ **5.** 4 **7.** $\frac{26}{135}$

9. $2\frac{12}{13}$ **11.** $\frac{-7}{24}$ **13.** $\frac{-11}{15}$ **15.** $1\frac{4}{39}$

17. $\frac{-7}{108}$ **19.** $\frac{19}{30}$ **21.** $\frac{-184}{245}$ **23.** $\frac{-44}{645}$

25. $\frac{-1}{6}$ **27.** $\frac{10}{21}$ **29.** $2\frac{13}{15}$ **31.** $-6\frac{1}{4}$

33. $1\frac{59}{75}$ **35.** $\frac{5}{19}$

37. It is the smallest of all the common multiples.

39. There cannot be any primes common to both factorizations.

CHAPTER 3 REVIEW PROBLEMS

1. 6   **3.** 136 **5.** 74   **7.** 43   **9.** 64

11. 59   **13.** 7   **15.** 23   **17.** 94   **19.** 134

21. $\dfrac{33}{56}$ **23.** $\dfrac{25}{72}$ **25.** $1\dfrac{13}{99}$ **27.** $\dfrac{-23}{120}$

29. $2\dfrac{33}{104}$ **31.** $-2\dfrac{67}{76}$ **33.** $3\dfrac{64}{65}$

35. $-5\dfrac{119}{120}$ **37.** $-3\dfrac{97}{114}$ **39.** $1\dfrac{47}{126}$ **41.** $\dfrac{7}{40}$

43. $\dfrac{-21}{43}$ **45.** $\dfrac{10}{51}$ **47.** $\dfrac{-12}{49}$ **49.** $\dfrac{-2}{13}$

51. $\dfrac{5}{21}$ **53.** 84   **55.** $\dfrac{96}{151}$ **57.** $\dfrac{-75}{128}$

59. $-13\dfrac{3}{4}$ **61.** $\dfrac{32}{45}$ **63.** $\dfrac{3}{7}$ **65.** $-1\dfrac{47}{100}$

67. $4\dfrac{61}{225}$ **69.** $\dfrac{1}{35}$ **71.** $\dfrac{111}{256}$ **73.** $-4\dfrac{7}{32}$

75. $8\dfrac{17}{41}$ **77.** 2   **79.** $4\dfrac{1}{3}$ **81.** $\dfrac{1}{25}$ **83.** 1

85. 288 minutes or 4 hours and 48 minutes

87. $14\dfrac{7}{13}$ miles   **89.** $15\dfrac{3}{5}$ inches   **91.** \$50,875

93. 1. He gets back all \$500.   **95.** $11\dfrac{3}{4}$ feet

CHAPTER 3 PRACTICE TEST

1. $\dfrac{9}{19}$ **2.** $\dfrac{18}{19}$ **3.** $\dfrac{1}{3}$ **4.** $\dfrac{17}{20}$ **5.** $\dfrac{2}{3}$

6. $\dfrac{11}{12}$ **7.** $\dfrac{69}{51}$ **8.** $\dfrac{53}{15}$ **9.** $\dfrac{136}{48}$

10. $\dfrac{60}{100}$ **11.** $\dfrac{118}{96}$ **12.** $\dfrac{15}{42}$ **13.** 138

14. 102   **15.** 15   **16.** 30   **17.** 154

18. 161   **19.** $\dfrac{-59}{18}$ **20.** $-5\dfrac{1}{2}$ **21.** $1\dfrac{17}{30}$

22. $-1\dfrac{47}{54}$ **23.** $1\dfrac{5}{12}$ **24.** $-2\dfrac{1}{3}$ **25.** $\dfrac{-19}{36}$

26. $103\dfrac{1}{5}$ **27.** $\dfrac{124}{211}$ **28.** $\dfrac{11}{53}$

29. 1,644 miles   **30.** $140°F = 60°C$

31. $\dfrac{29}{130}$ years in 2 months and 3 weeks

32. $86\dfrac{5}{8} = \dfrac{693}{8}$ square feet.

CHAPTER 4
EXERCISES 4.1

1. $9 \cdot 1 + 3 \cdot \dfrac{1}{10} + 2 \cdot \dfrac{1}{100} + 5 \cdot \dfrac{1}{1,000}$

$\quad + 7 \cdot \dfrac{1}{10,000}$

$\quad 9 + \dfrac{3}{10} + \dfrac{2}{100} + \dfrac{5}{1,000} + \dfrac{7}{10,000}$

$\quad 9 + 0.3 + 0.02 + 0.005 + 0.0007$

3. $8 \cdot 100 + 6 \cdot 10 + 4 \cdot 1 + 3 \cdot \dfrac{1}{10} + 9 \cdot \dfrac{1}{100}$

$\quad 800 + 60 + 4 + \dfrac{3}{10} + \dfrac{9}{100}$

$\quad 800 + 60 + 4 + 0.3 + 0.09$

5. $7 \cdot 1 + 6 \cdot \dfrac{1}{1,000}$

$\quad 7 + \dfrac{6}{1,000}$

$\quad 7 + 0.006$

7. $1 \cdot 10 + 2 \cdot 1 + 5 \cdot \dfrac{1}{100} + 5 \cdot \dfrac{1}{100,000}$

$\quad 10 + 2 + \dfrac{5}{100} + \dfrac{5}{100,000}$

$\quad 10 + 2 + 0.05 + 0.00005$

9. $1 \cdot 100 + 9 \cdot 10 + 6 \cdot 1 + 7 \cdot \dfrac{1}{10} + 8 \cdot \dfrac{1}{100}$

$\quad + 9 \cdot \dfrac{1}{1,000} + 3 \cdot \dfrac{1}{1,000,000}$

$\quad 100 + 90 + 6 + \dfrac{7}{10} + \dfrac{8}{100} + \dfrac{9}{1,000}$

$\quad + \dfrac{3}{1,000,000}$

$\quad 100 + 90 + 6 + 0.7 + 0.08 + 0.009 + 0.000003$

11. tens   **13.** hundredths

15. hundred-thousandths **17.** millions

19. tenths

21. eighty-two and seventy-one hundredths

23. seven and two hundred nineteen thousandths

25. eight thousand and eight thousandths

27. fifty-nine millionths

29. two million, one hundred eighty thousand and ninety-nine ten-thousandths

31. 89.97   **33.** 20.046   **35.** 0.00011

37. 1,000,000.1   **39.** 9,000,027

41. $\dfrac{3}{5}$ **43.** $\dfrac{3}{4}$ **45.** $\dfrac{3}{625}$ **47.** $\dfrac{1}{8}$ **49.** $\dfrac{7}{16}$

51. $\dfrac{99}{20}$ **53.** $-\dfrac{35}{2}$ **55.** $-\dfrac{3,021}{1,000}$ **57.** $\dfrac{123}{1}$

59. $-\dfrac{17}{16}$ **61.** >   **63.** 11   **65.** $-\$35$

67. False. $-2 - (-4) = -2 + (+4) = 2$

69. False. $5 - 12 = 5 + (-12) = -7$

EXERCISES 4.2

1. <   **3.** <   **5.** <   **7.** <   **9.** >

11. 17.191   **13.** 26.6468   **15.** $60.71

17. -0.21 **19.** 8.889   **21.** -91.71

23. -4.781 **25.** -4.332 **27.** 2.3091

29. 0.88076   **31.** 86.9   **33.** 0.1361

35. -1.57 **37.** -4.61 **39.** -15.79

41. $65.43   **43.** 54.819   **45.** -967.01

47. 49.004   **49.** -8.9 **51.** 3.51

53. -1.8611 **55.** -1.251 **57.** 123.9

59. -821.27 **61.** 3.469   **63.** -189.262

65. -2.584 **67.** $11.68   **69.** 23.292

71. $755   **73.** 116.3   **75.** $67.11

77. -25.7 **79.** 64.621   **81.** 91.7 million km

83. 396 million km   **85.** 21.7 earth days

87. $299.95   **89.** 4 $20 bills   **91.** 1.242

93. $-99,999$ **95.** 60   **97.** $\dfrac{21}{10,000}$

99. When we say 7 is a factor of 21, we are using the word *factor* as a noun.

EXERCISES 4.3

1. -0.13 **3.** 0.0075   **5.** -0.2375

7. 486   **9.** 0.044296   **11.** -0.02682

13. 0.00004   **15.** 0.378   **17.** -0.0136

19. -0.64 **21.** 34.224   **23.** 846

25. $-2,970$ **27.** $-8,234,300$ **29.** 820,000

31. -0.00863 **33.** 4.84   **35.** 17.7241

37. -0.125 **39.** -5.29 **41.** 0.1225

43. -24 **45.** 63.3   **47.** $-1,000$ **49.** -43.44

51. -21.04 **53.** -0.336 **55.** 184.8

57. $-361,530$ **59.** $26.66, $421.66

61. $499.76   **63.** $21.42   **65.** 153.86 cm

67. 18 grams, 7.36 grams   **69.** 39.84 grams

71. 130.56 grams

73. 598,961,890; 598,962,000; 600,000,000; 600,000,000

75. $-1,864$ **77.** -765 **79.** 0

81. undefined

EXERCISES 4.4

1. 4.7   **3.** 1,458.7 .   **5.** 32.9   **7.** 8.0

9. 12.12   **11.** 221.00   **13.** 8.66   **15.** 50.00

17. 18.333   **19.** 861.005   **21.** 3.000

23. 1,000.000   **25.** 0.6194   **27.** 3.0

29. $28   **31.** -3.21 **33.** 75.62

35. 319.55   **37.** 14.286   **39.** -7.948

41. -0.814 **43.** -2.506 **45.** 4,400

47. 3.884   **49.** 405.8   **51.** $-3,589,000$

53. -126.154 **55.** 24.3   **57.** -0.08

59. -0.02839 **61.** 0.0000126   **63.** 0.003246

65. -0.6 **67.** $-0.\overline{714285}$ **69.** $0.\overline{8}$

71. 0.84   **73.** $0.8\overline{3}$ **75.** 1.875

77. $-1.\overline{571428}$ **79.** 0.382

81. 1,399 boxes of cookies   **83.** $266.77

85. 14.5 miles per gallon   **87.** 1.12 hours

89. 5 chocolate chip cookies   **91.** 3.04 hours

93. -1 **95.** 16   **97.** 7; 3; 343   **99.** 1

EXERCISES 4.5

1. 3   **3.** $\dfrac{5}{2}$ **5.** 8   **7.** 7   **9.** 0.5

11. 25   **13.** 94   **15.** 2.4   **17.** 29

19. between 3 and 4; 3.162

21. between 9 and 10; 9.950

23. between 11 and 12; 11.402

25. between 19 and 20; 19.748

27. 2.6, 2.646   **29.** 10.9, 10.954

31. 5.5, 5.477 **33.** 14.1, 14.142 **35.** 348

37. 22.338 **39.** 25.495   **41.** 31.623

43. $\sqrt{2.56}$ is rational because

$$\sqrt{2.56} = 1.6 = 1\frac{6}{10} = \frac{16}{10}$$

45. $\sqrt{62}$ is irrational because $\sqrt{62} \approx 7.874$

47. $\sqrt{\dfrac{49}{144}}$ is rational because $\sqrt{\dfrac{49}{144}} = \dfrac{7}{12}$

49. $\sqrt{961}$ is rational because $\sqrt{961} = 31 = \dfrac{31}{1}$

51. -42 **53.** 124   **55.** -5 **57.** 100

59. $\dfrac{1}{4}$ **61.** -40.18 **63.** -105.6

65. 10 meters **67.** 25 inches **69.** 61 feet

71. 3 seconds **73.** 16 feet **75.** 2

77. 2, 3, 5, 7, 11, 13, 17, 19, 23, 29

79. $2^3 \cdot 5^3$ **81.** $7 \cdot 13 \cdot 17$ **83.** $\dfrac{17}{15}$

EXERCISES 4.6

1. No **3.** Yes; $361 = 19^2$. **5.** No

7. Yes; $625 = 25^2$. **9.** No **11.** No

13. No **15.** Yes; $441 = 21^2$.

17. Yes; $1,600 = 40^2$. **19.** No **21.** $3 \cdot \sqrt{5}$

23. $2 \cdot \sqrt{5}$ **25.** $4 \cdot \sqrt{2}$ **27.** $4 \cdot \sqrt{7}$

29. $6 \cdot \sqrt{3}$ **31.** $9 \cdot \sqrt{2}$ **33.** $12 \cdot \sqrt{3}$

35. $8 \cdot \sqrt{5}$ **37.** $7 \cdot \sqrt{7}$ **39.** $14 \cdot \sqrt{2}$

41. not reducible **43.** not reducible

45. $11 \cdot \sqrt{35}$ **47.** not reducible

49. $19 \cdot \sqrt{7}$ **51.** $5 \cdot \sqrt{14}$ **53.** $14 \cdot \sqrt{3}$

55. $441 \cdot \sqrt{5}$ **57.** $13 \cdot \sqrt{10}$ **59.** $20,449 \cdot \sqrt{7}$

61. $3 \cdot \sqrt{41}$ **63.** $5 \cdot \sqrt{29}$ **65.** $10 \cdot \sqrt{15}$

67. $6 \cdot \sqrt{21}$ **69.** $7 \cdot \sqrt{13}$ **71.** $7 \cdot \sqrt{21}$

73. $6 \cdot \sqrt{35}$ **75.** $120 \cdot \sqrt{15}$ **77.** $252 \cdot \sqrt{21}$

79. $315 \cdot \sqrt{105}$ **81.** $120 \cdot \sqrt{7}$

83. $(4 + 5) + 6 = 4 + (5 + 6)$

85. $(9 \cdot 10) \cdot 11 = 9 \cdot (10 \cdot 11)$ **87.** $\dfrac{b}{a}$

89. To add two fractions requires first changing the fractions to a common denominator. To multiply two fractions does not require a common denominator. To multiply two fractions, multiply their numerators and multiply their denominators.

EXERCISES 4.7

1. $\dfrac{17}{100}$ **3.** $\dfrac{23}{20}$ **5.** $\dfrac{4}{5}$ **7.** $\dfrac{1}{8}$ **9.** $\dfrac{18}{25}$

11. 1 **13.** $\dfrac{2}{3}$ **15.** $\dfrac{3}{40}$ **17.** $\dfrac{1}{400}$ **19.** $\dfrac{53}{25}$

21. 0.19 **23.** 0.06 **25.** 0.82 **27.** 4

29. 1.25 **31.** 0.065 **33.** 0.0675 **35.** 0.0025

37. 0.075 **39.** 0.0025 **41.** 87% **43.** 8%

45. 70% **47.** 911% **49.** 112.5% **51.** 200%

53. $33\dfrac{1}{3}$% **55.** $5\dfrac{1}{2}$% **57.** 16.25%

59. 0.5% **61.** 70% **63.** $\approx$42.9% **65.** 98%

67. 250% **69.** $\approx$38.5% **71.** 67.5%

73. 84% **75.** $\approx$83.3% **77.** $\approx$91.7%

79. $\dfrac{6}{25}$, 0.24, 24% **81.** $\dfrac{17}{40}$, 0.425, 42.5%

83. 0.98% **85.** $\approx$57.1% **87.** $\approx$30.8%

89. 0.524 **91.** 0.165, $\dfrac{33}{200}$ **93.** false

95. 11 **97.** $\dfrac{41}{64}$ **99.** false

CHAPTER 4 REVIEW PROBLEMS

1. hundred-thousandths

3. $2 \cdot 1 + 9 \cdot \dfrac{1}{100} + 4 \cdot \dfrac{1}{1,000}$

$2 + \dfrac{9}{100} + \dfrac{4}{1,000}$

$2 + 0.09 + 0.004$

5. twenty and two tenths **7.** 504.0074

9. $\dfrac{5}{16}$ **11.** $-0.519 > -0.52$ **13.** 10.0

15. $0.1\overline{6}$ **17.** 35 **19.** 9.849

21. between 11 and 12; 11.4 **23.** $7\sqrt{2}$

25. $28\sqrt{5}$ **27.** $20\sqrt{5}$ **29.** $\dfrac{18}{25}$ **31.** 0.0525

33. 116.7% **35.** 6.75% **37.** -3.515

39. 0.0147 **41.** $\approx$16.718 **43.** -9.179

45. -0.0086 **47.** -5.1076 **49.** -110

51. -24.4305 **53.** -50 **55.** 692 **57.** -0.6

59. 109.2 **61.** 3.45 miles **63.** 20%

65. $13.32 **67.** $16.63 **69.** $-2,200$

CHAPTER 4 PRACTICE TEST

1. $2 \cdot 10 + 7 \cdot 1 + 8 \cdot \dfrac{1}{100} + 3 \cdot \dfrac{1}{1,000}$

$+ 1 \cdot \dfrac{1}{10,000}$

$20 + 7 + \dfrac{8}{100} + \dfrac{3}{1,000} + \dfrac{1}{10,000}$

$20 + 7 + 0.08 + 0.003 + 0.0001$

2. 17,000,000.055   **3.** $\dfrac{11}{16}$ **4.** $0.\overline{285714}$

5. 17.98   **6.** $\dfrac{18}{7}$ **7.** $560\sqrt{35}$ **8.** $5\sqrt{130}$

9. $\dfrac{2}{3}$ **10.** 0.0775   **11.** 93.75%   **12.** 90%

13. −15.87   **14.** −3.752   **15.** 6,000
16. 1.802   **17.** −3.58   **18.** −0.0108
19. 1,323   **20.** −0.92   **21.** −6.1836
22. −6.724   **23.** −22.827   **24.** 12.8 gallons
25. $747.88

CHAPTER 5

EXERCISES 5.1

1. $\dfrac{1}{25}$ **3.** $\dfrac{1}{49}$ **5.** $\dfrac{1}{9}$ **7.** $\dfrac{1}{125}$ **9.** 1

11. undefined   **13.** $\dfrac{1}{64}$ **15.** 1   **17.** 0

19. undefined   **21.** $\dfrac{1}{100}$ **23.** $\dfrac{1}{64}$ **25.** 1

27. −1   **29.** undefined   **31.** −32

33. $-\dfrac{27}{8}$ **35.** $\dfrac{9}{100}$ **37.** $-\dfrac{64}{27}$ **39.** 49

41. $-\dfrac{1}{512}$ **43.** 64   **45.** $-\dfrac{1}{216}$ **47.** $\dfrac{16}{225}$

49. $\dfrac{16}{25}$ **51.** $-\dfrac{4}{13}$ **53.** 31   **55.** 43

57. −17   **59.** $\dfrac{1,288}{125}$ **61.** $\dfrac{13}{4}$ **63.** −5

65. $\dfrac{1}{20}$ **67.** 0   **69.** $\dfrac{1}{2}$ **71.** Yes; $784 = 28^2$.

73. $4 \cdot \sqrt{30}$ **75.** $\dfrac{0}{5} = 0$ but $\dfrac{5}{0}$ is undefined.

77. $\dfrac{3}{8} = \dfrac{1}{4} + \dfrac{1}{8}$

EXERCISES 5.2

1. $\dfrac{1}{3}$ **3.** $\dfrac{1}{8}$ **5.** $\dfrac{1}{5}$ **7.** 1

9. 0.0001   **11.** 0.000001   **13.** $\dfrac{1}{2}$

15. You cannot apply exponent rules but the expression simplifies to $\dfrac{81}{8}$.

17. 1   **19.** 144   **21.** 309   **23.** 50   **25.** 9

27. $-\dfrac{1}{128}$ **29.** −216   **31.** 2^{16} **33.** $-\dfrac{1}{7^9}$

35. 27^{26} **37.** $\dfrac{1}{5^{14}}$ **39.** $\dfrac{1}{128}$ **41.** 1

43. $-\dfrac{1}{2^{23}}$ **45.** −27   **47.** 1   **49.** 8

51. $\dfrac{1}{144}$ **53.** 25   **55.** $\dfrac{1}{125}$ **57.** $-\dfrac{2}{39}$

59. 0 and 1   **61.** $(7 + 3) \cdot (-25)$

EXERCISES 5.3

1. -2^{15} **3.** -3^9 **5.** 4^{30} **7.** $\dfrac{1}{8^{15}}$

9. undefined   **11.** 2^{15} **13.** $\left(\dfrac{4}{3}\right)^{12}$

15. -3^9 **17.** 5^{42} **19.** undefined

21. $6^3 \cdot 9^3$ **23.** $\dfrac{1}{2^3} \cdot \dfrac{1}{17^3}$ **25.** $\dfrac{1}{4^8}$ **27.** $2^8 \cdot \dfrac{1}{7^8}$

29. $\left(\dfrac{5}{6}\right)^{30}$ **31.** $\dfrac{1}{2^4} \cdot \dfrac{1}{3^4}$ **33.** 1   **35.** 3

37. $\dfrac{-1}{512}$ **39.** −2   **41.** 1   **43.** division

45. 6th power
47. $(-5) \cdot 8 + (-5) \cdot 6 + (-5) \cdot (-4)$ **49.** 4

EXERCISES 5.4

1. 1,000,000   **3.** 0.1   **5.** 0.00001
7. 0.001   **9.** 100,000   **11.** 0.00000001

13. 1,000,000,000   **15.** 100   **17.** 306,840.

19. 341,100,000.   **21.** 17.259

23. 0.0000000088881   **25.** 0.0000006879

27. 63,090.   **29.** 0.00003792   **31.** 9.6701

33. 4,402.   **35.** 627,146.6   **37.** 50.5004

39. 146.751   **41.** 35,050.   **43.** 0.38259628

45. 7,923.52   **47.** 0.217   **49.** 1.7292

51. 0.0000001   **53.** 10,000.   **55.** −241,700.

57. −5,232.168   **59.** 207.673

61. subtraction, division, exponentiation.

63. 0

65. $|x|$ is the distance between the point on a number line that corresponds to the number zero and the point that corresponds to the number represented by x.

67. Every whole number greater than 1 is either a prime number or can be written in a unique way as a product of powers of prime numbers.

EXERCISES 5.5

1. $\frac{1}{2}$ is not in decimal form.

3. 92.76 is larger than 10 in absolute value.

5. 3.1 is not an integer power of 10.

7. −0.732 is less than 1 in absolute value.

9. $\frac{3}{5}$ is not in decimal form.

11. $\sqrt{2}$ is not in decimal form.

13. It is in scientific notation.

15. 1.236×10^0 **17.** 2.19×10^{-4}

19. $-1. \times 10^0$ **21.** $1. \times 10^{-6}$ **23.** $1. \times 10^{-3}$

25. 6.25×10^{-1} **27.** $4. \times 10^0$ **29.** $1. \times 10^{-2}$

31. $1. \times 10^2$ **33.** -6.25×10^{-2}

35. 9.99×10^3 **37.** 9.972524×10^3

39. 3.4×10^2 **41.** -1.64×10^{-1}

43. 1.0858×10^{-19} **45.** 1.428×10^2

47. -8.903×10^{-4} **49.** 4.0488×10^{-24}

51. 4.8×10^{11} **53.** $2. \times 10^0$ **55.** -1.6×10^{-2}

57. $8. \times 10^5$ **59.** $400 = 4. \times 10^2$

61. Since $10^8 > 3.1536 \times 10^7$ there are more shakes in one second than there are seconds in one year.

63. 0.3 second $= 3. \times 10^{-1}$

65. $900,000 = 9. \times 10^5$ **67.** $\frac{17}{19}$ **69.** $\frac{5}{101}$

71. There is an infinite number of odd composite numbers. For example, every multiple of 5 or 7 that is greater than 8 is an odd composite number.

EXERCISES 5.6

1. 6,500. kg   **3.** 0.00045 kg   **5.** 2.56 km

7. 20. kg   **9.** 280 ml **11.** 0.58 kg

13. 40. cg   **15.** 180,000. cm^2 **17.** 20. t

19. 4.6 mg   **21.** 27,000. m^2 **23.** 9,350. t

25. 8.44×10^5 l **27.** 0.0238 g

29. 4.07×10^5 g   **31.** 945. m^2 **33.** 7.25 kg

35. 862. kg   **37.** 0.0032 ml **39.** 2.4 cm

41. 7.6 cm $\times$ 12.7 cm   **43.** 10.0 cm $\times$ 6.3 cm

45. $4\sqrt{43}$ **47.** $\frac{27}{8}$ **49.** $18\frac{1}{2}$

CHAPTER 5 REVIEW PROBLEMS

1. $\frac{1}{25}$ **3.** $\frac{1}{9}$ **5.** 8   **7.** undefined

9. 0   **11.** $-\frac{3}{5}$ **13.** 1   **15.** 16   **17.** 1

19. $-\frac{27}{8}$ **21.** $\frac{1}{27}$ **23.** -5^{15} **25.** $\frac{1}{16}$

27. 8   **29.** -5^{14} **31.** 1   **33.** 0   **35.** 64

37. 3^6 **39.** $\frac{1}{2^{15}}$ **41.** $\frac{1}{4^{18}}$ **43.** −1   **45.** 0

47. −1   **49.** $\frac{1}{8^4}$ **51.** 2^{40} **53.** yes

55. No; 18.1 is larger than 10.

57. No; $\sqrt{3}$ is not written as a decimal between 1 and 10.

59. No; $-\frac{1}{2}$ is not a whole number.   **61.** yes

63. 2.3×10^{-4} **65.** -9.1×10^{-1}

67. 2.7×10^{12} **69.** 2.2×10^5 **71.** 1.02×10^5

73. 1.0×10^{-1} **75.** 5.0×10^2 **77.** −39

79. 99,000.9   **81.** 1   **83.** 2.6×10^{-4} kg

85. 6.24 m

CHAPTER 5 PRACTICE TEST

1. $\dfrac{1}{25}$ **2.** $\dfrac{1}{27}$ **3.** 16   **4.** 9   **5.** 0

6. undefined   **7.** undefined   **8.** 1

9. -8 **10.** 24   **11.** $\dfrac{1}{3^{12}}$ **12.** 2^{20}

13. $\dfrac{1}{12^{16}}$ **14.** $\dfrac{1}{2^{24}}$

15. No; $-\dfrac{3}{5}$ is not an integer.

16. No; $\left|-0.003\right| < 1$ **17.** No; $25.6 > 10$.

18. No; not a power of 10.

19. 9.095×10^4 **20.** -8×10^{-5}

21. 2.1×10^4 **22.** 2×10^{10} **23.** 3.1×10^4

24. -243 **25.** $-\dfrac{1}{72}$ **26.** $\dfrac{1}{9}$

27. $\dfrac{1}{4}$ **28.** 2.6×10^6 m   **29.** 3.6 cm^2

CHAPTER 6

EXERCISES 6.1

1. polynomial, monomial, degree = 0

3. polynomial, trinomial, degree = 3

5. not a polynomial

7. polynomial, binomial, degree = 1

9. not a polynomial

11. polynomial, trinomial, degree = 8

13. polynomial, trinomial, degree = 6

15. $21x$ **17.** $26x^2$ **19.** $6a^2$

21. not like terms   **23.** $-7x^2y$ **25.** $-7a^2b^4$

27. not like terms   **29.** $-3x^3y^2$ **31.** $33x$

33. $-3x^2y + 5xy^2$ **35.** $a^6 - 11a^5$

37. $-c^2 + c + 1$ **39.** $2x^4$

41. $-2x^3 + x^2 + 2x + 18$

43. $7x^5 + 4x^4 - 4x^3 + x$

45. $4ab^2c^4 - 5a^2bc^4 + 10a^2b^2c^4$ **47.** $60\sqrt{6}$

49. $-0.688 < -0.6869$ **51.** 1.36 **53.** 22.5%

EXERCISES 6.2

1. $18x^5$ **3.** $20x^9$ **5.** $18x^4y^6$ **7.** $24x^6y^5$

9. $-10a^4b^4c^4$ **11.** $12a^5b^5c^5$ **13.** $-18xy^5z^6$

15. $-\dfrac{3}{14}xyz^2$ **17.** $-24x^5y^{10}z^3$ **19.** $6a^4b^3c^6d^6$

21. $24x^3 + 40x^2$ **23.** $-18x^4 + 12x^3$

25. $72a^5 - 40a^4$ **27.** $-2x^4y^4 + 3x^5y^5$

29. $x^4y^6 + x^5y^5$ **31.** $28w^6 + 20w^5 + 8w^4$

33. $\dfrac{3}{2}p^5qr^3 + \dfrac{4}{5}p^2q^3r^3 + \dfrac{4}{7}p^2qr^4$

35. $-24x^5y^6 + 12x^4y^2 - 18x^5y^3$

37. $-24x^{10}y^{10} + 12x^7y^9 + 20x^6y^8 - 32x^2y^3$

39. $-3x^2 + x$ **41.** $2x^3 + 2x^2 - 6x$

43. $-17x^3 - x^2 - 5x$

45. $-3.64x^4y^5 + 1.29xy^3 + 9.94x^4y^2$

47. $6z^7 - 10z^5 - 7z^3$ **49.** $4a^2bc^5 + 7a^3b^2c^3$

51. $26w^6$ **53.** $-42a^7 - 9a^4$

55. $24x^5y^6 + 15x^5y^5$ **57.** $33y^5z^6 - 20y^5z^5$

59. $36x^7y^3 - 24x^7y^5$ **61.** $27y^4z^5 + 54y^4z^6$

63. $\dfrac{25}{36}$ **65.** 0   **67.** $\dfrac{24}{13}$

69. 2,048 is the 11th power of 2.

EXERCISES 6.3

1. $wx + sx + wz + sz$

3. $24x^2 + 38xy + 8y^2$

5. $-35w^2 + 41wx - 12x^2$

7. $-6x^2 + 28xy - 30y^2$

9. $-72a^2 + 77ab - 20b^2$

11. $-12x^2 - x + 63$ **13.** $12x^4 - 4x^3 - 40x^2$

15. $-8x^5 + 30x^4 - 18x^3$

17. $-12x^4 - 52x^3 + 138x^2 - 30x$

19. $16x^4 - 32x^3 - 17x^2 + 40x$

21. $27a^8 - 45a^7 - 18a^6 + 30a^5 + 21a^4 - 35a^3$

23. $-24y^6 + 58y^5 - 60y^4 + 50y^3$

25. $-15z^{11} + 6z^{10} + 10z^9 - 4z^8 + 40z^7 - 16z^6$

27. $12x^4 - 14x^3 - 22x^2 + 14x + 10$

29. $-5x^7 + 37x^6 + 10x^5 - 60x^4 + 24x^3$

31. Percent means per 100 or to divide by 100.

33. 120   **35.** 22.5% **37.** $\dfrac{16}{169}$

EXERCISES 6.4

1. $\dfrac{5x^2}{y^3}$ **3.** $\dfrac{-4b^2}{a^2}$ **5.** $\dfrac{-6x^3}{y^3}$ **7.** $\dfrac{4c^3}{a^4b^5}$

9. $\dfrac{6y^5}{x^4 z^8}$ **11.** $3a^7 b^{-2} c^{-5}$ **13.** $6x^2 y^{-5} z^3$

15. $14x^{-5} y^{-1} z^{-3}$ **17.** x^{-5} **19.** $x^{-3} y^3$

21. $5x^3$ **23.** $3x^2$ **25.** $\dfrac{5ab}{c^2}$ **27.** $8x^4 y^3$

29. $-3ab$ **31.** $-6ab^3 c^2$ **33.** $23x^3 + 18x$

35. $-5x^7 y^5 + 2x^8 y^3$ **37.** $5b^3 c^8 + 7a^2 c^8$

39. $\dfrac{3y^2 z}{x} - \dfrac{2}{yz}$ **41.** $\dfrac{-4y^6}{x^3} + 6x^4$

43. $\dfrac{-4z^2}{y^3} + \dfrac{5x^2 z^4}{y}$ **45.** $\dfrac{-4}{p^2 r^2} + \dfrac{6p^2}{r^2} + \dfrac{7r^2}{p^4}$

47. $\dfrac{-13a^5}{b^8} + \dfrac{10a^3}{b^5} - \dfrac{16}{b}$

49. $\dfrac{4x^8}{y^6} - \dfrac{5}{y^3} + \dfrac{10x^2}{y^2} - \dfrac{8x^3}{y^5}$

51. An expression is a collection of terms that are added or subtracted. A term is a collection of factors that are multiplied or divided.

53. 484 is a perfect square since $22^2 = 484$.

55. If $\sqrt{-16} = x$, we would expect to be able to check that $x^2 = -16$. But according to the rules for signs, there is no real number whose square makes a negative; x^2 is nonnegative.

57. Neither one; additions and subtractions are on the same level and neither must come before the other.

EXERCISES 6.5

1. 27   **3.** 207 people   **5.** 0.4 mile

7. 2,144.66 cubic feet   **9.** 412.5 lbs.

11. 14.4 inches   **13.** $109.34   **15.** $0.75

17. 123.0   **19.** 21.63   **21.** $\dfrac{38 \cdot \pi}{3}$

23. 0.89 second   **25.** -2 **27.** $\dfrac{-21}{29}$

29. $\dfrac{1}{2}$ **31.** $\dfrac{-3}{7}$ **33.** $\sqrt{148} \approx 12.166$

35. ≈ -3.7139 **37.** 34   **39.** 912

41. ≈ 6.3246 **43.** $\dfrac{-128}{33}$ **45.** $\dfrac{9}{13}$

47. Add the digits in the whole number and check if that sum is evenly divisible by 3.

49. 0

51. A complex fraction contains another fraction within either its numerator or denominator or both.

CHAPTER 6 REVIEW PROBLEMS

1. Polynomial, trinomial; degree = 2.

3. Polynomial, monomial; degree = 0.

5. Polynomial, trinomial; degree = 5.

7. not a polynomial   **9.** $8x^2 - 9x + 4$

11. 0   **13.** $-4x^2 - 6x - 1$

15. $5x^5 + x^3 - 18x$ **17.** $-4a^3 b^2 + 2a^2 b^3 - 5ab^3$

19. $2x^2 yz^3 - 35x^3 y^4 z^2$

21. $-2x^2 y^4 z - 17x^4 yz^2 - 30xy^2 z^4$

23. $18x^5 - 24x^4$ **25.** $4x^2 + 3x - 5$

27. $-20y^7 + 80y^5 - 60y^4$ **29.** $-3a + \dfrac{2}{a} - \dfrac{5}{a^2}$

31. $-20x^7 y^5 + 16x^5 y^5 + 24x^6 y^9$

33. $-6x^7 y^5 + 4x^9 y^6 + 9x^5 y$

35. $14x^8 + 40x^6 + 26x^5$ **37.** $17x^4 + 25x^2$

39. $\dfrac{-2}{7}$ **41.** 6   **43.** $\dfrac{1}{6}$ **45.** $-\dfrac{3}{2}$ **47.** $\dfrac{16}{9}$

49. $\dfrac{1}{18}$ **51.** 7   **53.** $V = 1{,}597.26$

55. $a = 140$ **57.** 180π **59.** $\dfrac{53{,}750\pi}{3}$

61. $6x^2 + 3x - 63$ **63.** $-14x^2 + 43x - 20$

65. $20a^2 - 17ab - 63b^2$

67. $27x^3 + 21x^2 - 28x + 20$

69. $-32x^3 + 16x^2 + 18x - 9$

71. $36x^6 - 75x^5 + 44x^4 - 6x^3$

73. $10x^4 - 36x^3 + 13x^2 + 28x - 15$

CHAPTER 6 PRACTICE TEST

1. Polynomial, trinomial; degree = 4.

2. Not a polynomial.

3. Polynomial, monomial; degree = 0.

4. Polynomial, trinomial; degree = 5.

5. not a polynomial

6. Polynomial, binomial; degree = 6.

7. $-3x^3 - 2x^2$ **8.** $7x^4 + 2x^5$ **9.** $4x^5$

10. 0   **11.** $25x^5 - 29x^3 + 9x^2$

12. $-a^4b^3 - 5a^5b^2 - 5a^2b^3$

13. $25x^5y^3 - 18x^2y^3 - 6x^3y^5$

14. $-18x^9 + 6x^7 + 21x^6$ **15.** $20a^9 - 6a^8 + 4a^7$

16. $\dfrac{-6x^7y}{z^4}$ **17.** $-7x^3 + 5x - \dfrac{3}{x}$

18. $-9a^3 + 7a - 4$ **19.** $6x^5y - \dfrac{11x^6}{y^7} + \dfrac{14x^4}{y^2}$

20. $-\dfrac{1}{2}$ **21.** 3   **22.** $\dfrac{3}{25}$ **23.** 79

24. $10x^3 - 48x^2 + 32x$

25. $-10a^3 + 20a^2b + 6ab^2 - 12b^3$

26. $12x^6 - 29x^5 + 15x^4 + 8x^3 - 6x^2$

27. $21a^5 - 26a^4 - 7a^3 + 10a^2$

28. 532π **29.** $\sqrt{10}$

CHAPTER 7

EXERCISES 7.1

1. 14 is a solution.   **3.** 3 is not a solution.

5. -2 is not a solution.

7. $\dfrac{5}{2}$ is not a solution.   **9.** $\dfrac{2}{3}$ is a solution.

11. 4 is not a solution.   **13.** 2.5 is a solution.

15. -3 is not a solution.

17. 1 is not a solution.   **19.** 121 is a solution.

21. -1 is a solution.   **23.** 0 is not a solution.

25. -1 is a solution.   **27.** 0.62 is a solution.

29. $-\dfrac{3}{2}$ is a solution.   **31.** $x^3 + 8$

33. $100 - x^4$ **35.** $2x - 7$ **37.** $\dfrac{1}{x} - 6$

39. $-6(84 + x)$ **41.** $\dfrac{x^6}{6}$ **43.** $\dfrac{1}{2}x - (-2)$

45. $\dfrac{-4x}{x^2}$ **47.** $(x + 5)^3$ **49.** $-9 - 2x$

51. $(2x + 10) - 3x$

53. $3(x - 4) - 6(-12 + x)$

55. $(2x + 16) - 8(x - 2)$

In problems 57–66, more than the following written expressions are possible.

57. The product of a number squared and three

59. $\dfrac{1}{4}$ of the sum of a number and 8

61. The square of a number subtracted from the cube of a number

63. Three times the difference of four and a number

65. Two times the difference of a number and seven subtracted from four times the sum of a number and six

67. trinomial   **69.** $6x^3 - 34x + 53$

71. $5 - \dfrac{3}{x} + \dfrac{10}{x^2}$

EXERCISES 7.2

1. $x = 84$ **3.** $x = 300$ **5.** $x = 204$

7. $x = -6$ **9.** $x = \dfrac{1}{12}$ **11.** $x = 1$

13. $x = 720$ **15.** $x = -125$ **17.** $x = 8.218$

19. $x = -9.102$ **21.** $x = 240$ **23.** $x = -24.3$

25. $x = -2$ **27.** $x = -25$ **29.** $x = 15$

31. $x = -190$ **33.** $x = 3.2$ **35.** $x = -28$

37. $x = -84$ **39.** $x = -3$ **41.** $x = 210$

43. $x = -6.12$ **45.** $x = -0.4$ **47.** $x = \dfrac{1}{2}$

49. $x = -0.009$ **51.** $x = -143$

53. $x = -13$ **55.** $x = 1.76$ **57.** $x = 0$

59. The number 30×10^7 is not in scientific notation because 30 is not a number greater than or equal to 1 and less than 10.

61. 9.3×10^7 miles   **63.** 1.08×10^1, 10.8

65. $4^3 = 4 \cdot 4 \cdot 4 = 64$

$4^2 = 4 \cdot 4 = 16$ $16 = 64 \div 4$

$4^1 = 4$ $4 = 16 \div 4$

$4^0 = 1$ $1 = 4 \div 4$

EXERCISES 7.3

1. $x = -9$ **3.** $x = -4.4$ **5.** $x = 65$

7. $x = 4$　　**9.** $x = -4$　　**11.** $x = -\dfrac{9}{2}$

13. $x = -\dfrac{1}{2}$　　**15.** $x = -8$　　**17.** $x = -10$

19. $x = -28$　　**21.** $x = 6$　　**23.** $x = -1$

25. $x = 40$　　**27.** $x = -14$　　**29.** $x = 10$

31. $x = 4$　　**33.** $x = -9$　　**35.** $x = 1$

37. $x = -1$　　**39.** $x = -4$　　**41.** $x = -19$

43. $x = 8$　　**45.** $x = -10$　　**47.** $x = 0.15$

49. $x = -9.1$　　**51.** $x = 7$　　**53.** $x = 30$

55. $x = 31.5$　　**57.** $x = -\dfrac{5}{32}$　　**59.** $x = \dfrac{9}{4}$

61. $x = 16$　　**63.** $x = 5$　　**65.** $x = -\dfrac{15}{2}$

67. $x = 72$　　**69.** $x = 98$

71. A rational number is a quotient of two integers. $\dfrac{3}{4}$ is a rational number.

73. Shifting the decimal points in a division problem is equivalent to multiplying by factors of 10. The principle that justifies the shifting is the principle of multiplying by 1.

75. A terminating decimal is one in which there are only 0s after a finite number of decimals. $\dfrac{5}{8} = 0.625$ is an example of a terminating decimal. The remainder in the division is eventually 0.

77. true

EXERCISES 7.4

1. $-6\dfrac{1}{2}$　　**3.** -64　　**5.** 0.33　　**7.** -22

9. 13　　**11.** -13　　**13.** $\dfrac{5}{2}$　　**15.** -50

17. -4　　**19.** 11　　**21.** -13　　**23.** -16

25. 45　　**27.** 42

29. The smaller is 11 and the larger is 51.

31. Jennie is 11 years old and Carrie is 14 years old.

33. Reyna is 11 years old, Mercedes is 22 years old, and Antonia is 27.

35. The home photocopier costs $500 and the office copier costs $5,000.

37. The slower car is traveling at 52 miles per hour.

39. 16 men and 29 women are in the class.

41. The nurse worked 8 hours on Wednesday, 5 hours on Thursday, and 10 hours on Friday.

43. The Coke costs $0.90.　　**45.** 144, 145

47. 67, 69　　**49.** 84, 86, and 88

51. $-136, -134$　　**53.** 29, 30, and 31

55. 6, 7, and 8　　**57.** 8, 10　　**59.** 18

61. 31, 33, and 35

63. Two thousand eighty-three and ninety-seven ten-thousandths.

65. The estimated product is -28. The exact product is -30.34.

67. $-7,600$　　**69.** $\dfrac{16}{9}$

EXERCISES 7.5

1. $x = 56$　　**3.** $x = 12$　　**5.** $x = 5$

7. $x = 7$　　**9.** $x = 16$　　**11.** 20 passes

13. 135 people participated in the taste test and 60 people preferred Diet Cola B.

15. $1,183　　**17.** 390 miles　　**19.** 120 feet

21. 2 earned runs

23. 1,968 defective light bulbs　　**25.** 31 days

27. 8 gallons　　**29.** 10 yards　　**31.** 74%

33. 24　　**35.** 16　　**37.** 27.5　　**39.** $66\dfrac{2}{3}\%$

41. 50 students　　**43.** $2.10　　**45.** 60%

47. 17.4 minutes　　**49.** 20%　　**51.** $950

53. 9% decrease　　**55.** 28%

57. The discount is $96 and the sale price is $204.

59. The sales tax is $0.24 and the total cost is $3.23.

61. 56, 72　　**63.** $-64, -20$

65. The first family pays $291 and the second family pays $388.

67. 25 men and 20 women are in the class.

69. The first friend gets $880 and the second friend gets $1,100.

71. yes　　**73.** LCM = 1,440　　GCF = 2

75. $\dfrac{7}{8}$　　**77.** false

EXERCISES 7.6

1. $s = \dfrac{P}{4}$ **3.** $t = \dfrac{d}{r}$ **5.** $b = P - a - c$

7. $T = \dfrac{PV}{nR}$ **9.** $m = \dfrac{y - b}{x}$ **11.** $h = \dfrac{V}{\pi r^2}$

13. $F = \dfrac{9}{5}C + 32$ **15.** $R = Pn + C$

17. $h = \dfrac{S - 2\pi r^2}{2\pi r}$ **19.** $P = \dfrac{A}{1 + rt}$

21. \$180 **23.** 18 months **25.** 9% per year
27. \$4,000 **29.** 12 miles per hour

31. 412.5 miles **33.** $7\dfrac{1}{2}$ miles per hour

35. $3\dfrac{1}{8}$ hours or 3 hours, $7\dfrac{1}{2}$ minutes

37. 12 miles per hour **39.** 5.4 feet
41. 44 inches **43.** 3 inches
45. 1,000 pounds **47.** 20°C **49.** 6 inches

51. 2,016 **53.** $-\dfrac{3}{8}$ **55.** 49

57. $6x^3 + 31x^2 - 4x - 110$

EXERCISES 7.7

1. $x < 3$

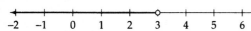

3. $x \geq 6$

5. $x > 0$

7. $x > 2$

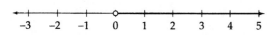

9. $x > 2$

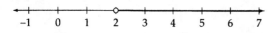

11. $x < 5$

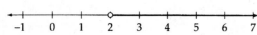

13. $x < 0$

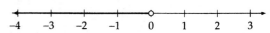

15. $x < 3$

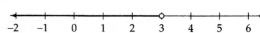

17. $x < \dfrac{5}{2}$

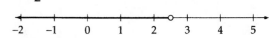

19. $x \geq 2.5$

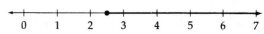

21. $x < -\dfrac{3}{2}$

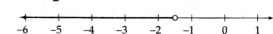

23. A ratio is a quotient of two numbers. A proportion is a statement that two ratios are equal.

25. $\dfrac{45y + 10z - 3}{2}$

27. 1. division by zero
2. square root of a negative number
3. zero raised to the zero power
4. zero raised to a negative power

29. 1. Zero has no sign.
2. Zero added to a number does not change the number.
3. Zero times any other number is always zero.
4. You cannot divide by zero.

CHAPTER 7 REVIEW PROBLEMS

1. -15 is a solution. **3.** $\dfrac{1}{2}$ is not a solution.

5. 4 is not a solution. **7.** $2x - 55$

9. $\dfrac{1}{x} + 86$ **11.** $x = -\dfrac{29}{20}$ **13.** $x = -69$

15. $x = -448$ **17.** $x = 539$ **19.** $x = -\dfrac{1}{2}$

21. $x = -11$ **23.** $x = -20$ **25.** $x = -33$

27. $x = -30$ **29.** $x = \dfrac{11}{2}$ **31.** $r = \dfrac{C}{2\pi}$

33. $t = \dfrac{2d}{c}$ **35.** $s = \dfrac{A - \pi r^2}{\pi r}$ **37.** $x = 1$

39. The daughter is 3 years old, the son is 11 years old, the mother is 33 years old, and the father is 36 years old.

41. A chair costs $50.

43. The integers are 66, 68, and 70.

45. They will win 96 games.   **47.** $156

49. $64\dfrac{2}{7}\%$ **51.** 350   **53.** 30%   **55.** 13%

57. 66,600 miles   **59.** 65 feet   **61.** $x < -4$

63. $x < -5$

CHAPTER 7 PRACTICE TEST

1. 2 is a solution.   **2.** -1 is a solution.

3. $x^2 - 5x$ **4.** $\dfrac{x}{6} - \dfrac{2}{3}(x + 12)$

5. $x = -5$ **6.** $x = -96$ **7.** $x = 48$

8. $x = -100$ **9.** $x = -3$ **10.** $x = -2$

11. $x = 60$ **12.** $x = 3$ **13.** $x = -64$

14. $x = -1.45$ **15.** $b = \dfrac{2A}{h}$ **16.** $R = \dfrac{A - P}{PT}$

17. -26 **18.** 11 men

19. $-37, -35,$ and -33 **20.** 135 gallons

21. 14%

22. Wendy receives $25,000 and Thad receives $20,000.

23. 8.2%   **24.** 4.5 hours   **25.** 10 inches

26. $x \le 3$ **27.** $x < -4$

CHAPTER 8

EXERCISES 8.1

1. $A(3, -2)$ **3.** $C(5, 3)$ **5.** $E(2, 1)$ **13.** $M(-9, -5)$ **15.** $O(-5, -6)$

7. $G(-10, -2)$ **9.** $I(4, -6)$ **11.** $K(-4, 5)$ **17.** Quadrant III   **19.** Quadrant III

The solutions to problems 21–31 are shown in the following figure.

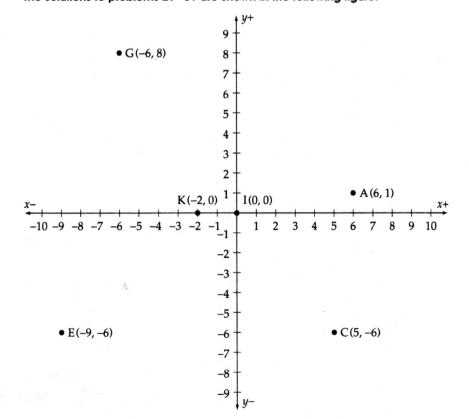

33. Vertically aligned: $d(A, B) = 78$.

35. Horizontally aligned: $d(A, B) = 12$.

37. Horizontally aligned: $d(C, D) = 26$.

39. Horizontally aligned: $d(C, D) = 11$.

41. Horizontally aligned: $d(A, B) = 36$.

43. $5(x^3 + y^2 + z)$ **45.** $x = -5$

47. $12\sqrt{5}$ **49.** $-2x^5 - 2x^4 - x^3$

EXERCISES 8.2

1. $\sqrt{65} \approx 8.0622577$ **3.** 25   **5.** 17

7. 29   **9.** 13

11.

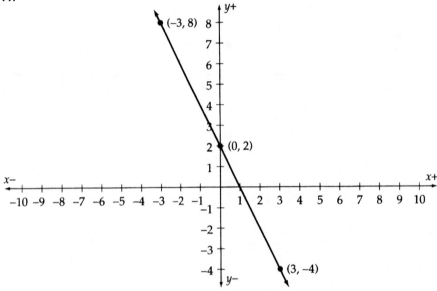

13.

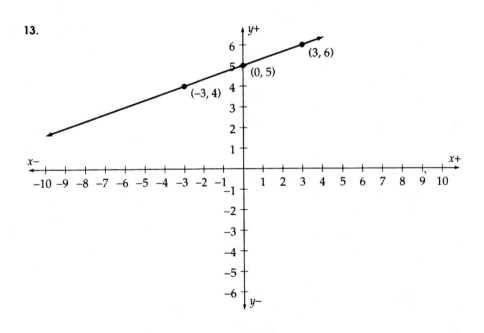

15.

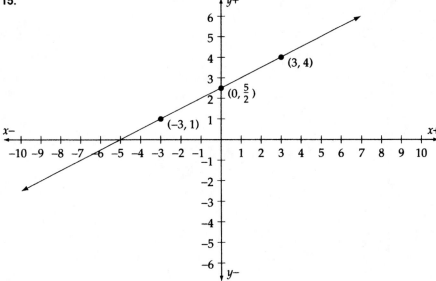

17.

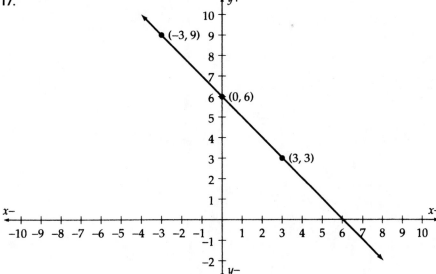

19.

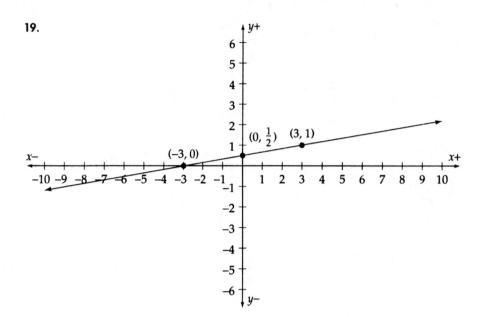

21.

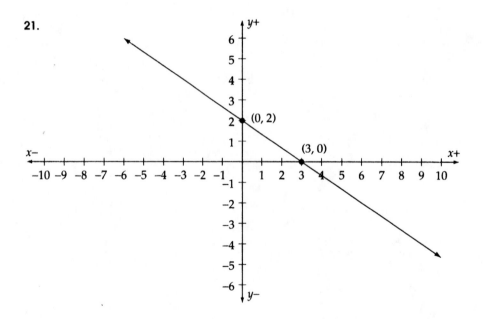

23.

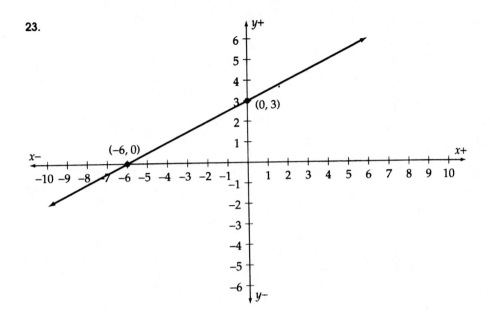

25.

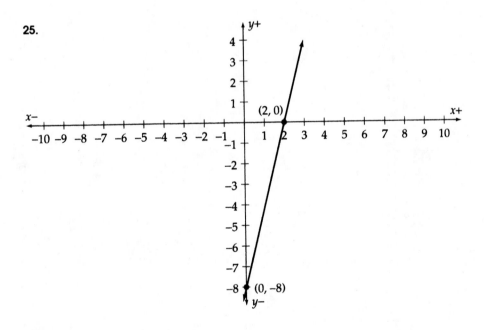

27.

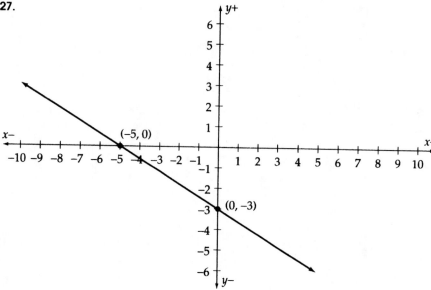

29.

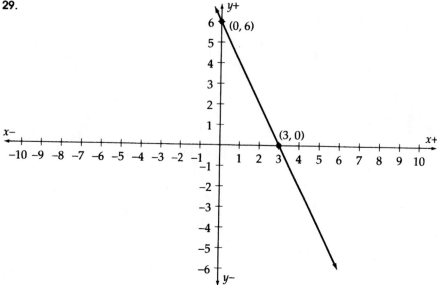

31. $y = \dfrac{-13}{6}x + \dfrac{5}{6}$ $\qquad m = \dfrac{-13}{6}$ $\qquad b = \dfrac{5}{6}$

33. $y = -3x - 4$ $\qquad m = -3$ $\qquad b = -4$

35. $y = \dfrac{9}{11}x + 9$ $\qquad m = \dfrac{9}{11}$ $\qquad b = 9$

37. $y = \dfrac{2}{3}x - \dfrac{4}{3}$ $\qquad m = \dfrac{2}{3}$ $\qquad b = \dfrac{-4}{3}$

39. $y = -3x - 54$ $\qquad m = -3$ $\qquad b = -54$

41. x^{21}

43. A binomial is a sum (difference) of two monomials.

45. A whole number is divisible by 3 if the sum of its digits is divisible by 3.

47. a signed whole number, including zero

EXERCISES 8.3

1. $\dfrac{-13}{7}$ **3.** $\dfrac{13}{5}$ **5.** undefined **7.** $\dfrac{2}{25}$

9. 0 **11.** $2\sqrt{5}$ **13.** 17 **15.** 41 **17.** 61

19. $\sqrt{73}$ **21.** $(10, 8), (14, 11), (18, 14)$

23. $(16, -24), (23, -26), (30, -28)$

25. $(32, -19), (40, -32), (48, -45)$

27. $(-20, 4), (-16, 15), (-12, 26)$

29. $(9, -27), (11, -34), (13, -41)$

31. $\Delta x = 36$ **33.** $\Delta y = -21$ **35.** $\Delta x = -52$

37. Move 35 units down: $(6, -25)$.

39. Move 45 units up: $(10, 44)$.

41. Move 75 units up: $(-23, 64)$.   **43.** $x = \dfrac{7}{12}$

45. 1.92 inches   **47.** $y = \dfrac{cd - ax}{b}$

49. No; $\sqrt{605} = 11\sqrt{5}$.

CHAPTER 8 REVIEW PROBLEMS

1. quadrant IV   **3.** quadrant I

5. quadrant III   **7.** quadrant II

9. quadrant III   **11.** quadrant II

13. Vertically aligned, distance = 21.

15. Horizontally aligned, distance = 6.

17. Vertically aligned, distance = 9.

19. 5   **21.** 17   **23.** 37

25.

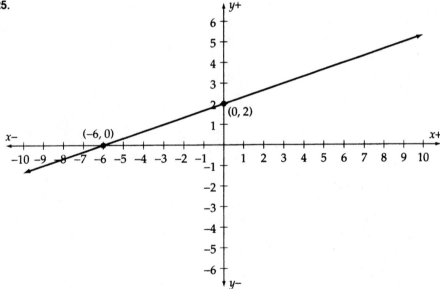

27.

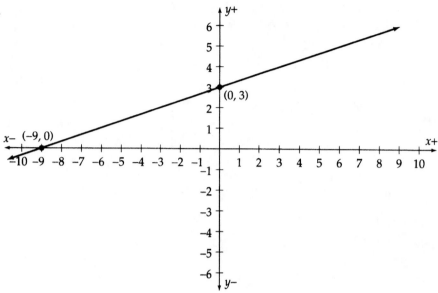

29.

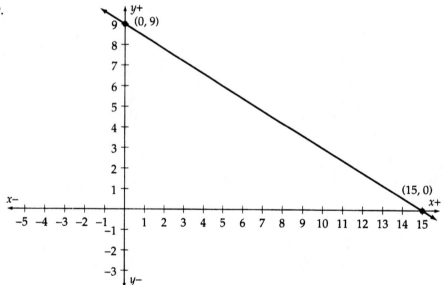

31. $m = \dfrac{4}{3}, b = \dfrac{17}{3}$

33. $m = \dfrac{8}{5}, b = \dfrac{16}{5}$

35. $m = \dfrac{-5}{16}, b = \dfrac{31}{16}$

37. $m = \dfrac{5}{7}, b = \dfrac{20}{7}$

39. $\Delta x = -8, \Delta y = -7, m = \dfrac{7}{8}$

41. $\Delta x = 9, \Delta y = -23, m = \dfrac{-23}{9}$

43. $\Delta x = -8, \Delta y = -7, m = \dfrac{7}{8}$

45. $\Delta y = -9$ **47.** Move up 30 units; $(-27, 45)$.

49. $\Delta y = 32$ **51.** Move up 45 units; $(-16, 31)$.

CHAPTER 8 PRACTICE TEST

1. quadrant II   **2.** quadrant IV

3. quadrant III   **4.** quadrant I

5. quadrant IV   **6.** quadrant II

7. horizontally aligned; distance = 1

8. vertically aligned; distance = 19

9. horizontally aligned; distance = 16

10. horizontally aligned; distance = 2

11. 5   **12.** 13

13. the line contains $(-8,0)$ and $(0,7)$

15. $y = \dfrac{5}{9}x + \dfrac{25}{9}; m = \dfrac{5}{9}; b = \dfrac{25}{9}$

16. $y = \dfrac{3}{4}x + -2; m = \dfrac{3}{4}; b = -2$

17. $\Delta x = 4, \Delta y = -2, m = \dfrac{-1}{2}$

18. $\Delta x = 1, \Delta y = 1, m = 1$

19. $\Delta y = -39$ **20.** $\Delta x = 75$

21. move up 16 units to $(-30, 25)$

22. move right 26 units to $(34, -17)$

FINAL EXAM PRACTICE TEST

1. billions

3. two million, seven thousand, eighty-one

5. 3,790,000,000

7. base = 3, exponent = 5; $3^5 = 243$

9. -26 **11.** yes   **13.** Yes; $511 = 7 \cdot 73$.

15. 80   **17.** associative law for multiplication

19. commutative law for multiplication

21. division   **23.** 44   **25.** true

27. $\left| -38 - (-117) \right|$ **29.** 4   **31.** -3

33. $\dfrac{76}{84}$ **35.** $\dfrac{5}{4}$ **37.** $-25\dfrac{13}{23}$

39. false   **41.** $\dfrac{119}{27}$

43. divisor $\times$ quotient + remainder = dividend

45. addition   **47.** $\dfrac{13}{400}$ **49.** 4.55   **51.** 0.925

53. 16   **55.** $490\sqrt{2}$ **57.** $\dfrac{7}{125}$ **59.** 0.245%

61. $\dfrac{-1}{8}$ **63.** 1   **65.** 0.0007269   **67.** 2×10^6

69. four   **71.** $-x^3 - 12x^2 - 4x$

73. $-15x^3 + 19x^2 - 6x$ **75.** $\dfrac{-4y^7}{x^7} - \dfrac{5y^9}{x^2}$

77. $x = -3$ **79.** 35 mph   **81.** 6.3 ounces

83. $x = \dfrac{3 - 2y^2}{9}$ **85.** true   **87.** $(0, 5)$

89. $\dfrac{5}{12}$

91.

93. 0.000350 k*l*

INDEX

×   (times symbol), 18, 301
·   (raised dot), 3, 18, 332
≠   (not equal), 58
≈   (approximately equal), 5, 226, 370
π   (number pi), 132, 200, 330
<   (less than), 75
>   (greater than), 75
≤   (less than or equal), 455
≥   (greater than or equal), 455

%   (percent symbol), 258
°   (degree), 72, 330
...   (ellipsis), 1
(x, y)   (ordered pair), 468
$d(A, B)$ (distance between A and B), 473
Δx (delta-x), 489
Δy (delta-y), 489
| | (absolute value), 73

"And," in reading decimals, 204
Abscissa, 471
Absolute value, 73–74, 93, 479
Addition
    of integers, 79
    of like fractions, 144
    of like terms, 336–337
    phrases in word problems, 387
    of polynomials, 339
    of positive and negative integers, 81
    property of equality, 393
    property of inequalities, 455
    rule for exponents, 283
    of signed decimals, 213
    two negative integers, 80
    unlike fractions, 148
    whole numbers, 8
Aggregation symbols, 35, 244

Algebraic expressions in word problems, 387
Analytic geometry, 467
Ares, 319
Associative laws, 59–60, 293
Astronomical unit, 404

Base, 29
Basic operation for an expression, 39, 393
Batting average, 235
Binomial, 334
Borrowing, 11, 212
Braces, curly, 35
Brackets (square), 35

Capacity, of a room, 364
Carrying, 9
Cartesian coordinate system, 471
cc (metric abbreviation), 318
Celsius temperature, 330, 364
centi- (metric prefix), 316
cg (metric abbreviation), 320
Checking solutions to equations, 385
Clearing fractions, 413
Clock pendulum, 372
cm (metric abbreviation), 317
Coefficient, 333
Common denominator, 143
Common factors, 124
Common multiples, 51
Commutative laws, 58–59
Comparing
    fractions and mixed numbers, 138–139
    signed decimals, 209
Complex fractions, 184–185
    procedure to simplify, 186

Composite number, 43
Compound interest formulas, 368–369
Conditional equation, 384
Cone (surface area), 379
Consecutive integer word problems, 423
Constant, 330
Converting
    decimals times powers of ten, 301
    decimals to percents, 260
    decimals to reduced fractions, 205
    fractions to decimals, 232–234
    fractions to percents, 260
    improper fractions to mixed numbers, 137
    mixed numbers to improper fractions, 136
    percents to decimals, 260
    percents to fractions, 259
    powers of ten to standard notation, 299
    to and from scientific notation, 307–308
    signed fractions to signed decimals, 234
Cross multiplication, 431
Cross products, 431
Cube, 30

deci- (metric prefix), 316
Decimal notation, 202
Decimal point, 202
    shifting the, 220, 230–232, 299–301
Decimal(s)
    nonrepeating, 242
    nonterminating, 242

Decimal(s) (*continued*)
　place value of, 202–204
　reading, 204
　repeating, 233
　rounding, 226–227
　signed, 209
　word names for, 202
　writing, in words, 204
Degree, of a polynomial, 335
deka- (metric prefix), 316
Delta x, 489
Delta y, 489
Denominator, 121
Discount
　price, 437
　rate, 437
Distance
　formula, 478, 480, 491
　rate and time formula, 449
　between two points on a number
　　line, 92–93
Distributive law, 60, 62, 211, 337,
　　338, 344, 350, 359
Dividend, 22
Dividing
　exponential expressions, 284
　nonzero number by itself, 123
　numbers in scientific notation,
　　310
　by one, 169
　polynomial by a monomial,
　　359–361
　by powers of ten, 229
　signed decimal by an integer,
　　228
　by zero, 103–104
　into zero, 103–104
Divisibility, 43
　tests, 45
Division
　algorithm, 22
　check, 23
　integers, 101–102
　property of equality, 399
　property of inequalities, 456
　signed decimals, 231
　signed fractions, 170
　signed mixed numbers, 171
　two monomials, 356–359
　whole numbers, 21
　by zero, 103–104
　into zero, 103–104
Divisor 22, 124

Ellipsis, 1
Equality of ordered pairs, 471

Equation(s), 383
　equivalent, 393
　linear, 393, 481
　literal, 445
　rule for eliminating variable
　　terms in, 408
　solving literal, 445. *See also*
　　Solving equations
　substitution in, 384
Estimating square roots, 243
Expanding
　decimals, 203
　fractions, 123
　power of a fraction, 278
Exponent(s), 29
　addition rule, 283
　multiplication rule, 291
　rules for signed, 295
　subtraction rule, 284
　summary of, rules, 295
Exponential
　notation, 28
　phrases in word problems, 387
Expression, 33, 387
Extremes, 430

Factor, 43, 124
Factors, 18, 100
Fahrenheit temperature, 330, 364
Finite decimal, 233
Focal length, of a photographic
　lens, 367
FOIL method, 350–352
Fraction(s)
　bar, 121
　complex, 184–185
　converting to a decimal, 232–234
　converting to a mixed number,
　　136
　converting to a percent, 260
　equivalent, 122
　improper, 135
　in lowest terms, 124
　signed, 133
Fundamental property of
　proportions, 431
Fundamental theorem of
　arithmetic, 46
Future value (FV), 332, 368–369

g (metric abbreviation), 320
GCD (greatest common
　denominator), 54
GCF (greatest common factor), 50,
　54–55, 128

giga- (metric prefix), 316
Gram, 320
Graphing solutions to inequalities,
　455
Greater than, 75
Grouping symbols, 35, 244, 410
　nested, 37
　with powers of powers, 293

hecto- (metric prefix), 316
Hero's formula, 369–370
Hollow dot, 455
Hyphen, use in word names, 3, 205
Hypotenuse, 239, 478

Identity, 384
Inequalities, 453
　reversing the sense of, 456–457
Inflation, and compound interest,
　369
Integers, 72
Inverse operations, 11
Irrational number, 242

kg (metric abbreviation), 320
kilo- (metric prefix), 316
kl (metric abbreviation), 318
km (metric abbreviation), 317

l (metric abbreviation), 318
Law, of the lever, 366
LCD (least common denominator),
　145–146
LCM (least common multiple), 50,
　52, 146
Less than, 75
Like terms, 336
Linear equation, 393, 481
Liter, 318
Literal equation, 445
Lowest terms, 124, 128

m (metric abbreviation), 317
Mass, 320
Means, 430
mega- (metric prefix), 316
Meter, 315
Metric system prefixes, 316
Metric ton, 320
mg (metric abbreviation), 320
micro- (metric prefix), 316
milli- (metric prefix), 316

ml (metric abbreviation), 318
mm (metric abbreviation), 317
Monomial, 333
Multiplication
    operation, implied, 332, 491
    phrases in word problems, 387
    polynomial by a monomial, 344
    property of equality, 397
    property of inequalities, 456
    rule for exponents, 291
    table, 19
    two monomials, 343
    whole numbers, 18
Multiplying
    exponential expressions, 283
    integers, 97–100
    numbers in scientific notation,
        310
    by one, 168
    signed decimals, 219
    signed fractions, 163–164
    signed mixed numbers, 167–168
    by zero, 20

nano- (metric prefix), 316
Negative
    exponents, 275–276, 357
    integers, 72
    number raised to a power, 110
    numbers, 71–72
    sign, 72
Nonnegative, 74
Nonpositive, 74
Number(s)
    even, 45, 423
    expanded form of, 3, 203
    irrational, 242
    line, 8, 72, 209, 468
    mixed, 135
    negative, 71–72
    odd, 423
    prime, 42
    rational, 121
    real, 242
    whole, 1, 241
    writing, in scientific notation,
        308
Numerator, 121
Numerical coefficient, 333

Operations
    mixed, 109, 176
    undefined, 103–104, 111, 244,
        274, 276

Opposites, 73, 82
Order, of operations agreements,
    34–36, 293
Ordered pair, 468
Ordering, 75
Ordinary notation, 298
Ordinate, 471
Origin, 470

"Point," in reading decimals, 205
Parabola, 370
Parentheses, 35
Percent, 258, 434
    proportion, 434
Perfect square, 241, 249
Periods, 2
pi, 132, 200, 224, 226, 330
pico- (metric prefix), 316
Place holder, 4, 202–204, 229
Place value, 2,
    of decimals, 202–204
Plotting points corresponding to
    equations, 481
Points
    horizontal distance between, 474
    horizontally aligned, 474
    vertical distance between, 474
    vertically aligned, 474
Polynomial, 334
Positive sign, 72
Power
    of a fraction, 278
    implied, 333
    of a product, 294
Powers of ten, 220, 229, 298
Present value (PV), 332, 368–369
Prime (relatively), 42, 55, 124
Prime factorization, 46, 48, 128, 253
Product, 18
    of powers, 283
    property of square roots, 250
    rule for exponents, 291
    rule for powers of powers, 291
Proper fraction, 134–135
Proportion, 430
PV (present value), 332, 368–369
Pyramid, 379
Pythagorean theorem, 239, 364, 478

Quadrant, 470
Quotient, 22
    of powers, 284

Radar detector, 365

Radical sign, 240
Raised dot, 3, 18, 301, 332
Rate, 430
Rate, distance, time formula, 449
Ratio, 429
Rational number, 121
Reciprocal
    of a fraction, 169
    of a number, 169, 276–277
Rectangular coordinate system, 470
Reducing
    fractions, 124, 128
    square roots, 249
Regular polygon (side length), 381
Regular price, 437
Relatively prime, 42, 55, 124
Remainder, 23
René Descartes, 467
Rounding
    decimals, 226–227
    whole numbers, 4–5

Sale price, 437
Scientific notation, 301, 306
Sieve of Eratosthenes, 44
Signed distance, 490
Signs, rules of, for products and
    quotients, 100, 102
Similar triangles, 493
Simple interest formula, 448
Simplifying
    complex fraction, 186
    fraction raised to a negative
        power, 278
    power of a product, 294
    square root, 249
Slope, of a line, 491–493
Solid dot, 455
Solution, to an equation, 384
Solving equations
    by combining like terms, 405
    containing fractions, 412
    containing grouping symbols,
        410
    with fractions, 412–413
    using addition, 393
    using division, 399
    using multiplication, 397
    using subtraction, 395
Specific gravity, 378
Square, 30
    perfect 241, 249
Square brackets, 35
Square root, 240
    completely reduced, 251
    estimating, 243

Square root *(continued)*
  of negative numbers, 244
  principle for eliminating, 252
Standard form, 3, 298
Standard notation, 298
Subscripted variable, 367
Subtraction
  phrases in word problems, 387
  property of equality, 395
  property of inequalities, 455
  rule for exponents, 284
Subtraction
  of integers, 88–89
  of like fractions, 156
  of polynomials, 345–346
  of signed decimals, 214
  of unlike fractions, 156–158
  of whole numbers, 10

tera- (metric prefix), 316
Term, 33, 331
Terminating decimal, 233
Tests of divisibility, 45
Theorem, 45, 239
Time sweep, for a clock pendulum,
  372

Torus, 378
Trapezoid, 379
Trial quotient interpretation, 47
Triangle(s)
  right, 239, 478
  similar, 493
Trinomial, 334

Undefined operations. *See*
  Operations, undefined

Variable, 20, 73, 330, 332
  subscripted, 367
  term in equations, 407–408
Vinculum, 233
Volume
  of a sphere, 366
  of a spherical cap, 371

Weight (mass), 320
Whole number perfect square, 241
Word problems
  with algebraic expressions, 387

with literal equations, 447
miscellaneous phrases in, 387
with more than one related
  quantity, 421
with proportions, 432
with ratios, 438
solving, using equations,
  418–419
steps for solving, 419

x-axis, 468
x-coordinate, 468
x-intercept, 484

y-axis, 468
y-coordinate, 468
y-intercept, 483

Zero
  division by, 103
  exponent, 273–274
  as a place holder, 204
  raised to the zero power, 274

TABLE OF COMMON MEASUREMENTS

Area

144 square inches = 1 square foot
9 square feet = 1 square yard
1 acre = 43,560 square feet
640 acres = 1 square mile

Circular Measure

360 degrees = 1 circumference
1 radian ≈ 57.29577951 degrees
1 degree ≈ 0.017453292 radian
60 minutes = 1 degree
60 seconds = 1 minute

Fluid Measure

1 teaspoon = $\dfrac{1}{3}$ tablespoon

1 tablespoonful = $\dfrac{1}{2}$ fluid ounce

16 fluid ounces = 1 pint

Mathematical Constants

$\pi \approx 3.14159265359$
$e \approx 2.71828182846$
Golden ratio = $\dfrac{1 + \sqrt{5}}{2}$
≈ 1.61803398875

Length

1 printer's point ≈ 0.013837 inch
1 inch = 2.54 centimeters
12 inches = 1 foot
3 feet = 1 yard
6 feet = 1 fathom
5,280 feet = 1 mile
1,760 yards = 1 mile
1 meter = 100 centimeters ≈ 39.37008 inches
1 kilometer = 1,000 meters ≈ 0.6214 mile
1 mile ≈ 1.609344 kilometers
1 astronomical unit = 93,000,000 miles

Metric System Equivalents

2.54 centimeters = 1 inch
1 meter ≈ 39.37 inches ≈ 3.28084 feet
1 kilometer ≈ 0.6214 mile
1 are ≈ 1,076.39 square feet ≈
    119.599 square yards ≈ 0.024711 acre
1 liter ≈ 61.024 cubic inches ≈
    0.26417 gallon ≈ 1.0567 quarts
1 gram ≈ 0.035 ounce
1 kilogram ≈ 2.205 pounds

Volume

1,728 cubic inches = 1 cubic foot
27 cubic feet = 1 cubic yard
2 pints = 1 quart
4 quarts = 1 gallon
1 gallon = 231 cubic inches
1 cubic foot ≈ 7.48 gallons
31.5 gallons = 1 barrel

Time

60 seconds = 1 minute
60 minutes = 1 hour
24 hours = 1 day
7 days = 1 week
365 days = 1 common year
12 months = 1 year
10 years = 1 decade
100 years = 1 century
1,000 years = 1 millennium

Weight

16 ounces = 1 pound
2,000 pounds = 1 ton
1 kilogram ≈ 2.205 pounds
1 gram ≈ 0.035 ounce
1 pound ≈ 0.493827 kilogram

Miscellaneous Physical Constants

Equatorial radius of the earth ≈ 3,963.34 miles
Acceleration due to gravity ≈ 32.1725 feet/second^2
Velocity of sound in air ≈ 1,087.1 feet/second
Velocity of sound in water ≈ 4,823 feet/second
Avogadro's number ≈ 6.02257×10^{23} grams/mole
Density of the earth ≈ 344.7 lbs/feet^3
Density of water ≈ 62.425 lbs/feet^3
Density of air ≈ 0.0807 lb/feet^3
1 gallon of water weighs 8.337 lbs
Speed of light ≈ 186,282.397 miles/second
1 light year ≈ 5.8746×10^{12} miles (approximate)
Distance from earth to the moon ≈ 238,857 miles
    (average)
Distance from earth to the sun ≈ 92,900,000 miles
    (average)
Diameter of the moon ≈ 2,160 miles
Diameter of the sun ≈ 864,000 miles
Diameter of the planet Jupiter ≈ 88,000 miles
Diameter of the planet Mars ≈ 4,200 miles

SPECIAL SYMBOLS AND ABBREVIATIONS

Symbol	Name	Meaning/Use
,	comma	period separator for whole numbers
.	decimal point	denotes the start of the decimal part of a number
×	times	denotes multiplication, especially in scientific notation
·	raised dot	denotes multiplication, avoids confusing × with x
+	plus	addition or positive
−	minus	subtraction, negative, or the opposite of
÷	divide	one of three notations used for division
—	fraction bar	denotes division and fractions (see also *vinculum*)
=	equal	denotes that two quantities have exactly the same value
≠	not equal	denotes that two quantities differ in value
≈	approximately =	denotes that two quantities have nearly the same value
√	square root	denotes the square root of a number
( )	parentheses	aggregation symbols to group parts of expressions
{ }	curly braces	aggregation symbols to group parts of expressions
[ ]	square brackets	aggregation symbols to group parts of expressions
π	pi	denotes the constant number pi ≈ 3.14159265359
)	division brace	denotes long division
| |	absolute value bars	denotes the absolute value operation
GCD	GCD	acronym for greatest common divisor
GCF	GCF	acronym for greatest common factor
LCM	LCM	acronym for least common multiple
LCD	LCD	acronym for least common denominator
<	less than	denotes that one quantity is less than another
≤	less than or equal	denotes that one quantity is less than or equal to another
>	greater than	denotes that one quantity is greater than another
≥	greater than or equal	denotes that one quantity is greater than or equal to another
±	plus or minus	denotes the same or opposite sign of a quantity
——	vinculum	aggregation symbol to cover repeating part of a decimal
%	percent	used to denote the number of parts per 100
FOIL	foil	acronym for First Outer Inner Last, used to multiply binomials
°	degree	denotes either temperature or angle measure in geometry
...	ellipsis	denotes a pattern to be continued
x_2	subscripted variable	x can be any variable letter, 2 can be any whole number
(x,y)	ordered pair	represents points in the x–y coordinate plane
$d(A,B)$	distance A–B	represents the distance from point A to point B
Δ^x	delta x	horizontal change in point coordinates, new x – old x
Δ^y	delta y	vertical change in point coordinates, new y – old y
PV	present value	standard financial variable name called the present value
PMT	payment	standard financial variable name for a periodic payment
FV	future value	standard financial variable name called the future value
km	kilometer	km is an abbreviation for kilometer
m	meter	m is an abbreviation for meter
cm	centimeter	cm is an abbreviation for centimeter
mm	millimeter	mm is an abbreviation for millimeter
kl	kiloliter	kl is an abbreviation for kiloliter
l	liter	l is an abbreviation for liter
ml	milliliter	ml is an abbreviation for milliliter
cc	cubic centimeter	cc is an abbreviation used for cubic centimeter
kg	kilogram	kg is an abbreviation for kilogram
g	gram	g is an abbreviation for gram
cg	centigram	cg is an abbreviation for centigram
mg	milligram	mg is an abbreviation for milligram
a	are	a is an abbreviation for are
○	hollow dot	indicates a point excluded from a graph on a number line
●	solid dot	indicates a point included in a graph on a number line